REGENERATION

REGENERATION

TORONTO'S WATERFRONT AND THE SUSTAINABLE CITY: FINAL REPORT

CANADA

Ontario

**HONOURABLE
DAVID CROMBIE
COMMISSIONER
TORONTO, CANADA**

Royal Commission on the Future
of the Toronto Waterfront

Regeneration: Toronto's waterfront and the sustainable city: final report

This report has been translated by the translation services of the Secretary of State, Canada, and is available in French under title:
Régénération : le secteur riverain de Toronto et la ville durable : rapport final

ISBN 0-660-14400-X
DSS cat. no. Z1-1988/1-1992E
Includes bibliographical references.

1. Waterfronts — Planning — Environmental aspects — Ontario — Toronto Metropolitan Area.
2. City planning — Environmental aspects — Ontario — Toronto Metropolitan Area.
I. Crombie, David, 1936 -   . II Title.

HT169.C32T6 1992   333.91'715'09713541
C92-099588-8

Cover: Domtar Cover Paper, Cream White 80 lb.
Domtar's Recycled Fine Paper is made exclusively (100%) from sorted paper waste that has been previously used and discarded by consumers. Made in Canada.

Fly Sheet: Eagle Recycled Text Natural 80lb. Acid free. Made in Canada.

Inside: 60 lb. Cream White Vellum
Phoenix Opaque is an Environmental Choice licensed book and offset paper made from 50% de-inked recycled paper of which 40% is post-commercial waste paper and 10% is from post-consumer sources. Made in Canada.

*Printed on
recycled paper*

TO HIS EXCELLENCY
THE GOVERNOR GENERAL IN COUNCIL

MAY IT PLEASE YOUR EXCELLENCY

      By Order in Council PC – 1988 – 589 dated March 30, 1988, I was
appointed Commissioner to inquire into and make recommendations regarding the future
of the Toronto Waterfront. I now beg to submit the attached Report.

      Respectfully submitted.

David Crombie
Commissioner

December 1991

Royal Commission on the
Future of the
Toronto Waterfront

Commission royale sur
l'avenir du
secteur riverain de Toronto

Commissioner
The Honourable David Crombie, P.C.

Commissaire
L'honorable David Crombie, c.p.

Executive Director and Counsel
Ronald L. Doering

Directeur exécutif et Conseiller juridique
Ronald L. Doering

TO HIS HONOUR,
THE LIEUTENANT–GOVERNOR OF
THE PROVINCE OF ONTARIO

MAY IT PLEASE YOUR HONOUR:

      By Order in Council O.C. 2465/89, dated the 12th day of October, 1989, I was duly appointed a Commissioner under the *Public Inquiries Act*. I am pleased to present to you the attached Report of the Royal Commission on the Future of the Toronto Waterfront.

      Respectfully submitted.

David Crombie
Commissioner

December 1991

171, rue Slater St., 11th Floor/11e étage
P.O. Box/C.P. 1527
Station/Succursale "B"
Ottawa, Canada K1P 6P5

Tel. No./No. de téléphone: *(613)* 990–3306
Fax. No./No. de facsimilé: *(613)* 990–4345

207 Queen's Quay West/Ouest ,5th Floor/5e étage
P.O. Box/ C.P. 4111
Station/Succursale "A"
Toronto, Canada M5W 2V4

Tel. No./No. de téléphone: *(416)* 973–7185
Fax No./No.de facsimilé: *(416)* 973–7103

ROYAL COMMISSION ON THE FUTURE OF THE TORONTO WATERFRONT

COMMISSIONER
The Honourable David Crombie, P.C.

EXECUTIVE DIRECTOR AND COUNSEL
Ronald L. Doering

EXECUTIVE ASSISTANT TO THE COMMISSIONER
Margaret Johnston

SENIOR DIRECTOR OF SPECIAL PROJECTS
David Carter

SENIOR DIRECTOR
William Roberts

DIRECTOR OF ENVIRONMENTAL STUDIES
Suzanne Barrett

POLICY ANALYST
Gord Garland

EXECUTIVE ASSISTANT TO THE EXECUTIVE DIRECTOR
Charity Landon

ASSISTANT TO THE SENIOR DIRECTOR OF SPECIAL PROJECTS
Deborah Williams

ASSISTANT TO THE DIRECTOR OF ENVIRONMENTAL STUDIES
Sarah Kalff

RESEARCHER
Soo Kim

PRODUCTION MANAGER/SYSTEMS ADMINISTRATOR
Marlaine Koehler

ADMINISTRATIVE ASSISTANTS
Joan Lea
Louise Madore-Payer

PUBLICATIONS CO-ORDINATOR
Irene Rota

SECRETARY TO THE EXECUTIVE DIRECTOR AND COUNSEL
Lisa Ohata

SECRETARY TO THE SENIOR DIRECTOR OF SPECIAL PROJECTS
Alice LeBlanc

PUBLICATIONS DESIGNER
Jiin Kim

SECRETARY TO POLICY AND RESEARCH STAFF
Martha Lopez

RECEPTIONIST
Anne Dixon

CLERK/MESSENGER
Wesley Birecki

CANADIAN WATERFRONT RESOURCE CENTRE
Janet Hollingsworth, Library Services Co-ordinator
Vera Kubelikova, Records Office Manager
Jean Sinclair, Library Technician

ACKNOWLEDGEMENTS

We wish to thank the following people, who brought to this and each of our publications their fortitude, hard work, and editorial talent.

Sheila Kieran, Editor
Margot Côté, French Editor
David Kilgour, Proofreader

We would like to acknowledge the contribution of the following people in the writing of this report:

Joe Berridge
Roger du Toit
Ken Greenberg
Michael Hough
Bryan J. Howard
Neal A. Irwin
John Jackson

Joanna Kidd
Michael Kirkland
Edward J. Levy
Paul Muldoon
Pat Ohlendorf-Moffat
Ronald A. Reid
Ric Symmes

We would like to express our appreciation to the following for their co-operation and contribution to our work:

The Governments of Canada and Ontario, City Mayors, their councils and departments; Regional Chairs, their councils, departments and conservation authorities; and various public and private agencies, boards, and associations.

Over the three years of the Commission's life, the work of many hands has made it possible to meet the challenges set before us. We sincerely thank the following persons for their assistance:

Brent Abbott ✤ Garry Adams ✤ Sharon Adams ✤ T. Bruce Adams ✤ Tom Adams ✤ John Addison ✤ David Agnew ✤ Ted Aikins ✤ Andrea Aitken ✤ Al Albania ✤ Ken Albright ✤ Gena Ali ✤ Duncan M. Allan ✤ David Allen ✤ Gene Allen ✤ Mary Ann Allen ✤ Paul J. Allsop ✤ Robert Allsopp ✤ Lorne D. Almack ✤ Martin Amber ✤ Carl Amrhein ✤ Howard Anders ✤ Douglas Anderson ✤ Paul Anozy ✤ Mark Anshan ✤ Randall Arendt ✤ Garth Armour ✤ Tim Armstrong ✤ Rob Arnott ✤ Wayne Arthurs ✤ Taline Artinian ✤ Lynn Artmont ✤ H. E. Ashley ✤ Brian Ashton ✤ Norman Atkins

✤ Bill Attewell ✤ Mike Attia ✤ Luigi Aurilio ✤ Peter Azeez ✤ Angela Azzopardi ✤ Wilbert Bach ✤ John Bacher ✤ Aubrey Bailey ✤ Giles Bailey ✤ George Baird ✤ Dave Baker ✤ Dennis Baker ✤ Randy Baker ✤ W. M. (Bill) Baker ✤ Wayne Baker ✤ John Band ✤ Marc Baraness ✤ Victor Barbeau ✤ Wayne Barrett ✤ John Barrington ✤ Vicki Barron ✤ Serge Bastien ✤ Diana Baxter ✤ Donald Baxter ✤ G. H. U. (Terk) Bayley ✤ Calvin Beach ✤ Russel Beach ✤ Frank Bean ✤ Max Beck ✤ Paul J. Beck ✤ Fred Beer ✤ Carl Beernath ✤ Moiz Behar ✤ Harry Behrend ✤ Phil Beinhaker ✤ Paul Beisel ✤ S. Dennis N. Belcher ✤ Lesley Bell ✤ William F. Bell ✤ Ginette Bellefeuille ✤ Terri Bellemore ✤ Peter Belling ✤ Sam BenDayan ✤ Yvonne Bendell ✤ Michael Bender ✤ David Bennett ✤ Gerry M. Bennett ✤ John Bennett ✤ Michael Bennett ✤ Beth A. Benson ✤ Murray Benyon ✤ Peter Bernard ✤ Chris Berzins ✤ J. B. Best ✤ Donald M. Biback ✤ Robert Bickerstaff ✤ Jane S. Billings ✤ David Bingham ✤ Ron S. Binnie ✤ Diana Birchall ✤ Roly Bird ✤ Christine Bishop ✤ Jim Bishop ✤ John Bitove ✤ Scott Black ✤ Jim Blair ✤ M. Bloess ✤ Steve Bloom ✤ Allan Blott ✤ Robert Bloxam ✤ Chris Blue ✤ Tony Blue ✤ Dirk Blyleven ✤ Trudy Bodak ✤ Christian Bode ✤ Nancy Boland ✤ Craig Boljkovac ✤ Carlo Bonanni ✤ Bob Bonner ✤ Rudi Boonstra ✤ Nars Borodczak ✤ Susanne Borup ✤ Ila Bossons ✤ Lucien Bouchard ✤ Peter Bougadis ✤ John Bousfield ✤ Charles Bouskill ✤ Ted Bowering ✤ Gary Boyd ✤ Patrick Boyer ✤ Bill Boyle ✤ Brian J. Boyle ✤ Cheryl Bradbee ✤ Mike Braden ✤ Jim Bradley ✤ Kevin Brady ✤ Graham Brand ✤ Andy Brandt ✤ Robert Brault ✤ Tim Brewsten ✤ Karen Bricker ✤ Margaret Britnell ✤ David Brock ✤ Robert Brock ✤ Marek Brodski ✤ Ian Bromley ✤ Calvin Brook ✤ Jeff Brooks ✤ John Brooks ✤ Pauline Browes ✤ Bob Brown ✤ Fergy Brown ✤ Hank E. Brown ✤ Ian C. R. Brown ✤ Veronica Brown ✤ Jeb Brugmann ✤ Marion Bryden ✤ Bill Brydon ✤ Ian Buchanen ✤ Brian Buckles ✤ Dianne Buckner ✤ Ian Budge ✤ Robynne Budish ✤ Michael Bulatovich ✤ Diane Bull ✤ John Bulloch ✤ Jim Bullock ✤ Robert G. Bundy ✤ Jane Bundze ✤ Rita Burak ✤ Heather Burgess ✤ Hernan P. Burgos Jr. ✤ Hernan P. Burgos Sr. ✤ Graham Burke ✤ Sheldon Burlow ✤ Bryan Burns ✤ Dan Burns ✤ David Burnside ✤ Barb Butler ✤ Bob Butler ✤ Everett Butsma ✤ Phillip Byer ✤ Caroline Byrne ✤ Niall Byrne ✤ Steve Byrne ✤ Orlando Cabrera ✤ Charles Caccia ✤ Lynn Calder Starr ✤ Dennis R. Callan ✤ June Callwood ✤ John Calvert ✤ Bernie Camacho ✤ Frank X. Camenzuli ✤ Jim Cameron ✤ Bill Campbell ✤ Karen Campbell ✤ Monica Campbell ✤ Nino Campitelli ✤ Tom Camps ✤ Tony Cancelliere ✤ Barbara Caplan ✤ Dennis Caplice ✤ Massimo Carbone ✤ V. Carette ✤ Elaine Carey ✤ John Robert Carley ✤ Victoria Carley ✤ Adam Carr ✤ Bruce Carr ✤ Brenda Carrigan ✤ Ken Carroll ✤ Patrick A. Carson ✤ Joe Caruana ✤ John Cary ✤ Daniel Cassidy ✤ Bruce Caswell ✤ Larry Cavanagh ✤ G. Cesario ✤ R. B. Chafe ✤ Stephen Chait ✤ Donald P. Chalmers ✤ C. H. Chan ✤ John C. Chan ✤ Victer G. Chan ✤ Thomas F. Chandler ✤ Grace Chang ✤ D. Chapman ✤ Joe Chapman ✤ Ron Chapman ✤ Jean Charest ✤ Micheline Charlebois-McKinnon ✤ David Charlesworth ✤ Edward Chart ✤ Peggy Chau ✤ Barrie Chavel ✤ Nancy Cherney ✤ Bob Chernicki ✤ Anna Chou ✤ David Christie ✤ Robert C. Christie ✤ Ron Christie ✤ P. Chronis ✤ Carolyn Chung ✤ Gardner Church ✤ Marilyn Churley ✤ J. Chyurlia ✤ Steve Clagg ✤ Bob Clapp ✤ Brad Clark ✤ David Clark ✤ Nancy J. Clark ✤ Scott W. Clark ✤ Alan Clarke ✤ Bill Clarklin ✤ Adrienne Clarkson ✤ Lorraine Clarkson ✤ John Clay ✤ Al Clayton ✤ Brian Cleeve ✤ John Clement ✤ Tom Clement ✤ Bill Clements ✤ Georges Clermont ✤ Tom Clifford ✤ Larry Close ✤ Steve Close ✤ John Coakley ✤ Tom Cobourn ✤ Sandy Cochran ✤ Dian Cohen ✤ Howard Cohen ✤ Dusty Cohl ✤ Theo Colborn ✤ Audrey Cole ✤ Rob Colli ✤ Murray Collican ✤ Frank Edward Collins ✤ Jack Collins ✤ Leigh Collinson ✤ Martin Collis ✤ Rosemary Colucci ✤ Brian Conacher ✤ Roger Concall ✤ Don Connolly ✤ Rick Connors ✤ Mark Conway ✤ Ken Cook ✤ William Cook ✤ Dave Cooke ✤ Tony Coombes ✤ Jack Cooper ✤ Kathy Cooper ✤ Jean Corbeil ✤ Ken Corbett ✤ Francine Côté ✤ Ron Coulas ✤ Darryl Coulson ✤ Jacqueline Courval ✤ Jane Coutts ✤ Eric Cowan ✤ Sandra Cowan ✤ Nigel Cowie ✤ Chuck Cox ✤ Samuel Craig ✤ Bill Cram ✤ Jack Cramer-Byng ✤ Margaret Cramer-Byng ✤ Maggie Cresswell-Weber ✤ David Crome ✤ James Crump ✤ Walter S. Culbertson ✤ L. Ross Cullingworth ✤ Ken Cumberland ✤ N. N. Cursio ✤ Joe D'Abramo ✤ Alex Dagg ✤ S. M. Daggupaty ✤ Harry Dahme ✤ Romesh Dalal ✤ Bob Dale ✤ Ralph Daley ✤ Harold S. Dalkie ✤ Beverly Dalys ✤ Nada Dancy ✤ Barnett Danson ✤ George Dark ✤ Amy Darker ✤ Dave Darker ✤ John Darling ✤ Al Davidson ✤ Anton Davies ✤ Ben Davies ✤ Bryan Davies ✤ Katherine Davies ✤ Paula Davies ✤ Tom Davies ✤ Walter Davies ✤ Wayne Davies ✤ Bruce Davis ✤ Cameron Davis ✤ Mark Davis ✤ Sylvia Davis ✤ Robert Dawes ✤ Ian N. Dawson ✤ John Day ✤ John Alexander Day ✤ Marie Day ✤ Wazir Dayal ✤ Robert de Cotret ✤ Michael de Gruchy ✤ Sheila de Zwaan ✤ Alyson Deans ✤ Sam Defelice ✤ Michael DeGroot ✤ Maureen DeJong ✤ Pat Delbridge ✤ Bruce Demara ✤ Bob DeMatteo ✤ Kathy Deming ✤ Brian E. Denney ✤ Michael Dennis ✤ Terry Denovan ✤ Kathy Dermott ✤ J. DeSchulthess ✤ Gene Desfor ✤ Anne-Marie Deslauriers ✤ Ian Deslauriers ✤ Wayne Deveau ✤ John Deverell ✤ Don Dewees ✤ Janet Dey ✤ Parviz Dhajani ✤ Con Di Nino ✤ Jack Diamond ✤ Bill Dibden ✤ Jennifer Dickson ✤ Les Digby ✤ Ben DiRamo ✤ Betty Disero ✤ Barry Ditto ✤ Frank Dixon ✤ Kenneth S. Dobb ✤ Tim Dobbie ✤ Jim Dobbin ✤ Rob Dobos ✤ Rod Dobson ✤ Doug Doherty ✤ Carole Donaldson ✤ Len Doncheff ✤ Laura Donefer ✤ Lee Doran ✤ Bob Doty ✤ Bob G. Douglas ✤ Dave Douglas ✤ Gordon Dowdell ✤ Elizabeth Dowdeswell ✤ Robert Dowler ✤ Donn Downey ✤ John Downing ✤ Derek Doyle ✤ Leo Drikx ✤ Alan G. Driver ✤ Leith Drury ✤ Douglas P. Dryer ✤ Aline Dubois ✤ Andrée DuBois ✤ Rick Ducharme ✤ Jim Duer ✤ Al Duffy ✤ Alexandra Duncan ✤ Bruce Duncan ✤ Brian Dundas ✤ Bill Dunphy ✤ Noreen Dunphy ✤ Steven Dunsford ✤ William Duron ✤ D. A. Durrant

✦ Barney Dutka ✦ Valerie A. E. Dyer ✦ Gary Dysart ✦ Ralph Eades ✦ Graeme Eadie ✦ Maggie Easton ✦ Arnold Edinborough ✦ Russ Edmunds ✦ Philip Edwards ✦ Tom Edwards ✦ Daniel Egan ✦ Jo-Anne Egan ✦ David L. Egar ✦ Arthur C. Eggleton ✦ Sam Ejnesman ✦ Susan Elbe ✦ Jack Ellis ✦ R. F. Ellis ✦ Mark Entwistle ✦ Danny Epstein ✦ Bob Evans ✦ David Evans ✦ Trevor Eyton ✦ Stephen Fagyas ✦ Paul Fairbrother ✦ George M. Fairfield ✦ Anne Fairley ✦ Helen Farley ✦ Paul Farley ✦ Tom Farrell ✦ Bob Farrow ✦ Milt Farrow ✦ Peter Fasullo ✦ Dale Faubert ✦ Peter Fay ✦ David Featherstone ✦ Robert Featherstonhaugh ✦ Paul Feitelberg ✦ David Feldman ✦ Tommy Fellion ✦ Elizabeth Feltes ✦ Jennine Feretti ✦ David Ferguson ✦ Derek Ferguson ✦ Jock Ferguson ✦ Robert Ferguson ✦ Claudia E. Fieder ✦ Larry Field ✦ Mike Filey ✦ Susan Filshie ✦ Richard A. Findlay ✦ Morris Fine ✦ Michael Firestone ✦ Susan Fish ✦ Ewen Fisher ✦ Gerry Fitzsimmons ✦ James Flagal ✦ Robert Flagal ✦ Gerry Flahive ✦ J. D. Fleck ✦ Eric Fleming ✦ Eugene A. Flichel ✦ Chuck Flink ✦ Tom Flood ✦ Doug Floyd ✦ Dennis Flynn ✦ Tom Foote ✦ Mark Forbes ✦ Rob Forbes ✦ F. Shane Foreman ✦ M. Forester ✦ Dennis Fortune ✦ Michael C. Fortune ✦ William Foster ✦ Bruce Fountain ✦ Ed R. Fox ✦ Glen Fox ✦ Ron Foy ✦ David Frame ✦ David Francis ✦ Bill Frankling ✦ Karen Fraser ✦ Sandra Frasson ✦ Ken Frederickson ✦ Barbara Freedman ✦ Louis Freedman ✦ Adele Freeman ✦ Bill Freeman ✦ Harry French ✦ Bruno Fresci ✦ Elene Ftohogiannis ✦ Ken Fukumoto ✦ Ed Fulton ✦ Tom Fulton ✦ Rem Gaade ✦ Holly Galway ✦ Don Gamble ✦ Ciaran Ganley ✦ Ken Gansel ✦ Francis Gardiner ✦ Fred Gardner ✦ Helen Garland ✦ Robert Garrard ✦ David Garrick ✦ John A. Gartner ✦ Peter B. Gass ✦ John Gault ✦ Gord Geeseburger ✦ Mario Gentile ✦ Ric German ✦ Denis Gertler ✦ Len Gertler ✦ Meric Gertler ✦ Ross Gervais ✦ John Ghent ✦ Brian L. Gibson ✦ Graeme Gibson ✦ Ian Gibson ✦ Janice Gibson ✦ Sally Gibson ✦ James Gillies ✦ Sam Gindin ✦ Daniel Girard ✦ Robert Giroux ✦ Donald Given ✦ Bob Giza ✦ Andrew Glass ✦ Marc Glassman ✦ Bill Glenn ✦ Chris Glerum ✦ Fred Gloger ✦ Robert Glover ✦ Nick Gobes ✦ Freya Godard ✦ Charles Godfrey ✦ Martin Goebel ✦ Lawrence S. Gold ✦ Lee Gold ✦ Mark Goldblatt ✦ Howard Goldby ✦ Judy Goldie ✦ Michael Goldrick ✦ Lorrie Goldstein ✦ Phillip W. Gooch ✦ Len Good ✦ Ted Goodchild ✦ Robert A. Goodings ✦ Gary Goodman ✦ David Gordon ✦ Richard Gordon ✦ Julius Gorys ✦ Ron Gotts ✦ Stephen Goudge ✦ Alain Gourd ✦ Katharine Gourlie ✦ Carole Goyette ✦ George Grant ✦ Jack Grant ✦ Henry Graupner ✦ Bill Gray ✦ Lou Greenbaum ✦ Ira Greenspoon ✦ Ellen Greenwood ✦ Bill Greer ✦ Douglas Grenville ✦ Marney Grew ✦ Ruth Grier ✦ Kathleen Griffin ✦ Richard Griffiths ✦ Lino Grima ✦ Randy Grimes ✦ George Gross ✦ Ellen Jane Grossman ✦ Carmen Guerreri ✦ Brad Guest ✦ Robert Gullins ✦ Ravi Gupta ✦ David Gurin ✦ Gigi Gurthrie ✦ David Guscott ✦ Katherine Guselle ✦ Stella Gustavson ✦ Gigi Guthrie ✦ Tibor Haasz ✦ Donald C. Hadden ✦ Glenn Hadley ✦ Derek Hagen ✦ Roseann Hahn ✦ Efraim Halfon ✦ Barbara Hall ✦ Howard Hall ✦ Ilona Hall ✦ Janet Hall ✦ Joe Hall ✦ John Hall ✦ Mark Hall ✦ Doug Hallet ✦ Andy Hamilton ✦ David Hamilton ✦ J. P. Hamilton ✦ John Hanbidge ✦ Brian Hancock ✦ Mac Hancock ✦ Trevor Hancock ✦ J. Moyra Haney ✦ Bob Hanna ✦ Gary S. Harding ✦ Michele Harding ✦ Peter Hare ✦ Jennifer M. Harker ✦ Lyn Harrett ✦ Glenn Harrington ✦ David Harris ✦ John Harris ✦ Carol Harris-Lonero ✦ Michael Harrison ✦ Don Hartford ✦ Ian Harvey ✦ Vanessa Harwood ✦ Khalid Hashmani ✦ Dave Hawke ✦ Bill Hawkes ✦ Dennis J. Hawley ✦ Mary Hay ✦ Stewart Hay ✦ Al Haynes ✦ Dan Heap ✦ Stan Heidman ✦ Steve Heineman ✦ Ariane Heisey ✦ Michael Heitshu ✦ Karl Hemmerich ✦ Jeff Hemming ✦ David Henderson ✦ Fred Henderson ✦ Paul Henderson ✦ Colleen Hennessy ✦ Gary Herrigel ✦ Patricia Herring ✦ Rob Hersey ✦ Marc Hewitt ✦ Fred Heywood ✦ Sharon Hicks ✦ Peter M. Higgins ✦ Tom Higgins ✦ Verna Higgins ✦ Bob Hill ✦ D. Jeremy Hill ✦ John Hillier ✦ Susan Himmel ✦ Jim Hodgins ✦ Darryl Hogg ✦ Kenneth Holder ✦ Bruce Holland ✦ Roger Hollander ✦ Brian Hollebone ✦ Irvine Hollis ✦ Brian Holmes ✦ Alex Home ✦ Glen Hooper ✦ Jean Hopkins ✦ Dick Horkins ✦ Kevin Hosler ✦ John Houweling ✦ Bob Howald ✦ Bill Howes ✦ Al Hoyne ✦ Lorraine Hubbard ✦ Dave Hulchanski ✦ Christopher Hume ✦ Manfred Humphries ✦ David Hutcheon ✦ Noel Hutchinson ✦ Robert Hutchinson ✦ Debbie Hymes ✦ Sandra Iaboni ✦ Brett G. Ibbotson ✦ Joseph Iglewski ✦ Jack Imhoff ✦ Bruce Ing ✦ Jonah Ing ✦ Inga Ingram ✦ Colin Isaacs ✦ Dorothy Izzard ✦ Raine Jaagumagi ✦ Laurie A. Jacklin ✦ William H. Jackman ✦ Gladstone Jackson ✦ Lorna D. Jackson ✦ Julian Jacobs ✦ Karl Jaffray ✦ Gloria W. James ✦ Lois James ✦ R. Scott James ✦ Rick James ✦ Royson James ✦ Terry Janczyk ✦ Milan Janecek ✦ Bruce Jank ✦ Diana Jardine ✦ Beth Jefferson ✦ Otto Jelinek ✦ Shirley Jen ✦ Alf Jenkins ✦ Hans Jensen ✦ Peter Jensen ✦ Walter Jensen ✦ Sam Jephcott ✦ Mike Jerrett ✦ Sabine Jessen ✦ Norman Jewison ✦ Paul Johannsson ✦ Judith John ✦ Andrew L. Johnson ✦ Bob Johnson ✦ David Johnson ✦ Fred Johnson ✦ Patricia K. Johnson ✦ Anne Johnston ✦ Gerry Johnston ✦ Richard Johnston ✦ Robert D. Johnston ✦ Allen Jones ✦ Glen Jones ✦ Jack Jones ✦ Laura Jones ✦ Wendy Joscelyn ✦ Wendy Joyce ✦ Helen Juhola ✦ Peter Jull ✦ John G. Jung ✦ John Jursa ✦ Phil Kaegi ✦ Ron Kanter ✦ Heidi Kaphengst ✦ Frederick T. Kasravi ✦ Nora Kassabian ✦ David Kaufman ✦ Kevin Kavanagh ✦ Michael Keating ✦ Walter Kehm ✦ Andrew Keir ✦ Susan Keir ✦ Morley Kells ✦ G. V. Kelly ✦ Susan Kelly ✦ Perry Kendall ✦ Ron Kennedy ✦ Byran Kerman ✦ Sharon Kerr ✦ Tom Kerr ✦ Frank Kershaw ✦ Bruce C. Ketcheson ✦ Carol Q. Ketchum ✦ Fareed W. Khan ✦ Rajib Khettry ✦ Ian Kilgour ✦ Don King ✦ Eldred King ✦ Rosina King ✦ John Kinkead ✦ Jeremy K. B. Kinsman ✦ John Kis ✦ Shane Kjertinge ✦ Laura Klager ✦ Mitchell Klein ✦ Randall R. Klein ✦ Ksenija Klinger ✦ Steve Klose ✦ Jo-Anne Knight ✦ Carl Knipfel ✦ Louise Knox ✦ Marilyn Knox ✦ Harold Kobold ✦

Risa Kogan ✤ Emil Kolb ✤ Raines Kolsy ✤ Heather Konefat ✤ Karl Konze ✤ Irving Korn ✤ Andrew Koropeski ✤ Ray Kosky ✤ S. C. Kosti ✤ Lawrence Kotseff ✤ Dick Krajewski ✤ Gordon Krantz ✤ Robert Kravel ✤ Elizabeth Kriegler ✤ Matthew Kronby ✤ Richard Kuchynski ✤ Brian Kurtner ✤ Michael Kusner ✤ Kelvin Kwan ✤ William Kwong ✤ P. Réal L'Heureux ✤ Huguette Labelle ✤ R. Lafleur ✤ Celia Laframboise ✤ Marilyn Lagzdins ✤ Michelle Lalonde ✤ Peter Lambert ✤ Wes Lammers ✤ Penny Lamy ✤ Donald Lander ✤ Alexis Landon ✤ Dennis Lang ✤ Peter Langdon ✤ Peter Langer ✤ David Langille ✤ Doug Langley ✤ David F. Larone ✤ Maureen Larsen ✤ Mel Lastman ✤ David Latchman ✤ Keith Laushway ✤ Mark Law ✤ Patrick L. Lawrence ✤ Jack Layton ✤ Michael Lea ✤ Allan Leach ✤ Don Learning ✤ Laurie LeBlanc ✤ Norman LeBlanc ✤ Patrice LeBlanc ✤ Stephen R. LeDrew ✤ Chang Lee ✤ Don Lee ✤ Jack Lee ✤ Erma Leesty ✤ Robert Lehane ✤ Horst Leingruener ✤ Vivian Leir ✤ Henry Leistner ✤ Ken Lem ✤ James Lemon ✤ Mary Lemyre ✤ Owen Lemyre ✤ Jill Leslie ✤ Iara Lessa ✤ C. A. Levesque ✤ Howard Levine ✤ Reg Lewis ✤ Vic Lim ✤ Clifford Lincoln ✤ Paul Lisanti ✤ Irwin Lithwick ✤ Arthur Little ✤ Greg Little ✤ John Livey ✤ Simon Llewellyn ✤ Rob Lockhart ✤ Jane Logan ✤ John Long ✤ Ross Long ✤ Bill Longden ✤ Harry Lopez ✤ Brian Loreto ✤ Frank Loritz ✤ Don Loucks ✤ Debbie Lovas ✤ W. Carl Lovas ✤ Amory Lovins ✤ David Low ✤ Harvey Low ✤ Rodine Lozada ✤ Rainer Lubbren ✤ Bob Luckhart ✤ Natalie Lue ✤ Peg Lush ✤ D. Luymes ✤ William Lye ✤ Donna Lynch ✤ Jim T. Lynch ✤ N. Barry Lyon ✤ Kim Lyons ✤ Larry Lyons ✤ Michael Lyons ✤ Heather MacAndrew ✤ Bob MacAuley ✤ David Macdonald ✤ Doug Macdonald ✤ Duncan MacDonald ✤ Helen MacDonald ✤ Jean MacDonald ✤ Lynda Macdonald ✤ Anne Macilory ✤ John Macintyre ✤ Barry Kent Mackay ✤ Elmer MacKay ✤ Hugh Mackenzie ✤ Eric Macklin ✤ James W. MacLaren ✤ Gord MacPherson ✤ Sandy MacPherson ✤ Diana Macri ✤ Chris Madej ✤ Paul Magder ✤ Marie Magee ✤ Steve Magee ✤ Fil Magnoli ✤ Chuck Magwood ✤ John Maher ✤ Janice Mahoney ✤ Garth Mailman ✤ Joyce Main ✤ Wally Majesky ✤ Frank C. Malatesta ✤ Douglas Maloney ✤ Robert Maloney ✤ Bob Malvern ✤ Andrew Manahan ✤ Ron Manfield ✤ Iggy Manlangit ✤ Thomas Manolakos ✤ Peter Mar ✤ Valerie March ✤ T. J. Marchant ✤ Alan R. Marchment ✤ Eva Marczak ✤ John Marczak ✤ Nora Mark ✤ Margaret Marland ✤ Jiri Marsalek ✤ R. Scott Marsh ✤ Stephen Marshall ✤ Tom Marshall ✤ Dale Martin ✤ Douglas Martin ✤ Jim Martin ✤ Luciano Martin ✤ Regan Martin ✤ Shirley Martin ✤ Deborah Martin-Downes ✤ Donald R. Martyn ✤ Al Mason ✤ John Roger Massingham ✤ Guy Mastrella ✤ Boris Mather ✤ Craig Mather ✤ Margary Mathews ✤ Marc Mattachini ✤ Burkhard Mausberg ✤ Jim Maxwell ✤ John Maxwell ✤ Robert Maxwell ✤ Doug Maybank ✤ Eileen Mayo ✤ Bob McArthur ✤ H. I. McBride ✤ Robert McBride ✤ Mark McBurney ✤ Fiona McCall ✤ Hazel McCallion ✤ Doug McCallum ✤ Patricia McCarney ✤ Frank McCarthy ✤ Shawn McCartney ✤ Anne McCauley ✤ Maureen McCauley ✤ David McClelland ✤ Michael McClelland ✤ David McCluskey ✤ Stephen McColl ✤ Jeff McCorkell ✤ M. Mike McCormick ✤ Mavis McCullum ✤ Gerard McDade ✤ John McDermid ✤ Dan Mcdermott ✤ Mark McDonald ✤ Maureen McDonnell ✤ Barbara McDougall ✤ Patricia McDowell ✤ Timothy McGee ✤ Nancy McGill ✤ Dan McGillivray ✤ John McGinnis ✤ Brian McHattie ✤ Donna McHoull ✤ David McHugh ✤ Craig McInnes ✤ Stewart McInnes ✤ Suzanne McInnes ✤ Erv McIntyre ✤ Trevor McIntyre ✤ Donald McKay ✤ Sheila McKay-Kuja ✤ Samm McKaye ✤ Pearl McKeen ✤ Lee-Anne McKenna ✤ Dan McKenzie ✤ Darcy McKeough ✤ Edward N. McKeown ✤ Jackie McKeown ✤ David McKillop ✤ Elizabeth McLaren ✤ David McLaughlin ✤ Madelaine McLaughlin ✤ Stephen McLaughlin ✤ Dan McLean ✤ Guy McLean ✤ Jim McLean ✤ Moira McLean ✤ William A. McLean ✤ Judith McLeod ✤ Lyn McLeod ✤ Charles McMillan ✤ John McMillan ✤ Scott McMillan ✤ John McNaughton ✤ Ray McNeil ✤ Gary McPeak ✤ Diane McPherson ✤ Laurie McPherson ✤ K. C. McReynolds ✤ Maureen McVarish ✤ Sean Meagher ✤ Sonya Meek ✤ Peter Meerburg ✤ Peter L. Meffe ✤ Ruth Melady ✤ Nelson Melnyck ✤ Tom Melymuk ✤ John Mende ✤ Eric Menezes ✤ Kathy Menyes ✤ H. Roy Merrens ✤ Jim Merritt ✤ Serge Metikosh ✤ Charles J. Meyers ✤ Mofeed Michael ✤ John Michailidis ✤ Michael Michalski ✤ Ed Mickiewicz ✤ Peter Middleton ✤ Frank Miele ✤ George Mierzyski ✤ Paul Migus ✤ John R. Mihalus ✤ Melanie Milanich ✤ Anthony Miles ✤ Joan Miles ✤ Tony Miles ✤ David Milgram ✤ Fred Millar ✤ Jim Millar ✤ Doug Miller ✤ Gavin Miller ✤ Glenn Miller ✤ Joe Miller ✤ John Miller ✤ Pam Miller ✤ Phyllis Miller ✤ Rodger B. Miller ✤ Russell Miller ✤ Sarah Miller ✤ Dennis Mills ✤ Frank Mills ✤ John Mills ✤ Robert E. Millward ✤ Michael Miloff ✤ Ann Milovsoroff ✤ David Mirvish ✤ P. K. Misra ✤ Paul Mitcham ✤ Ron Moeser ✤ Rasheed Mohammed ✤ Michael B. Moir ✤ Paul Moloney ✤ Laurie Monsebraaten ✤ Donna Montgomery ✤ David Moore ✤ Irene Moore ✤ Peter J. Moore ✤ Richard Moore ✤ Christopher Morgan ✤ Bruce Mori ✤ Beverly Morley ✤ Lawrence Morley ✤ Barry Morrison ✤ Don Morrison ✤ Harold Morrison ✤ Monica Morrison ✤ Larry Morrow ✤ Lynn Morrow ✤ Robert Morrow ✤ Wiebke Mortenson ✤ Desmond Morton ✤ Ian Morton ✤ Marlene Moser ✤ Elias Moubayed ✤ Diana Mourato ✤ Christine Moynihan ✤ Tom Muir ✤ Elizabeth Mulholland ✤ Thomas Mulligan ✤ Brian Mulroney ✤ Ann Mulvale ✤ Jon Munn ✤ Bill Munson ✤ Bruce Murat ✤ Rosa Murnaghan ✤ Claire Murphy ✤ Pat Murphy ✤ Barry Murray ✤ Don Murray ✤ Jack Murray ✤ David Myers ✤ Rollo H. H. Myers ✤ Frank Myron ✤ Huguette Nadeau ✤ Cynthia M. Nambudiri ✤ Jim Nash ✤ Ted Nasmith ✤ Nolan Natale ✤ Rashmi Nathwani ✤ Léonce Naud ✤ B. N. Nayak ✤ Mohamed Nayed ✤ Eha Mai Naylor ✤ John Neate ✤ Melanie Neilson ✤ Terry Neilson ✤ Earl Nestmann ✤ Julie Nettleton ✤ Robert Newbury ✤ Larry Newton ✤ Winnie Ng ✤ Elizabeth Nielson ✤ Jeanette Niggenaber ✤ Robert Nisbet ✤ Brian Nixon ✤ Wendy Noble

❦ Peter Noehammer ❦ Frank Norman ❦ Robert Norman ❦ Lynn Norris ❦ Barbara North ❦ Pat Northey ❦ Mike Northfield ❦ Kathy Nosich ❦ Heather Nourse ❦ E. R. Nurse ❦ Patricia O'Connell ❦ Gerri-lynn O'Connor ❦ Dan O'Halloran ❦ Brian O'Keefe ❦ Noreen O'Laughlin ❦ James O'Mara ❦ Catherine O'Neill ❦ Michael O'Reilly ❦ Larry O'Toole ❦ Norah Oakley ❦ Peter Oberlander ❦ Patrick W. Olive ❦ Gabe Oliver ❦ John Oliver ❦ Ben Ong ❦ Larry Onisto ❦ Eli Ophek ❦ Ian Orchard ❦ Walter Oster ❦ Ray Ostiguy ❦ Tom Ostler ❦ Steven Otto ❦ Cairine Oulton ❦ Ken Owen ❦ Jack Oziel ❦ Anna Pace ❦ B. Paehike ❦ Michael Page ❦ Shelley Page ❦ André Pageot ❦ Victor Pakalnis ❦ Janice Palmer ❦ Cyril Palod ❦ Aubrey Pancer ❦ Leslie Papp ❦ Victor P. Pappalardo ❦ John Parker ❦ Stan Parker ❦ Charles P. Parmellee ❦ Alison Parsons ❦ Karen Partanen ❦ Kevin R. Pask ❦ Dennis Pataky ❦ Mafat Patel ❦ Jeff Paterson ❦ Murray Paterson ❦ Doug Patriquin ❦ Richard Patten ❦ Joan Patterson ❦ Marjorie Patterson ❦ Nancy Patterson ❦ Norman Paul ❦ Chuck Pautler ❦ Annette Payne ❦ David Peakall ❦ Randall T. Pearce ❦ W. N. Pearl ❦ Jonathan Peck ❦ Eudora Pendergrast ❦ William Peppler ❦ Bob Perkins ❦ James K. Perkins ❦ Dennis Perlin ❦ David Perlman ❦ Lynda S. Peros ❦ Deo Persaud ❦ George Peter ❦ Brad Peterson ❦ David Peterson ❦ Eric Peterson ❦ Jim Petite ❦ Robert Petrella ❦ Don Peuramaki ❦ Robert Phaelke ❦ Thomas J. Phelan ❦ Kim G. Philip ❦ William Philips ❦ David C. Phillips ❦ Robert Phillips ❦ Karen Pianosi ❦ Peter Pickfield ❦ Darrell Piekarz ❦ Debbie Pierce ❦ Susan Pigg ❦ Alan Pilkey ❦ Juri Pill ❦ Herbert Pirk ❦ Jon Plank ❦ Rudy Platiel ❦ A.E. Pokotylo ❦ Margaret Polanyi ❦ Peter Pomeroy ❦ Lynn Poole ❦ Peter Poot ❦ George Post ❦ Russ Powell ❦ Gerald Pratley ❦ Bill Pratt ❦ Dick Pratt ❦ Charles Presswell ❦ Michael Price ❦ George Priddle ❦ Robert J. Pringle ❦ Bill Pristanski ❦ G. Punt ❦ Margaret Purcell ❦ Peter E. Purins ❦ R. A. Quail ❦ Elizabeth Quance ❦ Jack Rabba ❦ Jack Rabinowitz ❦ Donna Rachey ❦ Jan Raczkowski ❦ Mark Raczkowski ❦ Bob Rae ❦ Michael Raggett ❦ Debbie Ramsay ❦ Peter Ramsay ❦ Richard B. Ramsden ❦ Robert Ramsey ❦ Tim Rance ❦ Carol Randall ❦ Marianne Ratelle ❦ Kenneth Raven ❦ Ousama Rawi ❦ Angus V. Read ❦ Alan B. Redfern ❦ Alan Redway ❦ Wayne Reeves ❦ Henry A. Regier ❦ I. Reichenbac ❦ Alva Reid ❦ Bruce Reid ❦ David A. Reid ❦ Julyann Reid ❦ Mark Reid ❦ Audrey Reifenstein ❦ Paul A. Reimer ❦ Gloria Reszler ❦ Trefor Reynoldson ❦ David W. Rice ❦ Peter Rice ❦ Jim Richards ❦ Nigel H. Richardson ❦ Susan Richardson ❦ Wayne S. Richardson ❦ Dale Richmond ❦ Don Richmond ❦ John Richmond ❦ Tom Ridout ❦ Bob Riggs ❦ Suzanne Rioux ❦ Brian Ripley ❦ George Ritchie ❦ Ray Rivers ❦ Jim Robb ❦ Dave Robertson ❦ Ian Robertson ❦ James K. Robertson ❦ Jim R. Robertson ❦ Gerald Robinson ❦ Nancy Robinson ❦ Paul Robinson ❦ Keith Rodgers ❦ George Rodrigues ❦ Richard Rohmer ❦ S. Roitman ❦ Anthony Roman ❦ Brenda Roman ❦ Alfredo Romano ❦ Mario Romano ❦ William Rosart ❦ Lee Ross ❦ Mike Rostetter ❦ Phil Roth ❦ Richard Rotman ❦ William A. Rowat ❦ Andris Roze ❦ Norm Rubin ❦ Norm Rukavina ❦ George Rumble ❦ Somer Rumm ❦ Dallard Runge ❦ David Runnalls ❦ Zen Ruryk ❦ Deborah Russell ❦ George Rust-D'Eye ❦ Brian Rutherford ❦ Jim Ryan ❦ Louis Sabourin ❦ Peter J. Sagar ❦ Fran Sainsbury ❦ Carol Saint Laurent ❦ Edward R. Sajecki ❦ Nimrod Salamon ❦ Ted Salisbury ❦ Todd Salter ❦ Dereck Samaroo ❦ David Sampson ❦ Heather Saranpaa ❦ Eileen Sarkar ❦ Bill Saundercook ❦ David Saunders ❦ Charles Sauriol ❦ Paul Savoie ❦ Fred Scaffidi ❦ Henry Schefter ❦ Steve Schibuola ❦ Nigel Schilling ❦ Glen Schnarr ❦ John Schnayder ❦ N. Schonstedt ❦ Rhonda Schop ❦ Tom Schwartz ❦ Carolyn Scott ❦ Ian W. Scott ❦ Rosanna Scotti ❦ Paul H. Scrivener ❦ Robin Sears ❦ David Sefton ❦ Morley Sefton ❦ Farhad Seif ❦ Les C. Selby ❦ Alex Semeniuk ❦ John Sewell ❦ Geoff Shamie ❦ Walter Shanahan ❦ Peter Sharp ❦ Bob Shaw ❦ Martin Shaw ❦ Steve A. Shaw ❦ Derwyn Shea ❦ John H. Sheard ❦ James Shears ❦ Brian Shell ❦ Lou Shenfeld ❦ John Shepherd ❦ Griff Sherbin ❦ John Sherk ❦ Amanda Sherrington ❦ Richard Shibley ❦ Evelyn Shih-babor ❦ Ron Shimizu ❦ Karey Shinn ❦ Nick Shinn ❦ John Shipman ❦ Dalton Shipway ❦ Judie Shore ❦ Andrea Short ❦ Bob Short ❦ Glen Shortliffe ❦ John Shortread ❦ Steven Shrybman ❦ Anna Shumeko ❦ Gabriella Sicheri ❦ Marv Sidor ❦ Michael Sifton ❦ Sky Sigal ❦ Maria Kaars Sijpesteijn ❦ P. Silman ❦ Joe Silva ❦ Martin Silva ❦ Vykki Silzer ❦ John Simmers ❦ Robert Simmons ❦ Peter Simon ❦ Holly Simpson ❦ Jack Simpson ❦ Mary Simpson ❦ Lee Sims ❦ Bruce Sinclair ❦ John Sinclair ❦ Nancy Singer ❦ Safra Singh ❦ Karen Sita ❦ Andrew Skaab ❦ Michael Skafel ❦ George Sladek ❦ Robert W. Slater ❦ Joey Slinger ❦ Ron Sloan ❦ Richard Slowikowski ❦ Ed Slugocki ❦ Peter Sly ❦ Sharon Smalley ❦ David Smiley ❦ Albert R. Smith ❦ Beverly Smith ❦ David Smith ❦ Doug Smith ❦ Frank Smith ❦ Gordon Smith ❦ Julian L. Smith ❦ Karen Smith ❦ Paul K. Smith ❦ Ray Smith ❦ Robert D. Smith ❦ Rodney Smith ❦ Ron Smith ❦ Scott W. Smith ❦ Ken Snelson ❦ Sam Sniderman ❦ Simon So ❦ Richard Soberman ❦ Adam Socha ❦ Michael Soegtrop ❦ Rene Soetens ❦ Rachel Soffer ❦ Christopher Solecki ❦ Adrianna Solman ❦ Keith Solomon ❦ John Sousa ❦ Rosemary Spatafora ❦ Ray Spaxman ❦ Donald Speller ❦ Ted Spence ❦ Al Spiegel ❦ Laurel Spielberg ❦ David Springbett ❦ Bhartendu Srivastava ❦ Haymish St. Rose ❦ Elke Stahr ❦ Elizabeth Stanley ❦ Andrew Staples ❦ Becky Stapleton ❦ Charles Stearns ❦ Brian Stein ❦ Ross Stephen ❦ Murray Stephens ❦ Robert Stephens ❦ Judith Stephens-Wells ❦ Jan Stepien ❦ Feodora Steppat ❦ Mark Sterling ❦ Barry Sterparn ❦ Geoffrey Stevens ❦ Don Stevenson ❦ Greg Stewart ❦ Mary Stewart ❦ J. Anthony Stikeman ❦ Jeffery Stinson ❦ George Stockton ❦ Stewart Stolarski ❦ David Stonehouse ❦ Jeanne Strain ❦ Paul J. Strain ❦ Cynthia Strike ❦ Richard Stromberg ❦ Elaine Struke ❦ Jane Stubbington ❦ Richard Stultz ❦ Larry Sukava ❦ Barbara Sullivan ❦ Karl Suns ❦ Penti Suokas ❦ Kim Surgenor ❦ Hans Sustronk ❦ Sylvia Sutherland

THE WORK OF MANY HANDS . . . .

✤ John S. Sutherns ✤ Aine Suttle ✤ Howard Swadron ✤ Gail Swainson ✤ Anne Swarbrick ✤ Stanley B. Swartzman ✤ John Sweeney ✤ Austin Sweezy ✤ M. L. Swiggum ✤ Marv Sydor ✤ Tariq Syed ✤ Sandy Symmes ✤ Chris Szweda ✤ Peter Tabuns ✤ Catherine Talbot ✤ Larry Talbot ✤ Ken Tamminga ✤ R. T. (Bob) Tanaka ✤ Donald Tate ✤ Brian Taylor ✤ Carole Taylor ✤ Craig Taylor ✤ Dan Taylor ✤ Donna P. Taylor ✤ Irene Taylor ✤ Laura Taylor ✤ Marion Taylor ✤ Mark Taylor ✤ Raymond Taylor ✤ Robert Taylor-Vaisey ✤ Nicholas Teekman ✤ Bill Teron ✤ Chris Teron ✤ Paul Terry ✤ Christopher Thacker ✤ Lloyd Thomas ✤ Pan Thomas ✤ Peter Thomas ✤ Rondo P. Thomas ✤ Dave Thompson ✤ Denis Thompson ✤ Geoffrey Thornburn ✤ Michael G. Thorne ✤ Bev Thorpe ✤ Judith Tinkl ✤ Doug Tipple ✤ Richard Tobe ✤ George W. Todd ✤ Paula Todd ✤ Peter L. Todd ✤ Peter Tollefsen ✤ Peter Tomlinson ✤ Alan Tonks ✤ Rob Tonus ✤ Linda Torney ✤ John Tory ✤ Louise Tousignent ✤ Steve Tovee ✤ Robert Townsend ✤ David Toyne ✤ D. A. Trail ✤ Stephane Tremblay ✤ Joyce Trimmer ✤ David Troian ✤ Dave Trudeau ✤ Patrice Trupke ✤ Henry Tuero ✤ Blair Tully ✤ Brian Turnbull ✤ Brian Turner ✤ June Turner ✤ Mary-Frances Turner ✤ Raymond J. Twinney ✤ John Tylee ✤ Caroline Underwood ✤ Anthony Usher ✤ Marsha Valiante ✤ Jack R. Vallentyne ✤ Michael Valpy ✤ David V. Van ✤ John Van Burek ✤ Mark Van Elsberg ✤ Wal Van Riemsdyk ✤ Jack A. Vance ✤ M. VanDenTillaart ✤ Ben Vanderbrug ✤ Mark Vanderlaan ✤ Linda Varangu ✤ Nick Vardin ✤ Steve Varga ✤ James Vavaroutsas ✤ Brian Veinot ✤ Angela Vella ✤ Victoria Vidal-Ribas ✤ Peter Viducis ✤ Dieter Viereik ✤ David Villeneuve ✤ Ian Vincent ✤ Flora Voisey ✤ Andrew Volgyesi ✤ Ralph Volkhammer ✤ Joseph Volpe ✤ Rad Vucicevich ✤ Tony Wagner ✤ Sam Wakim ✤ Douglas A. Walker ✤ Gordon Walker ✤ Lennox Walker ✤ Michael Walker ✤ Nick E. Walker ✤ Peter Walker ✤ Tom Walker ✤ Thomas Walkom ✤ Brenda Wall ✤ James Wallace ✤ John Waller ✤ David Walmsley ✤ Lenore Wang ✤ Paul Wang ✤ Keith Ward ✤ Mary Beth Ward ✤ Craig Wardlaw ✤ Martha Warnes ✤ Basil Warren ✤ Randy E. Warren ✤ Robert Washburn ✤ Leon Wasser ✤ John G. Y. M. Wasteneys ✤ Dave Watt ✤ Garth S. Webb ✤ Larry Webb ✤ Madelyn Webb ✤ Peter Webb ✤ Richard A. Wedge ✤ Valerie Weeks ✤ Klaus Wehrenberg ✤ Henry Weissenberger ✤ Amber Welbelove ✤ Philip Weller ✤ Peter Wells ✤ Tammy Wells ✤ Gary Welsh ✤ Jane Welsh ✤ Jane Weninger ✤ Jim Wentzel ✤ Chip Weseloh ✤ John G. West ✤ Patrick West ✤ John Westgate ✤ Mark Whelan ✤ David White ✤ Drummond White ✤ Michael White ✤ Julie Whitfield ✤ Joseph Whitney ✤ Mike Whittle ✤ Ken Whitwell ✤ Reg Whynott ✤ Marnie Wigle ✤ Doug Wilkins ✤ Leslie J. Will ✤ Maldwyn Williams ✤ Marisa Williams ✤ R. A. Willson ✤ Bruce Wilmshurst ✤ Al J. Wilson ✤ John Wilson ✤ Katharine Wilson ✤ L. R. Wilson ✤ Mark Wilson ✤ Michael Wilson ✤ Peggy Wilson ✤ Trevor Wilson ✤ Jack Winberg ✤ Jim Wingard ✤ Chris Winter ✤ Ross Winter ✤ Lou Wise ✤ Jim Wiseman ✤ Jack Witherspoon ✤ Jim Witty ✤ Tony Wohlfarth ✤ Peter Wolf ✤ David Wolfe ✤ Chris Wong ✤ Hardy M. Wong ✤ Joe Wong ✤ Rosanna Wong ✤ Dickson Wood ✤ Nancy Wood ✤ Paul Woodall ✤ Bob Woodburn ✤ Carolyn Woodland ✤ Cathy Woods ✤ Julian Woods ✤ Lynda Kay Woodsworth ✤ Steve Woodward ✤ Barbara Woolley ✤ Gord Wooley ✤ John W. Wouters ✤ Chris Wren ✤ Donald Wright ✤ Mary Wright ✤ Wojciech Wronski ✤ Bill Wrye ✤ Franklin Wu ✤ Al Yagminas ✤ Armine Yalnizyan ✤ Yvonne Yamoka ✤ David Yap ✤ Haig Yeghouchian ✤ Kai Yew ✤ Richard Yoon ✤ James Young ✤ Jennifer Young ✤ Patricia Young ✤ Jack Youngberg ✤ John Yudelman ✤ Derek Yue ✤ E. H. (Eberhart) Zeidler ✤ Alena Zelinka ✤ Alex Zeman ✤ Joyce Zemans ✤ Orvin Zendel ✤ Gary Zikovitz ✤ Peter Zimmerman ✤

CONTENTS

PREFACE

AN ECOSYSTEM APPROACH TO THE REGENERATION OF CITIES

The city should be regarded as a natural ecosystem, requiring an integrated approach for addressing its problems.

Half the world's peoples will live in urban areas by the end of this decade. Whether we achieve a greater degree of environmental sustainability over that time will therefore be determined largely by our cities. Surely, sustainability is not possible in the long term unless we can soon find ways to regenerate our urban ecosystems, keep them in good health, and adopt more sustainable urban lifestyles.

But the environmental challenges facing cities receive relatively little attention — as any review of the literature on sustainable development quickly makes clear. Even the United Nations World Commission on Environment and Development (the Brundtland Commission) devoted little to the analysis of what it called the urban challenges. As Michael Hough said in his book **City Form and Natural Process** *(1989), "In a world*

increasingly concerned with the problems of a deteriorating environment, be they energy, pollution, vanishing plants, animals or productive landscapes, there is a marked propensity to bypass the environment most people live in — the city itself".

The City as Pestilence

Why do most environmental commentators engage in so little analysis of our urban ecosystems? Perhaps one reason is that many environmentalists continue to see cities as unnatural — or worse. Recently, for example, Canadian geneticist David Suzuki, a widely read analyst of social and environmental issues, offered his perspective on cities around the world:

> *We can't eradicate cities. Nor would we want to. But we must recognize that cities disconnect us from nature and each other. They exist by draining resources from the planet while spreading toxic materials and debris. And if we regard all living things on earth as an immense supra-organism (which some have called Gaia), then cities must be seen as the Gaian equivalent of cancer (1991).*

Dr. Suzuki's view of cities, however harsh, plays to a familiar bias in North American literature. Cities, in the accepted view, are not good things. ("Pestilential to our future," said Thomas Jefferson.) Bad things happen there. The countryside is a good thing. Good things happen there. "Nature" is at home in the countryside but not in the city, and God is clearly more knowable in the wide-open spaces than on city streets.

City bashing, therefore, is an easy occupation, but it makes the regeneration and renaissance of cities much more difficult for those who, like Lewis Mumford, see the city as a place where "the separate beams of life" are brought together and "the issues of civilization are brought into focus" — a place where ancient connections, origins, and identities merge with overwhelming events that suggest new opportunities, new dreams, and new questions.

The City as Beacon

It has not been all one-sided, though clearly the bashers have had their way. In a valiant brigade, city lovers such as Jane Jacobs, William H. Whyte, Ian McHarg, Tony Hiss, and others have struggled to frame a more positive view of the city, and have offered both philosophical perspectives and practical steps for a more hopeful future.

They are supported, of course, by the millions upon millions of ordinary people who over the centuries have chosen to leave the countryside in order to live in the city. Why do they come? Why have cities grown and grown? Why do people, if they have the choice, decide to live in the "pestilence" and "cancer" of the city?

Cities are desirable and important because they continue to be beacons of hope and freedom to each new generation. Travel on any continent and you will see young people taking the road to town, drawn by the magnetism of cities. Cities are places where fame, fortune, and the future seem ripe for the picking. They are places where you can try to be what you want to be — and where, if you're lucky, you will find a sense of

community that will serve your needs, shape your day-to-day experiences, give focus to your freedom and meaning to your hopes. For these reasons, as the Alberta Environment Council (1988) put it in its publication **Environment by Design**, cities continue to be "the habitat of choice for most people."

The City as Natural Phenomenon

But like us, a city is not separate from nature. Within cities we have vegetation, forests, fields, streams, lakes, rivers, terrain, soils, and wildlife. Hydrology, topography, and climate set the fundamental structure for human habitation and the building of the city itself. As Kevin Lynch (1981) wrote in **A Theory of Good City Form**, "People and their cities are as much natural phenomena as trees, streams, nests, and deer paths. It is crucial that we come to see ourselves as an integral part of the total living community".

Based on this understanding, we must begin the regeneration of our cities and waterfronts over the next decade. Only by understanding the city as a part of nature can we deal with the wounds inflicted on it, mend its ways, and design its form so that it functions sustainably to satisfy needs without diminishing opportunities for future generations.

The Environmental Revolution

There is, of course, no other choice. The Environmental Revolution is already here — as almost everybody knows. It developed out of the perspectives of the conservation movement at the turn of the century, and was quickened by the actions of anti-pollution activists in the last 25 years. As a result, the environmental imperative today is hitting the city with seismic force.

The fact is that, in pursuit of its needs and pleasures, our throwaway society has poisoned the air, polluted the rivers, and contaminated the earth, without worrying or caring to learn about the long-term damage caused to the environment or about the way we are foreclosing opportunities for future generations. Unswimmable beaches, undrinkable water, unfishable rivers that have become sewers — these are only some of the visible, touchable signposts of environmental carelessness and degradation.

People will no longer put up with it. Environmental consciousness has already begun to reorganize government policies and priorities, recast corporate strategies, and redefine community and individual responsibility and behaviour. And it is raising fundamental questions — spiritual questions — about the relationship of humankind to nature and to God. It has become a force strong enough to change the face, form, and function of cities around the world.

An Integrated Approach to Cities

It is for these reasons, among others, that the idea of using an ecosystem approach to the regeneration of cities has gained increasing acceptance. An ecosystem is composed of air, water, land, and living organisms, including humans, as well as the interactions among them. The concept has been applied to many types of interacting systems, among them lakes, watersheds, the biosphere, and cities themselves.

Traditionally, human activities have been managed on a piecemeal basis, treating the economy separately from social issues or the environment. But the ecosystem concept holds that these are interrelated, that decisions made in one area affect all others. Dealing effectively with the environmental problems in any city requires a holistic or ecosystem approach to managing human activities.

There are certain key characteristics of an ecosystem approach that help illustrate what is required. An ecosystem approach:

- includes the whole system, not just parts of it;

- focuses on the interrelationships among the elements;
- understands that humans are part of nature, not separate from it;
- recognizes the dynamic nature of the ecosystem, presenting a moving picture rather than a still photograph;
- incorporates the concepts of carrying capacity, resilience, and sustainability — suggesting that there are limits to human activity;
- uses a broad definition of environments — natural, physical, economic, social and cultural;
- encompasses both urban and rural activities;
- is based on natural geographic units such as watersheds, rather than on political boundaries;
- embraces all levels of activity — local, regional, national, and international;
- emphasizes the importance of species other than humans and of generations other than the present; and
- is based on an ethic in which progress is measured by the quality, well-being, integrity, and dignity it accords natural, social, and economic systems.

Because all environmental problems (and, in fact, all social and economic problems) cut across disciplines and jurisdictions, the multidisciplinary and multijurisdictional qualities inherent in ecosystem planning make this approach particularly necessary and appropriate.

Overcoming Jurisdictional Fragmentation

Unfortunately, most of society is not organized in a way that facilitates this comprehensive approach. In Canada, for example, four levels of government have jurisdiction in the Toronto city region, and more than 100 agencies exercise responsibility with little effective co-ordination among them. Indeed, in the past, the parochial pressures of bureaucracies and representative governments have almost compelled them to be unresponsive to cross-jurisdictional issues. When everyone is in charge, no one is in charge.

The result is bureaucratic and political paralysis — a situation in which almost any agency can stop projects, and no one can do anything. Because lines of accountability are completely distorted or hidden by this jurisdictional fragmentation, the citizen is left without any means of recourse. The implications for our democracy may be more crucial than we know. The jurisdictional gridlock throughout this region is the single biggest obstacle to its environmental (and economic) regeneration. And this is not a problem unique to the Toronto city region.

The ecosystem approach, then, requires new institutional arrangements. As the Brundtland Commission warned in its 1987 report, **Our Common Future**:

> Most of the institutions facing those challenges tend to be independent, fragmented, working to relatively narrow mandates with closed decision processes. Those responsible for managing natural resources and protecting the environment are institutionally separated from those responsible for managing the economy. The real world of interlocked economic and ecological systems will not change; the policies and institutions concerned must.

Common Features to Diverse Solutions

Each city region in the world will have to develop its own institutional adaptations in order to implement an ecosystem approach to planning. Each adaptation will reflect the history, culture, traditions, habits, and customs unique to that city. But it is also possible to see that cities will discover some common features in their new approach:

- the recognition of the primacy of natural boundaries and processes;
- the integration of land use with environmental planning in public process and law;
- the integration of urban and rural planning to link the city with its region;
- the creation of concurrent, rather than consecutive, planning processes;
- the integration of capital budgets of all government departments and agencies to ensure coherence, economies, and financial strength; and
- the recognition of the increasing importance of designing places and spaces that allow people to feel a part of nature while they take advantage of the immemorial human pleasures that only cities can offer.

These kinds of institutional adaptations will help cities develop their potential fully. **Environment by Design** could not express it better than by quoting Claude Lévi-Strauss:

> Cities have often been likened to symphonies and poems, and the comparison seems to me a perfectly natural one. . . . By its form, as by the manner of its birth, the city has elements at once of biological procreation, organic evolution and aesthetic creation. It is both a natural object and a thing to be cultivated; something lived and something dreamed. It is **the** human invention par excellence.

Adapted from the article written by David Crombie and Ronald L. Doering printed in Ecodecision Magazine, *No. 3, December 1991. Reprinted by permission of the publisher.*

Introduction: The Work of the Royal Commission on the Future of the Toronto Waterfront

> We shall not cease from exploration
> And the end of all our exploring
> Will be to arrive where we started
> And to know the place for the first time.
> —T.S. Eliot. Four Quartets. Little Gidding, V

The First Phase

On 30 March 1988, the Governor-in-Council, on the recommendation of the prime minister, approved the appointment of the Honourable David Crombie as Commissioner to:

inquire into and make recommendations regarding the future of the Toronto waterfront and to seek the concurrence of affected authorities in such recommendations, in order to ensure that, in the public interest, federal lands and jurisdiction serve to enhance the physical, environmental, legislative and administrative context governing the use, enjoyment and development of the Toronto waterfront and related lands.

More specifically, the Commission was directed to examine:

- the role and mandate of the Board of Toronto Harbour Commissioners;

- the future of the Toronto Island Airport and related transportation services;
- the issues affecting the protection and the renewal of the natural environment insofar as they relate to federal responsibilities and jurisdiction;
- the issues regarding the effective management of federal lands within the Toronto waterfront area; and
- the possible use of federal lands, facilities, and jurisdiction to support emerging issues such as the proposed Olympic Games and World's Fair.

The Commission was initially given a three-year mandate, from June 1988 to June 1991; that was later extended to 31 December 1991, in order to give the Commission time to complete added work requested by the Province of Ontario.

The Government of Canada's decision to establish the Commission was based on its recognition that the Toronto waterfront was an area offering many opportunities but had, to quote an Intergovernmental Waterfront Committee (IWC) that looked at the situation, "a number of urgent matters that must be studied and dealt with".

The IWC had been organized informally 18 months before the Commission was established, after the prime minister asked Mr. Crombie, then a cabinet minister from Toronto with a particular interest in urban issues, to make recommendations on the appropriateness of having the Government of Canada, through the Canadian Broadcasting Corporation (CBC) — a Crown corporation — involve itself in urban redevelopment in downtown Toronto.

In the course of discussing this project with representatives of the Province, Metropolitan Toronto, and the City of Toronto, it became evident to Mr. Crombie that there were some common concerns, particularly about waterfront issues and about the jurisdictional gridlock that had developed in dealing with them. This led to a decision to set up the IWC, with then-Premier David Peterson in the chair, and a membership comprising Dennis Flynn, then chairman of the Municipality of Metropolitan Toronto; the then-mayor of Toronto, Art Eggleton; and Mr. Crombie.

The IWC met over the next several months to identify common concerns on which concerted action might be taken, work that proved to be the foundation for tasks eventually assigned to the Royal Commission.

The Commission began by organizing five work groups that would look at broad waterfront issues, and planned a series of public hearings for the spring of 1989. In addition, Commission staff and experts under contract began to analyse the port, airport, land-use, and development activities of federal agencies on the waterfront.

From the beginning, the Commission conducted open inquiries, seeking to consider all perspectives and listening to all points of view. Openness included invitations to federal, provincial, and municipal governments to participate in the Commission's work groups and studies, alongside representatives of the private sector, labour, and academia. The Government of Canada, the Province of Ontario, and other invited participants accepted willingly and worked co-operatively from the start. Initially, however, municipalities were wary, fearing that the existence of the Commission might be an attempt by the federal government to extend its jurisdiction on the waterfront. As it became clear that this was not the case, and that the Commission intended to respect existing jurisdictions at all levels, a very high degree of intergovernmental co-operation was offered in every aspect of the Royal Commission's work.

It soon became evident to the Commission, as it had been to some others, that waterfront problems were both broader and deeper than the list of issues included in the Commission's federal mandate. They stemmed from historical forces related to the way society and the economy had evolved over the past 200 years, and to the impact each had on the waterfront and on the local and regional environment of which the waterfront is a part.

The public, ahead of governments, was aware of the nature of the problem. In the Commission's first sets of hearings, dozens of deputants delivered the same message: by all means sort out the issues of Harbourfront and the Harbour

Toronto Skyline, view from the Toronto Islands

Commissioners, but help us find out how to make our lake publicly accessible, fishable, drinkable, and swimmable. This cannot happen while the rivers that empty into the lake are contaminated, the air that connects to it is dirty, the groundwaters polluted, and the soils through which they pass contaminated.

During this first phase of its work, the Commission published seven major reports, as background for the public hearings and as the basis of its analysis of waterfront needs and opportunities: *Environment and Health: Issues on the Toronto Waterfront; Housing and Neighbourhoods: The Liveable Waterfront; Access and Movement; Parks,*

Pleasures, and Public Amenities; Jobs,
Opportunities, and Economic Growth; Persistence
and Change: Waterfront Issues and the Board
of Toronto Harbour Commissioners; and *The*
Future of the Toronto Island Airport: The Issues.

Fortunately, the Commission had not
been given specific boundaries as part of its
original mandate. Therefore, work groups
were encouraged to draw whatever boundaries they felt were necessary in considering
the issues placed before them. The limits
turned out to be broader (and vaguer)
in some instances (e.g., environment and
health) and narrower and more specific in
others (e.g., housing and neighbourhoods).

However, at this stage of the
Commission's existence, its principal
geographic focus was the waterfront of
the Regional Municipality of Metropolitan
Toronto, including the three local municipalities of Etobicoke, Toronto, and
Scarborough. In many instances, the word
Toronto came to be used as shorthand for all
the communities in the region, defining the
sense of place. In fact, a study conducted for
the Commission in 1991 reveals that, rather
than naming the individual municipalities
in which they live, seven of every ten area
residents think of themselves as coming
from Toronto.

By the end of the first year of operations, the Commission had reached its first
set of conclusions, which it conveyed to the
federal government and the public through
its first interim report, in August 1989. It
summarizes the first phase of the Commission's work, which had focused on the waterfront in the context of Toronto's history,
values, and contemporary issues:

Toronto was born on the waterfront. Long before the Simcoes. Long
before the Town of York. Deep in the

mists of aboriginal time, the Toronto
Carrying Place was a centre of trade,
stabilized by community and endowed
with spiritual significance.

When Toronto embraced the
Railway Era in the 1850s, there were
few hints of the City that would emerge,
the City the railways would help to create. And if the City was cut off from its
waterfront by dozens of sets of tracks
flowing in and out of each other in the
new lands south of Front Street — and
it was — it is also clear that the City and
its people benefitted mightily. Having
secured a major share of a new technology, and established a formula for economic success that remains potent to
this day, Toronto drew hundreds of
industries to its shores over the years.
And as energetic cities do, it began
to attract people from other parts of
Canada and from all over the world:
creative people, people with dreams
and ideas, people seeking freedom and
better prospects, people whose children
and their ensuing generations would
keep Toronto vigorous. And the City
prospered.

But as railways and then expressways cut people off from their waterfront, as people looked elsewhere to
live, work, and play, and as our economic drive brought greater prosperity
to more and more people, our perspective changed dramatically. The significance of waterfronts was lost and their
importance diminished; the great contribution of our river valleys was no
longer understood or taught and, save
for a few hardy souls, the essential role
of Nature in the City was all but forgotten.
Progress meant industry and industry

meant railways. Railways required land for track and cities agreed to separate themselves from their waterfronts in order to capture the opportunities the railways offered.

But in our time the railways have become more interested in profit from the land than in service from the tracks; ships have changed their technologies and their trade routes; the economic base of cities is being changed and there has been a significant shift in human values. People are coming back to our waterfronts for pleasure and solace in a way that their great-grandparents would have understood.

This is dramatic, powerful, and far-reaching historical change. The people of Toronto understand this. Time and again, they have expressed their belief that Toronto's way of doing things, its values, its civic traditions could and should be used to deal with the forces that affect the future of the waterfront and the city.

Three words define the values of Toronto at its best: opportunity, tolerance, and orderliness. With a few pauses, Toronto has been a place at the cutting edge, a magnet for new ideas, and a resource in realizing them. In Toronto, as in all vigorous cities, opportunities beget opportunities.

Moreover, there has always been an ongoing opportunity to affect the course of the city itself — a sense that Toronto is a work in progress and that its directions can be changed. People

who have been in Toronto for a while begin to develop a feeling of what they want it to be, what of its many facets would benefit from change, what should stay the same.

Tolerance has meant the near-total absence of violent confrontation. There are forums where people grapple with ideas, interests, and beliefs. When compromise is possible, compromise is made, but even when it is not possible, "losers" are left with the knowledge that, next time, they could just as easily be "winners": an idea has been rejected, not the person who proposed it. This climate of tolerance has also meant that sooner or later, "New Torontonians" (new arrivals or new generations, or both) will have their ideas and aspirations brought to the City's and the public's official attention and they will be given respectful consideration. Tolerance means that everybody learns that everybody counts.

Orderliness has been important in the building of Toronto. With all the transformations the City has experienced and all the conflicts it has had to resolve, nothing has ever truly gotten out of hand. That discipline (a better word, maybe, than orderliness) has been here from the beginning — a lingering legacy, no doubt, of Governor Simcoe's garrison days. It is a value, or a virtue, that has been drawn upon by each succeeding wave of New Torontonians, reinterpreted on occasion and adapted to specific circumstances, but always enriched along the way.

Toronto has been a place at the cutting edge, a magnet for new ideas, and a resource in realizing them.

Toronto continues to recognize that freedom remains alive only in an atmosphere of order, that life here is played by a set of rules, and that the rules are meant to work for everybody. From this comes the assurance that nothing will ever get out of hand or out of control; that the City will never grow beyond its ability to solve its problems; that, when things start to go wrong, order will be restored and the right thing done.

Well, that's the faith. Easier to say than to do. Forging consensus rooted in these core values is the dull, hard work of democracy — an unrelenting, never-ending task that requires the energies, interests, and imaginations of many people over long periods of time. Sometimes their voices are not heard. Sometimes the thread is lost — or their visions are blocked. And sometimes the soul-numbing experiences of day-to-day battle create a tempting cynicism that obscures the progress being achieved.

Indeed, the values that we call opportunity, tolerance, and orderliness work best when people believe they themselves can make a difference; when they feel that their dreams can expand their realities; and when they feel that Toronto holds its own unique promise for them, a promise that can be fulfilled by their efforts, both individually and in community with others.

Armed with this appreciation of Toronto's core values, the Commission turned its attention to a first set of recommendations. The Commission had already decided to make interim recommendations that would facilitate the ongoing process of analysis and help forge a consensus on required courses of action. It would make final recommendations on issues it felt capable of dealing with as early as possible in its mandate, in hope of obtaining early agreement and response from the community and from the governments involved.

The Commission made more than 60 recommendations in this first interim report, more than half of which dealt with environmental issues. Most of these suggestions were directed in the first instance to the federal government, but a number were generic and applicable to two or more levels of government. True to its mandate, the Commission was seeking the concurrence of affected authorities.

The single most important recommendation of the interim report was the proposal that a watershed approach be adopted to protect Toronto's vital ecosystem. The report said:

> To begin, a broad evaluation is needed to ensure that sufficient open space is maintained and that its environmentally significant features are preserved. Across the entire watershed, a "green" strategy [should] be devised to preserve the waterfront, river valley systems, head-waters, wetlands, and other significant features in the public interest. Such a strategy would physically link the waterfront to the river valley systems, which, in turn, would be linked by the preserved headwater areas. A

In the first interim report the most important recommendation was the proposal that a watershed approach be adopted to protect Toronto's ecosystem.

continuous trail system would guarantee public access to these natural and open spaces.

Major elements supporting the green strategy were the Commission's proposals that the Rouge River Valley be protected as a natural heritage park, Humber Bay Park East be protected as significant regional urban space, and the Leslie Street Spit be recognized as an urban wilderness park. The Commission defined "urban wilderness" as an extensive area in which natural processes predominate; there is public access without vehicles; and there are low-key, low-cost, unorganized recreation and contacts with wildlife.

The environmental recommendations made by the Commission in the report included proposals for:

- improving public access to the entire waterfront and extending public ownership;
- imposing a moratorium on lakefilling until a comprehensive lakefill policy is developed;
- establishing a waterfront-wide heritage policy;
- protecting all natural areas and wildlife along the waterfront, and rehabilitating and maintaining river valleys such as the Humber, the Don, and the Rouge;
- creating a watershed greenbelt;
- strengthening and more closely integrating the Ontario Planning Act and the Environmental Assessment Act, as well as strengthening the federal environmental review process; and
- controlling over-development, including high-rises, on the waterfront to prevent visual or physical barriers.

All these issues and recommendations were to be more fully analysed and considered in subsequent phases of the Commission's work.

In the same interim report, the Commission also made its final recommendations on the Toronto Island Airport and on Harbourfront, as well as its fundamental recommendations about the Board of Toronto Harbour Commissioners. They are summarized here and discussed in greater detail in Part III of this report.

The Commission recommended that the federal government terminate the Harbourfront Corporation and create a new entity, the Harbourfront Foundation, giving it a mandate to continue providing Harbourfront's wide variety of cultural, recreational, and educational programs, which would be supported by an endowment from the Harbourfront assets. The Commission suggested that lands not needed to endow the foundation should be disposed of, subject to negotiations with the City of Toronto; furthermore, the Commission felt that urban design improvements were also needed, to achieve the best physical integration of the Harbourfront area with the surrounding city and the water.

In considering the Toronto Island Airport, the Commission concluded that it should continue its dual role as part of a regional airport system. Within this system, it should serve general aviation and limited air commuter operations, in accordance with the terms and conditions of the 50-year Tripartite Agreement signed in 1983 among the City of Toronto, the Toronto Harbour Commissioners, and the federal Minister of Transport.

The Commission also recommended that a new airport plan be prepared, one

Bluffer's Park Marina, Scarborough

that would reflect that dual role and ensure that the airport would remain at its existing scale, be cleaner and quieter, and become more sensitive to the needs of its users. It also found a need for management improvements, including a new financial and accounting base, and improved public and user consultation processes.

The Commission recommended that the mandate of the Toronto Harbour Commissioners (THC) to operate the Port of Toronto be separated from planning or developing lands that do not serve the port function. The THC should retain its authority to operate the Port (and the airport) on behalf of the City of Toronto but should be limited to that task. The Commission suggested that, in addition to the proposed changes to the THC's mandate, greater local control of waterfront planning and a better system of accountability were needed.

The Commission indicated it would conduct studies during the next phase of its work, to evaluate how much land was needed for the port operation and which lands could be transferred to another body. It also recommended that an environmental audit of the entire East Bayfront/Port Industrial Area be carried out before there was further action to develop lands in those areas.

THE SECOND PHASE

On 30 August 1989, the same day the Commission's report was released, then-Treasury Board President Robert de Cotret responded on behalf of the Government of Canada:

> The government is in substantial agreement with the Royal Commission's recommendations on Harbourfront, is generally supportive of the recommendation

that the airport continue to serve general aviation and limited commuter traffic, and is open to discussions with the City of Toronto regarding the recommendation to transfer management of lands no longer required for port purposes from the Toronto Harbour Commissioners to another body.

Shortly thereafter, on 17 October 1989, the Province of Ontario also acted: then-Premier David Peterson announced broad provincial measures to ensure that Toronto's waterfront is preserved, protected, and used prudently as an accessible and attractive place for people.

These measures included:

- endorsing the Royal Commission's report;
- providing an additional, complementary mandate to the Commission, asking it to report to the Province on waterfront development issues along the entire western basin of Lake Ontario, from the eastern boundary of Durham Region to the western boundary of Halton Region;
- agreeing to join the environmental audit of the East Bayfront/Port Industrial Area, and issuing an invitation to Metropolitan Toronto and the City of Toronto to participate as well;
- declaring a Provincial Interest in that area under the Planning Act, "to prevent any major development . . . until it can be determined what is appropriate for the people and the environment";
- asking the Commission to recommend ways of linking and integrating the waterfront to the upstream watersheds

throughout the Greater Toronto region; and (in a companion move)
- appointing Ron Kanter, then MPP for St. Andrew-St. Patrick, to identify ways of protecting forever the headwaters and river valleys from the Oak Ridges Moraine to Lake Ontario.

Having said on numerous occasions that no one level of government can resolve all the issues related to the development of the waterfront in the public interest, Mr. Crombie called the new provincial mandate, added to that from the federal government, "a very strong signal of federal-provincial co-operation on these matters". Indeed, it made this Commission only the second in Canadian history to serve two levels of government. (The first had been the one called to investigate the Ocean Range disaster off Newfoundland in 1976.)

The mandate the Province gave the Commission was broad and comprehensive. Because of the waterfront's environmental significance; the extensive socio-economic pressures that characterize waterfront development; and the importance of rational planning and development of the waterfront to ensure future quality of life and the well-being of hinterland areas, the Province asked the Commission to inquire into and make recommendations concerning:

- appropriate allocation of waterfront lands to various uses — i.e., housing, open-space, industrial, and commercial uses;
- waterfront transportation in the context of the regional transportation system;
- housing and community development on the waterfront;

- employment and job opportunities relating to the waterfront; and
- initiatives to preserve and enhance the quality of the environment and the quality of life for people living in the region.

The Commission was asked to conclude its inquiries and submit its recommendations to the Province at the same time that it reported to the federal government.

In the second phase of its operations, the Commission used the same methods as in its first year: utilizing work groups, independent analysis, public hearings, and consulting with interested parties. Now, however, it was working in a much more fully regional context — looking at a region with a shoreline of some 250 kilometres (155 miles) covering 17 local municipalities, six conservation authorities, four regional municipalities, and four counties on the waterfront.

The Commission held three more sets of public hearings in this second phase, in Burlington, Toronto, and Oshawa, and published three more background reports: *A Green Strategy for the Greater Toronto Waterfront*; *Waterfront Transportation in the Context of Regional Transportation*; and the results of the first phase of the environmental audit, *East Bayfront/Port Industrial Area: Environment in Transition*.

The work ranged from theory to practice, policy to program, and from the scale of the Great Lakes to that of the region and its communities. Fundamental to all its efforts was the conviction that the

environment had to be the workbench on which all other aspects of the Commission's operations and conclusions would be built.

This need — to consider the environment first and make it the central theme — led the Commission to choose an ecosystem approach for analysing the state of the environment of the waterfront, the watershed, and the (bio)region, and for charting their future. Learning as it went, leaning heavily on thinkers (Jack Vallentyne, Andy Hamilton, Henry Regier, Don Gamble, Peter Sly, Katherine Davies, and Trevor Hancock, among others) who had been and are still working out underlying ecosystem concepts, the Commission sought to understand the approach in theory and, in its audit of the East Bayfront/Port Industrial Area, to apply it.

The emphasis on understanding environmental conditions as a prelude to planning courses of action brought the Commission into contact with many parties, among them:

- the International Joint Commission (IJC), in connection with its work on water quality and water levels in the Great Lakes;
- the four parties (i.e., environmental agencies of the U.S. and Canadian governments, the State of New York, and the Province of Ontario) responsible for creating the Lake Ontario Toxics Management Plan (LOTMP); and
- locally, various stakeholders associated with Remedial Action Plans (RAPs),

> *The environment had to be the workbench on which all other aspects of the Commission's operations and conclusions would be built. This conviction led to the ecosystem approach.*

which are designed to clean up contamination "hot spots" in areas around the Great Lakes, Toronto being one of them.

The Commission's second interim report, *Watershed* (1990), was submitted to the federal and provincial governments in September 1990; it begins with a definition of "ecosystem" and an explanation of the significance of the ecosystem approach:

> Simply put, an ecosystem is composed of air, land, water, and living organisms, including humans, and the interactions among them. The concept has been applied to many types of interacting systems, including lakes, watersheds, cities, and the biosphere.
>
> Traditionally, human activities have been managed on a piecemeal basis, treating the economy separately from social issues or the environment. But the ecosystem concept holds that these are interrelated, that decisions made in one area affect all the others. To deal effectively with the environmental problems in any ecosystem requires a holistic or "ecosystem" approach to managing human activities. . . .

The environmental audit is demonstrating the inextricable links among the East Bayfront/Port Industrial Area, other parts of Toronto, the Don River Watershed, and the Great Lakes. Similarly, the Greater Toronto Area waterfront being investigated by the Royal Commission is part of a region that includes the watersheds of the rivers leading into Lake Ontario from the GTA. Anything that happens within this area is tied ecologically to the health of the waterfront.

Therefore in order to truly understand the waterfront itself, we must gain an understanding of the biological region, or bioregion in which it lies.

Watershed then goes on to assess the state of the waterfront and of the Greater Toronto bioregion, defined by the Commission as the area bounded by the Niagara Escarpment to the west, the Oak Ridges Moraine to the north and east, and Lake Ontario to the south. In the words of the report:

> The assessment concluded that this is an ecosystem under considerable stress; one that is, to a large degree, "disintegrated", in which the carrying capacity — the ability of air, land, and water to absorb the impact of human use — is clearly strained, and cannot be sustained over the longer term unless fundamental changes are made.
>
> There is an urgent need for regeneration of the entire Greater Toronto Bioregion to remediate environmental problems caused by past activities, to prevent further degradation, and to ensure that all future activities result in a net improvement in environmental health.

The Commission recognizes that governments, working alone, cannot solve our environmental problems, and that the bioregion's six thousand industries and four million residents have responsibilities they must meet.

The ecosystem concept holds that economy, social issues, and environment are interrelated — decisions made in one area affect all the others.

Because the ecosystem approach highlights interactions among ecological, social, economic, and political systems in the bioregion, the Commission emphasized the importance of developing new administrative mechanisms that bring jurisdictions together to solve problems co-operatively and that help establish environmentally sound ways of living.

Watershed's second chapter focuses on the needs of the Greater Toronto waterfront in the context of its bioregion and offers a set of nine principles for planning, developing, and managing a healthy, integrated waterfront.

The Commission said the waterfront should be clean, green, useable, diverse, open, accessible, connected, affordable, and attractive. (There is a more detailed explanation of the interpretation, origins, and possible applications of these principles, both in *Watershed* and in this report.)

Watershed contains some 80 recommendations for implementing an ecosystem approach that will restore the health and usefulness of the waterfront. As in the first interim report, some suggestions are generic, involving the entire waterfront or region, while others are specific to particular areas or jurisdictions. Although many recommendations were directed to the federal government, most flowed from the Commission's provincial mandate.

Among the most important generic, region-wide recommendations were:

All federal, provincial, and municipal governments and agencies with an interest in or influence over the waterfront should adopt the ecosystem approach and principles outlined in this report as a basis for planning.

The Province should declare the waterfront from Burlington to Newcastle a Provincial Resource, and it should provide leadership, resources, and opportunities for collaboration amongst various parties, in order to integrate planning and programs as part of efforts to regenerate the waterfront.

The Province should establish Waterfront Partnership Agreements with municipalities, along the lines recommended in this [*Watershed*] report.

Over the next year, the Province should work with the Commission to review ways in which the philosophy and principles of the ecosystem approach could best be integrated into the Planning Act and other relevant provincial legislation, as it affects the Greater Toronto bioregion. . . .

The Province should plan, co-ordinate, and implement a Waterfront Trail from Burlington to Newcastle, to be completed by 1993 to celebrate both the bicentennial of the founding of York and the centennial of the Ontario provincial parks system. . . .

The Province should take immediate steps to preserve the ecological, scenic,

Watershed offers recommendations for implementing an ecosystem approach and developing the administrative mechanisms to bring jurisdictions together to solve problems co-operatively and to establish environmentally sound ways of living.

and recreational significance of the Oak Ridges Moraine, and to ensure that future land use in the moraine does not result in cumulative impairment of the ecological quality of downstream rivers or the waterfront. . . .

The federal and provincial governments should modify the RAP process by elevating each municipality from being one of many stakeholders, to being a joint partner in developing and implementing the RAP. Using the watershed approach, all municipalities within a given watershed should be asked to collaborate on the RAP. . . .

The Province should bring forward comprehensive lakefill policies for public review as soon as possible. The policies should require thorough environmental appraisal of all individual lakefill projects, and of their cumulative effects, across the Greater Toronto Waterfront. Until such policies are in place, there should be a moratorium on new lakefilling. . . .

The waterfront, the Oak Ridges Moraine, and river valleys of the Greater Toronto Area should be recognized as Provincial Resources in the public debate and decisions made by all levels of government on the urban form and structure of the region. . . .

In addition to the recommendations dealing with environmental regeneration at the regional scale, *Watershed* considered a wide range of specific matters, including:

- devising a concept for the route of a continuous Waterfront Trail from Burlington to Newcastle;

- examining the possibility of reducing the barrier effects of the Gardiner/ Lakeshore Corridor, by taking down the elevated portion of the expressway in phases and improving public transit and road systems in the area;
- creating a Waterfront Regeneration Trust, to co-ordinate the regeneration of the waterfront;
- defining and proposing the transfer of THC's non-port lands: to the City of Toronto for parkland and a wildlife corridor; to the Toronto Economic Development Corporation (TEDCO) for industrial purposes; and to the proposed Waterfront Trust for decontamination and redevelopment for mixed uses;
- creating a Centre for Green Enterprise and Industry; and
- drafting waterfront plans and projects in Halton Region, Mississauga, Etobicoke, Scarborough, and Durham Region.

When *Watershed* was released, Mr. Crombie said he was "encouraged over the past year by the continuing strong public interest in the waterfront and by signs of an emerging consensus among all levels of government concerning waterfront policies and priorities. The aim of this report", he continued, "is to provide the basis for governments to act now on the fundamental decisions that have to be taken to ensure that the people of Toronto have the waterfront they want and deserve".

There was widespread and positive community and government reaction to the Commission's principles, and to its recommended approach for regenerating the waterfront and watershed.

THE THIRD PHASE

Once more, the Government of Canada responded promptly. On 12 September 1990, Robert de Cotret, then Treasury Board president and Environment minister, said:

> I fully support the comprehensive eco-system approach that the Commission has adopted and which is integral to the *Great Lakes Water Quality Agreement.* The federal government has an important role to play in responding to *Watershed* and we will do our full share within our jurisdiction.

He also commented favourably on the proposed Centre for Green Enterprise, and promised that the government would look closely at recommendations to increase public access to the waterfront, and to transfer federal lands along the waterfront to other levels of government. Mr. de Cotret added, "Mr. Crombie has presented a useful framework for discussing the future of the Toronto Harbour Commissioners. The government will be discussing these recommendations with the City of Toronto, the Province, the Royal Commission, and other interests".

That same afternoon, Bob Rae, then premier-elect, welcomed *Watershed,* saying:

> The Government of Ontario will provide the strong provincial leadership needed to maintain the ecological integrity of the waterfront. We fully agree with the ecosystem approach to waterfront policies and priorities, and we are prepared to work closely with local governments and existing agencies to protect the ecology of the watershed and to create a diverse, integrated, and healthy waterfront.

Almost all municipalities across the waterfront also endorsed the report, as did representatives of business, labour, and environmental and community groups.

Shortly after the release of *Watershed,* the Commission organized another work group, to review how the philosophy and principles of the ecosystem approach might best be integrated into the Planning Act and into other legislation that affects the Greater Toronto bioregion. The group's conclusions and recommendations were published in *Planning for Sustainability: Towards Integrating Environmental Protection into Land-Use Planning.*

The Province of Ontario responded more fully three months after *Watershed* was released. On 17 December 1991, Ruth Grier, Minister of the Environment and minister responsible for the Greater Toronto Area, commended the previous government and John Sweeney in particular, for giving the Commission a broad mandate and for supporting the Commission; she continued:

> We endorse fully the principles put forward for the future direction of the waterfront area; a waterfront that is clean, green and attractive; a waterfront that is useable, diverse and open; and a waterfront that is connected, affordable and accessible.
>
> We intend to use these nine principles as a guide, not only for the waterfront, but to move beyond the waterfront — to the GTA urban structure process. We will provide a framework to ensure that greenlands and watersheds become an integral part of future plans for the Greater Toronto Area.
>
> Today, I would like to outline how we intend to implement key recommendations of the report.
>
> Firstly, we will establish a continuous Waterfront Trail which will

Watersedge Park, Mississauga

become the Green-Way that ties the GTA together from Burlington to Newcastle. It will link to the Bruce and Ganaraska Trail systems at either end. We see the waterfront trail as the highest land use for all public lands along the water's edge. The trail will be much more than a four foot strip of asphalt. This trail will connect the waterfront with river valleys and source areas and link up areas of natural and historic importance along Lake Ontario. It will be a place for people, for families and children to enjoy the out of doors and the natural environment on foot or bicycle.

Secondly, we accept the idea of Waterfront Partnership Agreements as a valid implementation vehicle for waterfront plans. We will negotiate agreements between local, regional and federal governments, along with conservation authorities, to prepare responsible development plans and implementation mechanisms for the waterfront consistent with the Crombie principles.

Thirdly, we will establish by legislation a Waterfront Regeneration Trust to co-ordinate regeneration activities.

Finally, we will move to halt the unnecessary privatization of the public shoreline and Crown resources such as water lots.

Mrs. Grier turned her attention to the remaining period of the Commission's mandate:

In the final year of the Royal Commission's work, we will ask Mr. Crombie to address:

The feasibility of relocating the Gardiner Expressway in consultation with Metropolitan Toronto and the Ministry of Transportation;

the pooling of lands and the integration of future plans for the Canadian National Exhibition,

Ontario Place, Fort York and HMCS York in consultation with the Ministry of Tourism and Recreation and the other authorities involved; and

policies, practices, technology and methods available to regenerate shoreline areas.

The Commission soon realized that these additions to its mandate could not be explored in the time still available. As a result, both the federal and provincial governments extended the Commission's life by six months, to December 1991.

In addition to publishing *Planning for Sustainability*, in the third phase of its work, the Commission completed the environmental audit of the East Bayfront/Port Industrial Area (*Pathways: Towards an Ecosystem Approach*) and the three tasks given it by the Province. The results of these efforts were published in three major reports: *Shoreline Regeneration*; *Garrison Common: Preliminary Master Plan*; and *The Toronto Central Waterfront Transportation Corridor Study.*

Adopting the ecosystem approach made the environment the key to the Commission's thinking. But that approach demands an understanding of the dynamic interaction among environmental, economic, and community issues. Therefore, in addition to work associated with the new elements of its mandate, the Commission carried out further research and mounted seminars to consider the broader implications of the ecosystem approach.

In addition, working papers were published on cumulative effects, soil decontamination, the regional economy, community profiles, and the waterfront in winter.

The Commission continued to communicate with a wide range of groups and individuals, using the *Newsletter*, speeches, presentations, consultations, and meetings. In the summer of 1991, it surveyed public opinion on waterfront issues, having the polling firm, Environics, add a number of questions to its regular survey of residents living in the Greater Toronto region.

Environics found that issues relating to the environment and the waterfront ranked high among elements identified as contributing to the quality of life in the region, and that people in the region view environmental protection as an economic issue.

THE FINAL REPORT

This final report summarizes all that has come before in the work and experience of the Royal Commission on the Future of the Toronto Waterfront. Throughout the Commission's existence, all those involved in it thought hard and listened carefully to the views and advice of people — thousands of people. Therefore, this is the work of many hands and minds; it embodies the values, aspirations, concerns, and hopes of these thousands of citizens.

In looking at our collective experience, those who were involved with the Commission in the course of its existence have come to the end of their work with a sense of optimism: the core values — orderliness, tolerance, and the seizing of opportunities — held by Torontonians are starting to be applied to the regeneration of the waterfront and the watersheds across the entire bioregion.

This final report treats waterfront regeneration as an opportunity that brings with it the long-term promise of a healthy environment, economic recovery and sustainability, and maintaining a liveable community.

The likelihood that these opportunities will be realized is strengthened by an emerging sense of order as governments, working with business, labour, community leaders, and ordinary citizens, recognize the degree of discipline and tolerance that is needed: discipline to perform one's role without blocking or ignoring that played by others, and tolerance of their needs and functions as all work together to deal with the waterfront or watersheds.

The title of this final report, *Regeneration: Toronto's Waterfront and the Sustainable City*, reflects the Commission's beliefs about what has to be done and what can be accomplished. The report itself consists of four parts.

Part I, "Planning for Sustainability", describes what the Commission found about the need for regional planning and co-operation, based on the ecosystem approach, and including concepts of sustainability, health, equity, stewardship, responsibility, and the bioregion as "home". After an updated assessment of the environmental state of the bioregion, the report articulates the Commission's philosophy and principles. The Commission's own efforts as an "agent of change" — applying the ecosystem approach — are described, and their value is assessed.

Part I concludes with a discussion of the Commission's ideas for ecosystem-based planning practice. This is based on the *Planning for Sustainability* report and the working paper on cumulative effects, as well

as on practical methods for ecosystem-based planning now being used or proposed by experts in the field.

Part II, "Environmental Imperatives", deals with a range of environmental imperatives that must be considered by each level of government if it is to help restore and maintain ecosystem health.

This second section includes: a critical review of the state of the Great Lakes ecosystem and efforts at regenerating it; measures for regenerating the Lake Ontario shoreline in the Greater Toronto bioregion; an explanation of the environmental, social, and economic importance of a greenway and trail system for the waterfront and the bioregion; and the advantages of considering winter conditions on the waterfront. It concludes with an analysis of the Don River watershed: its past, present, and future, treating the problems and opportunities of this watershed as typical of those throughout the bioregion.

Part III, "Places", surveys the various places along the waterfront, from Burlington in the west to Port Hope in the east. It includes summaries of responses to the Commission's previous area-specific recommendations, as well as encapsulating new research and recommendations for places across the waterfront, including the need for the integration of environment, land use, and transportation on the Central Waterfront.

This section reviews the Commission's own efforts to apply the ecosystem approach in its own work, in such projects as the

*

Regeneration *explores the opportunities to realize the promise of a healthy environment, economic recovery and sustainability, and a liveable community.*

environmental audit of the East Bayfront/
Port Industrial Area, the Garrison Common
Preliminary Master Plan, and the Toronto
Central Waterfront Transportation Corridor
Study. As well, it includes comments on the
initiatives undertaken by other bodies —
municipalities, conservation authorities,
federal and provincial ministries, and private-
sector owners and developers — now using
the ecosystem philosophy and approach.

The final section of the report,
"Regeneration and Recovery", discusses
issues related to implementation of the
Royal Commission's recommendations. It
includes the Commission's ideas about the
nature and structure of public administration needed to manage the waterfront: no
single level of government can or should
be in total control of the waterfront; each
should perform its role in its own jurisdiction, in partnership with others.

The section also offers the Commission's views on partnership agreements, the
issue of financing waterfront regeneration,
and a practical program of co-ordinated
action across the waterfront, including
consolidated capital budgets for the next
five-year period.

Sir Winston Churchill once said that
people create buildings and then buildings
create people. The same is true of the cities
and regions in which we live and their waterfronts. As a small element of two governments in a democracy, the Commission
offers a possible map to a better, healthier,
sustainable city. In a democracy, however,
the ultimate decisions — what maps to use,
whether to use a particular map, whether to
use any map at all — rest with and are made
real by the behaviour, attitudes, and actions
of its citizens.

CHAPTER 1:
THE ECOSYSTEM APPROACH

THE GREATER TORONTO REGION IS, BOTH LITERALLY AND FIGURATIVELY, AT A WATERSHED. NOT LONG AGO, SOCIETY BELIEVED THAT THE ENVIRONMENT WAS ENDLESSLY ABLE TO ABSORB THE DETRITUS OF A MODERN, INDUSTRIAL-BASED ECONOMY. MORE RECENTLY, THE ASSUMPTION WAS THAT THE ENVIRONMENT AND THE ECONOMY WERE INEVITABLY OPPOSED: OPTING FOR ONE MEANT DAMAGING THE OTHER.

TODAY, HOWEVER, IT IS CLEAR THAT THE TWO, RATHER THAN BEING MUTUALLY EXCLUSIVE, ARE MUTUALLY DEPENDENT: A GOOD QUALITY OF LIFE AND ECONOMIC DEVELOPMENT CANNOT BE SUSTAINED IN AN ECOLOGICALLY DETERIORATING ENVIRONMENT.

THE WAY WE CHOOSE TO TREAT THE GREATER TORONTO WATERFRONT IS CRUCIAL. IF GOVERNMENTS AND INDIVIDUALS RECOGNIZE — AND ACT ON — THE NEED TO RESOLVE PAST ENVIRONMENTAL PROBLEMS AND FORGE STRATEGIES TO PROTECT THE WATERFRONT NOW AND IN THE FUTURE, WE WILL, INDEED, HAVE SUCCESSFULLY CROSSED A WATERSHED.

— *WATERSHED* 1990

A REGION UNDER STRESS

So ended *Watershed*, the second interim report of the Royal Commission on the Future of the Toronto Waterfront. These conclusions — that the Greater Toronto waterfront is inextricably linked to its watersheds, and that environmental, social, and economic conditions in this region are highly stressed, and are mutually dependent — provide the foundation for this final report.

The waterfront, the place where land and water meet, has always been a key determinant in the location of urban settlements on the shores of Lake Ontario, starting with small forts and villages like Fort York, Fort Rouillé, and Port Hope. Gradually these grew into larger towns and cities, and are now part of the Greater Toronto region.

For thousands of years, aboriginal people created villages along the waterfront to take advantage of the wildlife of the lake and estuarine wetlands. When Europeans arrived in the 18th and 19th centuries, they were attracted by a safe harbour (now Toronto Harbour), the ready supplies of fresh water in Lake Ontario, and the abundant fish and waterfowl in the waters and wetlands. The major river valleys, like the

Humber and the Don, provided a transportation route into the hinterlands. The forests yielded game and timber, and, once cleared, fertile soils for farming.

Today, the Greater Toronto region is still dependent on the waterfront, although for different reasons. While water transportation no longer dominates, the lake still provides fresh water for millions of residents, and receives our wastewaters. Many recreational amenities, such as boating, shoreline parks, fishing, swimming, and nature appreciation, depend directly on the waterfront location.

Among other reasons for the waterfront's importance are its neighbourhoods, home to many people. Moreover, the lake provides abundant cold water to meet the cooling requirements of power stations. And, like waterfronts around the world, the Greater Toronto waterfront is a special *place* that draws people, fascinates them, satisfies their deep human need for contact with water and wildlife, and provides a constantly changing panorama of views, weather, and moods.

Just as the people of the Greater Toronto region are linked to their waterfront, so the health and life of the waterfront depend on the region. Ecologically, the waterfront is tied to its watersheds by the many rivers and creeks that flow into it, and the movements of wildlife and flows of stormwater along the valleys. Although there are many distinctive

The Greater Toronto waterfront is a special place that draws people, fascinates them, satisfies their deep human need for contact with water and wildlife, and provides a constantly changing panorama of views, weather, and moods.

neighbourhoods on the waterfront, to a great extent their future depends on regional and local municipal policies on such matters as affordable housing, community services, transit, parks, and the like. Similarly, the decline and renewal of different economic activities on the waterfront are influenced by regional trends in manufacturing, services, and commerce.

Just as the people of the Greater Toronto region are linked to their waterfront, so the health and life of the waterfront depend on the region.

Therefore waterfront-related strategies, plans, and programs to improve the quality of the environment, encourage community development or foster appropriate economic activities cannot be implemented in isolation: they must be undertaken in a regional context that recognizes the interdependence of the region and its waterfront, as well as the special qualities and characteristics of the waterfront itself.

It is appropriate therefore to begin this final report on the future of the Toronto waterfront by sketching some of the key environmental, social, and economic issues that must be faced in the Greater Toronto region, and by examining how they relate to the waterfront.

The geographic area considered in this overview is defined on the basis of natural boundaries, rather than political jurisdictions. This biological region, or "bioregion", comprises the major basin formed by the Niagara Escarpment on the west, the Oak Ridges Moraine to the north and east, and the Lake Ontario shoreline to the south. It is described by its natural characteristics: landforms, the lake, and the watersheds.

It should be noted that the Commission's 1990 *Watershed* report included a map of the Greater Toronto bioregion, based on provincial information about the Greater Toronto Area (GTA), which is defined as the regions of Halton, Peel, York, Metropolitan Toronto, and Durham. However, that does not cover the full extent of the bioregion, which extends into Simcoe and Dufferin counties in the northwest, and into Northumberland County as far as the Trent River in the east.

Information about the economic, environmental, and social conditions in the bioregion is currently collected on the basis of politically defined units, such as local municipalities, regions, the Greater Toronto Area or Statistics Canada's Toronto Census Metropolitan Area (CMA). Therefore, a great deal of what follows is based on information about the GTA or the CMA, both of which include the region's major urban centres.

For many people, the shoreline exerts an almost mysterious pull: it still offers a sense of country in our towns and cities. A walk with the dog along the water's edge, skipping stones over the lake's surface, finding a unique piece of driftwood, riding a bicycle on a trail through tall grass, or fishing off some rocks or a pier: these are just some of the ways people use the waterfront.

Royal Commission on the Future of the Toronto Waterfront. Shoreline Regeneration Work Group. 1991. *Shoreline regeneration for the Greater Toronto bioregion.* Toronto: Royal Commission on the Future of the Toronto Waterfront.

Map 1.1 Greater Toronto bioregion

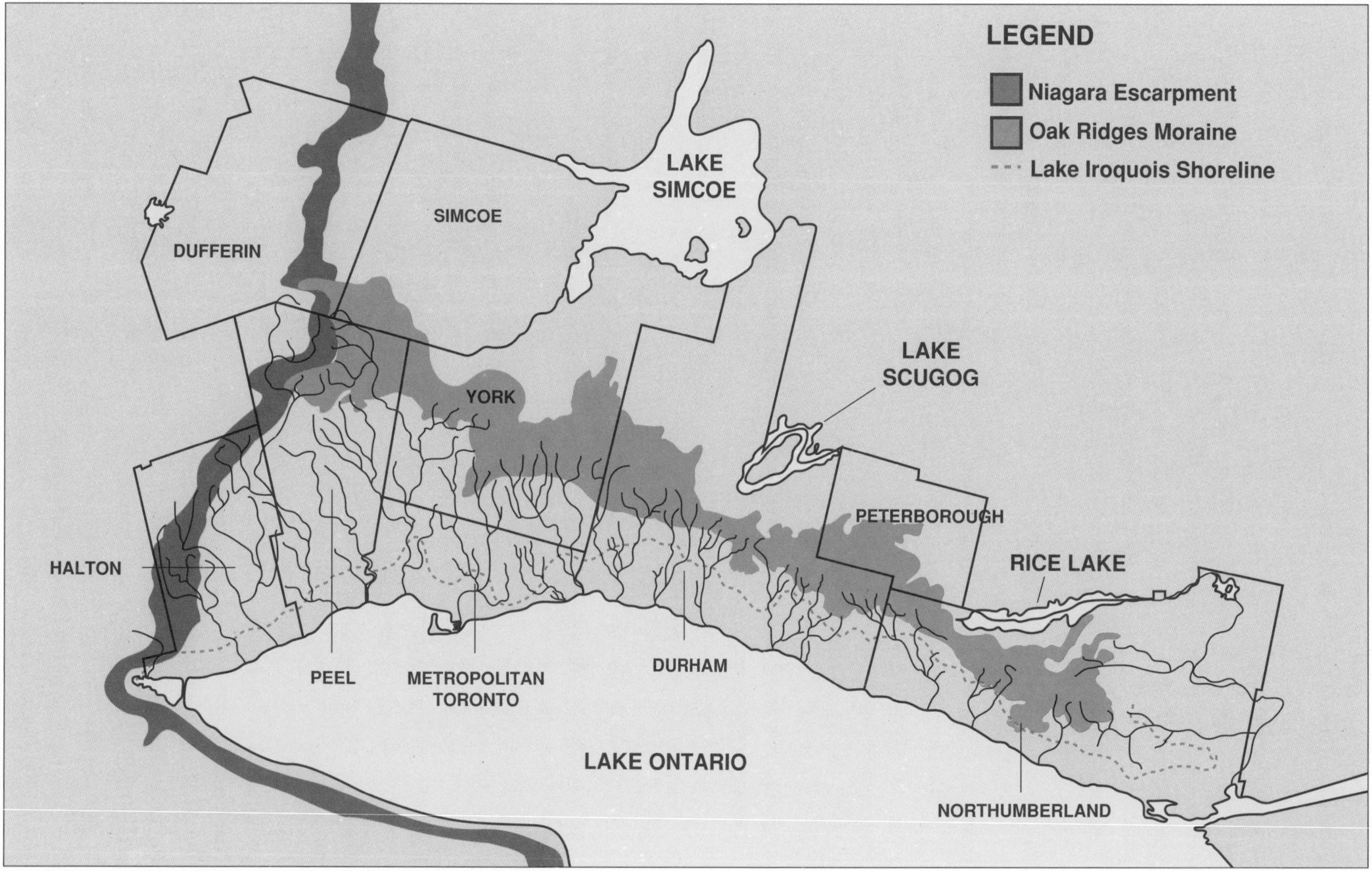

LEGEND

■ Niagara Escarpment
■ Oak Ridges Moraine
--- Lake Iroquois Shoreline

LAKE SIMCOE

LAKE SCUGOG

RICE LAKE

SIMCOE

DUFFERIN

PETERBOROUGH

NORTHUMBERLAND

YORK

DURHAM

HALTON

PEEL

METROPOLITAN TORONTO

LAKE ONTARIO

The Greater Toronto bioregion has important natural assets: beaches, wetlands, and bluffs along the waterfront; deep, wooded river valleys; the moraine's rolling, pastoral hills; majestic rock cliffs along the Niagara Escarpment; cool trout streams; fertile soils for agriculture; and more. Despite these blessings, there are many signs of environmental, social, and economic stress in the region. A better understanding of these stresses helps in devising strategies to deal with existing problems, and to meet future needs.

The following is a brief description of some of the challenges facing the Greater Toronto bioregion today, based on a more detailed discussion in the *Watershed* report.

POPULATION AND SETTLEMENT

The single greatest challenge facing the Greater Toronto region is probably the number of people who live here, and the expected high rate of population growth. The GTA has more than 40 per cent of Ontario's population (almost four million people) living on one per cent of the province's land base. Approximately 10 per cent of those live along the waterfront.

The GTA population has grown rapidly — from a pre-war population of about one million — and is expected to continue doing so, reaching about six million by 2021. That kind of growth places a tremendous strain on all sectors of society, trying to cope with the need to provide such basic necessities as housing, jobs, and health care, and to take care of services including transportation, waste disposal, and sewage treatment. It also threatens the quality of life that attracted many people in the first place: green spaces, recreational opportunities, clean air and water, a relatively safe city, good economic prospects, diverse amenities, and the like.

Even more important than the actual number of people living in the bioregion, however, is the pattern of settlement, and the way in which development occurs. The City of Toronto, and the centres of many other cities and towns in the bioregion, started as compact settlements kept compact by limitations of transportation by foot and horse. With the advent of streetcars, a more spacious form of settlement spread along early transit lines.

Most of the built-up parts of the bioregion, however, were developed for a society with a high degree of car ownership. As a result, there is low-density sprawl, inefficient in its use of land, energy, and other resources.

Not only have settlement patterns encouraged inefficiencies, they have tended to ignore existing natural features and processes (e.g., significant natural habitats, hydrological systems, landforms), as well as cultural and heritage values. The results are degraded environments and a blandness that comes from blurring the distinct attributes of different places.

GREENSPACE

Many of the green spaces in the Greater Toronto bioregion — particularly those of the Oak Ridges Moraine, Lake Ontario waterfront, and river valleys — have been harmed and fragmented, and are further threatened by patterns of development that ignore natural features and processes.

More than half the original wetlands in the bioregion have been drained for farms, bulldozed for housing or infilled to provide land for industry or transportation.

Most of the remaining wetlands have been debased by upstream pollution or surrounding land uses, and are subject to intense pressure from increased urbanization. Waterfront marshes at the mouths of rivers and creeks are at particular risk, because they are susceptible to changes in the flows, quality, and temperature of water from the watersheds, as well as to waterfront development, such as conversions to harbours and marinas.

Because of widespread forest clearing in Ontario in the past 200 years, only one-fifth of the GTA remains forest-covered today — and that includes parks, Crown land, conservation areas, and private woodlots. There is disturbing evidence that the trees still remaining — like their urban cousins — are under significant stress from drought, salt, and other pollutants.

WILDLIFE

Ever since the first European settlement, there has been a dramatic decrease in the diversity and abundance of wildlife in the bioregion, and remaining wildlife populations are under stress. The primary causes have been, and continue to be: loss, alteration, and fragmentation of habitat; fishing and hunting; pollution of ecosystems by excess nutrients and persistent chemicals; and the introduction of non-native animal and plant species.

As a result of these stresses, some species, like the passenger pigeon, have become extinct. Others, including the timber wolf, black bear, lynx, and elk, are no longer found in this bioregion. An increasing number of species are becoming rare: in the GTA today, there are as many as 114 provincially rare kinds of plants, reptiles, amphibians, mammals, and fish.

Muskrat

WATER SUPPLY

Most residents of the Greater Toronto bioregion get their water from Lake Ontario. However, a large part of York Region, including rapidly growing communities like Aurora and Newmarket, as well as the northern parts of Halton, Peel, and Durham regions, depends primarily on groundwater supplies.

This has caused serious water quantity and quality issues: first, there is evidence that in several areas, aquifers are actually being "mined" — water is being withdrawn faster than it is being naturally replenished. Second, in some areas, groundwater has been contaminated by a variety of sources including agricultural and industrial chemicals, leachate from landfills, road salt (groundwater in the lower Don Valley is as saline as seawater), and inadequate septic systems. Third, groundwater provides about 40 per cent of the water flow in the bioregion's rivers and streams, making them vulnerable to changes in water flows and purity. All three issues may be critical, limiting future growth in groundwater-dependent regions, unless water is piped from Georgian Bay or Lake Ontario.

Even in the areas supplied by Lake Ontario water, it is becoming evident that we need to reduce total consumption — not because of any lack of water (there is plenty in the lake), but there are the mounting costs of treating the water before it is used and of treating large volumes of sewage, as well as the impact on the environment of streams, rivers, and the waterfront that comes from stormwater and combined sewer overflows.

Water Quality

As explained earlier, the Metro Toronto waterfront is one of 43 "hot spots" around the Great Lakes, identified by the International Joint Commission as needing Remedial Action Plans (RAPs) because of water quality problems. In the Metro Toronto RAP area, bottom sediments are contaminated, organisms living in them show bioaccumulation of toxic substances, fish of some species have such high levels of contaminants they cannot be safely eaten by humans, aquatic life is stressed from pollution, and swimming beaches are frequently closed during the summer.

For the most part, sewage treatment plants in the bioregion meet provincial standards for concentrations of different pollutants they discharge, but they contribute massive loads of nutrients, heavy metals, and organic chemicals to the waterfront. It is clear that substantial improvements are required to most existing sewage treatment facilities, just to ensure that the wastes of the present residents of the bioregion are adequately handled. In addition, further capacity will be required to treat wastes generated by the expected increases in population over the coming decades.

The condition of the 60 or so rivers and tributaries in the Greater Toronto bioregion varies considerably. Although a few are still fairly healthy, many have been seriously degraded. Forest cutting has removed shade and caused banks to erode. Pesticides, fertilizers, and topsoil from farms, as well as a potent cocktail of rain-washed pollutants from urban areas, flow into the rivers. In some municipalities, when there are heavy rains, sewers overflow into rivers and the waterfront, carrying a bacteria-laden mixture of stormwater and sewage that means beaches have to be posted to warn people not to swim.

Aggregates

Glacial deposits of sand and gravel in the bioregion provide extensive aggregate resources, a fifth of those produced in the province. It is ironic, indeed, that the areas richest in aggregates — the Niagara Escarpment and the Oak Ridges Moraine — are the most sensitive to the extraction process. Removing aggregate from the Niagara Escarpment threatens its integrity as a landform and its natural habitats, while doing so in the moraine interferes with its hydrogeological functions as an aquifer and the source of many rivers.

Soils

In some parts of the bioregion, soils are contaminated with heavy metals and organic chemicals, often the legacy of industrial activities, lakefilling, transportation or waste dumping. Although the extent of soil contamination from industrial activities throughout the region is not known, there is reason to believe that many former and existing industrial and refinery sites are contaminated as the result of poor handling of hazardous materials in the past.

In this century, significant lakefilling has been carried out to create land for industry, transportation corridors, ports,

Importance of Water Clean-Up

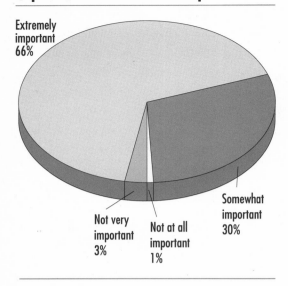

Extremely important 66%

Somewhat important 30%

Not very important 3%

Not at all important 1%

Two-thirds of the respondents believe it is "extremely important" that a major effort be made to clean up the Lake Ontario waterfront and rivers like the Don, the Humber, the Rouge, and the Credit so people can safely swim and fish in them again.

Source: Environics Poll. 1991.

N.B. Due to rounding figures may not add to 100.

and parks. Until very recently, and particularly along the central Toronto waterfront, this lakefilling included contaminated materials from construction sites, sewage sludge, incinerator refuse, and municipal garbage.

Inland, there are as many as 276 abandoned landfill sites throughout the GTA. Because waste dumping was virtually unregulated until about 20 years ago, there is little information about what may have been dumped in these sites or, for most of them, whether pollutants are now leaking into groundwater or nearby streams.

AIR

Air quality in the Greater Toronto bioregion is influenced by many sources, some of which are hundreds of kilometres away. For example, trace toxic organic chemicals can be carried long distances from other parts of Ontario, the United States, and beyond, and most chemical precursors of smog (ground-level ozone) come from American sources. Air quality is also influenced by activities in the bioregion itself — particularly from automobiles, coal-fired generating stations, incinerators, and industry, as well as from furnaces for heating homes, offices, and other structures.

Over the past few decades, levels of sulphur dioxide, particulates, carbon monoxide, and some metals have been declining, because of a combination of regulations controlling the sulphur content of coal and gas, a shift from coal and oil to natural gas, and replacement of leaded with unleaded gasoline. However, levels of nitrogen dioxide and volatile organic compounds (contributors to acid rain and ozone) have remained fairly constant and at high levels. Improved control of the main sources of these pollutants — automobiles, power plants, and certain industries — has been offset by increased numbers of automobiles on the roads.

For the last 10 years, levels of ground-level ozone have remained fairly constant, and are quite uniform across southern Ontario. However, they are highest in the City of Toronto, where they regularly exceed health-related guidelines on warm, sunny days in spring and summer.

ENERGY

Canadians consume more energy per capita than any other people in the world. The high proportion of Canada's population and industrial base in the Greater Toronto bioregion may make this one of the most energy-intensive regions in the world. Approximately 275 gigajoules of energy per person per year (the equivalent of 8,000 litres of gasoline) are consumed for transportation, heating/cooling, lighting, and industrial processes combined.

Some of the energy we consume is generated by the coal-burning Lakeview Generating Station in Mississauga and by the Pickering Nuclear Station. Once the Darlington Nuclear Station comes on line, a greater proportion of our electricity will be generated in the Greater Toronto bioregion. At the present, however, the bioregion is largely dependent on outside sources of electricity — on energy from distant nuclear and hydro plants, as well as on oil and natural gas brought by tanker, truck, and pipeline from other provinces and countries.

Because so much of the energy we use comes from outside the bioregion, we experience few of the direct effects of energy extraction and transformation. We do, however, suffer the consequences of energy consumption: burning fossil fuels to generate heat and electricity, and to power cars and trucks, releases greenhouse gases and contributes to rising global temperatures, acid deposition, and local air pollution. While nuclear energy avoids most of those air pollution problems, it raises other environmental, economic, and social issues — including the high costs of building nuclear reactors, uncertainty about their long-term safety and viability, health risks to people working in and living near nuclear stations, and how to dispose of nuclear fuel wastes.

Meeting our future energy needs will probably involve conservation programs and alternative energy supplies. It will be cheaper and more environmentally sound to conserve power than to build new generating plants. Further financial and environmental savings may be achieved through

Pickering Nuclear Power Station

alternative energy sources such as wind and solar power. Co-generation — using heat normally wasted when electricity is produced for industrial processes and space heating — may also play an important role in reducing the impact of our energy-consuming lifestyles.

TRANSPORTATION

In the past 10 to 15 years, very little has been invested in transportation infrastructure in the Greater Toronto bioregion, while transportation demand has far outstripped the supply of new roads, transit facilities, and parking spaces. The result is that roads are congested, commuting takes longer, energy is used inefficiently, air pollution increases, and people suffer more stress.

The volume of traffic has been growing, and is expected to continue to grow, at a rate of six per cent per year. If that happens, total traffic volumes will triple by 2011. The Province has few plans for major new highways in the area (although they will build Highway 407, complete Highway 403, and build a new Highway 6), so future transportation needs will have to be met in other ways, if severe gridlock is to be avoided.

At present, 64 per cent of all GTA commuters drive cars to work or school; 25 per cent use public transit; and 10 per cent walk or cycle. The percentage of transit use in the City of Toronto is much higher: in the downtown core, for example, 47 per cent of commuters use public transit.

If current trends continue, commuting between homes in one part of the Greater Toronto bioregion and jobs in another will continue to increase. In 1986, close to 270,000 commuter trips were made each day into Metro Toronto from the four surrounding regions. By 2011, this could reach nearly 500,000. Unless there is dramatically less dependence on cars for making these trips, and more people are able to work close to home, the road system will be unable to cope with traffic needs.

Transit systems must have a population density of at least 4,000 people per square kilometre (10,360 people per square mile). This is achieved in the central city, but densities in suburban regions are much too low. The density is 6,000 people per square kilometre (15,540 people per square mile) in the City of Toronto, and 3,500 (9,065 people per square mile) across Metro. But in developed areas outside Metro, the population density is only 2,100 (5,439 people per square mile). Unless densities in outlying areas increase enough to support public transit, or industry and commerce decentralize to allow people to live near their workplaces, the Greater Toronto bioregion could become "California North" — a nightmare of too many cars going too slowly on too few roads.

GARBAGE

Canadians produce more garbage per capita than the people of any other nation.

Every year, homes, institutions, industries, and commercial establishments in the GTA produce 4.5 million tonnes (5 million tons) of garbage — enough to fill six Skydomes to the roof. With existing landfill sites nearly at capacity and due to close in 1993 or 1994, the question of where to put all this garbage has become one of the most emotional and pressing in the bioregion.

To date, Halton is the only region in the GTA to successfully site a new landfill. Because the Province believes that the remaining regions should deal with their waste within their own borders, it created an Interim Waste Authority in June 1991 to search for landfill sites for the regions of Peel and Durham, and for the combined York Region and Metro Toronto.

Increased efforts at waste reduction, recycling, and composting programs, as well as higher tipping fees, are reducing the total amounts of waste going to landfill sites in the area. Diversion from disposal sites ranges from about six per cent in York Region to 21 per cent in Peel — short of the 25-per-cent reduction target set by the Province for 1992.

Increased tipping fees are having another effect: thousands of tonnes of privately collected garbage are being trucked to cheaper disposal sites elsewhere in the province and in the United States, creating losses of waste-disposal revenue in the bioregion, adding unnecessary air pollution from extra truck traffic, and raising questions about the ethics of transporting one community's garbage to another.

DEMOGRAPHIC TRENDS

The traditional structure of families in the bioregion, like that of families everywhere, is changing: there are more single-parent families, smaller family sizes, and an increasing number of dependent seniors. The age profile of the population is also shifting: there are a declining proportion of children and more older people. In 1991, 19 per cent of the GTA population was over 55, a figure that is expected to increase to 32 per cent by 2031.

The cultural diversity of the Greater Toronto bioregion is one of its most distinguishing characteristics: there are some 80 ethnic groups in the area. More than a third of all immigrants to Canada settle in the region, bringing with them special needs for language training and assistance in integrating into Canada's social and economic life.

These trends make increasing demands on communities and governments in the Greater Toronto bioregion. For example, a better supply of suitable housing is needed for different age groups and family types; there must be better transit networks; and social services and health care systems must be expanded.

SOCIAL NEEDS

The bioregion's demographic trends affect every part of it, from downtown Toronto to the older suburbs of Metro and the new suburbs of the outlying regions of York, Durham, Halton, and Peel. Similarly, social problems — poverty, homelessness, hunger, substance abuse, family violence, suicide — are no longer limited to the urban core, but strain the resources of municipal governments and non-profit groups throughout the region. The recession has exacerbated these problems, with increasing numbers of people competing for limited

social services, which are, in turn, being constrained by funding cutbacks.

Access to services is becoming an increasingly serious problem, for a variety of reasons. People from ethnic groups are often limited by cultural and language barriers. In the suburbs, lack of public transit means physical isolation, especially of women. Sometimes, appropriate services are simply not available, or have long waiting lists.

Thousands of people in the Greater Toronto bioregion are either homeless or living in overcrowded conditions. Causes include a shortage of suitable houses and apartments and an inability to pay high prices or rents. There are an estimated 20,000 homeless people in Metro Toronto alone; in 1986, nearly 28,000 families, seniors, and single people were on the provincial waiting list for geared-to-income non-profit housing.

A wide variety of housing types is available in the Greater Toronto bioregion with Metro offering the broadest range and about 76 per cent of all social housing in the GTA. The Region of York has the least diversity: 80 per cent of its housing comprises single-family detached houses.

> *T*housands of people in the Greater Toronto bioregion are either homeless or living in overcrowded conditions.

ECONOMY

The Greater Toronto region has traditionally been described as Canada's "economic engine", generating nearly one-fifth of the nation's income, with per capita incomes that are approximately 25 per cent higher than the national average.

In the past 15 years, the Greater Toronto region has been Canada's pre-eminent job-producing area. According to a paper prepared for the Commission by University of Toronto economic geographer Meric Gertler (1990), titled *Toronto: The State of the Regional Economy*, total employment in the Toronto Census Metropolitan Area (CMA) grew by an impressive 43 per cent between 1976 and 1990. Even higher growth rates — exceeding 70 per cent — occurred in community, business, and personal services, and in finance, insurance, and real estate. Although manufacturing remained a significant part of the economy, employment growth was slower there than in the service sector, reflecting a relative decline in the importance of manufacturing employment to the regional economy.

But there are signs of economic distress in the bioregion. The current recession has hit hard here, as in the rest of the country. There have been substantial declines in output and employment, and many observers suggest that the current downturn will be deeper and longer-lasting than first predicted. That makes it difficult to predict the future of the regional economy: its effects are mingled with other changes, more structural and fundamental, including the relative decline in manufacturing, the Free Trade Agreement with the United States (and the possibility that there will be a North American Free Trade Agreement, which will include Mexico), and imposition of the Goods and Services Tax.

One of the most notable trends of the past two decades is the decentralization of manufacturing activity from the City of Toronto — first to Metro's outer fringes and more recently to outlying regions in York, Durham, and Peel. However, it is impossible to predict whether this trend will continue, or whether industries will move out of the bioregion to other parts of Ontario, or go south to the United States or Mexico.

At the same time as manufacturing has declined, office-based employment, particularly in financial services, has grown in the City of Toronto and other urban centres; but there are different opinions about the extent to which this growth will resume after the recession. Some economists see the boom in financial services as a one-time event, made possible by financial deregulation, while others feel that the sector has considerable potential for continued growth, because: ongoing innovations in financial services products are meeting the needs of more sophisticated investors and borrowers; as the baby boom generation ages, there will be more demand for a variety of new savings vehicles; and many financial services are not easily automated and offer continued employment growth.

Another significant factor is the high quality of life the Greater Toronto bioregion can still offer, which attracts people in the financial services sector. This is in sharp contrast to New York City — Toronto's major competitor in the field — which is reaching limits to financial service growth, because of a combination of impending labour shortages, high house prices, decaying infrastructure, a deteriorating local education system, and an increasingly strained quality of life. Those responsible for the economy of the Greater Toronto bioregion would be well advised to consider New York's situation, which offers important lessons about the social, environmental, and cultural milieu necessary for sustained prosperity.

While some economists are optimistic about future increases in the office-based economy in the Greater Toronto bioregion, its role in stimulating the entire economy may be more limited than the one played by manufacturing-sector growth after the last

Most Important Consideration in a GTA Development Strategy

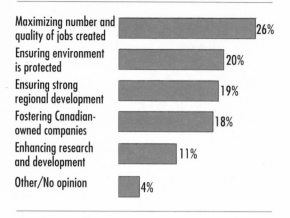

Maximizing number and quality of jobs created	26%
Ensuring environment is protected	20%
Ensuring strong regional development	19%
Fostering Canadian-owned companies	18%
Enhancing research and development	11%
Other/No opinion	4%

One-fifth of the respondents believe that despite the current recession, environmental protection should be a major part of an economic development strategy.

Source: Environics Poll. 1991.

recession. This is mainly because the intra-regional multiplier effects (purchases from other parts of the economy) from financial services do not even remotely match those from manufacturing industries.

These and other reasons should induce caution among those who would assume that, once there is a "recovery" from recession, it will herald an automatic return to business as usual. In fact, the major restructuring now occurring may result in quite a different economic picture, in terms of the key sectors, their relative rates of growth, the way they are distributed in the bioregion, and the types and numbers of jobs available.

CONCLUSIONS

These examples indicate the economic, social, and environmental pressures being exerted on the Greater Toronto bioregion, and make clear the fact that we can no longer take economic prosperity or quality of life in Greater Toronto for granted. Although it has many advantages, the bioregion's future health and environmental sustainability will depend on how we manage the assets we have: in addition to remediating problems caused by past activities, we must develop strategies to encourage more environmentally responsible lifestyles and development patterns, to nurture a vibrant regional economy, and to address pressing social needs.

It is also clear that tackling such issues means taking different approaches to problems, to decision-making, and to the way we get things done. It won't be easy. The Greater Toronto bioregion is governed by five regional municipalities, 53 local municipalities, four counties, six conservation authorities, and numerous federal and provincial ministries, departments, boards, agencies, and commissions. In an era when it has become clear that governments cannot solve environmental, social, and economic problems by themselves, the thousands of businesses and four million residents of the bioregion also have a role to play.

As the Royal Commission suggested in its *Watershed* report, the ecosystem approach appears to offer real and constructive alternatives to traditional ways of acting. The Commission has found the approach extremely helpful, as applied to its own work — a point that subsequent chapters of this final report will make clear. But, first, some observations about the ideas embodied in the ecosystem approach, and their relevance to the Greater Toronto waterfront and bioregion.

ECOSYSTEMS

The ecosystem approach is both a way of doing things and a way of thinking, a renewal of values and philosophy. It is not really a new concept: since time immemorial, aboriginal peoples around the world have understood their connectedness to the rest of the ecosystem — to the land, water, air, and other life forms. But, under many influences, and over many centuries, our society has lost its awareness of our place in ecosystems and, with it, our understanding of how they function.

What is new in the 1990s is a growing recognition that, unless we regain an awareness of humans as being part of ecosystems, and unless we respond to that awareness by changing the processes and criteria of decision-making, we will not be able to improve, and will even lose, the quality of life for which so many generations laboured.

In exploring the ecosystem approach, the Commission found that it integrates ideas from a variety of concepts and movements concerned about environmental and human well-being. Sporting different labels, but with many common elements, these include bioregionalism, green or eco-cities, the liveable metropolis, healthy communities, sustainable development, and the conserver society. A careful consideration of the philosophy behind all these concepts leads us to identify five fundamental themes of the ecosystem approach:

- the ecosystem as "home";
- everything is connected to everything else;
- sustainability;
- understanding places; and
- integrating processes.

THE ECOSYSTEM AS "HOME"

The ecosystem concept is an extension of the traditional view of the environment as all that surrounds us and influences us: something "out there", in the same way that a house comprises bricks and mortar. In contrast, an ecosystem is a "home", with a spiritual dimension transcending its physical structures. Ecosystems are dynamic, interacting, living systems; humans are part of them, not separate.

The "home" analogy is crucial to understanding our roles and responsibilities as co-habitants of ecosystems. Most people conceive of home as a special place providing more than shelter and a place to sleep. We cherish and care for our homes, and share them with our families, friends, and pets. Similarly, ecosystems provide for both our physical and our spiritual needs; in turn, we are responsible for part of maintaining and protecting their health. In the words of Professor Bill Rees of the University of British Columbia, "people must acquire in their bones a sense that violation of the biosphere is a violation of self".

The life of each of us is a fleeting moment in the history of the biosphere; we are stewards of the land and waters, but for a short time only. How do our lives affect our co-habitants — other people, wild animals, plants — in Toronto, in Canada, and in other countries? What legacy will we

Unless we regain an awareness of humans as being part of ecosystems, and unless we respond to that awareness by changing the processes and criteria of decision-making, we will not be able to improve, and will even lose, the quality of life for which so many generations laboured.

Economic Impact of Environmental Protection

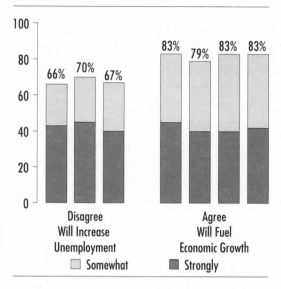

Two-thirds of Canadians disagree that environmental protection will harm employment in Canada. Four-fifths of Canadians believe environmental protection will fuel economic growth.

Source: Canada. House of Commons. Standing Committee on the Environment. 1991. Minutes of Proceedings, no. 6A, 26 September.

leave for the generations to come? These questions were addressed by the Brundtland Commission on Environment and Development (1987), which concluded in *Our Common Future* that:

> The Earth is one but the world is not. We all depend on one biosphere for sustaining our lives. Yet each community, each country, strives for survival and prosperity with little regard for its impact on others. Some consume the Earth's resources at a rate that would leave little for future generations. Others, many more in number, consume far too little and live with the prospect of hunger, squalor, disease and early death.

It is difficult, if not impossible, for most of us to see how, as individuals, we can even begin to respond to these global issues. However, there is a great deal of value in the environmental imperative to "think globally, act locally". It is there we must begin thinking about the Greater Toronto waterfront and its bioregion, guided by principles of stewardship and equity.

This implies caring for land, water, air, and living beings, including humans, other animals, and plants, in order to ensure their health in the long term as well as for today. It means that those with power and opportunities have a responsibility to act in ways that respect the needs of others, and the limits of the physical environment. And it means working to ensure that everyone has access to opportunities for a good quality of life — education, housing, jobs, social services, recreation, safety, a supportive community, attractive places, and a healthy environment.

The ecosystem concept recognizes that you are new, yet not new. The molecules in your body have been parts of other organisms and will travel to other destinations in the future. Right now, in your lungs, there is likely to be at least one molecule from the breath of every human being who has lived in the past 3,000 years; the air around you will be used tomorrow by deer, lake trout, mosquitoes, and maple trees. The same is true of water, sunshine, and minerals. Everything in the biosphere is shared.

Christie, W. J. et al. 1986. "Special contribution on: managing the Great Lakes Basin as a home." *Journal of Great Lakes Research* 12(1).

EVERYTHING IS CONNECTED TO EVERYTHING ELSE

A key to understanding ecosystems is to recognize that everything is connected to everything else. Therefore, we must examine the entire web of links among and within elements of ecosystems: air, soils, water, wildlife, land uses, communities, economic activities, and the like. By doing so, we can begin to understand how the parts affect, and are affected by, one another, and we can appreciate the complexities of the whole. For example, water pollution along Toronto's waterfront represents the combination, or cumulative effects of, many influences — from development in the headwaters of the rivers, to stormwater management in the suburbs, to sewage treatment on the lakefront, to lakewide inputs from the Niagara River.

In viewing a city as an ecosystem, we can look at supply, flows, transformation, storage, and disposal of energy and materials. For example:

- What energy, materials, capital, and labour go into the urban ecosystem?
- How are these transformed to provide services and produce goods?
- What are the waste by-products of our goods and services: heat, pollution, garbage, etc?
- How are these waste products managed? For example, is waste from one process used as the raw material for another, or is it simply discharged into the environment?

As a result of that kind of analysis, we can identify ways in which human activities can be reintegrated with ecological processes to ensure more efficient use of resources, reduce wastes and pollution, increase recycling, and conserve energy — measures that offer both environmental and economic benefits. There will have to be a shift in our thinking about environmental management: from the current emphasis on regulation and remediation, to a more proactive approach that focuses on preventing damage rather than fixing up problems after the fact. "End-of-pipe" pollution control and restoring already damaged ecosystems are clearly more expensive and less effective than dealing with problems at source, before they become problems.

Relationships within ecosystems can best be visualized as three interlocking circles: environment, community, and economy. However, most decision-making separates the three, with little understanding, for example, of the effects of economic decisions on community needs or environmental health. Too frequently, there is more emphasis on economic and social issues than on the environment.

The challenge now is two-fold: to understand the links in the ecosystem, and to redress the balance among them.

Therefore, studies and plans must be undertaken in an integrated way, examining the links among economic, social, and environmental matters. This is a major departure from current processes, which tend to regard environmental concerns as a separate area of study: the "green chapter" in a report unconnected to the remainder.

It is encouraging to note that efforts are now being made to recognize, and respond to, these links. For example, the "healthy city" concept is based on the realization that individual human health depends on many factors beyond the health

Figure 1.1 The Shift from Traditional to Ecosystem-Based Decision-Making

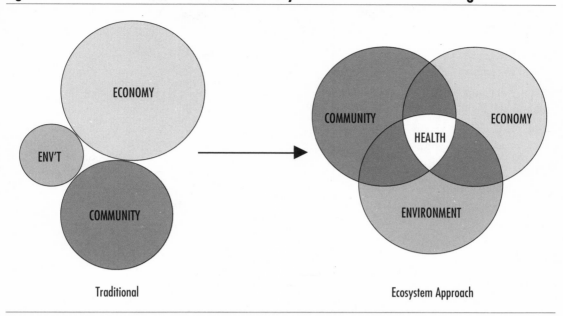

Traditional   Ecosystem Approach

care system and medical treatments. As a recent report by the Canadian Medical Association (1991) explained:

> Whereas in the 1970s there was a new emphasis on the effect of personal lifestyle choices on our health, in the 1990s it is becoming clear how seriously our collective lifestyle choices, and their impact on the environment, can threaten our health and well-being.

It is becoming increasingly clear that our health depends on the quality of the social, physical, and economic environments, and on equal access to the opportunities they provide: a "healthy city" is defined as one designed, built, and managed to truly contribute to the health and well-being of all its inhabitants. As Figure 1.1 shows, that means providing:

- an environment that is viable (i.e., supports human and non-human life), liveable, and sustainable;

- an economy that is equitable, sustainable, and adequately prosperous; and
- a community that is liveable, equitable, and convivial (Hancock 1990).

Since the 1980s, Toronto has played a key role in developing the healthy city concept and promoting it around the world. In 1989, in response to a report called *Healthy Toronto 2000* (1988), a Healthy City Office was created by unanimous Council decision, and given the mandate of working in partnership with government departments and the community to improve the quality of life in the City. The office focuses on three major issues — social equity, environmental protection, and community empowerment — and has established a wide range of programs — including those related to affordable housing, urban gardening, healthy workplaces, literacy, minimizing automobile use, main-street housing, report cards on the state of the city, and others.

Looking at economy/environment/community relationships from another perspective, communities must consider the quality of life they can offer as an important factor in attracting and keeping businesses, jobs, and a strong tax base. Table 1.1 shows how quality of life in a healthy community depends on a constellation of characteristics, including a good educational system, access to health care, economic opportunities, low crime rates, recreation and cultural facilities, clean air and water, and green space.

Just as municipalities are starting to consider the role of a healthy community in ensuring economic vitality and satisfying social needs, the business sector is beginning to recognize the value of maintaining environmental health. For example, in their book *Green Is Gold*, Patrick Carson and Julia Moulden (1991) advance a variety of compelling reasons for businesses to "go green". Among them:

- the rise of the "neo-traditionalist" consumer whose values are based on both the traditional and the new, and who seeks goods that are well-made, honestly presented, and reliable, and questions the environmental and moral implications of product choices;
- the power of local communities to demand clean industries and the NIMBY ("not in my backyard") syndrome in relation to undesirable facilities, such as landfill sites;
- tougher government regulations; and
- the significant bottom-line benefits that result from getting more out of less, reducing wastes, and preventing pollution.

Table 1.1 Examples of Indicators of Quality of Life for a Healthy Community

Economic Indicators
Average income level
Availability of employment
Diversified economic structure

Social Indicators
Availability of health care
Availability of social support systems
Good educational opportunities
Cultural and recreational facilities
Adequate affordable housing
Crime rate/personal security
Availability of public transit
Access to adequate food

Environmental Indicators
Clean air, soils, and water
Land-use patterns in relation to ecological processes
Diverse, healthy wildlife habitats
Noise
Safety from floods, erosion, and other hazards

Aesthetic Indicators
Community design — sense of place
Connections with cultural and natural heritage

Institutional Indicators
Public involvement in making community decisions
Role of volunteers
Role of community organizations
Integration among jurisdictions and agencies

Source: Adapted from Alberta. Urban Environment Subcommittee. 1988. Environment by design: the urban place in Alberta. N.p.: Alberta. Environment Council of Alberta.

A view has long been held that we must choose between jobs and the environment and there have been cases in which new environmental regulations have been the "straw that broke the camel's back" for an industry already facing difficulties. More realistically, however, a growing number of companies benefit from their "greenness", and are using it as a strong competitive edge over "dinosaurs" that refuse to change their ways. There is ready evidence of this trend in the products, services, and advertisements of companies that range from diaper manufacturers to food stores.

Carson and Moulden point out that our society currently treats nature as it treated workers 100 years ago when business did not calculate the cost, nor the benefits, of a healthy and socially secure work force. In the same way, society often fails to include the costs and benefits of a healthy and secure environment. Instead, we all bear the costs of diminishing resources, disappearance of valuable species, health problems, global warming, polluted rivers, unswimmable beaches, and the like. Fortunately, there is a growing understanding of the need to build true environmental costs into doing business in every economic sector.

Environmental costs may be added to those of production — for equipment or processes necessary for meeting stricter environmental regulations — and can then be passed on directly to the consumer. Similarly, as waste disposal costs escalate, prices of goods and services may go up. Alternatively, new uses for wastes can be found, with one company's garbage becoming another company's resource. Some current examples on the waterfront include the recycling of building materials generated by redevelopment of the Daniel's site in Etobicoke, and the Harkow proposal to build a recycling centre in the Port Industrial Area to sort and reprocess various construction materials.

Subsidies of several kinds can mask the true costs of providing services. For example, water rates paid by municipal customers in Ontario account for only 65 per cent of the money spent on providing water, treating sewage, and managing

stormwater; the balance comes from provincial subsidies, property taxes, and subdivision charges.

In addition, much more money is needed to replace and upgrade inadequate infrastructure, and meet today's expectations of a clean environment. A 1991 report by the Province's Municipal/Industrial Strategy for Abatement (MISA) Advisory Committee concludes that the full cost of providing improved municipal water and sewer services, rather than being the present average bill of about $70 per person per year, is actually about $250 (still considerably less than typical household energy costs). An additional benefit of full cost pricing is that by helping consumers to recognize the true value of water and sewer services, it would lead to water conservation and more careful management of pollution sources.

Right now, as we enter a more technologically intensive economic system, we have unparallelled opportunities to build high environmental quality and sustainability standards into such sectors as computers, electronic components, instrumentation,

> **O**ne of the dilemmas addressed by the "sustainable development" perspective is that modern industrial economies have dealt so effectively with the scarcity of food, manufactured goods, and services in developing their societies that they have created new scarcities of clean earth, clean air and clean water.
>
> Manitoba Environment. N.d. *Discussion paper: harnessing market forces to support the environment*. Winnipeg: Manitoba Environment.

Paying for River and Waterfront Improvements

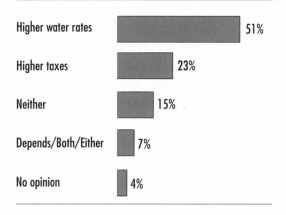

Higher water rates	51%
Higher taxes	23%
Neither	15%
Depends/Both/Either	7%
No opinion	4%

Half of the respondents favour higher water rates to fund improvements to Toronto's rivers and waterfront.

Source: Environics Poll. 1991.

health and medical supplies, and communication. As discussed in a recent report, *The New "Big Picture"* (Nuala Beck & Associates 1991), considering likely environmental implications of these sectors now is going to be much easier and more effective than imitating our current approach to most industries: attempting to regulate their activities, and cleaning up the degradation they cause — after they are well-established.

In his book, *Competitive Advantage of Nations*, Michael Porter (1990) concludes that environmental protection measures can benefit national economies. His research shows that countries with the most rigorous environmental requirements often lead in exports of affected products; he says that the right kind of regulations — those that stress pollution prevention rather than simply abatement or clean-up — can result in significant innovations with both environmental and financial benefits: companies are stimulated to develop less polluting or more resource-efficient products that save

industries money at home and are highly valued abroad.

SUSTAINABILITY

Another key concept inherent in the ecosystem approach is that, to have lasting value, efforts at ensuring health, stewardship, and equity must be sustainable: we must accept, and act on, the aphorism that we have not inherited the earth from our ancestors, but are borrowing it from our grandchildren.

Mohawk culture effectively integrates that perspective into decision-making by appointing someone to represent the seventh generation — to consider how the decisions being discussed today may be viewed seven generations from now. Given this kind of thinking, municipal decision-making (among other kinds) would have to take into account time well beyond the usual three or five years of a politician's term of office — beyond even the 10 to 20 years usually adopted as the context for official plans.

The idea of sustainability was most recently popularized by the Brundtland Commission on Environment and Development. It concluded that the only way to address issues associated with global development — poverty, hunger, and disease — at the same time as we deal with environmental degradation of the biosphere, is to pursue "environmentally sustainable economic development": development that meets present needs without compromising the ability of future generations to meet their own needs.

The Brundtland Commission report, made to the UN in 1987, evoked a proliferation of responses, reflected in growing international, national, provincial, and local awareness of the issues, at least in terms of words: speeches, papers, books, and reports abound. Although these can be important precursors, they are not change itself. That can be measured only by what is actually done.

The evidence is that we are taking relatively tiny steps (curbside recycling, for example), not the enormous strides required (changing to less consumption-focused lifestyles).

While there is general consensus that sustainability is a vital goal at all levels — global, national, provincial, and municipal — there is much less agreement about what it means and how it can be reached. It has been suggested that the Brundtland Commission was deliberately vague on this point, judging that the best way to put these new imperatives on the international agenda was to sell the idea that we can eat our cake (economic development) and have it too (a healthy environment).

But some of the tough implications of sustainable development were left undescribed. The Brundtland Commission suggested more rapid economic growth in both industrial and developing countries, in order to raise consumption standards in poorer nations. However, this ignores the sense that there will have to be fundamental changes in the way we use energy and materials, if we expect ecological processes and biosphere resources to provide First World living standards for a global population.

Understanding the ways in which ecosystems work makes it possible to understand the limits of the biosphere. Living organisms depend continually on energy, water, and nutrients. The water and nutrients (carbon, nitrogen, minerals, among them) cycle throughout the ecosystem: they are used, stored, transformed, and repeatedly reused. By contrast, energy, supplied by the sun, gradually dissipates as it is transferred from one organism to the next through the food chain. Thus, the growth of ecosystems is limited by the availability of materials and the rate of energy supplied by the sun.

On the other hand, many human economic systems are based on non-renewable forms of energy (oil, gas, and coal). The materials they use are not continually recycled but eventually wind up as pollutants in air, water or soil, or discarded in mountains of consumer waste in landfill sites. All this places further stress on ecosystems, reducing their productivity and ability to support life.

Perhaps we should look more closely at the related concepts of growth and development: if limitless quantitative growth is impossible, we should strive for development that offers "qualitative change in a physically non-growing economic system in dynamic equilibrium with the environment" (as described by Herman Daly and John Cobb (1989) in their book, *For the Common Good*). In other words, we have to sustain natural capital — forests, foodlands, clean air and water, minerals — and live off the interest. While that may sound simple, it in fact means making a fundamental shift from a consumer to a conserver society, reducing consumption and learning to do more and better with less.

> *"Environmentally sustainable economic development": development that meets present needs without compromising the ability of future generations to meet their own needs.*

Willingness to Change Lifestyle

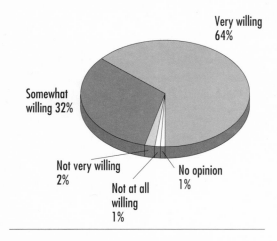

- Very willing 64%
- Somewhat willing 32%
- Not very willing 2%
- Not at all willing 1%
- No opinion 1%

Two-thirds of the respondents are "very willing" to make major changes in their daily lifestyles to help achieve an environmentally sustainable economy; a further third would be "somewhat willing" to make these changes.

Source: Environics Poll. 1991.

How do these issues affect the residents of the Greater Toronto region?

First, as biosphere co-habitants with others, we are responsible for ensuring that activities and lifestyles in this region contribute to global sustainability. More than 90 per cent of the GTA population lives in urban areas. This is similar to the global situation: nearly half the world's population lives in cities and towns and, in wealthier countries, more than 70 per cent are urban dwellers. Therefore, it is reasonable to assert that urban activities have a cumulative worldwide effect, as well as within their immediate environments. This global influence is the result of producing food for export; transporting food, energy, and materials; and polluting air and water, both locally and over a wide area. It is manifest in such problems as the long-range transport of airborne pollutants, destruction of rainforests, thinning of the ozone layer, and the greenhouse effect.

Second, as residents of the Greater Toronto bioregion, we must ask:

- How sustainable are the economy, natural environment, and quality of life here?
- What are the probable correlations among population growth, economic trends, and future environmental quality?
- As the population of this area grows, will we be able to maintain the current quality of life, let alone improve it?
- How will trends in economic activities affect the use of materials and energy, and the production of pollution and wastes?
- What is the carrying capacity of the bioregion, for people and wildlife?
- What are the natural limits of the ecosystem in supporting and tolerating human activities?

The signs of stress already evident in the Greater Toronto bioregion would seem to indicate that, if present trends continue, environmental health, the economy, and quality of life will not be at all sustainable. Clearly, therefore, strategies and plans for the future must be established in the context of sustainability that is fully and honestly explored, and constructively addressed.

UNDERSTANDING PLACES

Ecosystems may be understood on different scales: the largest one, of course, is the biosphere. Almost self-contained, it has its own atmosphere, water, minerals, soils, and life forms. However, like all ecosystems, the biosphere is not completely self-sufficient: it depends on energy from the sun, and is influenced by the gravitational forces of the sun, the moon, and other planets. Many interacting ecosystems are nested within the biosphere. As Figure 1.2 shows, a watershed in the Toronto region is part of the Greater Toronto bioregion, which, in turn, lies within the Great Lakes Basin, which is part of the larger Great Lakes–St. Lawrence system and so on.

One characteristic of ecological processes is that they rarely conform to political boundaries, such as city limits. Although the many interactions between ecosystems make it impossible to identify distinct boundaries, for practical purposes the key is to identify natural boundaries based on such characteristics as drainage patterns, landforms, vegetation, and climate.

As explained previously, the Royal Commission used the principle of natural boundaries to define the Greater Toronto bioregion: the Niagara Escarpment, the Oak Ridges Moraine, and Lake Ontario. Lands and waters in this bioregion share climatic and many ecological similarities, and the 60 or so watersheds all drain into Lake Ontario. Most of this area now falls within Toronto's commuter and economic orbit; in that sense it is our home — the ecosystem in which we live, work, and play.

Thinking about the whole bioregion helps focus attention on the interdependency and links that exist within it: between city and countryside, natural and cultural processes, water and land, economic activities and quality of life.

As Kirkpatrick Sale (1985) explains in his book, *Dwellers in the Land*, we must begin by understanding the bioregion: its geology and soils, weather, animals and plants, and human interrelations with those various elements. What natural processes are at work?

Figure 1.2   Ecosystems

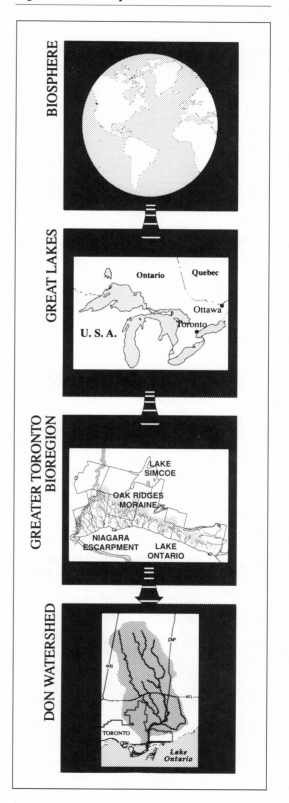

What do forms of wildlife need to survive? How have people affected the natural processes and how do they interact with wildlife? What is the aboriginal history of the place? What can we learn about ourselves from the settlement and development history of this area? In other words, how does this bioregion work and what distinguishes it from others?

Such thinking rekindles our sense of place, of rootedness, and of continuity with the past. It also shows what we have already lost, and what we stand to lose unless we begin making decisions based on an awareness of the region's full natural and cultural potential.

As "dwellers in the land", all of us — whether our families have been here for centuries or whether we are relative newcomers — need to feel connected with the natural world in a daily, physical way. The better we understand the bioregion in which we live, the more we will perceive it as "home", the more our decision-making and

behaviour will become harmonized with its special qualities, potentials, and sensitivities.

In his book, *Out of Place*, Michael Hough (1990) explores the tendency towards homogenization of urban places and the resulting loss of distinct regional identity. He says,

> . . . if it were possible to transport a visitor on a magic carpet around the world and set him down in the suburbs of Toronto, Bournemouth or Chicago, it is quite likely that he would have difficulty knowing where he was.

Since the Second World War, urban growth has occurred at an unprecedented scale and speed, frequently ignoring a place's unique natural and cultural attributes. Natural landscapes have become fragmented, the distinctions between town and country have been blurred, and a standardized pattern of freeways, subdivisions, malls, and strip development has become the norm.

A great deal of development that has taken place in the Greater Toronto bioregion since the end of the war ignored the bioregion's distinctive natural features and strong historical roots, creating landscapes that could be anywhere.

Instead, we should be taking advantage of the bioregion's true potential to create more distinct, memorable, and enjoyable places. A greater awareness of the bioregion's natural attributes — the bluffs and beaches of the Lake Ontario waterfront, the cliffs of the Niagara Escarpment, the rolling hills of the Oak Ridges Moraine, the deep river valleys and rivermouth wetlands — an understanding of how they were formed, and the processes they undergo, would help us to do this.

We also need to read, and learn from, the aboriginal and pioneer history evident

Likelihood of Developing an Environmentally Sustainable Economy

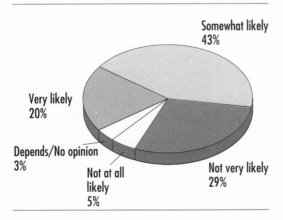

Somewhat likely
43%

Very likely
20%

Depends/No opinion
3%

Not at all
likely
5%

Not very likely
29%

There is optimism among the respondents that we can develop an environmentally sustainable economy over the next decade.

Source: Environics Poll. 1991.

42

This community could be anywhere in North America

in the countryside, the old downtown neighbourhoods, the port and industrial lands. All these and more remind us that we have a rich heritage of people interacting with each other and with this region. There is an opportunity now to retain what exists, rehabilitate what has been damaged, and work carefully with this heritage as we move toward the future.

Vistas are important and valuable in our experience of place because they help define and give character to the landscape. Vistas may be based on natural features, or created by people, over time, as they build cities or modify landscapes. Conversely, views may be lost or damaged if they are ignored when development or redevelopment takes place.

Compared with people of other major Canadian cities that have ocean or river waterfronts — Halifax, Vancouver, and Ottawa-Hull, for example — in modern times, Torontonians have not paid as much

If there is any scale at which ecological consciousness can be developed, at which citizens can see themselves as being the *cause* for the environmental *effect*, it is at the regional level; there all ecological questions are taken out of the realm of the philosophical and the moral and are dealt with as immediate and personal. People do not, other things being equal, pollute and damage those natural systems on which they depend for life and livelihood if they see directly what is happening; nor voluntarily use up a resource under their feet and before their eyes if they perceive that it is precious, needed, vital; nor kill off species they can see are important for the smooth functioning of the ecosystem.

Sale, K. 1985. *Dwellers in the land: the bioregional vision.* San Francisco: Sierra Club.

attention to public vistas as they might have. Halifax has strict guidelines about viewing planes between the Citadel and the water. Vancouver stringently protects views of water and mountains. Ottawa-Hull controls views of the Parliament buildings from across the Ottawa River, and limits downtown building heights to ensure they do not overwhelm the prospect of the Peace Tower.

This is more than mere symbolism: it helps protect and maintain the unique qualities of these cities, and influences urban form and structure just as powerfully as natural features or the configuration of roads and blocks.

Although often taken for granted, the vistas of the Greater Toronto waterfront are among the most powerful elements in creating memorable experiences there. The expanses of sky and water allow views across bays; from the land; from boats, islands,

and peninsulas to the waterfront; and views down on the entire waterfront panorama from aircraft. These are rarely the same from one day to the next: different weather, times of day, and seasons create ever-changing moods, colours, and lighting.

Monuments — such as the lion that marks the opening of the Queen Elizabeth Way 53 years ago, which is now situated near the Humber River, or the Princes' Gate at the Canadian National Exhibition — can be important aspects of vistas and help create a sense of place. They may commemorate an event, celebrate a place or interpret an aspect of history. But we have tended to neglect the importance and potential of monuments in place-making.

Some municipalities along the Greater Toronto waterfront have special provisions to take advantage of waterfront views, such as Burlington's Windows-on-the-Lake program.

A distinct and memorable place, Kensington Market

Overall, however, planning policies, design guidelines, development approvals, and other instruments could give more consideration to the special views that characterize waterfront places.

Having considered the unique attributes of the bioregion and how they can help us to protect and enhance its distinctiveness and diversity, making better places for living, playing, and working, attention must be given to the region's economy and the need to be sensitive to local and regional conditions and potentials, within larger national and international contexts.

As Meric Gertler (1990) explains in his working paper for the Commission, *Toronto: The State of the Regional Economy*, there are opportunities to develop regionally based economic strategies for the Greater Toronto region, building on existing advantages. These could look at the importance of quantity and quality of local goods and services, as well as at the local resource base, particularly its labour force and infrastructure. Local demand is essential in helping firms compete successfully in other regions and countries: sophisticated and demanding consumers in the market at home seem to act as the foundation on which firms compete effectively in other regions and countries. Competition with other firms in the same sector at home also spurs companies to innovate and produce superior products. And, as New York's experience shows, maintaining a high quality of life — a healthy environment, suitable housing, good social services, recreational opportunities, high-quality education, and so on — is crucial to a prosperous economy.

Despite that, no government entity is responsible for monitoring and responding to changes in the economic fortunes of this region as an integrated whole. The region is larger than any of the individual municipal or regional governments in the area, but smaller than the next largest level, the Province. However, despite the importance of the region's economy in the economy of Canada, neither provincial nor federal governments give it the care and attention it needs if it is to continue fulfilling this role.

INTEGRATED PROCESSES

The report of the World Commission on Environment and Development (1987) called for major alterations in the way we do business, and emphasized the need to integrate economic decision-making with environmental decision-making processes. It concluded, as has the Royal Commission, that sustainability requires a revolution in our thinking and in our institutional arrangements. Many traditional barriers will have to be overcome if we are going to respond to our current environmental and economic crises.

The past is important: it tells us where we have come from; what shapes what we are and influences what we will become. The built environment — historically, architecturally, and culturally rich buildings, districts and landscapes — gives us a sense of place. . . It provides a physical bond with a shared past and helps provide mental and physical stability in a rapidly changing world.

Parks, Pleasures, and Public Amenities Work Group. 1989. *Parks, pleasures, and public amenities.* Toronto: Royal Commission on the Future of the Toronto Waterfront.

Two of the most intractable obstacles to implementing an ecosystem approach — and to the economic and environmental regeneration it would provide — are rigidity of bureaucratic systems and fragmentation of jurisdictions. They combine to create a high degree of paralysis that pervades our systems of governance, and makes it difficult, if not impossible, to make sound, integrated decisions.

While it may now be considered trite to say that, *if we want to improve the kind of decisions we make*, we are going to have to change the *way* we make decisions, the fact is that the multidisciplinary, cross-sectoral, and multijurisdictional nature of today's environmental and economic problems means cutting across disciplines, sectors, and jurisdictions. Ten provincial round tables, two territorial round tables, a National Round Table, and hundreds of municipal round tables are examples of how new institutions can be created to adapt to this challenge. While still early in its existence, the round-table movement has already proven effective in bringing people together from diverse backgrounds so that they can talk and find ways to overcome old antagonisms, using innovative forms of consensus decision-making. Other advisory bodies, commissions, and task forces can also act as agents of change and vehicles to overcome institutional rigidities. Such catalysts as round tables can be important in fostering partnerships across sectors, among institutions within sectors, and across jurisdictions.

In the process of carrying out its mandate, the Royal Commission acted as a catalyst to promote change in the way we study, plan, and implement policies that will foster more sustainable waterfronts, cities, and regions, and its experience may suggest ways for others to do so. In fact, during the Commission's life, many people asked us to describe our methods, and have begun applying some of them: perhaps some aspects of our work may be usefully replicated in other areas (although, they may need to be adapted for different regions and circumstances).

The Commission's mandate required the Commissioner to seek full consultation with all interested parties and to seek the concurrence of affected agencies with his recommendations. In working to fulfil its mandate, the Commission used a cross-sectoral approach to its research and analysis and worked actively to see that its recommendations were implemented. By doing so, the Commission came to be an agent of change to help overcome the inertia it encountered. Its agent-of-change activities can be grouped as: linking resources, helping processes, acting as a catalyst, and finding solutions.

If we want to improve the kind of decisions we make, we are going to have to change the way we make decisions.

LINKING RESOURCES

In its multidisciplinary, multijurisdictional, and multi-stakeholder approach, the Commission linked agencies, organizations, levels of government, and individuals together — in some cases, those that had never worked with or even met each other before.

In the three years of its life, the Commission created 16 different teams to prepare reports, always drawing members

Figure 1.3 Contrasting decision-making processes

Fragmented

Round-Table

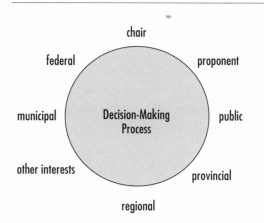

Source: Barrett, S., and J. Kidd. 1991. *Pathways: towards an ecosystem approach: a report of phases I and II of an environmental audit of Toronto's East Bayfront and Port Industrial Area.* Publication no. 11. Toronto RCFTW.

from different sectors, backgrounds, and interests: developers began talking with environmentalists, traffic engineers with landscape architects, scientists with community activists, and federal public servants with city officials. This often led to consensus, trust, and promotion of partnerships that would not otherwise have emerged. Furthermore, these interactions sometimes extended beyond the individuals directly involved, to link their networks — their colleagues, values, information, and resources.

The use of multi-stakeholder teams to produce discussion papers that focused consultations worked only because participants were asked *not* to act as stakeholders, to "park their team jackets at the door". They were to reflect but *not* represent their sector organizations. Many participants reported that this was quite liberating, enabling them to set aside territoriality, to escape cramped adherence to old ways of viewing problems and, instead, to see them on the basis of new information, understanding, and perspectives.

While the 15 work group reports and 14 technical papers, prepared at arm's length from the Commission, were particularly creative, they were also grounded in the hard reality that comes from subjecting each position or recommendation to the test of feasibility and acceptability.

HELPING PROCESSES

Just by providing "good offices" the Commission was often able to help a stalled process move forward; creating a steering committee, calling a meeting, acting as a facilitator (and sometimes mediator) allowed the Commission to analyse issues and promote change, breaking out of long-standing jurisdictional gridlock. Because the Commission was only advisory, took away no one's jurisdiction, and was temporary in its duration, it could act as an honest broker, to a greater degree than could a permanent body with legal powers.

The Commission's use of public hearings (described in the Introduction) helped the process: friendly and informed hearings ensured open communication and made lawyers unnecessary. The free flow of information opened many processes that had formerly been closed; several groups said they felt empowered by participating in an open forum at which they could express their positions in their own words.

The public is often consulted too early or too late: too early before a paper has been prepared to focus discussion and suggest options; or too late after most decisions have been developed, leaving citizens with the suspicion they were simply being used as window dressing. The Commission's hearings were always based on discussion papers prepared by the representatives of diverse stakeholders.

The Commission's "family" of regular deputants and interested parties were kept involved by a variety of means, not least the *Newsletter*. Desk-top published in-house at modest cost, it became an effective way of ensuring that participants knew what the Commission, and other groups, were doing. By the end of the Commission's life, it had a mailing list of more than 7,500 people.

ACTING AS A CATALYST

Royal commissions have the right to be independent, but are not obliged to be so. In preparing recommendations, the Commission often tested drafts with affected agencies, frequently with the help of work group members, and then worked to advocate positions it had taken.

This proactive and interventionist stance was not greeted warmly at first by all the many agencies and special purpose bodies that have jurisdiction in the region. By the second year, however, most of these

bodies had come to see the Commission's process as a way of breaking the debilitating constraints of fragmented bureaucratic systems.

The Commission's interim reports were essential to the success of its function as a catalyst. Very early on, deputants saw that they had been listened to; governments and their agencies were able to respond quickly, thereby giving credibility to the entire process. Problems could be solved as they arose, freeing the Commission to concentrate on other subjects.

By issuing interim reports, the Commission avoided the perception — and the reality — in which commission documents simply gather dust on a shelf: ours were not orphans in a bureaucratic system. Before being released, each had been the subject of a great deal of groundwork by the work groups and in the consultation processes. After the interim reports were released, we could continue actively working with other agencies that would adopt and implement our recommendations.

FINDING SOLUTIONS

After analysing and synthesizing many issues, and having focused debate, crystallized positions, and overcome inertia, the Commission made recommendations on possible solutions to what, in many cases, had been longstanding and persistent problems. Most major recommendations in the first two interim reports have now been adopted and implemented, either partially or fully.

Some workable solutions were found, in part, as the result of the broadly based, interactive consultation process used from the outset. If politics is the art of the possible, policy-making is the art of the feasible and there is no better way to find out what is possible than subjecting a discussion of ideas to full, open, and public critique. While many of our negotiated solutions were somewhat ragged, they were broadly acceptable. Rather than using conventional systems of policy-making, which often impose constraints on testing options openly, we could re-evaluate initial positions and, before making recommendations, adapt or retreat, in ways that would be difficult for governments and their permanent agencies.

INITIATIVES

The integrated processes used by the Commission helped to break down some of the existing barriers to research, analysis, decision-making, and implementation that threaten our ability to deal effectively with today's economic, social, and environmental problems. These efforts to implement the ecosystem approach are not without precedent: many steps are being taken in this direction, in Canada and worldwide.

In 1992, the United Nations will host a major conference on Environment and Development in Brazil, at which representatives from countries around the world will come together, share experiences, and develop, among other things, ways of addressing the cumulative effects of urban living on the biosphere. Given that nearly half the world's population lives in cities and towns, the conference has the potential to make significant changes.

The International Council for Local Environmental Initiatives (ICLEI) helps municipalities around the world address environmental issues. In the summer of 1991, it opened its World Secretariat and North American Headquarters in Toronto,

having chosen this region because of its reputation for actively promoting effective local environmental management. ICLEI will represent local governments to international organizations dealing with the environment, collaborate with municipalities worldwide on major environmental issues, and promote excellence in municipal management of the environment.

As ICLEI has found, many Ontario municipalities have already taken initiatives that reduce their impact on both global and local environments. New processes, planning studies, policies, by-laws, programs, environmental advisory committees, municipal environmental assessment processes, and development requirements help municipalities bring environmental considerations into their decision-making processes. Community initiatives have also become popular as citizens seek to address their local environmental priorities.

The City of Toronto's Healthy City Office demonstrates how processes can be adapted to facilitate co-ordinated municipal action. The Office acts as an agent of change, working with people in the community, in business, and government, with the goal of creating a good quality of life for everyone. For example, one of its recent projects focuses on transportation systems that are more socially and environmentally sensible than those now in use. The Office's recently published report, *Evaluating the Role of the Automobile: A Municipal Strategy* (Toronto 1991), was prepared by a work group that included representatives from municipal government, the Toronto Transit Commission, GO Transit, business, environmental groups, and ratepayers. It highlights the real costs of automobile use (energy use, air and noise pollution, health effects, use of land for roads and parking, etc.) and proposes a comprehensive strategy that could reduce the effects of automobiles by controlling emissions, reducing traffic, changing land-use patterns, and promoting alternative forms of transportation.

Increasingly, municipal planning studies are evolving to incorporate environmental concerns. For example, Halton Region (1990) has prepared a new regional plan that provides a vision of what its landscape and communities should be like in the very long term — 50, 100 or 500 years from now. Halton plans to reach its ultimate goal of sustainable development guided by two principles: land stewardship and healthy communities. The intention is to preserve landforms and inhibit urban sprawl so that there is a healthy balance among the social, economic, and environmental needs of the community.

A number of municipalities have also proposed new Official Plans that place much more emphasis on the environment than did previous versions. For example, Metro Toronto's *Towards A Liveable Metropolis* (1991) suggests innovative ways of dealing with the issues currently faced by its communities. These include a new framework for decision-making, based on the three components of liveability: environmental integrity, economic viability, and social well-being. Initiatives outlined in the report include integrating environmental, social, and economic considerations into a revised development review process, assessing the state of the environment in Metropolitan Toronto, and developing a strategy to ensure that corporate practices and policies are environmentally responsible.

The City of Toronto's *Cityplan '91* also has a strong environmental focus, based on the principle that:

> Toronto's residents, workers, and visitors have the right to an environment that is protective of their health and well-being, and . . . have the responsibility to maintain the environment for future generations.

Many of the plan's proposals are intended to protect and enhance the City's natural heritage directly, while others incorporate environmental considerations indirectly.

The Township of Mono, which recognizes the importance of managing water on a sustainable basis, has formed a committee to examine the cumulative effects of development taking place in the headwater areas of the northwestern part of the bioregion. Along with the local conservation authorities,

Most Significant Lifestyle Change

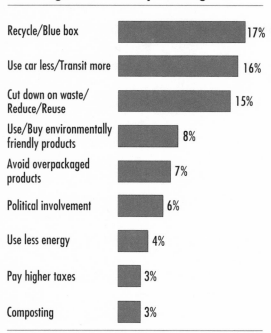

Recycling, using transit, and cutting down on waste are some of the changes the respondents are willing to make to achieve an environmentally sustainable economy.

Source: Environics Poll. 1991.

the Niagara Escarpment Commission, and the ministries of Municipal Affairs and of the Environment, Mono hosted a conference in October 1991 that examined the state of our water resources, current water planning practices, and responsibilities for water management.

The Credit Valley Conservation Authority (CVCA) has also been active in protecting and maintaining water resources, in this case the Credit River and its tributaries. In the late 1980s, the Authority recognized that the traditional approach to water management, stressing engineering, was not going to maintain the long-term health of the river. After undertaking extensive water resource studies, it developed an ecosystem approach to water management, which emphasizes understanding environmental conditions and only then developing sub-watershed plans. CVCA is currently involved in four sub-watershed plans with local municipalities, developers, and government agencies. Involving all interested parties has meant that, from the outset, decision-makers understand the constraints and opportunities that may exist in each sub-watershed.

In addition to participating in the CVCA sub-watershed planning exercise, the ministries of Natural Resources (MNR) and the Environment (MOE) have, with municipal and conservation authority representatives and other government agencies, been developing a framework for managing watersheds in urbanizing areas of Ontario. Founded on an ecosystem approach, draft interim guidelines for the preparation and implementation of sub-watershed plans and for the integration of water resource management objectives into Official Plans have been developed for discussion.

A number of municipalities have programs to protect environmentally significant areas. For example, Halton Region's Official Plan includes provisions for designating Environmentally Sensitive Areas (ESAs); it prohibits development in ESAs and requires an environmental impact study for development on land adjacent to an ESA.

In Halton, as in a number of other places in the bioregion, there is growing interest in maintaining more than the "islands of green" represented by ESAs. In 1989, the Metropolitan Toronto and Region Conservation Authority (MTRCA) adopted a *Greenspace Strategy for the Greater Toronto Region* (1989) encompassing integrated management of natural lands and resources within the region. Programs arising from the strategy include a proposed multi-stakeholder process for watershed planning in the Don Valley, and a Greater Toronto Region Trail System connecting the waterfront, the river valleys, and the Oak Ridges Moraine.

In 1989-90, Ron Kanter, then a Liberal MPP, working on behalf of the Province, studied options for a greenlands strategy in the Greater Toronto Area. His report, *Space for All* (1990), identifies existing greenland resources and calls for immediate action to secure them for the future, recognizing their importance to a good quality of life and a healthy environment.

As a contribution to Kanter's study, or in response to it, many municipalities (Halton, Scarborough, and Whitby, among them) prepared their own greenlands strategies. These would protect and link ESAs, valleylands, wetlands, groundwater recharge areas, woodlots, parks, waterfront lands, and the like.

The City of North York is a pioneer in working to expand and enhance existing natural areas through naturalization. By planting native vegetation, the City creates new habitat for wildlife and gives citizens a diverse and healthy environment in which to enjoy passive recreation. Naturalized parks are a step towards sustainability: because they are adapted to local environmental conditions, native species require less maintenance, fewer chemicals, and less water.

Governments at all levels are major consumers and can have a potentially significant role in stimulating the market for durable, reuseable, and recyclable products. The Regional Municipality of Metropolitan Toronto has asked its constituent municipalities to establish environmental purchasing policies, including such measures as using re-refined oil in municipal vehicles, reuseable eating utensils, and recycled paper.

Some municipalities are examining the state of the local environment as a quality-of-life issue and asking residents to offer ideas and a vision that will help focus long-term planning. For example, the Region of Waterloo appointed a Citizens' Advisory Committee on the Quality of Life, which is to gather opinions from members of the public and frame a consensus within which future community development can be guided. The committee found that sustainable development must become the basis for personal and community decision-making if the quality of life in the region is to be maintained and improved.

By-laws can also be used to promote sustainability. Recognizing the dangers of ozone-depleting substances to human and ecosystem health, the City of Toronto (1990) passed a by-law that prohibits and regulates the use, recovery, and disposal of products containing, or manufactured with, chloro-fluorocarbons, halons, and other ozone-depleting substances. Such equipment as refrigerators, air conditioners, and fire extinguishers must now be drained before they are discarded for disposal, chloro-flurocarbons and halons must be recovered from them, and the chemicals must be deposited at an authorized site.

The City of Toronto has adopted requirements for developments, to ensure that they are more environmentally responsible. An applicant must submit a noise impact statement forecasting noise emissions and ways to minimize their impact on the surrounding environment. All major development projects must now include waste reduction and recycling strategies in their proposals. New developments of more than 10,000 square metres (107,600 square feet) must meet water and energy conservation and efficiency standards. In order to minimize automobile use, a new proposal for a non-residential development, which would normally be required to include no fewer than 75 parking spaces, must now provide a traffic management plan suggesting alternative ways for future employees in the development to travel to work.

Citizens' groups have also taken powerful initiatives to protect and enhance the natural heritage: the Black Creek Project, begun in the early 1980s by several citizens in the Black Creek watershed, has fought for the protection and rehabilitation of the creek. It has planted more than 2,000 trees and shrubs in the creek valley, brought modifications of development proposals so they take environmental health into consideration, and tackled bank erosion with rocks that provide habitat. Funding from various levels of government and co-operation with the

Conservation Council of Ontario (CCO) has helped the Black Creek Project in its work.

CCO is also reaching out to other communities, encouraging them to become effectively involved in supporting a healthy environment. With its assistance, interested communities will develop environmental action plans that list their existing environmental and resource issues, and propose remediation strategies to be implemented over the next several years. The Regional Municipality of Metropolitan Toronto will be the first municipality to prepare an action plan and will focus on four key areas: waste reduction, natural areas, water conservation, and air quality.

Partnerships among various levels of government can facilitate environmental action. For example, as part of the Hamilton Harbour Remedial Action Plan, a program is being developed to restore 605 hectares (1,495 acres) of fish and wildlife habitat in Cootes Paradise and the mouth of Grindstone Creek. It is proposed that this work be undertaken as a joint project among the federal, provincial, and municipal governments, as well as with the private sector. Environment Canada recently allocated $4.2 million (one-third of the total projected costs) for the project, from the Great Lakes Clean-up Fund.

Provincial planning initiatives can also be important in promoting sustainability. The Niagara Escarpment Plan is one of the few land-use plans in Canada and the only one in Ontario that has jurisdiction on the basis of an ecological entity. The plan controls development that is incompatible with the natural environment and threatens the continuity of the escarpment and its vicinity.

Similar development pressures are occurring on the Oak Ridges Moraine, a hydrologically sensitive and important landform north of Toronto. The Province has undertaken a two-year planning study to develop a long-term strategy for the moraine. Until then, Provincial Implementation Guidelines on the Oak Ridges Moraine (1991) are intended to ensure that permission is given only to developments that are compatible with the environmentally sensitive nature of the Oak Ridges Moraine. For example, natural areas, groundwater recharge areas, and landforms are to be protected by the guidelines until the strategy is complete.

Growth pressures in the GTA prompted the Province to undertake the Greater Toronto Area Urban Concept Study, completed in 1990. It estimates infrastructure requirements, comparative capital costs, quality and effectiveness of urban services, and the environmental impact of three possible patterns of future development in the GTA — "spread", "central", and "nodal". Of the three, the "spread" concept, continued low-density development outside the existing built-up areas, was found to use the most rural land and natural resources; moreover, because it depended so heavily on automobile use, it would consume the most energy and contribute significantly to air pollution.

The "central" concept — new high-density growth concentrating development in existing built-up areas, particularly in Metropolitan Toronto, would be most energy- and land-use efficient, but would make it difficult to provide adequate open space in urban areas. The "nodal" concept, distributing new growth amongst nodes throughout the GTA, based on existing settlements and in a compact form, was judged least disruptive to existing communities;

STREAM REHABILITATION: THE BLACK CREEK PROJECT

Traditionally, cities and streams have not co-existed well: human settlements of any size usually herald habitat destruction, water pollution, and, in time, reshaping of a river's course to fit human habitation and infrastructure. This is more or less true around the world: the Seine in Paris, the Choa Phya in Bangkok, and the Vistula in Warsaw. Nor are Toronto's streams and rivers an exception. What is exceptional is the response of a group of citizens to the deterioration of their local stream — more specifically, the fight by the Black Creek Project for the health of Black Creek.

In 1982, Sandy Agnew, who grew up beside the river, and John Maher, who lived near Black Creek, got together with a few other neighbours and formed the Black Creek Project. Its goal was to protect and enhance Black Creek and its associated ecosystems — no small task, then or now.

Black Creek, a tributary of the Humber River, has suffered much since the first European settlement in the area. Most of the watershed was cleared for agriculture and later paved over by urban growth; a large proportion of the watershed was rendered impermeable by pavement and buildings; a great deal of water falling as rain and snow could no longer enter the soil to be released slowly into the river. Instead, precipitation hit pavement and roofs and was funnelled into storm sewers.

Today moderate to heavy precipitation results in sudden, powerful river flows. The high-velocity water is dangerous to both wildlife and humans, and severely erodes the riverbank. In parts of the stream that have been channelled, the water picks up speed as it rushes through the slick straight gutters.

Forcing the river into a concrete straightjacket also eliminates aquatic and shore habitat, and increases flood damage. Such artificial reaches of the stream are devoid of rocks under which water insects can hide, as well as the vegetation cover that is forage for small mammals and birds.

Some of Black Creek's tributaries are in even worse shape: they have been completely covered and are now part of the city's storm-sewer network; furthermore, like most urban streams, Black Creek and its tributaries suffer from pollution. Sediment from construction activity washes into the creek, blocking the light the aquatic community needs and blanketing the river bottom, which suffocates plant and animal life there. Discharges from industries in the storm sewershed; lawn chemicals; the soap people use in washing their cars; the oil and other chemicals we routinely pour down our drains — all make their way into the creek. Few species can survive in such a hostile environment.

One of the first rehabilitation activities of the Black Creek Project was to plant trees in the watershed. The restoration of some plant species that grew in the area before urbanization has enlarged wildlife habitat and slowed water percolation in the soil, giving the river a more stable water flow in planted areas.

Plantings of shrubs and trees have also helped stabilize riverbanks, while rocks placed along the creek banks have helped reduce erosion. The Black Creek Project usually has many planting days each year at which members and the public, frequently local students, work together to dig holes and plant trees in various parts of the watershed. There have been clean-up days involving the public as well as Environmental Youth Corps staff, at which garbage (including several hundred shopping carts) has been cleared from the river.

The Black Creek Project has also been instrumental in protecting the river by influencing development plans. In 1983, members persuaded the City of York to refuse creation of a snow-dumping ground, which would have further degraded Lavender Creek. In 1985, the Project stopped the bulldozing of a woodlot in Vaughan in order to create a stormwater management pond. The pond exists today — right beside the woodlot, in fact — but it is a positive addition to the woodlot's natural heritage because, acting in accordance with advice from members of the Project, designers ensured that it includes wetland areas.

Using funds from various levels of government and private donations, the Black Creek Project has supervised inventories of the natural heritage in the watershed, put in 300 metres (985 feet) of erosion control riprap, planned a bike path and nature trail system for the entire valley, and planted several thousand trees.

Pond in the Black Creek valley provides stormwater management and wildlife habitat

Future plans include replacing some of the channelled portions of the creek with natural stream beds and banks. At the mouth of the creek, this would allow fish from the Humber River to gain access to Black Creek again and would create habitat throughout the creek for many species of wildlife. Restoration is a slow process and there may sometimes be as many steps backwards as there are forwards. Ultimately, long-term success depends on the willingness of watershed residents to take on the role of stewards of the river.

provided the greatest diversity in types of housing, densities, and population/employment mixes; and wasted less energy and fewer resources than the "spread" concept.

Responses to the study show a general consensus in favour of some form of nodal growth; however, the study also recognized the need for more work on the idea: to define a shared vision for the Greater Toronto region; analyse future economic prospects and their impact on growth; examine human service needs; develop models for more compact, liveable communities; and improve understanding of environmental and open-space implications. The GTA office is currently preparing a "vision" paper as the basis for establishing common values and directions for this complex and dynamic region.

Niagara Escarpment, near Milton

PRINCIPLES FOR REGENERATING THE WATERFRONT

All these studies and initiatives indicate deep and growing concern about the future of the Greater Toronto region, and show that there is an emerging consensus about the need to act, and act soon, to secure a healthy and sustainable future. While people are responding to these challenges in a myriad of ways, there is a need now to co-ordinate efforts and place them in a framework that makes a larger, more effective whole. The Royal Commission believes this can be achieved by working to regenerate the waterfront and the bioregion.

We view regeneration as a healing process that restores and maintains environmental health, as well as anticipating and preventing future harm. This means striving to ensure that existing land uses and activities are adapted, and all new development is designed, to contribute to the health, diversity, and sustainability of the entire ecosystem: the physical environment, human communities, and economic activities.

To help meet these needs, the Commission's *Watershed* report identified nine principles that can be applied to make the Greater Toronto waterfront healthier and more sustainable: clean, green, connected, open, accessible, useable, diverse, affordable, and attractive. (Applications of the principles are discussed in *Watershed* and in subsequent chapters of this report.)

CLEAN

All activities and future development should work with natural processes to contribute to environmental health. Air, land, sediments, and water should be free of contaminants that impair beneficial uses by people and other living beings.

Polluted soils, groundwater, sediments, and water should be remediated. New development should include the best possible means of controlling stormwater flows and pollution, reducing energy use for heating/cooling, minimizing automobile dependence, reducing and recycling wastes, and reducing water consumption. Where possible, existing development should be adapted or retrofitted to achieve these goals.

GREEN

Natural features and topography should form a "green infrastructure" for the bioregion's cities, suburbs, and countryside. A green infrastructure may include natural habitat areas such as wetlands and forests; landforms such as bluffs, valleys, beaches, and cliffs; aquifer recharge areas; and parks and other open spaces.

The diversity and productivity of ecological communities should be protected and restored through measures that:

- preserve the genetic diversity of indigenous plants and animals;
- protect and restore healthy natural habitats and communities; and
- maintain natural ecological processes.

CONNECTED

Throughout the bioregion, connections with the region's natural and cultural heritage should be restored and maintained. This should include links among:

- wildlife habitats;
- city and countryside;
- social communities;
- past and present; and
- people and nature.

A network of greenways should connect the natural habitats and human communities of the waterfront, valley systems, tablelands, the Niagara Escarpment, and the Oak Ridges Moraine. As much as possible, greenways should connect and incorporate existing public lands, to form a "linked-nodal" pattern throughout the bioregion. Continuous pedestrian and bicycle trails should be developed in these greenways to provide recreational and commuting opportunities.

When redevelopment is undertaken, cultural and built heritage should be respected and incorporated, so that continuity with the past is protected and distinctive places are maintained.

OPEN

Existing vistas of Lake Ontario and its bays, bluffs, peninsulas, and islands should be maintained. Moreover, vistas made possible by the open expanses of water (e.g., views of the city from Ontario Place, or across Humber Bay) should be treated as important values in waterfront development. Density and design of waterfront structures should not be permitted to create a visual barrier to the lake or intrude on the water's edge.

ACCESSIBLE

Nodes and communities of waterfront activity should be serviced by public transit as well as by road, with transit increasingly emphasized. People should be able to get to, and enjoy, the waterfront on foot or by bicycle, with major improvements made where necessary to overcome the barriers presented by road and rail corridors. The waterfront should be safe and accessible to all sectors of society, including the disabled, children, and older adults.

Where feasible, the water's edge should be — and should be clearly identified as being — open to public access. New developments should include public access to and along the waterfront. Where continuous access to the waterfront is not possible, it should be provided at convenient intervals, with parallel connections back from the shore.

Providing regional access for visitors, in areas where there are already residential neighbourhoods on the waterfront, should be handled carefully and with respect for local needs for privacy and safety.

USEABLE

The waterfront should continue to support a mix of public and private uses that:

- are primarily water-related;
- permit public access, use, and enjoyment of the water's edge;
- enhance residential neighbourhoods and appropriate commercial and industrial uses;

- decrease need for commuting by providing a local balance of employment and residential opportunities;
- are environmentally friendly in form and function;
- minimize conflicts with adjacent communities or uses; and
- are designed and managed to improve microclimate and promote greater year-round comfort and use.

Design, use, and management of waterfront places should enhance safety and minimize risks caused by:

- threats to personal safety from other users;
- flooding and erosion; and
- incidents involving hazardous materials.

DIVERSE

The waterfront should provide diverse landscapes, places, wildlife habitats, uses, programs, and experiences. This will offer varied opportunities for visiting and resident people, as well as for resident, migrating, and over-wintering wildlife.

The mix of land uses and facilities for competing public demands within environmental limits should be balanced between:

- public and private;
- urban and rural;
- regional and local;

- residential and recreational;
- industrial and commercial;
- built and natural environments;
- large- and small-scale;
- active and passive;
- busy and quiet; and
- free and user-pay.

AFFORDABLE

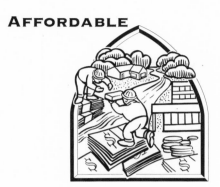

Waterfront development and management should be undertaken in ways that provide opportunities for economic renewal and for efficient use of limited government and private-sector resources.

Where possible, social, environmental, and economic objectives should be integrated with each other, in order to achieve them as effectively as possible. For example:

- projects might be more affordable if partners co-ordinate activities and share resources;
- projects could be designed to yield multiple benefits;
- a healthy environment is a more productive setting for economic activities.

A long-term view should be adopted when decisions are being considered so that the full societal and environmental costs of proposed activities become factors in whatever choices are made. For example, incorporating environmental protection at the outset may reduce the need for environmental rehabilitation later, thus improving long-term affordability and sustainability.

A range of waterfront parks and facilities should be available to provide opportunities for all income groups. Waterfront residential projects should offer a variety of housing types and prices, including affordable and rental housing.

ATTRACTIVE

Design and landscaping should protect, enhance, and create distinctive and memorable places along the waterfront. This means excellence in design of neighbourhoods and other developments, individual buildings, transportation elements, parks, recreational facilities, outdoor furniture, and other amenities.

Design on the waterfront should:

- protect vistas and views of the lake;
- provide a sense of continuity with the past;
- emphasize sensitive design and massing of buildings;
- consider the relationships among buildings, open spaces, and the water;
- use harmonious colours, textures, and materials; and
- include a range of landscape types, from wild and natural to manicured and formal.

SUMMARY

Ecosystem principles will help to make the most of the qualities of the Greater Toronto waterfront — the historic birthplace of our communities, the source of our drinking water, a home for wildlife, a place for recreation and relaxation, and the setting for vistas across the water.

This waterfront is inextricably linked, not only to the lake, but to the 60 watersheds that drain into it. Together, the waterfront, watersheds, Niagara Escarpment and Oak Ridges Moraine, form a major bioregion in Ontario. But the bioregion is under considerable economic, social, and environmental stress. We can no longer take its economic prosperity or quality of life for granted. It has also become clear that institutional arrangements in the bioregion are often part of the problem; bureaucratic systems are often rigid and jurisdictions fragmented.

In exploring these issues, the Commission found that the ecosystem approach offered some fresh insights and possible new ways of doing things.

By thinking of ecosystems as living systems, of which humans are a part, we can better understand our roles now and our responsibility to future generations. In the past, decision-making has often been based primarily on economic and social objectives, often at a cost to the environment. The ecosystem approach is based on the reality that everything is connected to everything else, which means that environmental considerations must be part of the decision-making process, so that relationships within ecosystems are viewed as comprising three interlinked circles: environment, community, and economy.

Viewing the bioregion as a whole helps to enhance the sense of place, as well as understanding of the links within it: between city and countryside, natural and cultural processes, water and land, economic activities and quality of life. It also shows how regionally based economic strategies can be developed for the Greater Toronto region, building on existing advantages.

It is apparent that, to achieve healthy, sustainable communities, we must find ways to adapt and improve many processes for studying, analysing, planning, reviewing, consulting, and decision-making. The changes already under way are reflected in various organizations and processes — the work of the Brundtland Commission; the existence of national, provincial, and territorial round tables on environment and economy; new initiatives by many municipalities, conservation authorities, environmental groups, and government agencies; and increased public awareness of the issues. The Royal Commission's work demonstrated how the ecosystem approach could be applied in specific areas and situations, as described in subsequent chapters of this report.

The bioregion's future health and quality of life, as well as its environmental and economic sustainability, will depend on how we choose to manage the assets we have. The Commission believes that using an ecosystem approach can help to assure a future that is indeed clean, green, connected, open, accessible, useable, diverse, affordable, and attractive.

CHAPTER 2:
PLANNING PRACTICE

According to the Royal Commission's publication number 12, *Planning for Sustainability* (Doering et al. 1991):

> As the work of the Royal Commission on the Future of the Toronto Waterfront has progressed, it has become abundantly clear — both from the evidence of deputants and from the Commission's own studies — that the present processes of land-use planning and environmental management do not offer even minimal environmental protection, let alone the "ecosystem approach to restoring and regenerating the Greater Toronto region" advocated in *Watershed* (RCFTW 1991).

The previous chapter describes some of the changes in decision-making processes that are needed to implement the ecosystem approach in the Greater Toronto region. Many involve some form of planning: for land uses in municipalities, for watershed management, for shoreline regeneration, for development, etc.

The ecosystem concept is so all-embracing, so multi-faceted, and so dependant on things only partially within any one politician's, planner's, designer's or developer's control, that there is a tendency to pay lip service and agree with the principle, but to avoid defining appropriate day-to-day practice. So, although the ecosystem approach to planning could and should be a revolution in planning practice, there is a real danger that it may become instead a descriptive veneer shallowly applied to doing things in the old way, just as such terms as "environmentally friendly" and "green" are sometimes used in advertising.

Because we want to focus on action rather than just on ideas or rhetoric, we offer in this chapter some thoughts on "ecosystem planning practice". For the sake of convenience, "ecosystem-based planning" has been shortened to "ecosystem planning", while "practice" is used to remind readers that performance is the ultimate test of our commitment to a healthy, sustained ecosystem. And it would be presumptuous to suggest that we can actually "plan" ecosystems: they are too complex, interconnected, dynamic, and often unpredictable. What we *can* do is undertake planning with an ecosystem perspective.

CONTEXT

Suggestions for practising ecosystem planning are offered in the context of a

> The structure of our metropolitan areas has long since been set by nature and man, by the rivers and the hills, and the railroads and the highways. Many options remain, and the great task of planning is not to come up with another structure but to work with the strengths of the structure we have — and to discern this structure as people experience it in their everyday life. . . . Grappling with these gritty realities, however, provides a far greater and more exciting challenge than the search for perfection somewhere else.
>
> Whyte, W. H. 1968. *The last landscape.* Garden City: Doubleday & Company.

number of recent and ongoing initiatives in Ontario; these have been established in response to the need to change planning processes so that we can cope with increasing and conflicting pressures on land, water, and natural systems. They include:

- the Commission on Planning and Development Reform in Ontario, chaired by John Sewell;
- the Ministry of Municipal Affairs' work on greening the planning process, a green guide to planning practice, streamlining the planning process, and identifying ways to develop provincial policies and plans;
- preparation of, and revisions to, many regional and local municipal Official Plans in the Greater Toronto region;
- co-ordination by the Ministry of Natural Resources of the Oak Ridges Moraine interim guidelines and planning study;
- the work of the Office of the Greater Toronto Area, including its *Urban*

Structure Concepts Study (Ontario 1990), and its vision statement for the Greater Toronto Area in 2021;
- former MPP Ron Kanter's (1990) study, *Space for All,* which describes options for a GTA Greenlands Strategy;
- the five-year review of the Niagara Escarpment Plan (Ontario 1985);
- investigations by the Ministry of Agriculture and Food regarding innovative ways to protect agricultural lands;
- the Ministry of the Environment's Environmental Assessment Program Improvement Project (EAPIP);
- work by the ministries of the Environment, Natural Resources, and Municipal Affairs on guidelines for integrating water resource management objectives into municipal plans;
- the Ministry of Natural Resources' review of the role, mandate, funding, and composition of conservation authorities; and
- the Metropolitan Toronto Remedial Action Plan.

For several reasons, these initiatives have tremendous potential to influence planning processes at a crucial time. First, as described earlier, the Greater Toronto bioregion is at a pivotal stage of growth. If future changes are not planned carefully, environmental quality will continue to be degraded and quality of life will suffer.

Second, many municipal Official Plans are currently being reviewed or prepared. Two regions, Peel and York, are still preparing their *first* Official Plans, while Halton and Durham are revising theirs and Metro Toronto is preparing its second Official Plan. At the same time, most local municipalities are undertaking Official Plan reviews, and many waterfront municipalities are preparing waterfront plans.

Plans now being prepared will have significant effects on patterns of development, environmental health, community life, and the economic vitality of this region for a long time to come. There are encouraging signs that some municipalities are shifting to more ecosystem-based planning; the challenge is to encourage this approach everywhere, so that these opportunities are used to ensure a healthy and sustainable future for the region.

Plans now being prepared will have significant effects on patterns of development, environmental health, community life, and the economic vitality of this region for a long time to come.

In recognition of these needs, *Watershed* proposed a review of

. . .the ways in which the philosophy and principles of the ecosystem approach could best be integrated into the Planning Act and other relevant provincial legislation, as it affects the greater Toronto bioregion.

The Royal Commission subsequently convened an interdisciplinary work group on environment and planning; it was asked to prepare a background paper on issues related to integration of environmental considerations into the land-use planning process and to suggest opportunities for better integration. The resulting report, *Planning for Sustainability* (Doering et al.), was published in June 1991, and is the basis for much of this chapter.

THE NATURE OF THE PROBLEM

Planning for Sustainability concluded that there is widespread agreement on the inadequacy of current provincial land-use planning processes to protect the environment, but there are many different views of the nature of the problem:

Environmentalists are concerned about the deterioration of the natural environment: loss of valuable natural areas such as wetlands, woodlands, and river valleys; disappearance of prime farmlands and rural landscapes; pollution of rivers; depletion of aquifers; and so on. Provincial and municipal governments are subject to conflicting demands for the use and protection of land, air, and water, but lack adequate resources to respond. Developers are concerned that environmental requirements are not clearly specified and that the processes being used to seek environmental protection create delays, increased development costs, and reduced options.

Clearly, the problems are many and complex. Following are some that have been highlighted during the Royal Commission's work.

PLANNING OR REGULATION?

Ecosystem planning practice has deep roots but its form is still emerging. Its roots can be traced to Henry Thoreau, Aldo Leopold, and some of the naturalists who came before and after them. The first views of Earth from space, during the 1960s, supported an ecological vision of Earth: when our planet was seen in its entirety — not as some kind of huge mechanical ball or geographic globe, but as a living, moving

Cooksville Creek, Mississauga: damaged by development practices, this channel is now under restoration by the Credit Valley Conservation Authority and the City of Mississauga

orb, beautiful and fragile — people's perceptions changed. In 1969, one of the key works in bringing the ecosystem into land-use planning was published: Ian McHarg's *Design with Nature.* It showed how human needs could be met within the framework of natural systems, rather than being imposed over them, with beneficial results for both people and nature.

During this century, most responses to growing awareness of ecosystem stress have tended to be more narrow and regulatory, rather than the proactive, ecosystem-based planning advocated by McHarg and others. According to that way of thinking, parks and reserves are created in response to habitat losses, to protect fragments of green. Regulations are applied to control development in hazard lands, as a reaction to flooding and erosion. If air and water are polluted, regulations are developed to control emissions. Instead of developing a clear vision for communities, using the Official

Plan process, growth proceeds on an incremental basis, with Official Plan amendments being made to accommodate individual development applications.

Consequently, a great deal of work and money have gone into devising appropriate regulatory structures, writing regulations, administering them, and responding to them — generally in an adversarial atmosphere, in which the *proponents* and *regulators* of development see themselves as being on opposite sides.

In such an atmosphere, developers, whether public or private, spend more time, energy, and money on manoeuvring a plan through the regulatory process than in designing it creatively. Similarly, environmental agencies spend more time on essentially negative regulations than on positive planning, and nonetheless feel they are protecting the public interest, because they are stopping others from doing harm. And many land-use planners — trained to conceive and propose plans in response to functional, ecological, and human issues — find that, when they enter public service, their jobs involve negotiating and administering regulations.

It is clear that, while regulations are an essential part of any environmental management system, they should not be seen as an alternative to good, ecosystem-based planning. We need to redress the balance, to spend more energy on developing practical, integrated techniques of planning and design, and use regulations to ensure that things happen as planned.

While regulations are an essential part of any environmental management system, they should not be seen as an alternative to good, ecosystem-based planning.

PROVINCIAL ROLE

In theory, the Planning Act provides opportunities for integrating environmental considerations into land-use planning and development control. In practice, however, its provisions are not being used effectively for this purpose.

The Province can comment on environmental matters when an Official Plan is being prepared, when it is being reviewed or amended, and when plans are being created for subdivisions and condominiums. However, the effectiveness of these review processes is hampered by limitations in the mandates of different provincial agencies, their general inability to reach consensus, the fact that they have inadequate resources, and the lack of enforceable and consistent standards.

These difficulties are exacerbated by the absence of clear provincial guidelines on environmental priorities and ecosystem approaches to planning. As a result, different municipalities take very different approaches to environmental matters, depending on political will, community priorities, resources, and expertise. Some municipalities only pay lip service to the environment, while others do what they can, with varying degrees of success. Such piecemeal and inconsistent approaches provide extremely patchy protection for ecosystems, and make it hard for developers to understand the rules of the game.

For example, Section 3 of the Planning Act allows the Province to issue policy statements to guide municipal planning on matters of provincial interest. So far, however, issuing policy statements has been a painfully slow, contentious process. The only ones currently in effect are for floodplains, aggregates, and housing. As *Planning for Sustainability* concluded:

> Inter-ministerial and inter-departmental turf wars over control and priorities make it difficult for governments to reach agreement on the substance of policy statements. Lack of political will, and the attitude that it is sometimes safer and easier to simply do nothing, impede provincial leadership. In the meantime, however, land-use decisions continue to be made without a clear statement of provincial priorities regarding the environment.

A case in point is the proposed provincial Wetlands Policy Statement. After ten years of discussions and paperwork, in September 1991 the ministers of Municipal Affairs and Natural Resources released yet another draft of the policy. The Province classifies wetlands according to the degree of provincial significance — based on their biological, social and hydrological values — and has seven such categories. The Royal Commission is pleased to note that the latest draft policy includes classes I to III in its definition of provincially significant wetlands to which the policy applies.

However, in many other respects the draft wetlands policy is disappointing. It does not have an ecosystem perspective and, if adopted in its present form, would provide very limited protection for wetlands in Ontario.

Like any policy statement under Section 3 of the Planning Act, the wetlands policy can only require municipalities to "have regard to" its provisions. This means that the policy statement must be seriously considered, and an explanation provided if it is disregarded — but it does not have to be used as the basis for decisions. Among other weaknesses of the draft policy statement, it:

- fails to emphasize the ecological relationships in wetland complexes, between wetlands and surrounding lands, or upstream influences;
- makes no provision for buffer zones around wetlands;
- has no clear definitions of compatible land uses, development, and wetland functions;

Carruther's Creek Marsh, Ajax

Map 2.1   Active development applications in the City of Vaughan

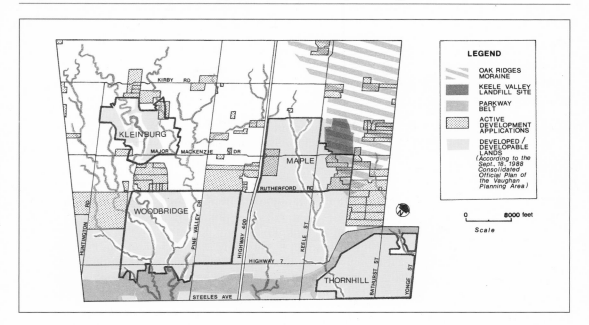

- does not prohibit public facilities and utilities from being placed in provincially significant wetlands;
- does not require planning documents (Official Plans, zoning by-laws, etc.) to be changed in a specified period to reflect the wetlands policy; and
- does not encourage municipalities to protect wetlands that are not classified as provincially significant (classes IV to VII), although these may be locally important.

MUNICIPAL PLANS

Although most municipalities in southern Ontario have Official Plans, as a rule these have not provided a long-term framework for change. Instead, distribution and form of growth have been reactive: Official Plan amendments were made in response to individual development proposals. In many places, therefore, it is assumed that development can be permitted almost anywhere, regardless of Official Plan designations for agriculture or open space.

In some cases, absence of an up-to-date Official Plan to guide development has been attributed to the Province's position that development can be approved only if proven servicing capacity (water and sewer) is available. Thus, in York and Durham regions, Official Plan amendments have been made incrementally, as excess capacity in various parts of the trunk sewer system has been identified.

This method of operation tends to discourage local municipalities in the regions from long-term planning. The apparent disregard for existing land-use plans is quite prevalent and is illustrated by comparing Official Plan designations with the distribution of development applications. Map 2.1 shows a typical situation, in this case in the City of Vaughan. It is worth noting that in 1989, concern about the implications of incremental development in Vaughan prompted a municipal policy review to examine future options and produce a policy framework for land use and development.

ECOSYSTEMS TRANSCEND MUNICIPAL BOUNDARIES

Another major limitation of municipal planning processes is that many ecosystem features and processes — rivers, groundwater, forests, wildlife populations and their migratory patterns, air movement — transcend municipal boundaries. This was well understood by the founders of conservation authorities in the 1940s. A. H. Richardson (1974), in *Conservation by the People*, quotes Professor A. F. Coventry's 1941 booklet, *Conservation and Post War Rehabilitation*:

A major limitation of municipal planning processes is that many ecosystem features and processes — rivers, groundwater, forests, wildlife populations and their migratory patterns, air movement — transcend municipal boundaries.

> Natural resources form a delicate balanced system in which all parts are interdependent and they cannot be successfully handled piecemeal. The present situation requires the coordination of existing relevant knowledge and its application where necessary, and then the development of a comprehensive plan for treating the natural resources on a wide public basis.

This perspective is evident in Section 21 of the Conservation Authorities Act, which states that an authority has power "to study and investigate the watershed and to determine a program whereby the natural resources of the watershed may be conserved, restored, developed and managed".

However, Section 28 limits authorities' regulatory powers to the use of water, alterations to watercourses, and filling and constructing in floodplains.

Because the Planning Act does not provide for planning in areas larger than regions and counties, there is no legislative framework for land-use planning for areas defined on an ecosystem basis: watersheds, the Oak Ridges Moraine or the Greater Toronto bioregion, for example. Although this situation could be remedied by municipalities and conservation authorities planning together for areas defined on an ecosystem basis, there are currently no incentives for them to do so. Such incentives could be provided, for example, by provincial requirements tied to funding for specific programs or capital projects.

There are a few exceptions to this general situation. The Niagara Escarpment Plan (Ontario 1985) is based on special legislation, the Niagara Escarpment Planning and Development Act of 1973, to protect the magnificent landform and nearby lands substantially as a continuous natural environment. The Province's recent guidelines and planning study for the Oak Ridges Moraine also represent significant recognition of the need for planning based on ecological systems.

On the whole, however, it appears difficult to implement ecosystem-based efforts such as watershed and remedial action planning. Despite the fact that all Ontario conservation authorities created plans in 1983, implementation has been hampered by lack of co-ordination and commitment among the jurisdictions involved, and because the Province does not require that watershed plan recommendations and strategies be incorporated into municipal planning and development control processes. These issues were recognized by the Environmental Assessment Advisory Committee in its report, *The Adequacy of the Existing Environmental Planning and Approvals Process for the Ganaraska Watershed* (Byer, Gibson, and Lucyk 1989). The Committee found that:

> ... the interjurisdictional character of the Watershed and the Moraine poses a considerable challenge for environmentally sensitive land-use planning, particularly because of the cumulative effects problem. Each municipality has its own set of priorities and objectives based on concerns within its jurisdiction. In the absence of special efforts, there is little likelihood that the separate municipal decisions will be consistent in their approach to environmental protection, or that they will reflect a comprehensive understanding of what is needed to protect the overall environmental quality.

The Committee went on to say that the Ganaraska Region Conservation Authority is restricted in its ability to address these issues because it has neither the mandate nor the authority to establish and implement planning policies for the watershed.

DESIGN AND STANDARDS

There are many examples of situations in which standards intended to ensure public safety or engineering efficiency have the unfortunate result of constraining design opportunities.

For example, street widenings often occur at the expense of trees, which are needlessly cut down at the apparent whim of traffic engineers, who could have saved them with only minor inconvenience to the

movement of cars and trucks. Unfortunately, this is not the result of whim but because engineers are hostage to standards of practice. No one — not those who commission street-widening projects or even the prime minister of Canada — can change the established parameters of design without subjecting the engineer to the penalties of professional misconduct. Because these standards are based, among other things, on concepts of public safety, the agency that commissions an engineer is also vulnerable if the design does not meet such standards. So the tree goes; it can stay only if standards are changed.

The form and pattern of urban growth are also influenced by standards: for lot sizes, setbacks, road widths, sidewalks, utilities, storm drains, and other elements. They affect the amount of land used to build a given number of homes, urban design, the extent of paved surfaces, types of drainage systems, and so on. It seems difficult, however, to change standards well entrenched in municipal planning and development approval processes. For example, many municipalities appear reluctant to respond to developers' requests for zoning that would permit smaller lot sizes — although these are an important aspect of establishing more compact communities, and of providing affordable homes. There is apparent concern that doing so would lead to "downgrading" of communities and a decline in nearby property values.

Development and infrastructure standards should be re-examined in view of current values and the demands of the environmental imperative. Although they represent the accrued wisdom of countless committees, ultimately they are based on human values, and can be revised if values change.

REVISITING SUBURBS

The growth of suburbs and the proliferation of automobiles evolved in tandem, enabling middle-class families to move away from the noise and activity of city commerce and industry to the country life promised in the suburbs. Ironically, but not surprisingly, as more people settled in the suburbs, the less country-like they became: the success of the settlement pattern led to its growing environmental, financial, and (for some) social inadequacies.

Moreover, as settlement continues to sprawl farther away from urban cores, more valuable farmland and natural areas are lost: each new low-density subdivision adds more congestion to the roads as more people drive longer distances to city centres for employment and recreation. Commuting, with its stalled traffic and idling engines, means increased air pollution and higher stress levels. And, sadly, this pattern of development is often socially isolating and inflexible, catering primarily to "typical family" households. Finally, low-density subdivisions engender high servicing costs and wasteful land use.

A recent housing proposal in Oakville by the River Oaks Group attempts to deal with many of these problems: it reflects new thinking on suburban planning, integrating overall quality of life with respect for the natural environment.

The plan envisions a community with densities comparable to those in traditional urban neighbourhoods, thus reducing the amount of land consumed. A range of housing types is proposed to meet current demographic trends — smaller households, an aging population, a rise in the number of single-parent families, and an increase in the number of households formed by people who are related or unrelated. Many of the units will be 'convertible' so that space can be expanded or reduced, depending on need, allowing residents to remain within the community despite changing personal or financial circumstances.

Low-density, single-use subdivisions are often socially isolating in two ways. First, in effect many are "bedroom communities" with limited opportunities for employment and entertainment. Second, the design of most suburbs emphasizes private (large closed-in yards, fences, etc.) rather than public spaces. River Oaks offers an alternative form of community in which street design emphasizes public values by carefully considering such elements as porches, balconies, sidewalks, street trees, lighting, and open spaces. The proximity to Oakville's new Uptown Business Core, as well as local corner stores, will provide commercial and other facilities within walking and biking distance.

Because of its smaller lots, lower servicing costs and "finish-later" options, River Oaks will offer more affordable housing than is available in the surrounding community; moreover, diversity and affordability will be further enhanced by the seamless integration of co-op and non-profit housing throughout the community, rather than in segregated housing blocks.

Another objective is to minimize the environmental impact of development and to connect the community to the natural environment. Instead of levelling the development site and removing all vegetation, as is commonly done during site preparation, natural topography and existing trees will be retained where possible.

This and other projects proposed by the River Oaks Group emphasizes stormwater management that encourages percolation of rain and snow through the soil, allowing

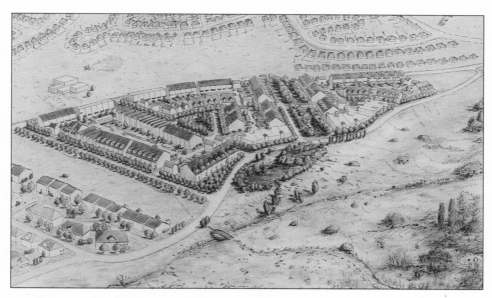

A recent housing proposal in Oakville takes a new approach to suburban development

slow recharge into groundwater and nearby creeks. This is in contrast to traditional stormwater management which forces large volumes of water into sewers connected to nearby streams, causing erosion and degraded water quality.

The proposal focuses on providing future residents with a high quality of life and a healthy natural environment. In order for such housing projects to proceed, land must be rezoned for mixed-use and convertible housing, and standards adjusted to accommodate proposed lot and street sizes, utility right-of-ways, and setbacks. If development standards evolve to support proposals like this one, and if other developments follow its lead, future suburban growth and development can be accommodated in a much more sustainable manner.

That has certainly been the case in the past — we did not always require that bedrooms have windows, for example — and they must continue to change if we are to retain or increase the health of our community.

ENVIRONMENTAL ASSESSMENT

There is growing concern that the environmental consequences of land-use planning and development decisions are not being fully considered. This is reflected in the number of requests that have been made to designate planning matters — such as Official Plan amendments, zoning changes or subdivision approvals — under the Environmental Assessment Act. *Planning for Sustainability* (Doering et al.1991) lists possible reasons for this situation:

- public concern that the municipal planning process is not addressing environmental concerns adequately;

73

- mistrust of the abilities and motives of city politicians and/or staff;
- mistrust of the provincial government review process;
- a desire to obtain intervenor funding (available for Environmental Assessment Board hearings, but not for Ontario Municipal Board hearings);
- a desire to shift the burden of proof from the complainant (the public or a government agency) to the proponent;
- a need to ensure consideration of alternatives to a proposal and alternative ways of carrying it out (neither of these is required by the Planning Act); and
- inadequate environmental information and analysis.

Complications also arise when the requirements of the Planning Act and Environmental Assessment Act (EAA) overlap. This frequently happens when municipal government activities are being considered — primarily to provide or upgrade infrastructure.

Building municipal infrastructure — roads, water supply, and sewage treatment — is subject to the EAA, through municipal class environmental assessment processes. In many cases, difficulties arise because class environmental assessment processes for infrastructure have not been co-ordinated with planning and approval processes for municipal development. For example, if Official Plan amendments have already been granted to permit development, it may be irrelevant to try to assess alternatives to providing infrastructure that supports the development, although this is required under the EAA. Developers waiting while the class environmental assessment process is undertaken face uncertainty and delays. Moreover, the processes for public involvement become complicated, requiring two streams of activity, each with its own reports, meetings, and administrative structures.

Another problem with environmental assessment on a project-by-project basis is that it becomes impossible to address cumulative effects: the combined effects of all activities in an area over time, plus the incremental impact of new stresses associated with individual projects. Accounting for them involves two basic components: a holistic understanding of all environmental conditions in the area, as well as an assessment of how these conditions are changing or are likely to change, given alternative scenarios.

Some examples of cumulative effects include:

- effects on waterfront water quality from many sources: sewage treatment plants, combined sewer overflows, storm sewers, rivers, and atmospheric deposition;
- fragmentation of wildlife habitats as a result of many land-use changes;
- indirect effects such as development in a river's headwaters causing sedimentation of a downstream wetland;
- the synergistic effects of different pollutants, such as the formation of ground-level ozone from nitrogen

A problem with environmental assessment on a project-by-project basis is that it becomes impossible to address cumulative effects.

A channelized portion of Black Creek

dioxides and volatile organic compounds in the presence of sunlight.

Incremental decision-making actually contributes to cumulative effects: it may be possible to build a bridge over a creek with minimal environmental impact, but there may be damage if a new trunk sewer is added, a well dug, part of a wetland filled, and a bend in the creek straightened. Under the Environmental Assessment Act, each of these projects is examined by a separate process and there is no mechanism to assess their combined effects. This raises critical questions:

- Can municipal planning and environmental assessment efforts be co-ordinated so that the former fulfil some of the requirements of the latter?
- Should the environmental assessment process be used to evaluate alternatives and assess individual projects in the absence of a comprehensive, ecosystem-based plan for land use and infrastructure?

Such considerations prompted Halton Region, working with the ministries of Municipal Affairs and the Environment, to propose a process that dovetails the Halton Urban Structure Review with environmental assessment requirements for infrastructure services (water, sewers, stormwater, and roads) for future growth in the region. If it is successful, this ground-breaking exercise may provide a useful example of integrating the municipal planning and environmental assessment processes.

SUMMARY OF KEY PROBLEMS

Without doubt, it is urgent to adopt an ecosystem approach to planning. We can no longer afford the past luxury of taking for granted an expanding economy and seemingly limitless natural resources. The region, with some four million residents, is already under considerable environmental, social, and economic stress. Even if the population remained stable, these stresses would have to be dealt with if the ecosystem were to be restored to health and vitality. However, given projections that, by 2021, the population could increase by 50 per cent — to about six million people — there are serious questions about how to accommodate such growth without causing further deterioration of the bioregion.

Unfortunately, current practices are not equal to the tasks. They suffer because of an over-reliance on regulations to control land use and development, based on outdated policies and standards. Our ability to plan on an ecosystem basis is limited by municipal, politically defined boundaries, and by jurisdictional gridlock that frustrates attempts at co-operation. And while people plod through numerous planning studies, policy development exercises, and reviews of legislation, environmental damage and losses continue.

TOWARDS ECOSYSTEM PLANNING PRACTICE

By contrast, improved processes for land-use and watershed planning could play a significant role in directing future development to environmentally appropriate places, and carrying it out in a manner that protects and enhances ecosystem values.

The Commission's own work explored some ecosystem planning practices. In *Watershed* it established nine principles and showed how they could be applied across the waterfront. The environmental audit of the East Bayfront/Port Industrial Area focused on ecosystem health and recommended ways to protect, restore, and enhance the area's ecosystem. In *Planning for Sustainability*, the Commission explored ways to integrate environmental protection into land-use planning. A Commission workshop on assessing cumulative effects culminated in a technical paper, *Towards Ecosystem-Based Planning: A Perspective on Cumulative Effects* (Davies 1991). Several practical planning exercises were commissioned and are summarized in this final report, in "Healing an Urban Watershed: The Story of the Don", "Garrison Common", and "Toronto Central Transportation Corridor".

Using that work, this chapter looks to the future and offers a broad outline of the practical aspects of ecosystem planning. As mentioned earlier, it is all too easy to put a "green spin" on the wording of traditional comprehensive plans. The task before the Toronto region's planning community is much greater and more exciting: to translate ecosystem theory into pragmatic methods of improving quality of life; establish land-use patterns; balance demand, capacity, and technology; accommodate economic development; and evaluate possible scenarios for the future. This must be done for natural and built environments at all planning scales, from region to individual site, for both public- and private-sector activities. We start by considering how ecosystem planning differs from most traditional approaches.

ECOSYSTEM HEALTH, SUSTAINABILITY, AND QUALITY OF LIFE

One of the key differences between ecosystem and traditional land-use planning is that the former emphasizes the need to balance ecosystem health, quality of life, and economic vitality. Traditional planning, on the other hand, is more inclined to focus on distributing land uses in accordance with social and economic imperatives. In ecosystem planning, policies and proposals are not judged solely on their economic merits, or on the way they contribute to housing, recreation or other social objectives. They are also judged on whether they add to regenerating and improving a region's ecological health.

In ecosystem planning, *interactions* in ecosystems — for example, between land-use practices and fisheries or among urban sprawl, automobile use, and air pollution — become a major focus of research, analysis, and decision-making. This means more effective and creative solutions can be found to issues that are the invariable result of complex relationships.

Ecosystem planning also involves a long-term view of change, rather than expedient short-term solutions. The longer view helps people and organizations develop sustainable strategies — stretching time horizons for planning, beyond the usual ten-year life span of Official Plans or the three to five years of a politician's term of office. We need to think in terms of what communities, and their environments, will be like in 50 years or more.

DIVERSITY

Ecosystem planning differs from many traditional methods by emphasizing, in various ways, the importance of natural and cultural diversity.

Natural ecological systems are usually complex assemblages of species and habitats. Similarly, cities that have evolved slowly and organically usually have a rich juxtaposition of places for work, play, and family life, as well as a blend of styles and structures from many decades and even centuries. Therefore, ecosystem planning is more likely to encourage a fine-grained pattern of mixed uses, rather than large, isolated districts for single-purpose uses.

It is also useful to think about the diversity within types of land use. While the Inuit have several words for snow, we have one, because snow is not as critical in urban life as it is in the Arctic. Similarly, a land-use

Cabbagetown, Toronto: residents enjoy a rich juxtaposition of nearby places for work, play, and family life

plan often has only one word — open space — for all the unbuilt lands in an area, but contains many words for settled areas: housing, commercial, industrial, transportation, institutional. As we pay greater attention to the needs of, and variations within, the natural system, we will devise new descriptive terms for land use in open areas.

GREEN INFRASTRUCTURE

The organization of settlements — the pattern of movement, uses, built form, and landscape — affects their health, beauty, and function. Simply put, some streets and blocks, buildings, parks, tracks, and expressways have been laid out in ways that make them safer, healthier, more beautiful, and/or more functional than others.

The traditional way to organize a community is by the system of services (usually underground sewers) and streets — the infrastructure. In general, major natural features are accommodated by being obliterated or avoided. The result in the Greater Toronto region is that settlements simply cut across the natural system. This sometimes leads to interesting juxtapositions, but it is a hit-and-miss affair.

In many land-use plans, natural areas and other open spaces are often cynically described as SLOAP: Space Left Over After Planning. Typically, the planning process begins by allocating spaces for residential, commercial, institutional, and industrial land use, with the road system as the primary link. Allocations are based on expected demand for these land uses, as well as suitability of location and infrastructure to support them.

In many land-use plans, natural areas and other open spaces are often cynically described as SLOAP: Space Left Over After Planning.

But what if we were to start with the demand for natural systems? How much land should be allocated to nature? How much to other kinds of open spaces? What ecological, aesthetic, urban design, and recreational functions can they fulfil?

This would lead to a different way of structuring urban form, using a fully linked, continuous "green infrastructure", based on natural systems, and recognizing open space — not as an absence of buildings but as a land use in its own right. This will be as important and effective a part of the public realm as the street system, and will have as strong an effect on urban form. The "Greenways" chapter of this report points out that such greenways can also provide a host of ecological, recreational, and economic benefits. A green infrastructure may include natural habitat areas; landforms such as bluffs, valleys, tablelands, beaches, and cliffs; aquifers and recharge areas; rural lands; heritage landscapes; parks, trails, and other open spaces; and archaeological sites.

HERITAGE

As discussed in Chapter 1, an ecosystem approach to the bioregion requires an understanding of, and an ability to work sensitively with, its natural and cultural heritage. Conventional development often sweeps the past aside in favour of all that is new and modern. Instead (as "Healing an Urban Watershed" illustrates), the natural topography and countryside can be used to define urban form, ensuring a sense of continuity with the past and maintaining valued elements of the landscape.

Similarly, in existing settlements, there are opportunities to adapt and reuse old buildings and to retain historic street, rail, and open-space patterns. In downtown Toronto, for example, many old industrial and commercial buildings along Front, King, Adelaide, and Richmond streets have been adapted for a variety of users, such as engineering or advertising companies. In contrast, the heritage of the Central Waterfront from Yonge to Bathurst streets has been virtually obliterated (notable exceptions being the Queen's Quay Terminal, Pier 4, and the Power Plant). Fortunately, there will be opportunities for more sensitive integration of built heritage on the waterfront when redevelopment begins in such places as Garrison Common, the East Bayfront, and the Port Industrial Area.

With care and imagination, the process of working with the existing world yields a more interesting and varied city in which to live and work, makes economic reuse of resources, offers a better understanding of collective history, and engenders a sense of personal attachment to the community. The landscape around us changes slowly and in a way that we can absorb and comprehend.

CAPACITY AND TECHNOLOGY

While capacity is a commonly used planning concept, ecosystem planning gives it a new connotation, one that is different from that generally found in traditional planning. For example, traffic capacity is used as a measure of how "good" a road plan is: if it is inadequate, the road size is increased and designed for ease-of-flow. An ecosystem plan places more emphasis on

Pier 4 on Toronto's waterfront in 1947 (upper) and 1987 (lower): old buildings can be adapted and reused

Throughout the world, from Sydney's Power House Museum to Thameside warehouse/apartments and across Canada, from Granville Island's art school to Harbourfront's Pier 4 and Power Plant Gallery, essentially humble industrial structures have been given distinguished new careers through imaginative architectural design at the same time as their historic form and other essential traits have been maintained for posterity.

Stinson, J., and M. Moir. 1991. Built Heritage of East Bayfront. Toronto: Royal Commission on the Future of the Toronto Waterfront. Draft.

environmental capacity as a measure of the value of the plan.

The capacity of the ecosystem — the amount of a given human activity that it can tolerate — is not fixed, but exists on a sliding scale. It depends not only on the intensity of activity, but also on societal values, current technology, and management techniques. Carrying capacity can change over time, depending on the interaction of these factors.

A century ago, for example, Toronto Bay had reached its capacity to absorb the effluent created by what we now think of as a tiny settlement. Providing sewage treatment set capacity at a new threshold, which has been exceeded again, both because population has increased and because water quality standards are higher. Now the emphasis is on improving treatment efficiency and reducing pollution at source rather than relying on "end-of-pipe" solutions. This will probably set another capacity threshold.

An ecosystem plan should seek to define and stay within a place's various capacities to accommodate the density and impact of people, buildings, vehicles, and wastes. It should also enhance capacity by adopting new ways of operating: solar orientation of buildings, composting and recycling, stormwater ponds, better transit, chemical-free landscaping, and so on. Thus, the notion of capacity should be used to establish both creative and restrictive measures — strategies of *what to do*, as much as *what to stop doing* — in order to maintain and expand the economic and natural health of our growing community.

FLEXIBLE BOUNDARIES

In ecosystem planning, the limits of areas being studied are decided on the basis of natural features and processes, rather than merely on political jurisdictions — which often means they are larger.

It may also mean that there are different boundaries for different ecological processes. For example, understanding water and rivers may require a watershed perspective, while soil contamination may be confined to a relatively small area, depending on the local migration of groundwater. The sources of soil contaminants may include historical land uses, recent landfill activities, and/or atmospheric deposition from long-range transport of air pollutants. In other words, establishing the parameters for ecosystem studies must be a flexible, open-minded process that fully explores all the known sources, interactions, and outputs.

Expanding the boundaries of research does not necessarily mean increasing planning beyond one's own jurisdiction. For example, in its waterfront planning process, the Regional Municipality of Metropolitan Toronto is using the concept of "geo-sheds" to encompass the links between watersheds, urban and natural drainage systems, coastal processes, and the shoreline. While this means studying ecological processes in jurisdictions beyond Metro's boundaries — to help understand key ecosystem relationships in planning for Metro's waterfront — it does not mean planning for those other jurisdictions.

There may be cases, of course, where looking beyond political boundaries to understand ecosystem processes shows that some interjurisdictional planning is essential. For example, the work of the City of Toronto's Task Force to Bring Back the Don has demonstrated that, without concerted effort throughout the Don watershed, actions to improve water quality in the lower Don will have limited success. The Metropolitan Toronto and Region

Conservation Authority is now working to establish a task force to address regeneration of the whole Don watershed.

In addition to boundaries based on natural processes, ecosystem planning may use boundaries defined by cultural features of places — neighbourhoods for example. Along the waterfront, some jurisdictions have a tendency to treat the area between the water's edge and the nearest major road as a planning unit. In many cases, this unit should be expanded to take in entire neighbourhoods — including parks, housing, shopping areas, etc. — and to encourage the sense of waterfront community.

ASSESSMENT OF LIKELY EFFECTS

Another fundamental aspect of ecosystem planning is that it includes assessment of the likely environmental, social, and economic effects of possible scenarios for the future, and enables planners, at an early stage, to consider the potential cumulative effects of many activities and projects.

The Environmental Assessment Act process focuses on finding the alternative *with the least unacceptable impact* — a laudable but essentially negative goal. Instead, assessing effects in the context of planning for a whole municipality or a watershed encourages evaluation of all effects, positive and neutral as well as negative. The goal is to find creative solutions that offer the greatest benefit, rather than simply trying to mitigate the consequences of harmful proposals. This makes it possible to take a proactive approach to improving ecosystem health, and to provide incentives that reward successful action. The goal of "net environmental gain" can be applied to ensure that future development makes a positive contribution to ecosystem health, by including measures to restore or re-create natural habitats.

INVOLVEMENT

Finally, ecosystem planning involves all key stakeholders working together in an open, public, fair, and efficient process. Relationships have to be worked out among many interests — the public, different levels and agencies of government, the private sector, special-interest groups, and others. Processes should be designed to facilitate co-operation, encourage conflict resolution, and build consensus. This should result in more timely and efficient decision-making, with fewer antagonistic procedures than often occur in traditional planning and environmental assessment processes.

A SUGGESTED FRAMEWORK FOR ECOYSTEM-BASED PLANNING

Given these basic elements — the goal of a healthy, sustainable ecosystem; a process involving communal efforts at reaching that

> **To arrest the degradation of natural resources and to restore in some measure their lost productivity involves replacing the unplanned individualistic exploitation of the past hundred years by planned management based on knowledge and recognizing public as well as private interest.**
>
> From Professor A. F. Coventry's brochure "Conservation and Postwar Rehabilitation" prepared for the 1941 Guelph Conference, quoted in Richardson, A. H. 1974. *Conservation by the people: the history of the conservation movement in Ontario to 1970.* Toronto: University of Toronto Press.

Importance to Family Life

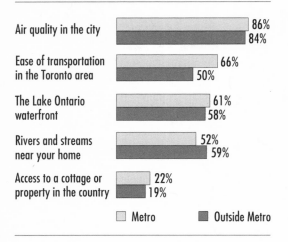

	Metro	Outside Metro
Air quality in the city	86%	84%
Ease of transportation in the Toronto area	66%	50%
The Lake Ontario waterfront	61%	58%
Rivers and streams near your home	52%	59%
Access to a cottage or property in the country	22%	19%

More than four-fifths of the respondents consider local environmental quality and ease of transportation to be very important to their family's quality of life.

Source: Environics Poll. 1991.

goal; and an integrated system of planning, design, and regulation — it is possible to suggest a framework for ecosystem planning, one that can be applied at different scales and in different contexts. For example, it could be used for a special region like the Oak Ridges Moraine, for remedial action planning in an area of concern on the Great Lakes, for a watershed, a regional municipality, a local municipality or a waterfront area. Moreover, the principles embodied could be applied to either public or private development.

The suggested framework includes aspects of planning and environmental assessment that are normally part of specific legislation. The following is an attempt to integrate some of the most valuable ideas embodied in legislation. It does not imply specific recommendations for changing the laws, only creative ways of combining activities to achieve the overall goal of ecosystem planning. Perhaps the best method for testing the feasibility and practicality of this sug-

gested framework would be to establish some demonstration projects, working closely with the agencies responsible for approving planning and environmental assessment processes.

DEFINING THE PURPOSE AND SCOPE OF THE PLAN

This involves addressing such questions as the need for the plan, its geographic scope, who should be involved, how long it should take, and its key issues.

DEFINING ROLES AND RESPONSIBILITIES OF PARTICIPANTS

Considerations might include information management, how participants will work together, who will make decisions and how, research and monitoring, funding for planning and implementation, and accountability for action.

ESTABLISHING GOALS

Although the overall goal of ecosystem-based planning is a healthy ecosystem, defining it and the best means of achieving it varies in different communities. Given such differences, the concept of sustainability requires, at a minimum, that goals be based on the community's long-term interests, its economy, and the environment that supports them. They should, therefore, take into account such concerns as a diverse economy, a safe environment, and the need for housing, jobs, recreation, etc.

At the same time, the ecological imperative of varied, high-quality, interconnected habitats for wildlife and for maintaining environmental processes should be addressed. Where possible, targets and indicators should be identified so that the current and future health of the ecosystem can be measured.

GATHERING INFORMATION

Good decision-making requires good information, gathered in an organized process that addresses the identified needs of the planning process. Unfortunately, existing information is often patchy, scattered, and difficult to consolidate. As recommended in the chapter "Water", an integrated network for ecosystem science in the Greater Toronto bioregion should be established; it would be of immense value to municipalities and others undertaking land-use planning.

Synthesis of information about all aspects of the ecosystem reveals relationships within it, as well as between a study area and its surroundings. It also highlights gaps in the available information, which may be filled by further research.

At some point, it may be necessary to balance the need for sound information with the need for action: although a planning team should seek enough information to make sensible decisions, a point is reached in any process at which lack of information may become an excuse for inaction. Therefore, uncertainties associated with missing information must simply be recognized and taken into account, and the effects of any project carefully monitored and necessary adjustments made.

ASSESSING ECOSYSTEM HEALTH, LIMITS, AND VALUES

Assessing ecosystem health can involve a set of criteria derived from the established goals; such criteria may include levels of toxic chemicals in the air, water, and soils; quality, variety, and quantity of wildlife habitat; species diversity; connections with natural and cultural heritage; economic vitality; social problems; availability of jobs, housing, recreation opportunities, community services, etc. This should lead to an understanding of:

- values to be restored, maintained or enhanced;
- opportunities;
- issues/problems to be addressed;
- constraints and hazards;
- needs/demands for facilities and services; and
- carrying capacity.

DESIGNING AND ASSESSING ALTERNATIVE SCENARIOS

Any planning process involving many people and groups will create a range of possible future scenarios. Their probable cumulative effects — on social, economic, and biophysical conditions — should be predicted and assessed in relation to the criteria used to evaluate ecosystem health. This will identify the extent to which each scenario meets the specific goals, principles, and targets of the plan, as well as any unwanted effects on the ecosystem. Technology can be adapted to suit the capacity and suitability of the ecosystem for different activities and measures can be designed to prevent or mitigate unacceptable effects.

The concept of sustainability requires, at a minimum, that goals be based on the community's long-term interests, its economy, and the environment that supports them.

> To date, there has been a tendency for the "savers" and "builders" in our communities to organize in separate camps and compete over change based on short-term issues instead of long-term planning objectives. Both camps must learn to work together so that their combined efforts can produce desired long-term development and protection results.
>
> Lemire, R. A. N.d. *Keeping our garden state green: a local government guide for greenway and open space planning.* New Jersey: New Jersey Department of Environmental Protection.

REACHING CONSENSUS ON FAIR AND USEFUL DECISIONS

Deciding which scenario to adopt and how to implement it usually lies with an elected body, such as a regional or local municipal council, or the provincial Cabinet. One of the many advantages of ecosystem planning is that it enables the planning group to present a proposed plan to a decision-making body in a way that makes the process explicit, clearly identifies the likely effects of the alternative scenarios, acknowledges uncertainties, and recognizes any remaining conflicts. A decision usually involves trade-offs among different goals, but at least the ecosystem planning process provides a clear understanding of the expected short- and long-term consequences of action.

REVIEW AND APPROVALS

One of the sources of delay and frustration in current planning and environmental assessment processes is the slow and unco-ordinated approach to review and approvals by provincial agencies. This could be alleviated by several measures. As recommended later in this chapter, provincial policies should be developed to bring more clarity and certainty to provincial requirements. Time limits on review periods could be established, with de facto approval if no review is undertaken during the specified time period. All agencies could be required to present their comments at the same time, in a public forum, and to make decisions concurrently (instead of the present step-by-step process).

MAKING COMMITMENTS FOR IMPLEMENTATION

Many good plans sit on the shelf because key stakeholders were not involved and/or because plans do not include an implementation process. Details of implementation will vary depending on the purpose and scope of the plan but, at a minimum, it is necessary to decide who will do what and when, and who will pay, perhaps through such arrangements as partnership agreements and cost-sharing programs.

MONITORING

Program monitoring should be established as early as possible, preferably before the plan is implemented, so that baseline conditions can be established. Monitoring should be designed to:

- assess changes in ecosystem health;
- evaluate compliance with the plan's goals and performance requirements; and
- provide information to assist those making decisions about individual projects.

Results should regularly be made available to the public so that implementation can be evaluated.

ENSURING THAT PROJECTS COMPLY WITH PLANS

A plan will include individual projects that have been identified during the planning process, which should justify the need for each project, examine alternatives to it, and assess its likely environmental, social, and economic effects. The remaining task is to design and assess each project to ensure that it meets the goals of the plan, that its effects are understood, and that it is carried out in the way that best protects and enhances the ecosystem.

To assist in this process of design and assessment, the plan could provide principles and performance requirements for individual projects; these might include requirements for energy and water conservation, stormwater management, recycling, health and social facilities, control of emissions to air and water, habitat protection, job creation, etc.

Projects will also be proposed that were not envisaged in the planning process. These should be assessed, in the context of the existing plan and its information base, to find out how they would affect the ecosystem. Proponents should be required to provide a statement describing likely social, environmental, and economic effects of the proposed development.

EVALUATING AND REVISING THE PLAN

Evaluation should be undertaken on a predetermined schedule to assess progress in relation to goals and targets, as well as to any changes in community needs, economic conditions or the environment. If necessary, parts of the planning process should be revisited, and the plan modified.

CONCLUSIONS

It is often said that environmental considerations add yet another layer of complexity, inefficiency, and delay to decision-making processes. The proposed framework is intended to truly integrate environmental matters, provide a fair and consistent process, and ensure that information, evaluation, and decision-making are shared and accessible. This will lead to greater efficiency and may shorten the time required for studies and approvals.

The ecosystem approach makes it possible to achieve a better understanding of systems, including economic, social, and environmental factors, and the relationships among them. This allows trade-offs to be made openly on the basis of comprehensive, balanced information in the context of a shared vision.

RECOMMENDATIONS

PLANNING ACT

The work group on *Planning for Sustainability* recommended that a provincial inquiry into land use and environmental protection be established and report back to the government within two years. In June 1991, the Province set up such a study, the Commission on Planning and Development in Ontario. It is charged with recommending changes that will entrench good planning into the land-use development process. While the scope of the Commission is not as broad as recommended in *Planning for Sustainability*, it will consider:

- meaningful public participation;
- integrating the Planning Act and the Environmental Assessment Act;
- the future of rural lands;

- urban sprawl; and
- environmental protection and cumulative effects.

The Planning Commission expects to submit a final report in 1993, which will be followed by legislative changes.

However, as *Planning for Sustainability* emphasized, it is not necessary or desirable to place all efforts at improving planning processes on hold while the Planning Commission is under way. There are a number of initiatives, many of which have already been started, that can be continued in the context of the existing Planning Act. In fact, they should be accelerated to ensure that significant environmental damage does not occur during the work of the Planning Commission. Accordingly, immediate action should be taken on the following.

PROVINCIAL POLICIES

The Province should set out clearly its expectations regarding land use, settlement patterns, and environmental protection. This means improving government processes to deal with turf wars, define common objectives and policies, provide better information services, and undertake co-ordinated reviews. Section 3 of the Planning Act, which gives the Province an opportunity to develop policies on matters of provincial interest, has been little used so far. At present, policy statements exist for floodplains, aggregates, and housing, and there are draft statements on wetlands and foodlands.

Clearly stated goals and targets should be developed by the Province in the context of a complete set of policies. In specific cases it is likely, however, that conflicts

Farmland is threatened by future development

will arise between different applicable policies; therefore, it may be helpful to develop criteria or principles to resolve potential conflicts and ensure environmental protection.

There should be built-in review mechanisms to deal with reactions to policy implementation and suggestions for improvement. Finally, policies should be mandatory, requiring municipalities to ensure that their planning, zoning, and development control processes comply.

The Province's endorsement of the nine principles and the ecosystem approach to planning, announced by the Honourable Ruth Grier on 17 December 1990, should be formalized and refined under Section 3 of the Planning Act.

RECOMMENDATIONS

1. The Royal Commission recommends that the Province prepare a comprehensive, integrated set of ecosystem-based policy statements under Section 3 of the Planning Act. These should include:

   - waterfront planning and development, including shoreline regeneration, based on the Commission's nine principles;
   - greenway concepts as described in Chapter 5;
   - watershed management;
   - natural heritage protection;
   - integration and conservation of cultural heritage;
   - rural lands and agriculture;
   - compact forms of development and redevelopment;
   - transportation and land use;

   - resource conservation (water, energy, timber, soils, aggregates, and others);
   - protection and rehabilitation of air, water, and soil quality; and
   - land-use compatibility.

2. The Commission further recommends that, as soon as possible and while policy statements are being prepared, interim guidelines be made available to establish provincial expectations for planning and development decisions.

3. While the waterfront policy statement is being prepared, all planning jurisdictions should ensure that Official Plans, waterfront plans, Secondary Plans, and other planning documents for areas on the waterfront incorporate the ecosystem approach and the waterfront regeneration principles.

PROVINCIAL REQUIREMENTS FOR PLANNING PRACTICES

While the Planning Act provides processes for planning and controlling development, it offers little guidance for the form and content of Official Plans. To ensure that its commitment to the ecosystem approach can be reflected in municipal planning, the Province should provide guidance and set out its expectations for ecosystem-based planning and development approval practices.

RECOMMENDATIONS

4. The Royal Commission recommends that the Province, in consultation with

municipalities, other agencies, professional organizations, and interest groups, prepare guidelines for ecosystem planning practices to be used in the preparation of Official Plans, waterfront plans, Secondary Plans, watershed plans, and other planning instruments.

5. The Commission further recommends that the Province, in consultation with municipalities, other agencies, professional organizations, and interest groups, develop environmental performance requirements so that there is greater certainty and consistency in the development approval process. These requirements might include greenspace protection, setbacks/buffers between natural areas and other uses, habitat restoration, energy efficiency, ambient and indoor air quality, dust control, waste management, noise restrictions, microclimatic conditions, stormwater management, and integration of built heritage.

WETLANDS POLICY STATEMENT

The recently released draft Wetlands Policy Statement should be revised to provide effective protection for Ontario's remaining wetlands. Draft implementation guidelines have not been released for public review, making it difficult to evaluate the draft statement.

RECOMMENDATION

6. The Royal Commission recommends that the Province strengthen its proposed Wetlands Policy Statement and bring it into effect as quickly as possible. Implementation guidelines should be made available as soon as possible. Changes should include:

- full protection for all (classes I to III) provincially significant wetlands;
- refusal to permit loss or impairment of significant wetland functions;
- consideration of ecological relationships within entire wetland complexes when making decisions about protection requirements;
- inclusion of requirements for buffer zones;
- the same treatment of public utilities/facilities as private development;
- encouragement of municipalities to protect wetlands of local significance (classes IV to VII);
- clarifications of interpretations of compatible uses and development; and
- a requirement that revisions of planning documents be made within a specified period to reflect the wetlands policy.

SITE PREPARATION

Municipalities have little power to control activities undertaken by landowners during landscaping or renovations, or by developers preparing sites for building (which often occurs even before development approvals have been given). These activities may result in irreversible damage to soils, groundwater, watercourses, aesthetic qualities, and/or wildlife habitats.

Although the Trees Act enables municipalities to pass by-laws restricting the destruction of trees, most municipalities have not done so and the by-laws that have been passed are difficult to enforce. A recent review (1991) of this issue conducted by the Tree Bylaws Advisory Committee (including representatives from the Association of Municipalities of Ontario and the Ministry of Natural Resources) recommended a new Trees Act to provide more effective protection for trees and woodlots.

The Topsoil Preservation Act, administered by the Ministry of Agriculture and Food, enables, but does not require, municipalities to pass by-laws to regulate or prohibit the removal of topsoil.

RECOMMENDATION

7. The Royal Commission recommends that the Province, in consultation with municipalities and interest groups, amend the Trees Act, the Topsoil Preservation Act, and the Planning Act, as appropriate, to require municipalities to regulate such activities as removal of trees and other vegetation, grading, removal of topsoil, filling, and drainage. These regulations should apply to new development, redevelopment, and other activities. Interim control measures should be put in place while the legislative changes are being developed and enacted.

STANDARDS

Standards intended to ensure the safety and/or efficiency of buildings, roads, sidewalks, drainage systems, and associated facilities often constrain creative design. As a result, it is sometimes difficult to implement new ways of maintaining or enhancing environmental quality and creating more liveable places for people.

Careless site preparation damages soils, watercourses, and wildlife habitats

8. The Royal Commission recommends that the Province convene an interdisciplinary conference of engineers, designers, and non-government groups to explore new approaches to establishing standards of development that will accommodate emerging social and environmental objectives.

NIAGARA ESCARPMENT

The Niagara Escarpment forms the western side of the Greater Toronto bioregion. Natural landscapes associated with the shallow soils, slopes, and wetlands along this 450-million-year-old landform create a significant natural corridor across southern Ontario. The escarpment serves as a source for many of the streams and rivers feeding into the western and central parts of the Greater Toronto waterfront.

Land uses along the Niagara Escarpment are regulated by the Niagara Escarpment Planning and Development Act, which works through an ecosystem-based plan administered by the provincially appointed Niagara Escarpment Commission. In 1990, in recognition of the escarpment's unique character, as well as the protection afforded by the Act, UNESCO named the escarpment a World Biosphere Reserve.

While planning mechanisms for the Niagara Escarpment are not perfect (for example, they rely heavily on top-down, regulatory approaches) they do provide one of the most advanced models of ecosystem planning in Ontario. The Niagara Escarpment Plan (Ontario 1985) is currently undergoing its first five-year review, and changes are proposed that would provide stricter control over pits and quarries, land severances, and some types of recreational developments.

The review offers an opportunity to examine how adequately the plan incorporates the ecosystem approach, and the strengths and weaknesses of the escarpment planning process. Such an evaluation would be useful to others seeking insights into the effectiveness of different planning tools in implementing the ecosystem approach, whether in the context of planning for municipalities, watersheds, shoreline regeneration or the Oak Ridges Moraine.

There has been no comprehensive monitoring of environmental health along the escarpment, which makes it difficult to evaluate the effectiveness of the Niagara Escarpment Plan. Long-term environmental monitoring and socio-economic research would provide valuable benchmarks to determine how well protection measures are working, and to assess their effect on land values, development costs, and so on.

RECOMMENDATIONS

9. The Royal Commission recommends that, as part of the five-year review of the Niagara Escarpment Plan, the Niagara Escarpment Commission assess the degree to which proposed revisions embody the ecosystem approach, and strengthen the plan, where necessary, to ensure it becomes a model of ecosystem planning.

10. The Commission further recommends that the Province establish a long-term environmental monitoring system along the Niagara Escarpment, to

document the plan's effectiveness in protecting and rehabilitating the environment. This monitoring effort should become part of the research and information network for the Greater Toronto bioregion, proposed in the "Water" chapter.

11. The Province should examine how the ecosystem planning approach used by the Niagara Escarpment Commission could assist in development of more ecologically responsible planning in all jurisdictions, especially in interjurisdictional planning for such features as the Oak Ridges Moraine and the shoreline.

OAK RIDGES MORAINE

The Oak Ridges Moraine, spanning about 160 kilometres (100 miles) from the Niagara Escarpment to the headwaters of Cold Creek (a tributary of the Trent River) is a ridge formed of the silt and debris left by receding glaciers during the last Ice Age. Its rolling hills, basins, kettle lakes, and wetlands are among the most scenic landscapes in southern Ontario.

The moraine also has great ecological significance. Its porous layers of sand, silt, and gravel provide deep aquifers, sources of groundwater that feed springs and coldwater streams, many of which flow south, forming larger rivers that end in Lake Ontario. The aquifers also supply drinking water to many hamlets and towns on the moraine.

In *Watershed*, the Royal Commission recommended that the Province take immediate steps to preserve the values of the Oak Ridges Moraine and to undertake a planning study regarding conservation, groundwater

protection, trail locations, cumulative effects, and future development.

In July 1990, the government expressed a Provincial Interest in the Oak Ridges Moraine. In June 1991, Implementation Guidelines for interim protection were published and a planning study was initiated to develop a long-term strategy for protecting and managing the moraine.

Unfortunately both the guidelines and the planning study are limited to the portion of the Oak Ridges Moraine that lies within the Greater Toronto Area — which excludes major parts east and northwest of the GTA boundaries.

Although the guidelines are comprehensive and well-intentioned, they may be vulnerable to misinterpretation and might not be strictly applied to protect the moraine. This concern was recently highlighted by the chair of the Ontario Municipal Board (OMB). In commenting on an application for a development on the Oak Ridges Moraine (Kirby Heights, a proposed 14-estate-lot subdivision in Durham Region), Morley Rosenberg said the guidelines are not applicable to OMB decisions because they have no legal status under the Planning Act.

In addition, some potentially harmful activities are "generally exempt" from the Oak Ridges Moraine Guidelines, including aggregate extraction, minor variances, building permits, and individual consents.

The terms of reference for the Oak Ridges Moraine planning study do not include examining possible implementation mechanisms. But this is a crucial element of ecosystem planning, needed to ensure that action is consistent among jurisdictions and that it addresses interjurisdictional concerns.

Albion Hills Conservation Area, Oak Ridges Moraine

RECOMMENDATIONS

12. The Royal Commission recommends that the Province extend the expression of Provincial Interest, Implementation Guidelines, and the planning study to include the entire Oak Ridges Moraine — not just the portions in the Greater Toronto Area (See Map 1.1).

13. The Commission further recommends that the Province, the Ontario Municipal Board, and the municipalities in the Oak Ridges Moraine ensure strict compliance with the guidelines, and that they carefully scrutinize proposals that could be exempted.

14. The Oak Ridges Moraine planning study should be expanded to include a description and evaluation of possible implementation mechanisms for the long-term strategy, taking into account the experience of the Niagara Escarpment Commission in conserving a similar landform feature and associated ecosystems.

WATERSHED PLANNING AND MANAGEMENT

Over the past four years, the Province has undertaken several reviews of conservation authority funding, organization, membership, and mandate.

In *Watershed*, the Royal Commission recommended that the Province review the mandate and functions of conservation authorities, in order to determine whether the current review should include more fundamental reforms. It also recommended that conservation authorities assume a greater role in, and receive core funding for, managing watersheds and protecting natural habitats.

This role was recognized in a 1991 draft of "A Conservation Strategy for the Conservation Authorities of Ontario":

> The Conservation Authorities of Ontario have as their vision watersheds of ecological integrity where human needs are met in balance with the needs of the natural environment (Association of Conservation Authorities of Ontario).

However, current proposals by the Ministry of Natural Resources (MNR) focus primarily on identifying core and non-core activities for the authorities. This reflects a preoccupation with what MNR will fund, rather than the potential of conservation authorities to employ a watershed perspective in protecting and managing resources. In fact, the core/non-core list doesn't even mention watershed planning or strategies.

A number of other issues affect the ability of conservation authorities to work effectively in ecosystem conservation. Their limited regulatory powers — focused primarily on flood and erosion control — are among several factors that severely restrict the ability of conservation authorities to protect natural areas and systems, and to undertake comprehensive, proactive watershed planning and management. Other factors include the narrow range of activities funded by the Province and, especially in smaller authorities, insufficient staff, resources, and expertise.

The result is fragmentation of watershed management among different government agencies. Because of their watershed jurisdictions and wide-ranging activities, however, conservation authorities work in areas of interest to departments of many ministries, including Municipal Affairs, Natural Resources, the Environment, Agriculture and Food, Tourism and Recreation, and Education.

It might be more appropriate to consider partnerships between individual conservation authorities and other government agencies, so that each could build on existing strengths in different parts of the Province. In addition, interministerial co-ordination of funding and programs would help to meet conservation authorities' needs in an integrated way.

Another factor that restricts the effectiveness of conservation authorities as ecosystem stewards is the way authority members are chosen. When the government of the day formed a Conservation Authorities Branch in 1944, it was understood that conservation was a grass-roots matter. According to A. H. Richardson (1974), in *Conservation by the People,* Dana Porter, then-Minister of Planning and Development, speaking at the 1944 London Conference on River Development in Southern Ontario, said:

> The main necessity in a programme of this kind is that it must have, to be really effective, the fullest possible co-operation and the fullest understanding. . .on the part of the people who are living in the region. . . .Unless we can keep the public fully advised and fully aware of the nature of the problems and unless we can carry their continued support, any policy that may be attempted by any government will be sure to fail.

Most members of an authority are appointed by municipal councils, and are frequently municipal politicians and staff.

(In addition, a maximum of three members may be appointed by the Province.) Although this ensures accountability to municipal government, in most areas it means that few authority members have the appropriate training or commitment for ecosystem-based planning and natural resource management.

Watershed strategies initiated by conservation authorities (e.g., the Rouge River Watershed Management Strategy co-ordinated by the Metropolitan Toronto and Region Conservation Authority) and/or Remedial Action Plan processes (such as the Metro Toronto Remedial Action Plan) are not necessarily integrated with municipal land-use planning and development approval processes. As a result, ecosystem-based watershed management may be thwarted, resources may be haphazardly expended, and opportunities to protect, restore, and/or enhance ecosystems may be lost. Work under way by the ministries of the Environment and Natural Resources, in consultation with the Ministry of Municipal Affairs, conservation authorities, and municipalities, on the integration of water resource management objectives into municipal plans should help to address these issues.

RECOMMENDATIONS

15. The Royal Commission recommends that the Province, in consultation with conservation authorities, municipalities, and non-government organizations:

   - recognize ecosystem-based watershed management and conservation as a primary role of conservation authorities and amend Section 28 of the Conservation Authorities Act to give them regulatory powers consistent with this role;

   - examine ways to assist co-operative initiatives among conservation authorities and provincial government agencies; and

   - revise the basis for appointing members to conservation authorities so that more representatives of local non-government environmental/conservation groups are included, while strong municipal representation is maintained.

16. The Commission further recommends that municipalities work with RAP teams and conservation authorities to integrate remedial action plans and watershed strategies into land-use planning and development approval processes.

PART II:
ENVIRONMENTAL IMPERATIVES

The original mandate of the Royal Commission was to examine the shoreline: the Greater Toronto waterfront. But a growing understanding of ecological principles led inexorably to expanding the scope of the Commission's enquiry to encompass the watersheds, Lake Ontario, and the Great Lakes Basin. This section of the final report addresses certain key environmental imperatives of waterfront regeneration: water, shorelines, greenways, and the winter waterfront.

First, and on the broadest scale, are the waters of Lake Ontario and its watersheds, constantly moving and ever-changing; we depend on them for drinking, washing, cooling, industrial use, shipping, and recreation. The natural systems and wildlife of the bioregion are dependent on the cycling of water (groundwater recharge, springs, streamflow, etc.) and on aquatic habitats: ponds, creeks, rivers, wetlands, the lake.

Second is an examination of the interface between land and water, the Lake Ontario shoreline. Its shape once formed by the power of the lake, the shoreline is now radically altered by human activities.

Third, we explore the possibilities of renewing ecological and recreational links between the waterfront and its watersheds, through greenways from the shoreline up the river valleys and into the hinterland.

Fourth, we explore the potential to improve year-round use of the waterfront, by careful consideration of microclimates, access, safety, landscaping, urban design, programming, and facilities.

Regeneration of the waterfront depends on restoring the environmental health of Lake Ontario's waters, its shoreline, and the river valleys. Therefore, we take an ecosystem approach to examining current problems, and to recommendations for regeneration. Because of the interdependence of ecosystems, a comprehensive strategy for regeneration must combine many objectives, so that each action fills a variety of needs, and complements actions being taken elsewhere.

For example, we cannot expect to regenerate the shoreline without addressing the health of both the lake that laps at its shore and the rivers that feed it. Similarly, actions designed to enhance year-round recreational use of the waterfront, or to provide linked trails in the bioregion, will be more valuable if efforts are undertaken at the same time to restore ecological health.

CHAPTER 3:
WATER

Early in its work, the Royal Commission realized that it could not consider the Greater Toronto waterfront in isolation from the area surrounding it. Ecological principles tell us that it will both affect areas outside itself and be affected by external influences. Moreover, the Greater Toronto waterfront is part of a much greater whole — in fact many greater "wholes". First (and closest to home), it is linked ecologically to the Greater Toronto bioregion by the river valleys and streams flowing south to the lake.

At the same time, as Map 3.1 makes clear, water quality along the Greater Toronto waterfront is tied to that of Lake Ontario, and the Lake Ontario Basin. The basin drains an area of about 64,000 square kilometres (24,710 square miles) in south-eastern Ontario and northern New York State.

But Lake Ontario does not sit in isolation. It is the fifth and most downstream in the chain of Great Lakes. About 80 per cent of the water entering it comes from upstream through the Niagara River. Although there is much that must and can be done in and around Metropolitan Toronto's waterfront, restoration of water quality is in part dependent on the health of the Great Lakes. For example, we can do little, acting independently, to tackle the problems of persistent toxic chemicals throughout the waters of the basin. That kind of problem requires a much broader perspective, one that can be gained only by examining the Great Lakes Basin ecosystem.

The Greater Toronto waterfront is but 250 kilometres (155 miles) of what has sometimes been called "North America's fifth coast" — 8,000 kilometres (5,000 miles) of continuous coastline bounding the Great Lakes and the St. Lawrence River. The earliest European explorers and settlers sailed up that coastline looking for a "land of plenty" and found almost unimaginable natural riches in an area sparsely settled by native people. The lakes provided a seemingly inexhaustible supply of fresh water for drinking. Stands of timber stretched as far as the eye could see. The rivers draining into the lakes could be used for transportation into the interior and floating timber out for powering grist and sawmills.

Wetlands, inland and at the mouths of rivers, supported thriving communities of fish, reptiles, and waterfowl. The forests

Map 3.1 The Great Lakes Basin, areas of concern

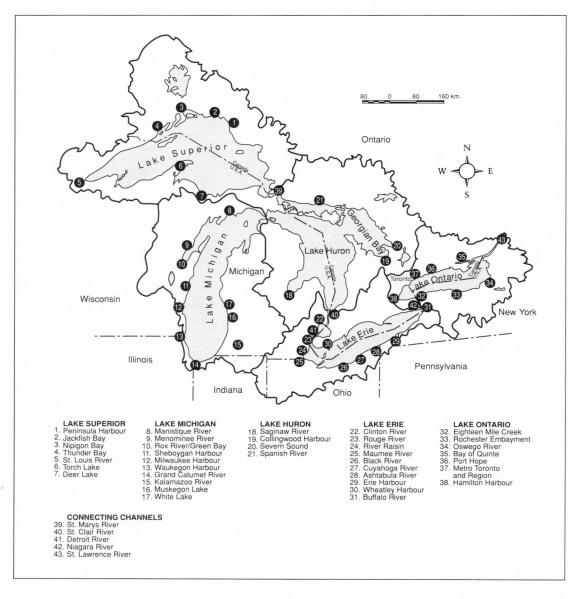

LAKE SUPERIOR	LAKE MICHIGAN	LAKE HURON	LAKE ERIE	LAKE ONTARIO
1. Peninsula Harbour	8. Manistique River	18. Saginaw River	22. Clinton River	32. Eighteen Mile Creek
2. Jackfish Bay	9. Menominee River	19. Collingwood Harbour	23. Rouge River	33. Rochester Embayment
3. Nipigon Bay	10. Rox River/Green Bay	20. Severn Sound	24. River Raisin	34. Oswego River
4. Thunder Bay	11. Sheboygan Harbour	21. Spanish River	25. Maumee River	35. Bay of Quinte
5. St. Louis River	12. Milwaukee Harbour		26. Black River	36. Port Hope
6. Torch Lake	13. Waukegon Harbour		27. Cuyahoga River	37. Metro Toronto
7. Deer Lake	14. Grand Calumet River		28. Ashtabula River	and Region
	15. Kalamazoo River		29. Erie Harbour	38. Hamilton Harbour
	16. Muskegon Lake		30. Wheatley Harbour	
	17. White Lake		31. Buffalo River	

CONNECTING CHANNELS
39. St. Marys River
40. St. Clair River
41. Detroit River
42. Niagara River
43. St. Lawrence River

that touched the Great Lakes shores were home to fur-bearing mammals, which could be trapped, and to deer, which were hunted for food. The lakes supported an abundance of fish — lake trout and herring, whitefish and sturgeon, Atlantic salmon and American eel, and many others.

Small wonder people flocked here. Today, 10 per cent of the American population and almost a third of all Canadians live in the Great Lakes Basin, which is the economic heartland of Canada. It includes 28 cities with populations of more than 50,000 people, as well as 13,400 manufacturing and industrial plants. Those who live in the basin depend on the Great Lakes for water used for drinking, irrigation, industry, waste receiving, power generation, transportation, and recreation, as well as for fisheries and wildlife habitat.

Now, almost two hundred years after European settlement began in earnest, the Great Lakes Basin has been dramatically transformed by human activities. Most of the great forests that once lined its shores were logged in a frenetic flurry of activity that lasted from 1850 to 1920. Development and the loss of habitat drove large mammals such as bear and deer inland. As the result of overfishing, dam construction, and habitat destruction, many once-abundant species of fish became rare or extinct. However unwittingly, the decision to build canals and the international movement of goods and people opened the door to the sea lamprey, purple loosestrife, and other exotic non-native species. In 1890 and 1891, one man's somewhat eccentric idea of importing into New York species of all birds mentioned by Shakespeare introduced the ubiquitous European starling to North America while, more recently, the release of bilge water from a foreign vessel brought us the zebra mussel. With few natural enemies, such opportunistic species have flourished in the basin and elsewhere, and have pushed out less hardy native species.

Natural areas — woodlands and wetlands — as well as valuable agricultural land have been gobbled up by indiscriminate development. Rivers have been befouled, and streams placed underground or paved over. One legacy of the intense resource extraction and manufacturing activities carried out in the basin is the presence of heavy metal and chemical pollutants; these can be found in the Great Lakes waters, in the sediments on the bottom of lakes and rivers, in landfill sites dotted across the landscape, and in soil and groundwater on industrial sites.

The landscape today is very different from the one that greeted European explorers. Natural resources, once so rich, are sadly diminished. This chapter briefly describes the state of the Great Lakes, particularly water quality and the health of humans and wildlife, and examines why there has been so little progress in restoring the Great Lakes ecosystem, which is crucial to the regeneration of the Greater Toronto waterfront.

THE STATE OF THE LAKES

An exhaustive review of the state of the Great Lakes is beyond the scope of this report; moreover, many excellent books have recently been published on the subject. This section focuses on three specific environmental problems in the Great Lakes

Beginning with the nineteenth-century cities and continuing through our post-war reshaping of cities, suburbs, and countryside, we have been making changes in the environment at an unprecedented rate. Today's world not only looks very different from the eighteenth-century world but also sounds very different and smells very different. Whatever else these changes have brought us in the way of human benefits or environmental degradation, they have offered us an unparalleled chance to look at how our health and well-being are affected by changing what we can experience in a place.

Hiss, T. 1990. *The experience of place.* New York: Alfred A. Knopf.

CHANGES TO THE GREAT LAKES FISH COMMUNITY

The first settlers on the shores of the Great Lakes were astounded by the bounty of fish. *The Jesuit Relations*, a journal published annually describing the experiences of Jesuit missionaries, reported that, "A single fisherman will catch in one night twenty large sturgeon, or a hundred and fifty whitefish, or eight hundred herring in one net" on the south shore of Lake Superior. It was reported that, at Sault Ste. Marie, whitefish in the St. Marys River ran so thick that, standing in the water, a person could reach out and easily grab a thousand. By the early 19th century, commercial fisheries had been established on the lakes, initially supplying mining and lumbering companies and, later, the booming cities of the U.S. midwest.

As early as 1879, more than a million pounds of lake trout and nearly two million pounds of whitefish were being harvested annually from Lake Ontario. By the beginning of the 20th century, commercial fishing was big business in the Great Lakes, involving 10,000 people — twice as many as 20 years earlier. "But as fishing intensity increased, and human-initiated changes to environment accelerated", the delicate web within which the fish community existed began to unravel.

Fish stocks declined, and some species disappeared forever, primarily as the result of overfishing. For example, the black-finned and short-nosed ciscoes were much sought after but, by 1900, these deep-water herring-like fish were commercially extinct. Other species were deliberately destroyed: the long-lived sturgeon (some live as much as 150 years) was hunted and destroyed because its external body armour easily tore nets set for smaller fish. Once they caught the sturgeon, fishers "piled them like cordwood, on the beaches, dousing them with oil and burning them."

Still other species were lost or declined as the result of a combination of factors. For example, overfishing, compounded by decreasing habitat, led to the demise of Lake Ontario Atlantic salmon. As settlers cleared the land, water flow in the summer decreased and siltation increased. Without trees to shade the rivers, temperatures rose, denying salmon the cool clear waters necessary for reproduction. Furthermore, saw mills blocked spawning routes and released saw dust that blanketed the river bottoms and marshes, suffocating fish eggs and larvae. The last Lake Ontario Atlantic salmon was seen in Wilmot Creek in 1896.

The final major blow to the Great Lakes fisheries came when, deliberately and accidentally, foreign fish species were introduced. Already vulnerable fish stocks could not compete with the new arrivals, changing forever the Great Lakes' ecosystem. Rainbow smelt, added to the Great Lakes as a food source for an unsuccessfully introduced salmonid, thrived and probably fed on the prey of whitefish and herring, thus bringing about the decline of these species. Carp, introduced as a food source for humans, destroyed aquatic vegetation, thereby affecting many fish species dependent on wetlands.

There are two fish species — lamprey and alewife — that have played a major role in degrading the Great Lakes fisheries; they are thought to have gained access via the canals that were constructed to link the fresh-water seas with the Atlantic Ocean. Lampreys, parasites that suck fish dry of their vital juices, have decimated whitefish and lake trout populations. Alewives do damage by virtue of their sheer numbers: they consume prey species used by lake herring, chub, and whitefish.

We are left with a Great Lakes fishery that has been drastically altered. The foreign species have become the most abundant; now, our sport fisheries rely almost exclusively on coho and chinook salmon raised in hatcheries, because these types do not reproduce very successfully in the lakes.

Because of diminished stocks, and also because of the relatively new threat of toxic contamination, commercial fishery operations cannot be sustained in the Great Lakes. The chemical soup produced by the agricultural and urban communities that rim them makes many fish unfit for consumption by either humans or wildlife. Today, the blue pike and lake trout are gone from Lake Erie, while Lake Ontario has lost the lake herring. Furthermore, six of seven species of chub are now extinct in the Great Lakes. It took 10,000 years for the fish community to evolve in the Great Lakes, and only a few decades to change it forever.

Sources: Ashworthy, W. 1986. *The late, Great Lakes: an environmental history.* Toronto: Collins; Weller, P. 1990. *Fresh water seas: saving the Great Lakes.* Toronto: Between the Lines.

Basin: water quality (especially as it affects the health of humans and wildlife), wetlands and river systems, and water quantity.

WATER QUALITY

The degraded water quality in the Great Lakes Basin is not just a recent concern. In Toronto, for example, pollution of the harbour and Ashbridge's Bay was a civic preoccupation as early as the 1880s. Prior to that time, the waters of the harbour had been viewed, in the main, as a convenient (and inexhaustible) dumping ground for human and animal wastes, and any other unwanted garbage. But as the stench along the waterfront became unbearable and understanding of waterborne disease grew, attitudes began to change. In order to protect public health, by 1910 the City of Toronto had built its first plant to treat sewage.

Toronto, of course, was not alone and its problems were being duplicated around the lakes, in Buffalo, Chicago, Cleveland, and other rapidly growing urban centres. To remedy the situation, in 1912 the Canadian and American governments asked the fledgling International Joint Commission to study the matter — the first bilateral environmental initiative undertaken in the Great Lakes.

In retrospect, building sewage treatment facilities and implementing measures to control nutrient loadings in the lakes have been the highlights of pollution control in the Great Lakes Basin. Until quite recently, sewage treatment initiatives there were a patchwork but, by the late 1960s, it was becoming apparent to scientists, policy makers, and the general public that the lower lakes were suffering badly from nutrient pollution. High levels of nutrients such

Massey Creek, Toronto

as phosphorus and nitrogen were causing eutrophication of the lakes — uncontrolled growth of aquatic plants, lowered levels of oxygen, and an environment in which many fish could not survive. Lake Erie, in particular, was in severe trouble and, as the "dying lake", became a powerful symbol of what was wrong in the basin.

Of course, excess levels of nutrients were by no means the only pollution problem at the time: waterways were receiving huge amounts of what are called "conventional pollutants" — oils and greases, oxygen-depleting organic matter, and suspended solids — in addition to barely treated industrial effluents and spills. The conditions in the 1960s were captured graphically by Phil Weller (1990) in his book, *Fresh Water Seas: Saving the Great Lakes*:

The severity of the problems produced a catalogue of bizarre phenomena. The weeds in Rondeau Bay on the north shore of Lake Erie became so dense that they looked like a "field of wheat" and an aquatic weed cutter was purchased to fight back the growth. The Cuyahoga River running through Cleveland was so clogged with oils and greases that it caught fire in 1969. The city had to build a fire wall and declare the river a fire hazard. . . . In March 1967 a deadly combination of cold weather and industrial pollution killed five thousand ducks along the Detroit River. Wood fibres, chips, pulp-paper mats, and oil slicks clogged the St. Marys River. Oil slicks and discoloured water were common on the Niagara River. . . . In January 1967 a worker's acetylene torch accidentally ignited the oils on the Buffalo River, a tributary of the Niagara. Flames leaped high into the air, burning pilings for a bridge and melting glass fixtures thirty feet above the surface of the water.

In 1964, in response to public demands for action, Canada and the U.S. asked the International Joint Commission to investigate and recommend remedial measures to stop the deterioration of the lakes. Following the IJC's report in 1970, concerted binational action was initiated. In 1972, the two governments signed the first Great Lakes Water Quality Agreement (GLWQA); it dealt specifically with eutrophication in lakes Ontario and Erie.

The agreement set the stage for co-ordinated prevention activities on both sides of the border; it set effluent targets for sewage treatment plants, and contained a schedule for reducing phosphorus loadings into the lakes. Canada's federal government took the lead by restricting phosphate concentrations in detergents and providing funds to upgrade sewage treatment plants. The Province of Ontario set tougher guidelines for effluents from treatment plants and also assisted municipalities to pay the costs of upgrading. The outcome was significant: the fishery in Lake Erie eventually recovered, and the thick green mats of algae, once so common, are now rarely seen.

This does not mean that conventional pollutants like phosphorus, suspended solids or bacteria have disappeared: site-specific problems still exist. In Toronto, for example, phosphorus levels across the waterfront are still too high, and some old combined sewers, which spew raw sewage into the nearshore of Lake Ontario in heavy rain storms, still exist. As a result, beaches have to be closed every summer because of high bacterial levels, and recreational opportunities

Sunnyside Beach

are reduced for swimmers, boardsailors, rowers, and others. In Toronto and 42 other places around the Great Lakes, these site-specific problems are being addressed within the framework of Remedial Action Plans to improve water quality.

However, the overall success of programs triggered by and agreed to under the 1972 GLWQA clearly demonstrates what can be achieved on the basis of co-ordinated action. Indeed, as pointed out in the report, *The Great Lakes in the 1990s*, "the rapid improvement in the condition of these lakes after 1972 encouraged Canada and the USA to sign a new agreement in 1978" (Jackson and Runnalls 1991).

The new agreement — the 1978 Great Lakes Water Quality Agreement — contains both an eloquent vision and a bold statement of purpose. While the 1972 document focused on eutrophication in two of the Great Lakes, the 1978 Agreement set out as its purpose nothing less than the restoration and maintenance of "the chemical, physical, and biological integrity of the Great Lakes Basin ecosystem" (International Joint Commission 1988). It bound both federal governments to consider the whole ecosystem in the basin, not just parts of it, and to examine the quality of the ecosystem (air, water, soil, humans, wildlife, and the connections among them).

The problems that had been addressed by the 1972 agreement were conventional pollutants — the so-called "lumps and solids" — the impact of which was visible in the form of scum, slicks, algae growth, and dead fish. The 1978 agreement tackled more complex problems — including one that was largely invisible: the myriad of synthetic toxic chemicals that could often be neither seen nor smelled. Therefore, the IJC's Water Quality Board (its principal advisory body) began compiling lists of synthetic toxic chemicals discovered in Great Lakes waters. Year by year, as detection methods improved, the list grew.

It now includes 362 compounds, of which 32 are metals, 68 are pesticides, and 262 are other organic chemicals. Of the total, at least 126 have been shown to be toxic to living beings, but there is little or no information about the toxicity of the remainder to humans or wildlife. Acceptable standards for the presence in water of many of these compounds do not exist: the IJC has set objective levels for 28 compounds in water, while the Province of

Ontario has water quality objectives for 87 compounds.

By 1985, after 13 years of compiling data, the IJC was able to target a sub-set of pollutants of great concern. They include:

- three industrial chemicals (PCBs, mercury, and alkylated lead);
- five pesticides (DDT, dieldrin, toxaphene, mirex, and hexachlorobenzene); and
- three waste by-products (dioxins, furans, and benzo (a) pyrene).

These were singled out in the basin because of their persistence in the environment, and their toxicity to wildlife and possibly human health.

The Water Quality Board has recently subjected six of the 11 pollutants — PCBs, DDT, dieldrin, toxaphene, mirex, and hexachlorobenzene — to further scrutiny. The manufacture and use of these chemicals have been significantly restricted for years; for example, most uses of DDT were stopped in Canada in 1970. The use of toxaphene virtually ceased in the early 1980s. Dieldrin, once widely used, may no longer be utilized for termite control. Because of restrictions on their use and manufacture, these chemicals are found in much lower levels in the environment now than 20 years ago. In fact, the levels found in the water of the Great Lakes are lower than the objectives set under the GLWQA and (in respect of these six pollutants) is "safe". It would seem that the problem should be solved.

But it has not been solved. Despite the significantly lower levels in the environment that resulted from actions taken, the IJC Water Quality Board concluded in their

Table 3.1   Critical pollutants in the Great Lakes Basin ecosystem

Total polychlorinated biphenyls* (PCBs)
Insulating fluid in electrical transformers and in production of hydraulic fluids, lubricants and inks. Includes 209 related chemicals of varying toxicity. Enters from air or in sediments.

DDT and its components (including DDE)**
Insecticide. Still used heavily for mosquito control in tropical areas on other continents. Enters from air or in sediments.

Dieldrin**
Insecticide used on fruits. Enters from air or in sediments.

Toxaphene**
Insecticide developed as a substitute for DDT. Used on cotton. Enters from air or in sediments.

2,3,7,8-tetrachlorodibenzo-p-dioxin (TCDD)
Chemicals in herbicides used in agriculture and for prairie and forest management (contaminant in Agent Orange herbicide used in Vietnam). Also a by-product of burning fossil fuels and wastes, and of pulp and paper production processes. This chemical is the most toxic of 75 forms of dioxin.

2,3,7,8-tetrachlorodibenzofuran (TCDF)
Chemicals in herbicides used in agriculture and for prairie and forest management. Also a by-product of burning fossil fuels and wastes, and pulp and paper production processes. This chemical is the most toxic of 135 types of furan.

Mirex***
Fire retardant and pesticide to control fire ants. Breaks down to more potent chemical, photomirex, in presence of sunlight. Enters from air or in sediments.

Mercury
Used in metallurgy, and a by-product of paint, chlor-alkali and electrical equipment production. Also occurs naturally in soils and sediments.

Alkylated-lead
Fuel additive and used in solder, pipes and paint. Also released when burning fuel, wastes, cigarettes and from pipes, cans and paint chips.

Benzo(a)pyrene
Produced when fossil fuels, wood, wastes and charcoal are burned and from automobile exhaust. One of many forms of polyaromatic hydrocarbons, or PAHs.

Hexachlorobenzene (HCB)
By-product of burning fossil fuels and wastes, and in manufacturing chlorine. A contaminant in chlorinated pesticides.

---

*   Manufacture and new uses prohibited in the United States and Canada
**   Use restricted in the United States and Canada
*** Banned for use in United States and Canada

Source: International Joint Commission. Great Lakes Water Quality Board. 1991. *Cleaning up our Great Lakes: a report from the Water Quality Board to the International Joint Commission on toxic substances in the Great Lakes Basin ecosystem.* Windsor: International Joint Commission.

1991 report to the IJC, *Cleaning up Our Great Lakes*, that reductions of the 11 critical pollutants:

> . . . are not as comprehensive as we now think necessary. Studies suggest that these substances actually have or threaten to have continuing important, if very subtle effects on human health and wildlife, even in very low concentrations. (IJC Great Lakes Water Quality Board 1991).

PERSISTENT TOXIC SUBSTANCES AND THE HEALTH OF WILDLIFE AND HUMANS

How can "safe levels" of toxic chemicals in water cause problems in humans and in wildlife? The answer lies in the characteristics of the chemicals and how they move through the food chain. The 11 on the IJC's list (and many others found in the Great Lakes Basin) are persistent: they take a very long time to break down into less toxic forms. In the case of toxic metals such as mercury and lead, breakdown never occurs.

At least eight of the 11 share one other important characteristic: they have the potential to "biomagnify". In other words, the levels of dieldrin or mirex or PCBs found in animal tissues get progressively higher as one moves up the food chain. In order to understand the problems of toxics in the Great Lakes, it is important to know why this happens.

When a kilogram of a persistent toxic chemical is discharged into water, some will remain dissolved in the water, and some will become attached to particles and sink to the bottom sediment. In either case, the chemical is "available" to aquatic organisms. Bottom-dwelling invertebrates (such as clams or worms) will accumulate the toxin in tissues as they ingest sediment or water. If levels are high enough, toxic effects will be seen in the organisms. If levels are lower, the invertebrates themselves will be fine, but a problem can still appear farther up the food chain.

In the animal world, almost everything is a potential dinner for something else. The food web is illustrated in Figure 3.1. It shows that invertebrates are near the bottom of the food chain and get eaten by forage fish such as smelts or alewives which, in turn, are eaten by larger fish — pike or lake trout, for example — which are eaten by aquatic birds such as gulls or cormorants, or by humans.

Although levels of persistent chemicals in water may be "safe" (because they meet the standards that have been set), as a consequence of biomagnification, levels are often too high in the fish to make them safe food for humans or wildlife. In the Metro Toronto area, because of chemical biomagnification, there are restrictions on eating some sizes of eight species of fish. Similar restrictions are found elsewhere around the lakes. Because of the biomagnification process, herring gull eggs may contain levels of PCBs 10 million times greater than those found in Great Lakes waters.

Biomagnification illustrates one of the weaknesses of the traditional approach to managing chemicals: water quality standards are set for the "most sensitive receptor", often to ensure the survival of sensitive species such as trout. But our water quality standards are *not* set to protect the gull that eats the smelt, or the human who eats the trout that ate the smelt.

The levels of persistent toxic chemicals found in the waters or tissues of animals in the Great Lakes are generally not high enough to cause acute toxic effects, including immediate death. Rather, scientists worry about chronic effects, the more subtle effects that can occur in humans or wildlife after years of carrying a chemical burden of PCBs or dioxins or toxaphene in body tissues. These effects can manifest themselves as cancer or reproductive failures; recently, scientists have begun to examine

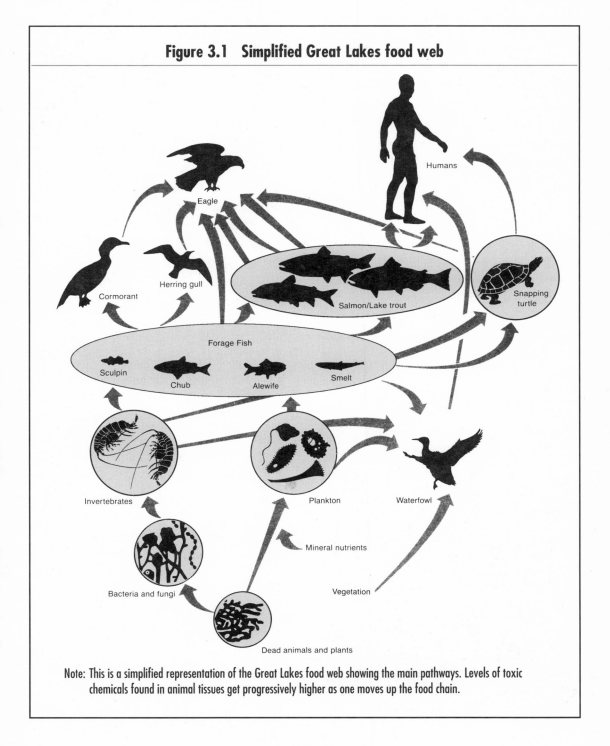

Figure 3.1   Simplified Great Lakes food web

Humans

Eagle

Cormorant

Herring gull

Salmon/Lake trout

Snapping turtle

Forage Fish

Sculpin

Chub

Alewife

Smelt

Invertebrates

Plankton

Waterfowl

Mineral nutrients

Bacteria and fungi

Vegetation

Dead animals and plants

Note: This is a simplified representation of the Great Lakes food web showing the main pathways. Levels of toxic chemicals found in animal tissues get progressively higher as one moves up the food chain.

the possibility that there are other, more subtle effects, such as hormonal or behavioural changes.

Since the 1950s, persistent toxic chemicals have been implicated in problems suffered by some 14 species of wildlife near the top of the food chain in the Great Lakes Basin. (See Table 3.2). They include reproductive problems, deformities, and sometimes dramatic population declines. They have been noted in two species of mammals (otter and mink), reptiles (snapping turtles),

and in three species of fish (lake trout, brown bullhead, and white sucker).

Similar difficulties have been noted in eight species of fish-eating birds around the basin: caspian, common, and Forster's terns, ring-billed and herring gulls, double-crested cormorant, black-crowned night heron, and bald eagle. Because of levels of chlorinated organic chemicals such as DDT in the environment, the populations of all these birds declined sharply in the 1960s. In fact, some decreases were so great that, according to the IJC Water Quality Board in its 1991 report:

> . . . records show that there was no known successful breeding of double-crested cormorants on Lake Ontario between 1954 and 1977. By the early 1960s and 1970s, this breeding failure had spread to lakes Michigan and Superior. . . . By the late 1960s some fish-eating birds in lakes Ontario and Michigan were found to be among the most contaminated birds in the world.

After uses of chemicals such as DDT were restricted and environmental levels dropped, populations of most of these birds recovered. In Toronto, we have night herons and cormorants nesting again. Even so, obstacles remain. Across the basin today cormorants are still being born with club feet and hideously crossed bills. Common and caspian terns still suffer from deformities and embryonic mortality. Bald eagles are unable to reproduce normally along the shores of the Great Lakes. Why is this happening?

Studies of animal tissues over time indicate that the levels of persistent chemicals such as DDT, dieldrin, and PCBs have stopped declining and are remaining at a stable level in the environment. Continued use and unseen sources — sediments, leaking landfill sites, deposition from the air — have resulted in a steady equilibrium in the environment and these residual levels in the environment are causing problems in wildlife. The evidence suggests that we will be living with these chemicals for a very long time.

Humans share the top rung on the food chain ladder with fish-eating birds and mammals: we breathe the same air and drink the same water. Some of us — especially hunters, anglers, and natives — eat fish and waterfowl from the basin. What about the effects on humans of exposure to these low levels of persistent toxic chemicals?

Table 3.2   Species of fish and wildlife known to be affected by contaminants in the Great Lakes

Species	Population decrease	Effects on reproduction	Eggshell thinning	Congenital malformations[1]	Behavioural changes	Biochemical changes	Mortality	Alterations in recruitment
Mink	X	X	NA	NE	NE	NE	X	?
Otter	X		NA	NE	NE	NE	?	?´
Double-crested Cormorant	X	X	X	(X)		X	?	?
Black-crowned Night-Heron	X	X	X	X		X	?	?
Bald Eagle	X	X	X	NE		NE	NE	?
Herring Gull		X	X	X	X	X	X	
Ring-billed Gull				X		NE	X	
Caspian Tern		X		X	NE	NE		X
Common Tern		X	X	X		X		
Forster's Tern		X		X	X	X		
Snapping Turtle	NE	X	NA	X	NE	NE	NE	NE
Lake Trout		X	NA			X		
Brown Bullhead			NA			X		
White Sucker			NA	X		X		

X = effects documented   NE = not examined   NA = not applicable   ? = suspected since population declined

[1]Unpublished records of congenital malformations (gross birth defects) exist for double-crested cormorant, great blue heron and the Virginia rail.

Source: Canada: Environment Canada, Canada. Dept. of Fisheries and Oceans, and Canada. Health and Welfare Canada. 1991. *Toxic chemicals in the Great Lakes and associated effects*. Toronto: Canada. Environment Canada, Canada. Dept. of Fisheries and Oceans, and Canada. Health and Welfare Canada.

Deformed bill on a double-crested cormorant

Historically, concerns about human health and persistent toxic chemicals in the Great Lakes Basin have centred around the risk of cancer. However, as our understanding of the effects of persistent toxic chemicals on wildlife has grown, researchers have begun to look for more subtle, less easily measured health effects. As the IJC Water Quality Board noted in its 1991 report:

> In news reports, the possibility of cancer is the risk most frequently associated with toxic chemicals. But there is growing evidence that some of the toxic chemicals identified in the Great Lakes ecosystem are likely to affect the nervous system, fertility, the development of young and immunity to disease.

Few detailed epidemiological studies have been carried out on the effects of persistent toxics in the Great Lakes on humans. One detailed survey did compare the health of children whose mothers regularly ate contaminated fish from Lake Michigan with a control group whose mothers did not. It found that the mothers who ate fish were carrying higher-than-average body burdens of PCBs and other chemicals.

Researchers also found significant differences in the children whose mothers ate an average of 6.7 kilograms (15 pounds) of Lake Michigan fish annually. They were born earlier in the pregnancy, weighed less, and had smaller heads than the control children. They startled more easily and had abnormally weak reflexes. On visual memory tests given when they were seven months' old, the babies of fish-eating mothers scored lower than those in the control group. Tested again at four years, babies of mothers who had eaten Lake Michigan fish had poorer verbal skills and poorer short-term memory. Researchers in this ongoing project will continue to study the children as they grow.

The Lake Michigan story indicates two things: first, exposure to existing low levels of Great Lakes chemicals may be causing subtle neurological or other effects we just have not been looking for. As the IJC Great Lakes Science Advisory Board concluded in its report, *1991 Report to the International Joint Commission* :

> The traditional public health approach to monitoring for cancer and unusual birth outcomes is too blunt to capture the subtle reproductive effects of Great Lakes contaminants. Subtle health effects observed in wildlife provide clues for the design of experimental approaches for determining if the same or similar effects occur in human populations.

Second, it underlines how babies are exposed to chemicals and their effects, either in the placenta or in breast-feeding. A mother's blood, which circulates to a baby through the placenta, and mother's milk can contain high levels of fat-soluble persistent toxic chemicals. The "acceptable intakes" of chemicals usually based on an adult diet do not address the exposure of children and breast-feeding infants whose immune systems are still developing. This shortcoming is described in *Toxic Chemicals in the Great Lakes and Associated Effects*, published in 1991 by the federal departments of the Environment, Fisheries and Oceans, and Health and Welfare:

> Several factors can increase the intake of contaminants by children and infants. Children usually consume more food per kilogram of body weight and have a higher absorption rate than adults. In addition, breast-fed infants are exposed to higher concentrations of fat-soluble contaminants than those found in adult foods. Although these exposures are for a relatively short period of time, they occur during a critical period of development.

The Lake Michigan study is worrisome because it indicates that children of high-risk mothers (those eating Great Lakes fish) may be at risk because of persistent toxic chemicals. Some observers suggest that children of women who are *not* high-risk — who do not eat Great Lakes fish — may also be at risk from persistent toxic chemicals. There is no doubt that people in areas around the Great Lakes (as in other highly industrialized areas of North America) are exposed to a complex mix of persistent chemicals. These chemicals are present not only in breast milk, but in food, air, soils, surface waters, and bottom sediments.

WETLANDS AND RIVER SYSTEMS

An examination of the Great Lakes' condition would not be complete without describing the health of the tributaries that feed those lakes, and of nature's own filters, the wetlands. Both are critical to a healthy, integrated ecosystem.

The Great Lakes Basin is rich in surface waters. It encompasses more than 80,000 inland lakes and an estimated 750 kilometres (466 miles) of rivers and streams. No overall assessment of their health has been undertaken in Ontario.

In general, acidification can be said to be a pressing problem in the lakes located in the northern part of the basin, while the effects of agricultural run-off are of great concern to those in the southern parts. Near urbanized areas, inland lakes and rivers are subject to the stresses of populated areas: direct discharges of toxic and conventional pollutants; effluent from sewage treatment plants; run-off from streets, roofs, and parking lots.

Many rivers in the basin have been structurally altered. Toronto's Don River is a classic example: dammed, straightened, and, in its lower reaches, encased in a straitjacket of concrete. Many rivers that were bottom-scoured by logging in the last century are silted today from urban storm run-off or erosion of their banks. Many of these degraded rivers — the Black, the Cuyahoga, the Fox, the St. Clair, and the Don, among others — lie in areas in which Remedial Action Plans are being developed.

While there may be few truly pristine rivers and streams in the basin, there are still many of good quality — streams and rivers that provide good spawning areas for cold- and warm-water fish, and offer aesthetically beautiful, diverse habitats for aquatic life. On the Metro waterfront, the Rouge is one such river, still remarkably unscathed by the development that surrounds it. Such rivers are a dwindling, invaluable resource, and should be protected.

It is also crucial to protect our remaining wetlands. At the water-land interface, they provide incredibly rich habitats for aquatic birds, mammals, reptiles, amphibians, and fish. Left undisturbed, wetlands filter and purify water, recharge groundwater, help to control erosion, and protect against floods. Sadly, however, as pointed out by the IJC Great Lakes Science Advisory Board in the *1991 Report to the International Joint Commission*:

> . . . despite their worth, the wetlands of the Great Lakes continue to experience irretrievable losses in both quantity and quality.

Even now, wetlands are still being filled for agricultural use, paved over as mall sites, and destroyed to make room for housing subdivisions, marinas or golf courses. Losses due to development have been staggering: in southern Ontario, an estimated 80 per cent of original wetland areas have been lost. In Michigan the figure is 71 per cent, and in Illinois it is 90 per cent!

Under the 1987 Great Lakes Water Quality Agreement, Canada and the U.S. agreed to establish a process to identify and preserve (and, where necessary, to rehabilitate) significant wetland areas in the Great Lakes Basin. The IJC is geared to research on wetlands, not on action. To date the parties have failed to develop a basin-wide inventory of wetlands and their health.

In the main, the Canadian government's Green Plan ignores wetland issues. The most recent version of the long-awaited provincial wetland policy under the Planning Act was released for review in September 1991. Many of those who worked on the issue for years were devastated by weaknesses in the proposed policy. As chapter two

Pumphouse Marsh, Oshawa: one of the few remaining natural wetlands in the Greater Toronto bioregion

described, it appears that the draft Wetland Policy Statement falls far short of providing the clear direction required to protect wetlands in Ontario.

In its report, *A Green Strategy for the Greater Toronto Waterfront* (1990), the Royal Commission made recommendations concerning the wetlands along the Greater Toronto waterfront, arguing that they are an immeasurable regional resource, and identifying critical habitat areas that require protection.

WATER QUANTITY

The Great Lakes are so large that explorer Samuel de Champlain called them "mers douces" — Sweetwater Seas. The largest, Superior, is 405 metres (1,325 feet) in depth and covers 82,000 square kilometres (32,000 square miles). In fact, it is so huge that it would take a molecule of water dropped in at Duluth 191 years to reach the Soo Locks and get into the St. Marys River. But it is one of the great ironies that the "Great" Lakes, despite their vastness — they hold one-fifth of the world's supply of fresh water — are a finite resource.

Nonetheless, we continue to use the waters in the Great Lakes Basin as if they were unlimited. People in Canada and the United States use more water per capita than those in any other of the world's countries — as they use more energy and many other natural resources. On average, an Ontario resident uses 360 litres (80 gallons) of water a day — water use has risen steadily over the past 20 years. It is estimated that, if trends continue, Ontario municipalities will double their per capita use of water by 2011.

There are Great Lakes Basin communities already experiencing water supply problems, some of which are related to upstream contamination by chemicals, which is what has happened at Walpole Island, in the St. Clair River. Niagara-on-the-Lake, which once drew its water from the highly polluted Niagara River, is now linked to Lake Erie by an umbilical cord of fresh-water pipes. It is likely that, in the future, more fresh water will be piped over long distances in the Great Lakes Basin.

Other areas such as Kitchener-Waterloo or parts of Halton, York, Peel, and Durham regions are experiencing water supply problems because groundwater resources are being depleted faster than natural processes can replace them. In the rapidly growing Region of York, limitations on water availability are constraining development. In the Oak Ridges Moraine, groundwater has lain in deep underground aquifers for thousands of years. This groundwater is important, not only for municipal, industrial, and agricultural use, but as a source of water for the streams feeding into the Great Lakes: 40 per cent of the water flowing in southern Ontario streams comes from groundwater and if supplies are exhausted, feeder streams will dry up, affecting fisheries, wildlife, and conservation.

Policy makers have recently begun to understand that our patterns of water use are not sustainable. In the Great Lakes Basin, we use more water than we return to the system. Some of the water removed from the Great Lakes is lost to evaporation or diversion and ends up outside the basin. Future pressures may come from the water-poor areas of the American sunbelt, which want to divert large quantities of water from the Great Lakes. Global warming will exacerbate the problem, as higher temperatures bring less rainfall, increased evaporation, and a greater demand for irrigation.

The quest for safe, clean water for drinking and household use, as well as commercial and industrial purposes, does not come cheaply. In *Water Conservation in Ontario: Implementing the User Pay System to Finance a Cleaner Environment,* a report prepared by the Municipal/Industrial Strategy for Abatement (MISA) Advisory Committee, it was concluded that in total, Ontario's municipalities have about $50 billion invested in water and sewage treatment infrastructure. The province contains about 37,000 kilometres (23,000 miles) of watermains and 30,000 kilometres (19,000 miles) of combined or sanitary sewers. In 1991, Ontario municipalities spent about $1.7 billion (more than one per cent of the Gross Provincial Domestic Product) on the infrastructure needed to treat and distribute drinking water and treat sewage. This was nearly triple the amount spent in 1980.

Not surprisingly, much of this investment is crumbling as it reaches the end of its useful life. On average, Ontario's sewers are about 50 years old, and some contain components that are older than Confederation! Leakage rates in these old sewer systems can range as high as 30 per cent.

More than 100 municipalities still have some old combined sewers, which contribute substantially to the bacterial and chemical loading of our waterways. Estimates of the current replacement value of municipal water supply systems are $30 billion, or about $3,750 per capita served. The costs of replacing sewage treatment systems have been estimated at $20 billion, or about $3,040 per capita served.

As discussed in Chapter 1, many Ontario residents are not paying the true costs of the water that they use. Of houses in Ontario that are supplied by municipal water systems, about 43 per cent pay a flat rate, regardless of the amount of water used. Another 30 per cent pay a declining block rate: as more water is used, the cost per unit drops. A mere 27 per cent of houses in the province are metered.

Wasteful water use, deteriorating infrastructure, and lack of full-cost pricing have serious economic and environmental consequences. Building ever-larger water and sewage treatment plants requires huge amounts of money, chemicals, and energy. Unless demand for water is reduced, and efficient use is made of water resources, municipalities will continue on this treadmill.

The alternative is to become more water-efficient: treatment plants would purify less water, operate more efficiently, and pollute less. Less water would be drawn from wells, protecting groundwater and Ontario's wetlands and streams. Processing smaller amounts of water would save energy and money, reduce chemical use, and defer the need for expensive new plants and equipment.

There are some hopeful signs that things are changing: in the summer of 1991, the Ontario Ministry of Natural Resources announced it would develop a provincial water efficiency strategy. Many municipalities, among them Metro Toronto, are establishing their own plans for becoming water-efficient.

WHY IS PROGRESS STALLED?

After hearing the litany of environmental problems in the Great Lakes Basin, it seems only logical to ask: why is the situation so grim? After all, we have had

environmental ministries and laws to protect the environment for 20 years. Millions
of dollars of public and private money are
spent every year on environmental regulation, enforcement, monitoring, and control. Why can't we eat the fish in the Great
Lakes, or swim in their waters, or preserve
wetlands from development? Why can't we
protect the aquatic life living in the lakes?
What is wrong?

JURISDICTIONAL
FRAGMENTATION

One of the most obvious reasons for
lack of progress is that jurisdictions are fragmented in the Great Lakes Basin: environmental responsibilities are shared among
two federal governments, one province,
and eight Great Lakes states. Within each
state and province are dozens of regional
governments, hundreds of municipal governments, and hundreds of special-purpose
agencies (such as conservation authorities).
Each has its own priorities and mandates.
In *Environment in Transition: A Report on
Phase I of an Environmental Audit of Toronto's
East Bayfront and Port Industrial Area*, a 1990
report of a study carried out for the Royal
Commission, the authors, speaking of the
situation in Canada, noted that:

> The existing regulatory framework is
> characterized by overlap and duplica-
> tion by different levels of government,
> by joint action on some issues, and
> by failure to exercise authority that is
> already in place. . . . The framework is
> fragmented, with different instruments
> governing separate aspects of the envi-
> ronment which makes it difficult to
> apply ecosystem goals and principles.

Citizens battling the regulatory
dragon are frustrated by the fragmentation:

with as many as five layers of government
involved in the Great Lakes Basin, with
more than a hundred agencies in the
Greater Toronto bioregion alone, it is easy
for any one group to say, "It isn't my fault."
Pinpointing responsibility is difficult and, in
some cases, futile. At a time when constitutional reform is being debated, it is useful
to read the 1990 federal Auditor General's
report, which asked: "Is Canada's Constitu-
tion environmentally friendly?" and concluded that:

> The consequence of these federal-
> provincial and interdepartmental divi-
> sions in responsibility for environmen-
> tal matters is a patchwork that makes
> it almost impossible to assign public
> accountability for safeguarding
> Canada's environment. There is no
> focal point of responsibility or account-
> ability to the Canadian people in
> respect of this crucial issue.

Resolving the complex environmental
problems of the Great Lakes Basin will
require dedicated, co-ordinated action. This
is not occurring. Nor is there any one body
taking responsibility for arranging the
actions of the various agencies. As the IJC
Great Lakes Science Advisory Board
lamented in its 1991 report:

> Policies in each country are developed
> through a process of inter-agency nego-
> tiation within general parameters of
> fiscal and foreign policy laid down by
> the governments of the day. To the
> extent that Great Lakes issues are not
> first-order concerns of the political par-
> ties or chief executives, policy questions
> devolve among the bureaucratic agen-
> cies, each with its own limiting man-
> dates and interests in the lakes. These
> interests may conflict and sometimes

affect agency personnel, programs and budgets.

And, the Board adds in what must surely be an understatement, ". . . this process is not necessarily conducive to setting a coherent policy for the lakes".

There is one body that could play a major role in ensuring the clean-up of the Great Lakes Basin — the International Joint Commission. The IJC was set up, by treaty, more than 80 years ago and, when asked by both the United States and Canada, is empowered to investigate and report on any matter along the common border. The IJC has the capacity to bring together officials and technical personnel from different levels of governments and other institutions in both countries. These individuals are invited to participate on IJC boards and committees in their "personal and professional" capacity, and to provide the Commission with knowledgeable expertise for analysing problems and considering possible solutions when framing recommendations to governments.

The IJC's powers are limited, for example, it only makes recommendations to governments. Nevertheless, over the years the IJC has ably completed many assignments primarily, but not exclusively, relating to the quality, quantity and uses of boundary waters. Perhaps its most important role in recent years has been to review government progress in achieving the goals of the Great Lakes Water Quality Agreement (GLWQA). Through its work, the IJC has developed a reputation as an unbiased watchdog over the environment in the basin.

However, many people and groups are concerned that the Commission's ability to function as an independent body, as required by the GLWQA, is being eroded. Attention is focused on the Water Quality Board described in GLWQA as "the principal adviser to the Commission . . . composed of an equal number of members from Canada and the United States, including representatives from the parties, and each of the State and Provincial governments".

Most observers agree that the Water Quality Board, once recognized as a key intergovernmental group dedicated to Great Lakes issues, is now generally considered an empty body. Many environmental groups, having seen the IJC's substantial committee structure being dissolved since 1987, believe the Water Quality Board has been gutted. They have made repeated calls for additional members on the Board, including aboriginal and environmental representatives, as one way of making it more accountable.

Some feel that the IJC approach of asking experts from federal, provincial and state agencies to wear two hats (one as an IJC committee member, the other as a government bureaucrat) hasn't been working. Since 1987, members of the Water Quality Board have made no pretense of serving two functions: they simply and unabashedly defend their government's interests.

The IJC has provided an important means for government officials in Canada and the United States to discover ways to resolve differences and achieve shared goals. The complexity of problems and the economic implications of possible solutions require imagination, co-operation, and competence. At its best, the Commission encouraged these qualities in the deliberations and findings of its boards and committees. Some observers feel that without effective mechanisms for inter-governmental co-operation, the objectives of the Great Lakes Water Quality Agreement will not be reached.

A FERRY TALE: AWASH IN JURISDICTIONS

Five years ago, the ferry *Prince Edward Island* motored into Whitby Harbour and started a chain of events that Franz Kafka would have found worthy of inclusion in his novels — just one local example of how jurisdictional fragmentation paralyses action.

The *PEI* was owned by a locally based numbered company and it carried an unusual cargo: two transformers filled with 2,275 litres (500 gallons) of PCBs. Originally meant to become a floating generating station in the Caribbean, the *PEI* found a temporary haven at the Whitby Harbour wharf when that deal fell through. The owner of the ferry soon found himself in a tangle of provincial and federal regulations governing PCB storage and export. He decided to do nothing for the time being.

In September 1986, worried about possible leaks of PCBs, the Town of Whitby made its first attempt to have the ferry and its cargo removed. Because the boat was in the harbour — which is under federal jurisdiction — neither the Town nor the Province had any power to intervene in the case. Ontario would have had authority to act if the transformers had been deemed to be PCB waste, but because they were deemed still "in use", the transformers were not covered by provincial regulations governing PCB wastes. A 1988 attempt to have the ferry removed was thwarted because, unbeknownst to the Town, one arm of the federal government (the Department of Transport) had been inadvertently collecting docking fees from the ferry's owner since 1986.

In February 1989, the owner of the *PEI* tried to move the ferry out of Canadian waters, but Environment Canada refused to allow him to do so — because there were PCBs on board! The owner then took the position that, while he would like to be able to comply with the Town's wishes and move his boat, he could not because he had no place to put the PCBs.

In early 1990, the Town was successful in having its harbour reclassified as a small craft harbour, which transferred jurisdiction from the federal Department of Transport to the federal Department of Fisheries and Oceans, and gave the Town of Whitby control of the wharf, pier area, and harbour waterlots. In May 1990, the Town gave the ferry's owner formal notice to remove the ferry from its property and move the PCBs to a location approved by the Ontario Ministry of the Environment.

While these jurisdictional battles were taking place, the very fear that had first triggered the Town's concern became reality: the ferry caught fire — not once, but twice, in July 1987 and October 1989. The vessel broke its moorings in January 1989; in December 1990, the vessel sank to the bottom of the harbour (although its deck remained above water). This sinking prompted a flurry of activity: Environment Canada issued a series of orders instructing the boat's owners to remove the transformers.

The orders were ignored and, after the boat was eventually refloated, the ferry's bilge water was found to be contaminated with PCBs. The slick was eventually skimmed off and stored on the deck of the vessel, alongside the transformers. At that time, Environment Canada issued two more orders, requiring the owner to store the contaminated bilge water properly. These, too, were ignored.

In summer 1991, a tentative agreement was reached to remove the PCBs. It involved the ferry's owner, the Town of Whitby, Whitby Hydro (which had agreed to store the PCBs temporarily, prior to their eventual destruction), and the Ontario Ministry of the Environment. The agreement fell through after the ferry owner refused to put up the agreed-on security for removing and destroying the PCBs.

In September 1991, the ill-fated ferry was still sitting docked at the wharf, leased from the federal government by the Town. An increasingly frustrated municipality had spent $12,000 to take the ferry's owner to court, where it successfully sued the owner in an action for trespass. He was fined $250, but he appealed. In October, the Town sought a mandatory injunction for the removal of the PCBs. The parties reached an agreement in court that, by 15 December 1991, the owners would remove the transformers from the boat and, by 31 December 1991, would remove the boat from the harbour. It remains to be seen whether this actually happens.

The last word belongs to David Sims, the Town of Whitby's frustrated lawyer, who lamented in provincial court that "the Second World War has been fought and won in less time than it will take to get the ship out of the harbour".

LACK OF ECOSYSTEM THINKING

Because restoration of the integrity of the Great Lakes ecosystem is the prime objective of the Great Lakes Water Quality Agreement, meeting it will require an ecosystem approach to managing, remediating, and rehabilitating. That approach demands comprehensive and systematic planning; management based on ecological units rather than political boundaries; an emphasis on long-term planning; and respect for the needs of future generations. It is obvious that an ecosystem approach has not been taken in the Great Lakes Basin, and it is equally obvious that this is a major reason for lack of progress in cleaning up the system.

There are no consistent rules across the Great Lakes Basin. Although the many governments involved have developed laws to protect air, water, sediments, soil, wildlife, and humans from pollution, standards set under these laws vary from jurisdiction to jurisdiction. For example, water quality standards for PCBs range from 14 parts per quadrillion in Minnesota to 1,000 parts per quadrillion in Ontario and New York.

An ecosystem approach requires management based on ecological units — bioregions or watersheds, for example. In general, however, policy-makers are still parochially confining their interest to what lies inside their boundaries, whether those are municipal, regional, provincial, state or federal. For example, there is no comprehensive management in the Don Watershed, or for the Rouge or Humber rivers. No one is taking responsibility for protecting the Greater Toronto bioregion, the Lake Ontario or the Great Lakes Basin.

There is little comprehensive ecosystem planning being carried out in the basin on a watershed or basin-wide scale. Environmental plans are not being integrated into other land-use planning initiatives. Remedial Action Plans are being developed to clean up

17 Canadian pollution "hot spots" in the basin but it isn't clear how these will relate to other initiatives, such as plans for fisheries and habitat management, land use, economic development, transportation, and housing.

One illustration of the piecemeal approach which has been taken in environmental planning is the PCB story. It illustrates how partial solutions have failed to address the very problem they were intended to deal with.

In the late 1970s, when PCBs were identified as an environmental contaminant, production was stopped. Nevertheless, PCBs are still in use in tens of thousands of pieces of electrical equipment around the Great Lakes. Most of the PCBs removed from service sit in storage in basements and out-buildings. In total, 52 per cent of the PCBs ever used in Canada are still in use; about 16 per cent remain in storage. Both types can leak and — as dramatically illustrated at St.-Basile-le-Grand in 1988 — can catch fire. Those not destroyed are potential new sources of environmental contamination.

Despite the actions taken since the 1970s, PCBs remain an acute problem. IJC estimates indicate that seven tonnes (6.9 tons) of PCBs fall from the air into the Great Lakes every year, predominantly as the result of leaks, spills, and fires. PCB levels in lake trout throughout the Great Lakes still exceed IJC objectives, while herring gull eggs around the basin contain high levels of PCBs, highest in contaminated areas such as the Detroit River and Saginaw Bay.

Remedial Action Plans are being developed to clean up 17 Canadian pollution "hot spots" in the basin but it isn't clear how these will relate to other initiatives, such as plans for fisheries and habitat management, land use, economic development, transportation, and housing.

Nonetheless — and despite the fact that substitutes exist — there is no deadline in Canada by which PCBs must be taken out of service and — while there are proven technologies for destroying PCBs in storage — there is no requirement that they be destroyed.

The PCB experience is echoed in other compounds. Of the 11 pollutants considered critical by the IJC, only one — mirex — has been totally banned by Canada and the U.S. The long-lived pesticides DDT, dieldrin, and toxaphene are still permitted for some purposes in the two countries and both mercury and alkylated lead are still widely used. There are no comprehensive strategies to reduce the presence of the critical pollutants (such as dioxins and furans) produced as by-products of industrial or combustion processes.

Some of the sources of these chemicals are far beyond the Great Lakes Basin: they are imported in food, or are carried long distances through the air to land in the basin. To protect ourselves from these persistent toxic chemicals, concerted action will be required worldwide.

Restoring the Great Lakes Basin ecosystem and preventing future problems means that our planning policies at all levels must look beyond the horizon of a single political term. But as the IJC Science Advisory Board points out in its 1991 report:

Conventional political wisdom calls for visibly addressing the problems of the day, not the problems that may (or may not) become politically significant tomorrow. There is little political payoff today for long-range anticipatory planning that will yield benefits only at some indefinite time in the future.

LACK OF ACCOUNTABILITY

An examination of events since 1978 highlights the remarkable failure of accountability mechanisms: too often, governments failed to meet their obligations under the Great Lakes Water Quality Agreement. In some cases, this has been in the form of unmet deadlines while, in others, programs have not been delivered as required under the agreement. The result is a string of broken promises that has contributed to the lack of progress in cleaning up the Great Lakes.

As signatories to the 1978 Great Lakes Water Quality Agreement, the governments of Canada and the U.S. pledged to:

Make a maximum effort to develop programs, practices and technology necessary for a better understanding of the Great Lakes Basin ecosystem and to eliminate or reduce to the maximum extent practicable the discharge of pollutants into the Great Lakes System (International Joint Commission 1988).

The policy directive was clear and, by signing the GLWQA in 1978, both parties agreed that the overall objective should be that "the discharge of toxic substances in toxic amounts be prohibited and the discharge of any or all persistent toxic substances be virtually eliminated". Thirteen years later, and after weighing the evidence, it is difficult to avoid the conclusion that the two parties have not made a "maximum effort" and that the goal of virtual elimination of persistent toxic substances is as remote now as it was in 1978.

It is actually more instructive to look at what has not been achieved under the GLWQA than what has. To date, the Canadian and U.S. governments have failed to:

- develop a binational strategy for managing persistent toxic chemical use in the basin;
- set targets for interim goals;
- set up mechanisms for achieving short-term and long-term targets; and
- develop a comprehensive database to guide decision-making.

The need for an overall strategy was articulated in the IJC's 1982 report, *Biennial Report under the Great Lakes Water Quality Agreement of 1978*, which recommended that Canada and the U.S. develop an "overall management plan for directing and guiding the activities of the parties and the state and provincial governments in controlling pollution in the Great Lakes system." Nine years later, this has still not happened. Indeed, in the *Fifth Biennial Report*, in 1990 (as in every one in the eight intervening years), the IJC again recommends that Canada and the U.S. immediately set up a "bi-national toxic substances management strategy to provide a co-ordinated framework for accomplishing, as soon and as fully as possible, the Agreement philosophy of zero discharge." It is nowhere in sight.

No interim targets have been set for reducing loadings of persistent toxic chemicals in the basin. While the U.S. has recently released its much-vaunted "33/50" program (under which releases of toxic chemicals are to be reduced by 50 per cent by 1995), it is voluntary and applies to only 17 chemicals, which were chosen on a nation-wide basis. The list of targets does not include many of the persistent bioaccumulative chemicals of most concern in the Great Lakes; indeed, only two of the IJC's critical 11 make the list. Neither the Government of Canada nor the Province of Ontario has set targets for reducing loadings of persistent toxic chemicals.

A number of commitments made by Canada and the U.S. under the GLWQA had timetables. Great Lakes United, a binational umbrella group of non-governmental organizations, recently analysed these commitments; of the 16 that had deadlines, eight (50 per cent) are three or more years behind schedule. One program — for joint disposal of hazardous wastes — is 11 years behind schedule! (Great Lakes United's list of commitments and notations on whether they were met can be found in Table 3.3.)

In their report, *The Great Lakes in the 1990s*, Ian Jackson and David Runnalls (1991) point out that:

> Whatever the original wording of agreements such as the Great Lakes Water Quality Agreement, as time passes they come to be defined in terms of what actually happens. Some elements are pursued, others are forgotten, or come to be regarded as not feasible, or even as window-dressing, whatever the original intent. Even in an ecosystem agreement such as the 1978 GLWQA, which rests on the principle that everything is connected to everything else, there is a clear danger that during the 1990s, ten to twenty years later, major items in the Agreement will be tacitly abandoned. If this happens, it is difficult to see how the ecosystem approach can be sustained.

The Province of Ontario's efforts at reducing the inputs of toxic chemicals into Ontario waterways are concentrated under the Municipal/Industrial Strategy for Abatement (MISA) program. It was launched by the previous government with great flourish in 1986, and was intended to move towards the goal of "virtual elimination of toxic chemicals" by setting tough new standards for eight industrial sectors and municipal sewage treatment plants. The Ministry of the Environment assured the public that the first of these rigorous new regulations would be in place by January 1988.

Almost six years after the program was launched, and four years after the first regulations were to be put in place, not a single abatement regulation has been promulgated under MISA. The program, first billed as the flagship of the Ministry of the Environment's pollution control initiatives, today looks more like a leaking dory. The overall MISA program has been mired in inaction and, under the most optimistic scenario,

Industry on the Mississauga waterfront

Table 3.3   Commitments made under GLWQA by Canada

Commitment	Completed	Date Commitment to be Achieved by	Time Lapsed beyond Commitment Deadline
Put programs in place to control pollution from industries	Partially	Dec. 31/83	9 years
Revise standards in Annex 1 of GLWQA	No	July 1/88	4 years
Agree to standard methods for assessing toxicity of substances	No	April 1988	3.5 years
Identify point source impact zones (mixing zones)	No	Sept. 30/89	2 years
Inventory raw materials, processes, by-products, waste sources and emissions of point sources	No	January 1982	9.5 years
Develop joint program for disposal of hazardous wastes	No	1980	11 years
Develop joint program for transportation of hazardous wastes	Yes	1980	6 years
Evaluate methods for quantifying transfer of contaminants from and to sediments	Partially	Dec. 31/1988	3 years
Agree to procedure for managing contaminated sediments	No	Dec. 31/1988	3 years
Develop joint demonstration program to manage contaminated sediments	No	June 30/1988	3 years
Complete three lists of toxic chemicals	Yes	Dec. 31/1988	11 months
Meet to review effectiveness of phosphorous load reduction plans	Yes	Dec. 31/1988	14 months
Confer on integrated atmospheric deposition network	Yes	Oct. 1/1988	17 months
Evaluate sediment management technologies	Yes	Oct. 31/1988	
Report to IJC progress under 11 Annexes to GLWQA (every two years)	Yes	Dec. 31/1988	2 months
		Dec. 31/1990	9 months

there will be no new standards in place for industrial sectors before 1995, at the earliest — fully ten years after the program was initially launched. Work on the municipal sector — sewage treatment plants — and industries discharging to sewers has barely begun. And as the days and months pass, the industries and municipalities around the basin continue the discharge of pollutants into Ontario lakes and rivers.

FAILURE TO ADOPT A PREVENTIVE APPROACH

For almost two decades, environmental groups and scientists have urged that society move to an "anticipate and prevent" approach for environmental problems, rather than the conventional "react and cure". "Anticipate and prevent" strategies include comprehensive ecosystem planning and environmental assessment of all projects, programs, and policies before they are implemented. It also includes avoiding or minimizing waste and pollution. This can be accomplished through the increased efficiency that results from changing or redesigning products, good management practices, the use of closed-loop systems, and substituting non-hazardous for hazardous raw materials. The "anticipate and prevent" approach also includes rigorously screening new chemicals for possible environmental and health effects, and banning chemicals found to cause undue environmental or health problems.

The tendency in pollution control, too often, is still to treat at the "end of the pipe": build a bigger sewage treatment plant, tack

Society needs to move to an "anticipate and prevent" approach for environmental problems, rather than the conventional "react and cure".

on another piece of pollution control technology, or engineer a better garbage dump. Too often these kinds of solutions merely transfer persistent pollutants from one medium to another. The filter on the industrial discharge pipe may stop pollutants from entering the river, but the filter (and the pollutants it traps) must eventually be put in a landfill site where groundwater can become contaminated, or it must be incinerated, thus spewing pollutants into the air, from which they will fall out on water or land.

React and cure strategies date from that time before we understood that we live in an ecosystem where pollutants cycle endlessly from air to water to soil to tissues, before we acknowledged that such practices are not sustainable over the long term.

There is some indication that a shift in attitudes and behaviour is starting to occur. As noted above, there are moves to ban chemicals — which, in fact, may be the only way to achieve zero discharge of persistent toxic chemicals, the goal of the Great Lakes Water Quality Agreement.

In 1990, the United States Council on Environmental Quality reported to the president that:

It appears that the only chemicals to have declined significantly in the Great Lakes ecosystem are those whose production and use have been prohibited outright or severely restricted.

In September 1991, Ontario Environment Minister Ruth Grier announced her intention to refocus the Municipal/Industrial Strategy for Abatement (MISA) program to emphasize prevention. She said the new MISA program would move towards zero discharge by developing a list of specific persistent toxic chemicals that are to be banned from the discharges of all facilities regulated under MISA. While this initiative deals only with discharge into water (and does not consider discharge into air), it is the first move by a government in the Great Lakes Basin to develop a process for banning persistent toxic chemicals.

Mrs. Grier's announcement came hard on the heels of reports from the IJC's Water Quality and Science Advisory boards, and from its Virtual Elimination Task Force. All three recognized the need to ban some persistent toxic chemicals.

The Water Quality Board recommended targeting six of the IJC's list of 11 critical pollutants as a first step. In its opinion, traditional approaches to controlling pollution were clearly failing to protect the health of humans and wildlife. It found that Canada and the U.S. had not adequately dealt with the manufacture, import, use, storage, transportation, and disposal of persistent toxic chemicals. "Many of these persistent toxic chemicals," said the Board, "are so troublesome as to require clear and absolute bans" (Great Lakes Water Quality Board 1991). The Board went on to recommend that the GLWQA parties develop a process with a fixed timetable and schedule to identify other chemicals that should be added to the list.

In addition to the parties' failure to develop a binational toxic substances strategy, outlined earlier, is the failure of governments at all levels to legislate the anticipate and prevent approach to set enforceable targets with deadlines for reducing persistent toxic substances. Where they exist, pollution prevention initiatives around the basin are discretionary and voluntary. This is the case with Environment Canada's $25 million Great Lakes Pollution Prevention Initiative, announced in March 1991 as part of the Green Plan. It includes programs aimed at achieving voluntary reductions in discharges in three areas: the automobile industry; small-quantity waste generators; and residential communities through citizen action. Similar activities are being conducted in the U.S. under the Great Lakes Pollution Prevention Action Plan.

In its 1990 *Fifth Biennial Report*, the International Joint Commission recognized the need to change the voluntary approach and enunciated the following principle, which was "universally supported" in submissions made to it:

> That principle was that, with respect to both the enactment of preventive measures and the enforcement of penalties for infractions, there must be an end to the 'business as usual' attitude: there must be strict application and enforcement of zero discharge and other restrictions as appropriate, and meaningful penalties for violations. The theme that the time has come when the principle of the Agreement must be given the force of law, providing for prohibition of the creation and/or discharge of dangerous substances and for appropriate penalties for breach, and that attention to this requirement should be given top priority, was either specific or inherent in the great majority of submissions made at the meeting.

In its recommendations, the IJC went on to urge that all parties "co-operatively develop and implement appropriate legislation, standards and/or other regulatory measures that will give enforceable effect to the principles and objectives of the Agreement on a Basin-wide basis."

LACK OF INFORMATION

Good policy development requires good information. Developing a strategy to achieve virtual elimination of persistent toxic chemicals requires knowledge of who is discharging what into the Great Lakes. That is why the GLWQA parties agreed in 1978 to produce, by January 1982, a "complete inventory of raw materials, processes, products, by-products, waste sources and emissions involving persistent toxic substances" (International Joint Commission 1978). It is almost ten years after the target date, and no such inventory has been developed.

The interim report released by the IJC Virtual Elimination Task Force in 1991 concluded that information on sources of toxic chemicals is inadequate. It found that, while approximate loadings could be determined for lead and PCBs, "for most other persistent toxic substances, information about sources and quantities entering the ecosystem is fragmentary or non-existent".

It is known that tens of thousands of tonnes of toxic chemicals are dumped into the air and water of the Great Lakes Basin every day. Exactly how much, however, is not known. In 1988, in the American states around the Great Lakes, 2,041 tonnes (2,009 tons) of toxic chemicals were emitted into the environment or transferred off-site each day. According to the U.S. General Accounting Office, because of the exemptions allowed in the U.S. reporting system, this may account for as little as five per cent of the total releases.

From the Canadian side, loadings of pollutants to the Great Lakes cannot even be guessed at. A federal initiative asking industries to produce Toxic Release Inventories will not provide figures until 1994 at the earliest.

The irony of trying to assess the health of the Great Lakes ecosystem is that, despite all the gaps, there is a huge amount of data generated every year. But data are not information. The data collected are all too often inconsistent in methodology and therefore not useful for analysing spatial trends or trends over time. Data are often stored in a manner that makes retrieval by others difficult or impossible. Information is scattered among agencies. Sometimes, there is no synthesis and interpretation of information and, when it does occur, the results are often communicated to decision-makers in obscure language. The Royal Commission's *Pathways: Towards an Ecosystem Approach: A Report of Phases I and II of an Environmental Audit of Toronto's East Bayfront and Port Industrial Area* described the problem as:

> . . . a lack of comprehensive approaches to measuring the health of the ecosystem, or its component systems (air, water, soils). Like someone working on a jigsaw puzzle, there are many research programs under way in different departments at all levels of government, but not one of them is responsible for assembling the pieces into a whole picture, or for ensuring that no pieces are missing. Co-ordinated, comprehensive research, modelling, and monitoring programs would help to ensure that pathways in the ecosystem are explored, that cumulative effects are assessed, that remedial programs can be evaluated, and that indicators of ecosystem health can be developed and applied (Barrett and Kidd 1991).

LACK OF ADEQUATE RESOURCES

Under the GLWQA, Canada and the U.S. have pledged to restore water quality in 43 toxic hot spots around the Great Lakes Basin, 17 of which are in Ontario. Since 1987, the federal government has spent $4.86 million on developing Remedial Action Plans (RAPs) for these areas. In the same period, the Ontario Ministry of the Environment has spent $7.58 million. Some participants in the RAP process argue that these expenditures are much too low, and that the lack of adequate funding has seriously hampered progress on the plans.

The IJC's *Review and Evaluation of Great Lakes RAP: Remedial Action Plan Program, 1991*, confirmed that one of the principal barriers to the implementation of RAPs is resource limitations, especially with regard to reducing the impact of agricultural pollution, combined sewer overflows, and contaminated sediments. Estimates are that it will cost as much as $19 billion to restore water quality in Canadian hot spots.

The Remedial Action Plans are site-specific, and are only part of an overall strategy for the Great Lakes Basin. Restoring ecosystem integrity will take basin-wide initiatives, as well as RAPs. The necessary actions and their costs have not yet been determined.

Perhaps the most basic need is to upgrade sewage treatment systems around the Great Lakes to meet the GLWQA's objectives. This is a commitment spelled out in Annex VI, in which Canada and the U.S. (in co-operation with state and provincial governments) agree to the "provision of financial resources to ensure prompt construction of needed facilities" (International

Metro Toronto's Main Sewage Treatment Plant

Joint Commission 1988). This commitment has not been fulfilled.

One untapped source of revenue for improving and upgrading sewage treatment systems is "full-cost pricing", under which municipalities charge users the full cost of water and wastewater services, on a metered basis. In addition to providing funds for upgrading infrastructure, that would reduce fiscal pressures on senior levels of government while reducing water use and associated pollution.

Canada's GLWQA commitments are funded under the Canada/Ontario Agreement (COA), which spells out federal and provincial governments' responsibilities in cleaning up the Great Lakes, and allocates funds for various activities. The last COA, signed in 1985, capped total spending at on average $3.7 million a year for six years. While that does not include all the money spent by either party, it is hardly sufficient, given the evidence that cleaning up the Great Lakes will require expenditures of a different order of magnitude.

LACK OF ENFORCEMENT OF EXISTING LAWS

While restoring the Great Lakes Basin ecosystem will require new strategies, approaches, and laws, there is a question of what existing (albeit imperfect) laws and regulations are being fully used. Could we, at this moment, be cleaning up at least some of the problems, using existing technologies and regulations?

The U.S. score in this respect is impressive: only one of 37 direct industrial dischargers to Lake Ontario is *not* meeting Best Available Technology Economically Available (BATEA) limitations for toxic pollutants. (This is in contrast to the Canadian situation where, as already mentioned, we are at least three years away from setting BATEA regulations through the MISA program.) In the meantime, 25 of 44 industries (or 57 per cent) discharging into Lake Ontario are not in compliance with even the existing weak requirements.

The record for Ontario's municipal sewage treatment plants is almost as distressing. In 1989, 108 of 364 (or 30 per cent) of the province's sewage treatment plants did not meet provincial guidelines for discharges of conventional pollutants. (At present, there are no guidelines for metals or organic chemicals.) Fifty of these treatment plants have not complied for at least three years. Perhaps most distressing is the fact that 61 of the non-complying plants are owned and/or operated by the Ontario Ministry of the Environment!

Nor are these industries and sewage treatment plants being prosecuted for exceeding allowable effluent guidelines. Of the 93 industrial polluters who were not in compliance in Ontario in 1989, eight were investigated by the Ministry's Investigations and Enforcement Branch, and one was prosecuted and convicted. With regard to the 108 sewage treatment plants not in compliance in 1989, two municipalities were charged by the Ministry. One pleaded guilty; the other case was dismissed and is currently under appeal.

While the Province has jurisdiction in many environmental matters, the federal government has some responsibility for environmental protection. The aim of the federal Environmental Protection Act, for example, is to comprehensively manage chemicals "from cradle to grave". In fiscal 1989-90, Environment Canada carried out 3,412 inspections under the Canadian Environmental Protection Act. These led to

280 enforcement actions, which resulted in 266 warnings and eight "directions". In a mere three cases, prosecutions were undertaken and convictions were obtained.

One of the federal government's potentially most powerful enforcement tools is the Fisheries Act, which is designed to protect fisheries and physical habitat. Under the pollution prohibition component of the Act, effluent limits have been set for seven industrial sectors, including pulp and paper. In addition, under its general prohibition section, the Act prohibits depositing of "deleterious substances" of any type in water frequented by fish. Despite these available powers, however, the Fisheries Act is rarely used. In 1988, for example, 21 charges were laid; there were 16 convictions, for which fines averaged $3,180. Considering that both the Fisheries Act and the Environmental Protection Act cover the entire country, these figures hardly reflect either the seriousness of the issue or the potential harm caused to the environment.

LACK OF RESPONSIBILITY

There is a fundamental conflict in carrying out Canada's responsibilities in the Great Lakes Basin. While the federal government has signed an international agreement to restore water quality in the Great Lakes, it is disinclined to pay the costs of clean-up. Environment Canada staunchly maintains that cleaning up the Great Lakes is the responsibility of Ontario and municipalities around the basin and says it will pay only for remediation related to federal lands or federal agencies.

But, as pointed out in *The Great Lakes in the 1990s* (Jackson and Runnalls 1991), when it comes to paying some of the costs of clean-up:

Responsibility for Water Problems

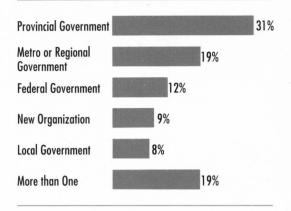

Provincial Government	31%
Metro or Regional Government	19%
Federal Government	12%
New Organization	9%
Local Government	8%
More than One	19%

One-third of the respondents feel the provincial government should be most responsible for addressing water quality issues in the Toronto area.

Source: Environics Poll. 1991

There are those who feel that a substantial federal commitment is unavoidable, both because of the large total sums that will be required, and because "it comes with the territory": if Canada commits to an international agreement to restore and maintain Great Lakes Water Quality, and if the federal government is to take credit for such an initiative, it cannot avoid paying its way.

Moreover, GLWQA's Article II states it is the policy of Canada and of the United States that "financial assistance to construct publicly owned waste treatment works be provided by a combination of local, state, provincial and federal participation" (International Joint Commission 1988).

In recent years governments have attempted to pass the buck for Great Lakes clean-up (and environmental protection in general): under the guise of "personal responsibility" there has been a tendency to finger the public (that is, everybody who is not government) as the major player in environmental protection. Then, if nothing happens, the reason given is that "the public wasn't ready to move" or "the public refused to pay". Environment Canada's Pollution Prevention strategy, for example, is based on having industrial sectors and the public set their own targets for reducing pollution and reaching them voluntarily, rather than having enforceable limits set federally. In a similar vein, the IJC Water Quality Board stated in its 1991 report, *Cleaning Up Our Great Lakes*, that:

> Although governments must pass regulations, provide some funding and co-ordinate research, much of the work of cleaning up and protecting the lakes has to be done by businesses and citizens. This means that all of us have to understand the importance of pollution prevention and learn how to practice it in our daily lives.

There is no question that, by themselves, governments cannot restore the Great Lakes to health. Individuals, by changing their attitudes and personal actions, will play a vital role in clean-up. However, they will need guidance from governments, and assurance that governments are doing their part. Furthermore, individuals can do just so much. Only governments can upgrade sewage treatment plants or regulate industrial discharges into the lakes or regulate the use of chemicals.

The IJC's 1986 *Third Biennial Report Under the Great Lakes Water Quality Agreement of 1978 to the Governments of the United States and Canada and the States and Provinces of the Great Lakes Basin* states unequivocally that:

> ... the primary responsibility for carrying out the programs needed for the success of the 1978 Agreement rests with governments. They also have the principal funding and enforcement capabilities.

SUMMARY

The lack of progress in cleaning up existing problem areas, and the lack of progress in developing strategies for preventing future problems, has led to a crisis of confidence in government. Informed observers and the general public have little confidence in the ability of governments and other institutions to restore the health of the Great Lakes Basin ecosystem, or even to prevent further deterioration. This institutional paralysis people perceive comes at a time when they believe action on the environment *must* take place.

Because Remedial Action Plans operate on a local basis, and involve so many members of the public, those closest to the RAPs are most cognizant of Great Lakes problems, and most frustrated by events. At the 1991 IJC biennial meeting, Great Lakes United member Sarah Miller asked the commissioners, "Are RAPs healing the Great Lakes?" and used the analogy that RAPs were intended to provide holistic treatments for sick Great Lakes. She concluded that:

> I am here today representing the exhausted and discouraged friends of the Great Lakes to communicate our fear that your experiment may be failing. There are grave signs that the patient is weakening while waiting for full treatment and for those in charge of this experimental treatment to agree to act. The original intent of the RAP cure was to fast-track the patient's recovery but the Great Lakes have been allowed to languish now for six years since your announcement of the RAP cure.

An Environics poll conducted in the Greater Toronto Area in June 1991 showed that only five per cent of those polled felt that water quality in the rivers and along the waterfront was good. There was universal support for cleaning them up so that people can safely swim and fish again. Eight of every ten respondents felt that cleaning up area waterways was an achievable goal which could be accomplished in a decade. A significant number of those polled expressed a willingness to pay for environmental clean-up and, significantly, they believe bureaucratic complexities and lack of political will — not money or technology — stand in the way of progress on environmental clean-up.

Restoring the health of the Great Lakes Basin ecosystem may be the single greatest challenge facing people living in the Great Lakes Basin. In the words of the IJC Water Quality Board in its 1991 report:

We who live around the Great Lakes are at an historic point. After years of experience with pollution, we now have a very good idea of what must be done to restore a healthy ecosystem. We have the know-how to clean up our lakes, but to do so we now have to make serious decisions.

Now, in order to illustrate the complex water quality problems in the Great Lakes Basin, we look closer to home — at the Metro Toronto Remedial Action Plan.

THE METRO TORONTO REMEDIAL ACTION PLAN

The Metro Toronto waterfront is one of 43 polluted areas around the Great Lakes in which a Remedial Action Plan (RAP) is being developed. RAPs were initiated in 1985, when the IJC recommended that governments on both sides of the border develop them to restore water quality. They were intended to be blueprints for remedial and preventive measures, and to be developed using an ecosystem approach. The requirement to carry out these RAPs was

Problems Preventing a Clean up

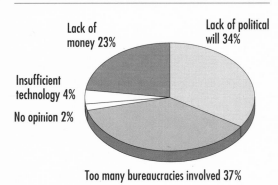

The respondents believe that lack of political will and too many bureaucracies are two of the biggest obstacles to cleaning up Toronto's waterfront and rivers.

Source: Environics Poll. 1991

River and Lakefront Water Quality

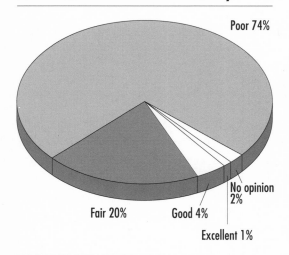

Three-quarters of the respondents rate the water quality in the area's rivers and waterfront as poor.

Source: Environics Poll. 1991

enshrined in the Great Lakes Water Quality Agreement when it was renegotiated in 1987.

The Metro Toronto and Region Remedial Action Plan was originally envisaged as a strategy for cleaning up the waterfront between Etobicoke Creek and the Rouge River. But, as it became apparent that cleaning up the waterfront would be impossible. without cleaning up the rivers that drain into it, the RAP's geographic area was expanded. It now includes the watersheds of the Etobicoke, Mimico, and Highland creeks, and the Humber, Don, and Rouge rivers — an area of some 2,000 square kilometres (772 square miles) which crosses many political boundaries, and includes five regional governments and 17 local municipalities.

The Ontario Ministry of the Environment is the lead agency in the Metro RAP, working closely with Environment Canada. A RAP steering committee (the RAP Team), which guides the process, is made up of senior representatives from the federal and provincial governments, and others from Metro Toronto, the Metropolitan Toronto and Region Conservation Authority, and the municipalities of Toronto, Scarborough, and Etobicoke.

Scientific and technical advisory committees, comprising government staff, provide assistance and advice to the RAP Team. A voluntary Public Advisory Committee, which offers ongoing feedback and community outreach, has broad representation from

Map 3.2   Metro Toronto and Region Remedial Action Plan area

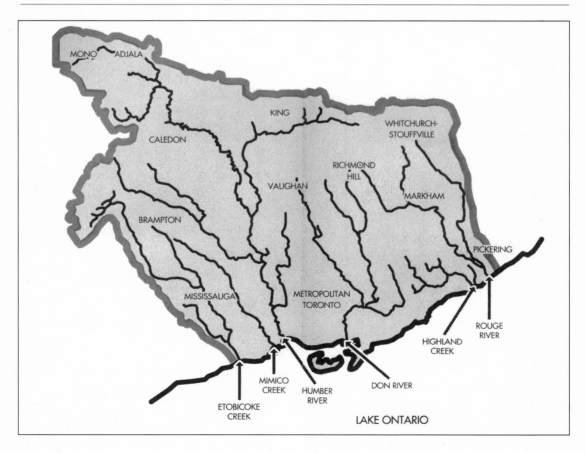

many sectors, including industry, tourism, agriculture, environmental groups, labour, recreation, municipalities, and others.

The RAP is intended to build on the work already carried out in the area. This includes the Waterfront Remedial Action Plan, completed by the City of Toronto in 1987. The RAP also builds on extensive studies carried out in the early 1980s under the Toronto Area Watershed Management Studies (or TAWMS). The RAP process is intended to bring "value added", which was not part of earlier studies like TAWMS, through the use of a comprehensive ecosystem approach, and to involve the public at every step of the process.

THE ENVIRONMENTAL PROBLEMS

Of the 17 Canadian areas on the Great Lakes where RAPs are being carried out, perhaps none faces more complex problems than those on the Metro Toronto waterfront. Some 2.5 million people live in the Metro RAP area, the southern part of which is highly urbanized and suffers stresses typical of dense population — the impact of sewage; contaminated stormwater from urban streets, roofs, and parking lots; physical restructuring of the natural environment; sewer dumping of toxic chemicals from households and small industries; and other problems.

The northern part of the RAP area is still largely rural, and there agricultural run-off of soil, pesticides, and fertilizers degrades streams and rivers. There, too, development pressures destroy rural lands to provide housing, and run-off during construction causes silting of streams and rivers.

If one were to fly over the Metro Toronto RAP area, the physical restructuring that has been carried out would be plain to the eye. First, of course, there are the urban areas — islands of heat, light, and air pollution — linked by a network of roads and bridges. The lower courses of all the area's streams and rivers (except the Rouge) have been dramatically altered. Blocked by dams, straightened and encased in concrete channels, they provide a hostile environment for aquatic life. Some feeder streams have been lost altogether. Habitats for terrestrial wildlife have been fragmented and lack continuity. Wetlands have been paved over, and built dock walls mean that, in many places along the waterfront, there are no shallows for fish. After a hundred years of lakefilling, erosion control, and other alterations, little of the natural shoreline remains.

The waters of the Metro Toronto RAP area suffer from population stresses as well: they contain high levels of phosphorus due to combined sewer overflows and sewage treatment plant effluents. Beaches are closed routinely every summer because of high bacterial levels that result from combined sewer overflows. Levels of heavy metals in water occasionally exceed Provincial Water Quality Objectives, especially in highly degraded areas such as the Keating Channel and the Inner Harbour. Bottom sediments are laden with heavy metals and organic chemicals. Consumption of some fish is restricted because of contamination.

The largest sources of pollution are the sewage treatment plants, combined sewer overflows, and stormwater run-off. The four sewage treatment plants in the area, which can treat 1,240 million litres (273 million gallons) of sewage a day, are the main sources of phosphorus, and they also pass through significant amounts of heavy metals and organic chemicals from

homes and industries. There are highly polluted zones around the outfall pipes of
these plants.

In heavy rainstorms, combined sewers
overflow and send a mixture of stormwater
and untreated sewage through 35 outfalls
into the Don and Humber rivers and,
through another 34 outfalls, directly into
Lake Ontario.

In an urban environment, stormwater
is a mixture of rain and various pollutants
from streets, roofs, parks, gardens, and
parking lots. Urban stormwater carries a
significant load of bacteria, metals, and
organic chemicals, and is funnelled through
some 2,250 outfalls into the streams, rivers,
and waterfront of the Metro RAP area.

Other sources of pollution include
deposition from the air; groundwater contaminated from industrial activities; agriculture or leaking landfill sites; historic contaminants in bottom sediment; and sources
"upstream" in the Great Lakes, including
the Niagara River.

PROBLEMS WITH THE RAP PROCESS

By necessity, remedial action planning
is an arduous, time-consuming task. There
is no cookbook in which to find the recipe
for a Remedial Action Plan, complete
with ingredients and the methods to be
employed. Each RAP deals with a unique
set of problems and is being developed
differently. Some, it would appear, are
having more success than others. Observers
of the Metro Toronto RAP process have
identified a number of problems with the
RAP process as it has been undertaken in
Toronto.

One criticism often levelled at the
Metro Toronto RAP is the amount of time

being taken to develop it: the original target
date set by the IJC to complete RAPs was
1987. This date was overly optimistic, and
did not reflect the complexity of the task at
hand. Work did not start on the Metro
Toronto RAP until 1986, and almost nothing but research was carried out for the first
two years. Since that time, efforts have concentrated on developing goals and principles to guide the process, on defining the
problems, and on identifying potential
remedial options.

Five years after the RAP was initiated,
and four years after it was originally to be
finished, selection of remedial options has
yet to begin. The current target date for the
draft Stage 2 document is late 1992.

Remedial Action Plans are developed
in stages: Stage 1 defines the problem;
Stage 2 selects remedial options; and they
are implemented in Stage 3. The scope of
the problems facing the Metro waterfront,
and the sources of those problems, were
detailed in the draft Stage 1 RAP document, *Environmental Conditions and Problem
Definition*, released in September 1988. The
recent IJC review of this report found that
the problem definition and description
were inadequate, and that the document
focused on conventional pollutants and did
not satisfactorily describe the sources and
causes of ecosystem impairment due to persistent toxic substances.

In April 1990, the RAP Team released
the *Draft Discussion Paper on Remedial Options*.
At the Royal Commission's second set of
hearings on the environment, this document
was criticized as unintelligible to the average
reader, and not useful for the process of
selecting remedial options. In its 1990 report,
Watershed, the Royal Commission recommended that the remedial options paper be

rewritten to make it more understandable, that it be reorganized on a watershed basis, and that it clearly link the RAP goals, the impaired uses, and the remedial options. Environment Canada and the Ministry of the Environment indicated to the IJC in September 1991 that they would not be rewriting the *Draft Discussion Paper on Remedial Actions*, but would be updating the remedial options in the Stage 2 document.

If it is to be implemented successfully, a Remedial Action Plan must have broad public support. In the Hamilton Harbour RAP, for example, continuous efforts have been made to inform the general public, to get people excited and involved in the RAP.

This has not been the case in the Metro Toronto RAP, where public outreach has generally been limited to contact with Public Advisory Committee members and representatives of their sectors, with a few newsletters being sent to a wider audience. In general, the Metro Toronto public does not know that a RAP is being developed and has not been involved in goal-setting or debates over remedial options. An outreach program scheduled for the winter of 1991/92 is intended to begin this process by widely distributing the Strategies document, which intended to raise the public profile of the RAP, outline the problems, and indicate the general direction in which the RAP is proceeding.

Developing a Remedial Action Plan that can actually be implemented is possible only if all stakeholders are involved. We have already commented on the lack of a strategy to involve the general public, but it would also appear that some of the municipalities and regions that should be part of the process are not involved in any meaningful way. For example, traced to its sources,

the Humber River's main branch starts in Mono Township in Dufferin County, while the east branch originates in Richmond Hill in the Region of York. But there is no evidence that these municipalities and regions pay heed to the RAP in their land-use planning, budget processes or public works planning. Although the municipal sector is represented on the Public Advisory Committee, and representatives of some "downstream" municipalities sit on the RAP Team, it does not appear that all five regional and 17 municipal governments are true partners in developing the RAP.

This lack of involvement by all stakeholders is one aspect of a larger, more troubling problem: the lack of an ecosystem approach. While, from the start, the RAP Team's intentions have been to use an ecosystem approach, in general it has failed to do so thus far. Problems in the draft Stage 1 report include: lack of integration and synthesis of information; concentration on the waterfront and lack of attention to the problems affecting the watersheds; little information about wildlife habitats, land use adjacent to the waterfront and watersheds, and contaminants in aquatic birds. Most important, the information collected to date, and the potential remedial options, are *not* organized on a watershed basis. Instead, the Metro RAP area is treated as a 2,000-square-kilometre (772-square-mile) monolithic block.

As noted, the IJC has said that lack of resources is a problem endemic to RAPs throughout the basin. The Royal Commission has twice commented on the limited resources for the Metro RAP, recommending increased funding, both to the Public Advisory Committee (in *Watershed*) and the overall program (in *Pathways*). In the past

Rouge Valley at Lake Ontario

two years, funding levels have increased to a limited extent.

One of the most serious criticisms levelled at the Metro Toronto RAP is that its development has had the effect of delaying beneficial projects that would otherwise have proceeded in the wake of TAWMS and other studies. Since the RAP started in 1986, some projects have indeed proceeded; for example, a detention tank in Toronto's Eastern Beaches has been built to reduce beach closures by detaining stormwater and combined sewer overflows during rainstorms. Repairs to sewers have been carried out, and work has been done to trace and disconnect illegal sewer hook-ups. Beaches have been cleaned and physically improved. Unfortunately, there is no way to judge whether or not remedial actions would have proceeded more quickly in the absence of the RAP planning process. In part this is

because, while municipalities are spending money on items that can be considered "remedial", in some cases the costs of remedial actions are buried in those of routine maintenance and operations.

The potential for delay is a problem in any long-term planning exercise — the need to balance action against the need to develop a strategic, unified, and comprehensive plan. Recognizing this, one of the principles adopted in the Metro RAP is that parties should proceed with remedial actions that are "consistent with RAP goals and principles" while the RAP itself is being developed. This echoes the "two-track" recommendation of the IJC (1988) *Revised Great Lakes Water Quality Agreement of 1978 as Amended by Protocol Signed November 18, 1987*, which encourages acceleration of existing programs while RAPs are under development.

One burden RAPs everywhere (including Toronto) have had to bear is that of too-great expectations. For many reasons — lack of knowledge, bureaucratic buck-passing — RAPs have been touted as the answer to any and all water quality problems in areas such as Toronto. This is simply not true. The Metro Toronto Remedial Action Plan is a site-specific clean-up plan; as such, it deals best with problems originating within its boundaries. Through the RAP, programs can be developed to do such things as keep the beaches open, preserve and rehabilitate local wildlife habitat, manage stormwater better, improve sewage treatment plants, and, to some degree, reduce sewer dumping of chemicals.

But there are problems that require a basin-wide approach, especially when sources lie outside the Metro RAP area. It will take basin-wide efforts to ban persistent chemicals, set multi-media standards for chemical exposure for humans and wildlife, and control deposition of toxic chemicals from air. They will also be required to reduce pollution from "upstream" in the Great Lakes, develop standards for sediment quality, technologies to treat sediments, and prosecute those not in compliance with environmental laws and regulations.

GRASSROOTS ACTION

In recent years, a number of grassroots initiatives have emerged, aimed at cleaning up waters in the Metro RAP area. These come from groups that include the Task Force to Bring Back the Don, the Black Creek Project, Save the Rouge Valley System, and Action to Restore a Clean Humber (ARCH). All sprang up to fill what was perceived as a void in government action; the work of ARCH is a good example.

ARCH, formed in 1989, is the newest of these citizens' groups; it is a non-governmental body made up of experts from various disciplines, and of others who have a stake in the Humber. Among its current projects: monitoring development that might affect the watershed and developing a computerized database to assist in clean-up actions. The organization sees its overall purpose as being to resolve the current jurisdictional logjam and to define an effective mechanism for implementing water quality programs on the Humber. To meet these goals, ARCH acts as a catalyst with government and the private sector, urging that clean-up action begin.

ARCH believes that we know how to clean up the Humber River, and that the impediments to progress are not technical or scientific, but institutional. Therefore, ARCH proposes to build on the substantial work already done in the Humber watershed, including the *Humber River Water Quality Management Plan*, completed in 1986 under TAWMS. This plan contains a host of recommendations for restoring water quality in the Humber River watershed, including measures to eliminate combined sewer overflows, reduce flooding, address sewer dumping from homes and industries, and control erosion, among others. According to ARCH, only a few recommendations of minor consequence from the Humber River Water Quality Management Plan have been implemented by Metro Toronto; most remain as "potential remedial options" in the list generated in the RAP process.

In June 1991, ARCH submitted an unsolicited proposal to the Metro Toronto RAP Team for funding to develop a

Map 3.3 Humber River watershed

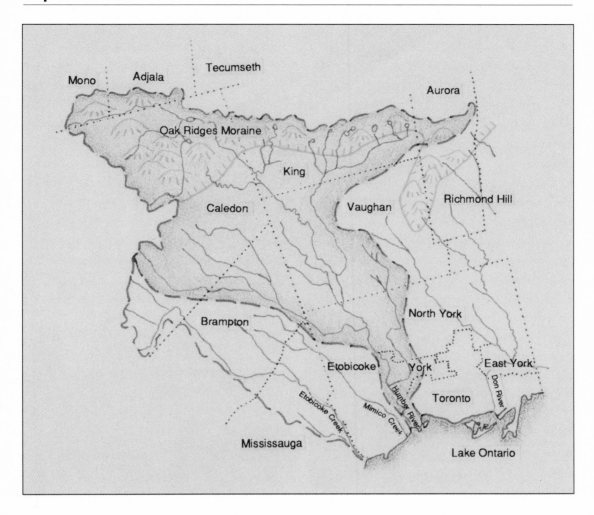

watershed-based mechanism for implementation of the RAP. The idea was to use the Humber River as a prototype for implementation based on the "watershed partnerships", as articulated by the Royal Commission in *Watershed*. This could then be used as a model for co-ordinated action in the other watersheds. ARCH argued that the Humber River was a logical choice because it has the largest watershed, and affects the greatest number of municipalities. By early December 1991, Environment Canada, the Ontario Ministry of the Environment, and Metro Toronto had

agreed in principle to the ARCH proposal, and funding for the project was imminent. While the initiative is laudable, it is unfortunate that ARCH is having to develop a prototype for implementation in the advance of the actual plan — the RAP.

From the earliest days of the RAPs, those involved in developing the plans have been haunted by the question of how to implement them. ARCH is focusing on two of the keys needed to unlock the implementation puzzle: involvement of all key players and use of a watershed approach. The group comprises people who, first and foremost, like their river, feel some sense of stewardship for it, and want to see it restored. Founding members living near the mouth of the river established connections with upstream dwellers and found that people in York and Peel regions and Dufferin County like their river, too! But the members of ARCH realized that merely involving citizens was not enough; all the players had to be at the table — every level of government, and the private sector as well. Therefore, they proposed a study to determine the best way of doing just that.

The ecosystem approach requires that activities be managed based on "ecological units". What is an appropriate ecological unit? For ARCH's members, logic suggested a unit that was manageable and understandable — the watershed of a river. Watershed planning is firmly grounded in a scale people can comprehend, where they can feel a sense of stewardship.

There is no doubt that support for such a strategy extends beyond the Humber River watershed. Speaking of Watershed Partnerships, the Commission's *Watershed* report said:

> Public support for this collaborative approach is very high. Indeed it is clear that people are prepared to back a common vision that takes into account the long-term health and well-being of the waterfront and its river valleys. The hundreds of deputants before the Commission bore witness to that fact.
>
> They may be well ahead of their governments. Clearly, they want their various levels of government to build on this consensus and move toward restoring the integrity of the waterfront and the ecosystem that sustains and determines it.

ACTION ON THE GREAT LAKES

The health of the Greater Toronto waterfront, as measured by the quality of water, is inextricably tied to the health of the Great Lakes Basin ecosystem. If we are going to clean up our waterfront, we must act regionally (perhaps even globally) as well as locally. This review of the state of the Great Lakes has touched on many of the complex problems facing us, and the institutional stumbling blocks that have so far impeded progress on clean-up. The public pressure for action on remediation grows and grows. But where do we go from here?

Waves breaking, Newcastle

The Royal Commission believes that there is a clear need to clean up the waters along the Greater Toronto waterfront and its watersheds. The following eight major recommendations are made to accelerate the process of regeneration.

THE GREAT LAKES WATER QUALITY AGREEMENT

In moving to improve water quality in the Great Lakes, it seems natural to start with the Great Lakes Water Quality Agreement (GLWQA). First signed by Canada and the U.S. in 1972, expanded in 1978, and reaffirmed in 1987, in many ways the GLWQA is a heartening document. Its overall goal is framed in ecological terms: to restore the integrity of the Great Lakes Basin ecosystem. The agreement contains both general and specific objectives for measuring ecological health.

It also includes commitments by the parties to develop many programs to prevent pollution from industrial, municipal, and agricultural sources, as well as from dredging, shipping, and other activities. In addition, the parties commit themselves to carrying out surveillance and monitoring programs, and to developing Remedial Action Plans, Lakewide Management Plans, and more. The GLWQA is filled with noble intentions, good words, and logical strategies to help clean up the Great Lakes Basin. Nonetheless, it is obvious that many of the most fundamental commitments made under the GLWQA have not been kept.

It is important to understand that point because we are close to the time (in 1992) when the GLWQA is due to be renegotiated. During that process, there is a temptation to "improve" the agreement by broadening its scope, refining its strategies, and adding more annexes. Those in favour of renegotiation argue that the GLWQA can be improved by better defining terms, setting priorities, and articulating the ecosystem approach more clearly.

The Royal Commission sees risks inherent in trying to renegotiate the Agreement now, especially the risk of expending bilateral effort on theoretical discussions at a time when the public is demanding action on Great Lakes clean-up. The Commission is not convinced that adding more words to the GLWQA will solve the problems in the Great Lakes in any way. Rather, we believe that "improving" the GLWQA would probably only generate more deadlines that will not be met, and more commitments that will not be kept.

In short, the Royal Commission considers that the problems of Great Lakes water quality are not primarily attributable to GLWQA shortcomings. The Great Lakes Water Quality Agreement is, if not perfect, a good foundation on which to build a strategy for restoring the Great Lakes. But there are structures *outside* the agreement that must be improved if meaningful progress is to be achieved in cleaning up the Great Lakes. Two changes, discussed in the next sections, are essential if that is to happen: a more effective International Joint Commission and a better Canada/Ontario Agreement.

THE INTERNATIONAL JOINT COMMISSION

The International Joint Commission has played a valuable and unique role as the independent watchdog of progress on environmental matters in the Great Lakes, and as a facilitator of intergovernmental co-operation. However, since 1987, there has been a steady erosion of the Commission as the result of cutbacks in funding, loss of trained staff, and changes in its committee structure that have left today's IJC unsure even of its role.

Attempts to restore the Great Lakes ecosystem will benefit from a strong and focused IJC which can act as a catalyst, an integrator, an independent fact-finder, observer, and watchdog. To be able to do this, the IJC should be supported with sufficient resources to carry out its obligations. This would allow the Commission, for example, to increase its in-house expertise rather than having to depend on the governments it monitors to provide it.

Since the IJC's 1985 biennial meeting in Kingston, public input has played an ever-increasing role in its reports on progress in cleaning up the Great Lakes. This input has been significant in increasing the Commission's attention to accountability.

Public interest in Great Lakes issues will probably continue to increase in the years ahead, as remediation starts. The Royal Commission believes that the public in the basin area can offer the IJC valuable expertise and opinion, and that a mechanism should be set up to formalize this transfer of information on an ongoing basis. This could be done through a standing Citizens' Advisory Committee which could advise the IJC and its boards on matters coming before them.

RECOMMENDATION

17. The Royal Commission recommends that the Government of Canada work with its U.S. counterpart and the IJC to:

- strengthen the role of the IJC and clarify its responsibilities;
- ensure that the IJC has sufficient, secure, multi-year funding to carry out its responsibilities; and

- set up a standing Citizens' Advisory Committee to provide ongoing advise to the IJC.

THE CANADA/ONTARIO AGREEMENT

Most Great Lakes watchers focus on the relationship between Canada and the U.S., as articulated and defined by the GLWQA. But that overlooks the jurisdictional realities in Canada, where responsibility for many environmental issues lies with the provincial, not the federal, government. Therefore, in implementing commitments under the GLWQA, the relationship between Canada and Ontario is more important than that between Canada and the U.S. It is articulated in the Canada/Ontario Agreement (COA).

The COA is one of the best-kept secrets in the environmental world, almost unknown to the general public, and little understood even by many environmental groups active on issues in the Great Lakes Basin. This is more than somewhat ironic, given the fact that COA is the key (on the

Relationships and responsibilities for Great Lakes water quality

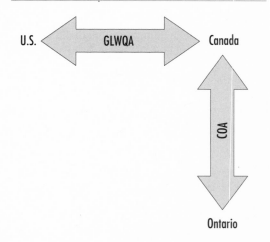

U.S.   GLWQA   Canada

COA

Ontario

Canadian side) to implementing the Great Lakes Water Quality Agreement. Just as the GLWQA spells out Canadian and American responsibilities in cleaning up the Great Lakes, the COA spells out federal and provincial government responsibilities in cleaning them up.

There have been Canada/Ontario agreements concerning the Great Lakes since 1971. The current COA was signed in April 1985, and expired on 31 March 1991. (It has since been temporarily extended for an indefinite period.) The COA contains the same principles as the GLWQA: the virtual elimination of persistent toxic substances, shared funding of publicly owned waste treatment works, and co-ordinated planning processes to control all sources of pollution. It also uses the same general and specific clean-up objectives found in the GLWQA.

The fundamental objective of the COA is to restore the Great Lakes Basin ecosystem. Its purpose is to "renew and strengthen co-operation between Canada and Ontario in meeting the obligations assumed by Canada under the revised [GLWQ] Agreement" and "to provide for the cost-sharing of specific programs which Ontario will undertake to assist Canada in meeting these obligations" (COA 1985).

In the 1985 version, Canada and Ontario agreed they would contribute equally to the costs of programs carried out under the COA (except for construction of sewage treatment facilities). The Agreement also placed a cap on the amount of money that would be spent: a total of $22.1 million over six years. Echoing the GLWQA, this version spelled out what Canada and Ontario would undertake in controlling pollution in the Great Lakes.

It included programs and other measures to deal with:

- treatment of municipal and industrial wastes;
- phosphorus management;
- pollution from shipping and dredging;
- pollution from land-use activities;
- hazardous polluting substances and persistent toxic substances;
- Remedial Action Plans; and
- annual inventories of polluters and compliance rates.

Canada and Ontario need to renegotiate the Agreement and the Royal Commission believes it is imperative that the COA be changed to allow the GLWQA's objectives to be reached. Observers have suggested a number of improvements that should be made during the renegotiation process.

First, COA negotiations between Canada and Ontario should be carried out publicly rather than, as in the past, by bureaucrats behind closed doors. While this approach might have been acceptable as recently as 1985, today's public demands a role in the development of such important tools. For example, in 1987, when the GLWQA was renegotiated by Canada and the U.S., then-Secretary of State for External Affairs Joe Clark appointed two members of non-governmental organizations to the Canadian negotiating team. Such appointments would ensure accountability at a critical time in the Great Lakes Basin clean-up process. Moreover, because municipalities will play a large role in funding local clean-up initiatives, they, too, must be given a role in negotiations.

> **W**e are moulded, we say, by the conditions and surroundings in which we live; but we too often forget that environment is largely what we make it.
>
> Carman, B. 1904. *The kinship of nature.* Boston: Page.

Second, the new COA must be more results-oriented, better designed for implementation. As it stands, the agreement is largely a mechanism for co-ordination. But if it is to achieve the objective for which it was designed — to meet the obligations assumed by Canada under the GLWQA — the COA must provide a framework within which GLWQA commitments can be implemented. This means that the COA must include strategic targets, administrative structures, measures of performance, and timetables. Furthermore, it should articulate clearly the roles and responsibilities of the various players involved.

Third, the COA must address program funding to meet GLWQA commitments, including reasonable apportioning of costs between the parties. It also must ensure that sufficient funds are provided to enable targets to be reached. Clearly, the funding cap set in the 1985 COA (on average, $3.7 million a year) is totally inadequate in dealing with the problems at hand. Under the Remedial Action Plans alone, the estimated costs for clean-up on the Canadian side are in the $19-billion range. Add to that the costs of Great Lakes monitoring, and programs to control pollution from industrial and municipal sources, rural and urban run-off, atmospheric deposition, dredging, and others, and it is clear that funding must be of a very different order of magnitude.

If the two governments cannot afford to provide this, they should say so candidly, to ensure that the public is not misled. In the very near term, significant funding will be required for Remedial Action Plans' so-called Track I options. These, as defined by the IJC, are existing programs that can be accelerated before the Remedial Action Plan is entirely complete.

Fourth, there is the matter of accountability. Every two years, Canada and the U.S. report to the IJC on their progress, and it then reports on overall progress in the Great Lakes Basin. The Canadian report, however, is essentially a list of programs under way. The COA parties should develop a set of indicators to measure progress of RAPs. These should be simple and easy to understand — the number of beaches posted to warn of pollution, the number of species of fish restricted for human consumption or the incidence of reproductive problems in aquatic birds.

The parties should make annual public reports on what they have accomplished, referring to this set of indicators, and should reveal which parties have spent what monies. This will allow the Canadian public to ascertain where its tax dollars are being spent, and measure tangible progress.

Fifth, on an ongoing basis, the public should be part of COA activities. This could be accomplished by giving a seat to members of the public on the various COA committees, or by creating a standing committee of citizen advisors.

RECOMMENDATION

18. The Royal Commission recommends that the federal and provincial governments renegotiate the Canada/ Ontario Agreement and:

- conduct public negotiations, with the explicit involvement of municipalities and non-governmental organizations;
- ensure that the new COA contains strategic targets, administrative structures, and timetables against which progress can be measured;
- explore funding options including full-cost pricing of sewer and water services;
- ensure that the new COA contains mechanisms for apportioning the costs of clean-up between the parties, that adequate funds are available to carry out programs to meet the commitments made under the GLWQA, and that funds are available to accelerate Track I RAP programs;
- develop a set of indicators of progress under Remedial Action Plans, and report annually to the Canadian public on progress made, as measured by those indicators, and by monies spent; and
- include the public on an ongoing basis in COA activities and monitoring.

MUNICIPAL/INDUSTRIAL STRATEGY FOR ABATEMENT

At this time, the Municipal/Industrial Strategy for Abatement (MISA) program is Ontario's prime vehicle for reducing the flow of toxic pollutants into Ontario waters. While it is intended to set tough new standards for direct industrial dischargers, municipal sewage treatment plants, and indirect industrial dischargers (who discharge to municipal sewage systems), the program, as we have seen, has been plagued with delays: control of direct industrial dischargers is almost four years behind

schedule, while virtually nothing has been done with the municipal and indirect industrial sectors. This is not acceptable.

During the three years of its existence, the Royal Commission has viewed with mounting frustration the lack of progress on MISA. Combined with the lack of enforcement of existing regulations, it places Canada in a poor position relative to American efforts at pollution control in the Great Lakes.

RECOMMENDATION

19. The Royal Commission recommends that the Province of Ontario move quickly to reduce pollution entering the Province's waterways, specifically by developing MISA as rapidly as possible so that it:

- sets regulations for direct industrial dischargers;
- decides on a program, including targets and timetables, to control pollution from the municipal sector, and moves to implement such a program; and
- decides on a program, with targets and timetables, to control industries that discharge to municipal sewage treatment systems, and moves to implement such a program.

THE METROPOLITAN TORONTO AND REGION REMEDIAL ACTION PLAN

The success of the Canadian Remedial Action Plans depends, in large part, on a renegotiated Canada/Ontario Agreement. Without a COA that provides funding agreements and funds for cleaning up the

Great Lakes, it will be impossible to implement RAPs effectively. The same is true of RAP planning, which ends with development of a Stage 2 document spelling out responsibility and timetables for paying for clean-up activities. In addition to a strong, effective COA, there are other planning issues that must be addressed in developing Metro's RAP.

The Metropolitan Toronto RAP, which has encountered its share of difficulties since it was started in 1986, is an attempt to develop a blueprint for cleaning up an immense and complex set of problems created by the fact that 2.5 million people live, work, and play in a relatively small area.

The most serious of these is the lack of a true ecosystem approach to tackling Metro's waterfront and watersheds. Using such an approach requires a fundamental shift from traditional ways of thinking — the compartmentalized approach to environmental protection, concerned with managing the external environment. The ecosystem approach, on the other hand, stresses integration, not compartmentalization, and is based on managing human activities *within* a natural system of which we are just one part. Shifts to ecosystem thinking cannot be legislated but are the result of changes to personal philosophy and values. Nonetheless, there are two concrete actions that can help move the Metro Toronto RAP to an ecosystem approach.

First, the IJC has asked that the Stage 1 (problem definition) document be rewritten to better reflect the problems and set the groundwork for an ecosystem approach in developing the RAP. The *Draft Discussion Paper on Remedial Options* also needs updating and reorganization on a watershed basis. While the RAP Team intends to make updates as part of the Stage 2 document, the Commission believes these should be done before Stage 2 is finished, particularly because ecosystem/watershed ideas are the building blocks needed in order to select remedial options for the final plan.

Second, as articulated in *Watershed*, we believe that a watershed approach should be taken in the Metro Toronto RAP: remedial options should be arranged and tied to restoring water quality in each of the six major watersheds, co-ordinated and integrated by the overall RAP. Because, according to the ecosystem approach, activities must be managed according to ecological units, we also think that the municipalities within these watersheds should be brought into the RAP development process as true partners.

To be effective, the RAP requires three additional improvements: adequate funding, solid public backing, and quick implementation. The Royal Commission is not convinced that the Metro Toronto RAP has received the resources necessary to fulfil its objectives. Of the 17 Canadian RAPs, this initiative is arguably the most complex, covers the largest area, and potentially affects the greatest number of people.

The Metro RAP has never effectively reached out to the general public to elicit support for cleaning up the watersheds and waterfront. However, broad public acceptance and support of the RAP is critical to implementing it successfully. Without it, a plan — however worthy — is likely to sit on a shelf gathering dust.

The RAP Team is taking steps to involve the general public through activities planned around the release of a document outlining its strategies. But this is only part of what is needed. The Team must develop an ongoing, comprehensive program of outreach to raise awareness and involve Metro Toronto's general public. Perhaps the best way to do this is by using a watershed approach, creating enthusiasm in people for cleaning up their own river, creek or stretch of waterfront.

Finally, the delays in the RAP process are unfair to those members of the public who have invested so much time and effort in its development. These hold-ups also threaten to make the RAP redundant: while development of the RAP has been dragging, regions and municipalities have proceeded on projects costing millions of dollars — all in the absence of a unifying framework.

For example, Metro Toronto has carried or is carrying out environmental assessments on expanding the Main Sewage Treatment Plant, the R. L. Clark Filtration Plant, and the Don Trunk Sanitary Sewer. It is also studying the future of the North Toronto Sewage Treatment Plant and developing a water conservation strategy. The City of Toronto is conducting a Sewer System Master Plan. Each of these projects has implications for water quality in the watersheds and along the waterfront, and should be taking place with guidance from the RAP. But expanding the Main Sewage Treatment Plant, for example (the subject of one of Metro's environmental assessments), has not been selected as a preferred remedial option because option selection has not yet taken place.

Clearly, completion of the Stage 2 Remedial Action Plan is a priority. The Royal Commission believes that the federal and provincial governments should take whatever action is necessary to guard against further slippage in deadlines for completing the Metro Toronto RAP.

RECOMMENDATIONS

20. The Royal Commission recommends that the federal and provincial governments use an ecosystem approach in developing the Metro Toronto and Region Remedial Action Plan. This means that:

- as soon as possible, and in advance of the draft Stage 2 document, the problem definition should be rewritten to

For if there is any scale at which ecological consciousness can be developed, at which citizens can see themselves as being the *cause* for the environmental *effect*, it is at the regional level; there all ecological questions are taken out of the realm of the philosophical and the moral and are dealt with as immediate and personal. People do not, other things being equal, pollute and damage those natural systems on which they depend for life and livelihood if they see directly what is happening; nor voluntarily use up a resource under their feet and before their eyes if they perceive that it is precious, needed, vital; nor kill off species they can see are important for the smooth functioning of the ecosystem.

Sale, K. 1985. *Dwellers in the land: the bioregional vision.* San Francisco: Sierra Club.

better reflect current information on the causes and sources of ecosystem impairment, and the potential remedial options should be updated to incorporate current information, as well as the input received from the reviews of the RAP committees;

- a watershed approach should be used to identify the problems, select remedial options, and measure progress; and municipalities should be involved as partners in developing the RAP on a watershed basis.

21. The Royal Commission further recommends that the federal and provincial governments allocate more resources to the Metro RAP, to reflect the actual complexity and scope of problems here, and the size of the population affected.

22. The federal and provincial governments should carry out an effective, continuing program of public awareness and involvement to raise the profile of the RAP and build support for its implementation.

23. The federal and provincial governments should take all steps necessary to eliminate further delays in developing the RAP and should ensure that the target date for completing the draft Stage 2 RAP (late 1992) is met.

GREATER TORONTO BIOREGION PROGRAM: RESEARCH AND INFORMATION NETWORK

Good scientific information, in a form that can be integrated and made readily available to all stakeholders and interested parties, is a key prerequisite of ecosystem-based decision-making. Throughout its work, the Royal Commission found that there was a great deal of information about the Greater Toronto waterfront and bioregion, but it is scattered in many locations and is difficult to synthesize because of differences in approach and methodology.

In discussing these issues in *Pathways*, its report on the environmental audit of the East Bayfront/Port Industrial Area, the audit team recommended that a research and information network be established, devoted to ecosystem studies in the Greater Toronto bioregion. It noted that many information systems and databases already exist; the fundamental need is to link them together, co-ordinate research efforts, and make information accessible to government agencies, non-profit groups, the private sector, and the public.

Subsequently, the Canadian Centre for Inland Waters (CCIW) convened several exploratory meetings of representatives from interested federal and provincial departments, the Royal Commission, universities, and the private sector. They agreed that a Greater Toronto bioregion information program is essential for future decision-making and management of the environment in the region. Among the initiatives that require such a program are the Metro Toronto Remedial Action Plan, pollution prevention strategies, the Oak Ridges Moraine planning study, the proposed Greater Toronto shoreline regeneration plan, watershed strategies, and ecosystem-based municipal plans.

A prototype information system, RAISON (Regional Analysis by Intelligent

Systems on a Microcomputer), has been developed by the National Water Research Institute at CCIW. It has been used successfully in evaluating the issue of acid rain, and was recently judged by NATO to be one of the most advanced systems of its type in the world.

An information network and ecosystem-based research initiative for the Greater Toronto bioregion is fully compatible with the federal government's Science and Technology Framework for the Green Plan. That plan emphasizes the desirability of partnerships under which the federal government will be able to work with other levels of government to achieve common objectives, applying an ecosystem approach. It also proposes to establish a national environmental information network to support state-of-the-environment reporting and environmental forecasting.

The suggested Greater Toronto Bioregion Program could be a vital part of such a network, focused on supporting decision-making in Canada's area of greatest population concentration, population growth, and environmental stress. This practical program has great potential to begin the vital process of building cooperation among governments, institutions, the private sector, and non-government organizations.

RECOMMENDATION

24. The Royal Commission recommends that the federal government, in concert with other interested parties, establish a research and information network for ecosystem studies in the Greater Toronto bioregion. Such a computer-based network should:

- use new technologies in artificial intelligence and expert systems to compile, synthesize, and output information;
- address existing gaps in scientific understanding of the complex links between socio-economic activities and environmental quality;
- transfer knowledge and technologies to decision-makers in the Greater Toronto bioregion and to the private sector for worldwide marketing; and
- be implemented by a new ecosystem research alliance. Such an alliance could include scientists and environmental managers from regional universities and colleges; representatives of the federal, provincial, and municipal governments; the Centre for Green Enterprise and Industry, the Canadian Waterfront Resource Centre; conservation authorities; the computer industry; environmental consultants; and non-government organizations.

The Royal Commission believes that the eight recommendations in this chapter will move us towards the Metro Toronto RAP goals of "swimmable, fishable, and drinkable" water. If they are implemented, these recommendations should provide, through the IJC, a strong and credible watchdog to oversee clean-up of the Great Lakes. Through a revamped Canada/Ontario Agreement, they should ensure that the commitments made under the Great Lakes Water Quality Agreement are met. Adopting a true ecosystem approach in the Metro Toronto RAP will provide a sound planning framework in which to develop the plan, and a renegotiated Canada/Ontario Agreement will ensure that funding is available for implementation.

An accelerated MISA will reduce dramatically the pollution entering Ontario's waters and provide a base on which to build future, more comprehensive programs.

Finally, establishing a program to collect comprehensive, integrated, and accessible information on the state of the environment will allow better ecosystem planning, monitoring, and analysis.

CHAPTER 4:
SHORELINE

In the past decade, there has been increased concern about the nature and extent of lakefilling, measures used to control shoreline erosion, and other shoreline modifications in the Greater Toronto bioregion. Reports prepared for the Ministry of the Environment (MOE) during the 1980s revealed the existence of extensive heavy metal and organic contamination in some soils used for lakefill. The Royal Commission's first interim report (1989) described other concerns as well:

The [Ministry of the Environment] analyses clearly revealed that, while lakefilling operations have had little or no short-term impact on surface-water quality, they do contribute to general sediment contamination, with potentially damaging effects on the biological food chain.

. . . extensive modifications of the Lake Ontario shoreline have altered natural coastal processes, causing contaminants to accumulate in sediments; in the past, such pollutants would have been transported offshore.

There has been no comprehensive assessment of the cumulative impact of lakefilling on Toronto's waterfront.

While understanding that lakefilling and other forms of shoreline modification can have beneficial effects, the Commission reiterated its concern about these practices in *Watershed*, its 1990 interim report. In that document, the Commission confirmed that it believed the situation was serious enough to require a moratorium on new lakefill projects, pending further study. The Commission recommended that the Province bring forward comprehensive lakefill policies for public review as soon as possible.

The provincial response was prompt: as a first step, in December 1990 the Minister of the Environment told the Legislature that she had asked the Royal Commission to address ". . . policies, practices, technology, and methods available to regenerate the shoreline areas".

The minister's choice of the phrase "regenerate the shoreline" was regarded as significant. Clearly, she wanted something much broader than a study of lakefill: the word "regeneration" suggested a desire to establish a shoreline that was healthier and more beneficial to the surrounding community. Lakefill would be a significant consideration in the study, but would be placed in the context of the broader issues of a sustainable environment, economy, and society.

The Commission created the Shoreline Regeneration Work Group, nine people with diverse backgrounds and expertise, who were asked to investigate issues and options. The Work Group first met in February 1991, and its report, *Shoreline Regeneration for the Greater Toronto Bioregion*, was released the following September. The report, combined with submissions at earlier public hearings and with other presentations, gave the Commission broad information about the problems and opportunities posed by shoreline regeneration.

HISTORY OF SHORELINE MODIFICATION

It is important to recognize that the shoreline of Lake Ontario has evolved since the retreat of the glaciers about 15,000 years ago. We can neither return the lakeshore to "the way it used to be" nor hold it in its current state: forces beyond human control ensure that it constantly changes.

Until the 18th century and the arrival of European settlers, human inhabitants of areas around Lake Ontario adapted themselves rather than attempt to change the waterfront. The forces of wind, water, frost, and ice sculpted the shore: frost shifted the ground, cracked the rocks, and hastened erosion of river, stream, and lake banks. Wind gave the waves energy. The waves pounded relentlessly against the shores, dislodging rocks and soil. Sand eroded from the shore was augmented by sediment discharged from the mouths of rivers and streams; this gritty material tumbled in the shallow nearshore waters and eroded the lake bottom and shore.

While sediment was the grindstone, ice propelled by waves was the battering ram: ice and wave-borne sediment attacked the shores and peninsulas, which retreated gradually. In sheltered areas, as waves and currents lost their ability to carry sediment, they deposited sand, which created and nourished beaches, bars, peninsulas, and islands. Erosion from what we now know as the Scarborough Bluffs, augmented by discharge from the Don River, created a peninsula and, later, the Toronto Islands.

Littoral sediments constantly replenished the bars that provided the essential barrier for many river and stream mouth marshes; these protected the marshes from invasion by icy water from Lake Ontario's depths. The warm waters of the marshes provided a rich nursery for all kinds of aquatic plants, fish, birds, and animals.

Eighteenth-century European explorers and traders found native inhabitants, and a lush and vibrant natural community around the mouth of each river and stream. Protected by spits or gravel bars, a wide variety of fish fed and multiplied. Large quantities of wildfowl inhabited the marshes found at the mouths of tributaries, like Bronte and Sixteen Mile creeks, and rivers such as the Credit, Humber, and Don.

The beaches, woods, marshes, and islands provided rich and varied habitat for deer, lynx, beaver, black bear, and many other species of flora and fauna. More than 50 species of fish, 270 types of birds, and countless animals inhabited the region. Abundant shelter and food provided attractive incentives for European settlement. Then, as now, humans attempted to change

The stone hookers' last stand at Port Credit

the shore, and to bend it to their needs. The first modifications, primitive piers, were constructed to allow deep draft sailing vessels to load and discharge directly on the shore.

Sailing ships required ballast, and buildings needed stone for foundations and walls. Loose rock from beaches and shallow waters was easily gathered and delivered to shipping and construction companies; soon a thriving fleet of "stone hookers" was at work along the shore, their crews using devices like pitch forks with the tines bent at right angles. These tools were employed to loosen and lift stone from the bottom. In the 1830s, the stone hookers removed as much as 43,000 tonnes (47,000 tons) of stone annually.

Unfortunately, the full value of these nearshore stones to the lake was unrecognized at the time: they served as armour for the lake bottom and shore and, once they were removed, erosion of the lakeshore banks accelerated. Farmers, alarmed by the loss of their shorefront property and pasture, successfully urged the Legislature to pass the so-called Three-Rod Law, in 1857. The law, which prohibited stone hookers from operating within three rods (15 metres) of the shore, came too late, after much of the damage had been done. Fish habitat was destroyed, shoreline facilities and farming land were damaged or lost.

It was a pattern often repeated to the present day: those involved in a worthy enterprise (such as gathering stone, an essential foundation for development) failed to consider the consequences for the natural environment. Nor did they fully consider the damage to the shoreline economy (farming and fishing). The activity was unregulated at first; only when the damage

Table 4.1 Major lakefill projects in the Greater Toronto bioregion

Project	Area	
	(hectares)	(acres)
J.C. Saddington Park	10	24
Lakefront Promenade Park	30	74
Colonel Samuel Smith Waterfront Area	28.5	70
Humber Bay Park — East and West	40	99
Ontario Place	38	94
Tommy Thompson Park (land and water)	470	1,161
Ashbridge's Bay	17	42
Bluffer's Park	42	104

Source: Reid, R., R. Lockhart, and B. Woodburn. 1990. *A green strategy for the Greater Toronto waterfront*. Publication no. 8. Toronto: Royal Commission on the Future of the Toronto Waterfront.

became serious were limits set, a reaction that effectively "closed the door after the horse had escaped".

In the next 130 years, shoreline modifications of increasing magnitude dramatically changed the shape of the Greater Toronto bioregion's shore. The largest of these initiatives, filling the Ashbridge's Bay Marsh to create 428 hectares (1,057 acres) of land for industrial and recreational use, emerged from the 1912 Waterfront Plan of the Board of Toronto Harbour Commissioners (THC). Most of the fill material was sediment dredged from the Inner Harbour, but included construction debris, excavated soil, sewage sludge, incinerator refuse, and municipal garbage.

More recently, the 1967 Waterfront Plan for the Metropolitan Toronto Planning Area proposed massive lakefilling, chains of artificial islands, public open space, and marinas with a combined capacity of 5,000 boats (Metropolitan Toronto). The 1967 plan inspired a series of artificial

headlands configured to protect boat clubs and marinas. Since the 1950s, 676 hectares (1,668 acres) of land have been created through lakefill, and plans exist for many more. In *Pathways* and in *Shoreline Regeneration*, Royal Commission publications 11 (Barrett and Kidd 1991) and 13, lakefill projects and the associated decline in water quality are described in more detail.

Many projects and modifications have taken place on the shore of the Greater Toronto bioregion, and the nature of change varies. *Shoreline Regeneration* includes the following description of the Greater Toronto bioregion waterfront.

A BIRD'S-EYE VIEW OF THE SHORE TODAY

Flying over the western shoreline of Lake Ontario, one is struck by the intensity of development: from the sand beach of the Burlington Bar to Oakville, much of the shoreline is protected with hard coverings (revetments) of concrete, rubble, and large quarried stone (armourstone), as well as with short groynes jutting into the lake. Occasional narrow cobblestone or gravel beaches remain, but the evidence of change is everywhere.

At the harbour entrance to Oakville Creek, the lack of beach at either side of the groynes suggests that littoral transport is not great. To the east, the St. Lawrence Cement Co. and Gulf Oil Co. concrete piers stretch offshore to navigable water. Residential development surrounds one of the few remaining wetlands, the Rattray Marsh, which is protected from the lake by the barrier formed by its tree-covered bar. Even further east, as the shale subsides below lake level, a different shore forms — one that is low and sandy, created from fine glacial material near Lorne Park, west of Port Credit.

At Port Credit, commercial and industrial development mixes with public open space built on reclaimed land behind steep stone revetments. A major lakefill structure east of the Credit River provides marina facilities next to the heavily armoured shoreline of the Lakeview Generating Station and Lakeview Sewage Treatment Plant.

The dominant features on the Metro Toronto waterfront are lakefill structures: the Colonel Samuel Smith project at Kipling Avenue projects 700 metres (770 yards) from a low-density residential area. Four kilometres (2.6 miles) to the east are two adjacent lakefill headlands at the mouth of Mimico Creek that provide shelter for boats as well as parkland. A breakwall, constructed as part of the 1912 Toronto Harbour Commissioners' plan, protects low parkland that stretches east from the Humber River

to the lakefill structure that supports Ontario Place.

The west shore of the Toronto Islands offers one of the longest sand beaches remaining on the waterfront. The south shore has been fortified with a rubble mound breakwater, groynes, and a concrete seawall. Cut off from its sand supply by the Leslie Street Spit, the shore is being eroded more quickly. The Ward's Island beach, anchored by the new Eastern Gap entrance structure, has reoriented itself to face southwest. Nearly all the Inner Harbour shore is vertical concrete and steel; the Outer Harbour has been created by the Leslie Street Spit, a lakefill structure extending five kilometres (three miles) into 16 metres (52 feet) of water, protected by a veneer of eroding concrete, brick, and asphalt rubble.

Mouth of the Rouge River

Immediately next to the spit is the Ashbridge's Bay lakefill, where the east-facing embayment has filled with littoral sand. Beyond the groynes and breakwalls along the Eastern Beaches rise the Scarborough Bluffs, where the Metropolitan Toronto and Region Conservation Authority (MTRCA) is installing shore protection structures of fill and rubble. The sharp incline of the bluffs is caused by erosion, the result of wave action on their underwater base. Unprotected, they retreat at a rate averaging a third of a metre (one foot) per year. Bluffer's Park lakefill at the foot of Brimley Road occupies nearly two kilometres (1.2 miles) of shoreline and extends 600 metres (660 yards) offshore, intercepting all littoral drift from the east.

Residential development at the top of the bluffs near East Point gives way to open space and scattered industrial use. Much of the shoreline is in a natural state, although occasional storm-sewer outfalls intrude.

Further east, Frenchman's Bay is separated from Lake Ontario by a natural sand bar broken by an entrance structure that permits navigation. Part of the Pickering Generating Station is built on reclaimed land with heavy armourstone revetments and cooling water intake groynes.

From Pickering to Whitby the shoreline is characterized by low bluffs two to seven metres (14 to 23 feet) high, with low-density residential or agricultural uses predominating. Various creeks have small estuarine wetlands behind gravelly beaches and bars; the estuary at Whitby has long been a commercial harbour with entrance groynes interrupting the sand and gravel bar. From Whitby to Oshawa, the shoreline varies from seven-metre (23-foot) bluffs descending to stream estuaries, each fronted by a small beach. Much of the land is low-density residential or cottage-lined beaches.

On the east side of the Oshawa Harbour entrance groynes, reclaimed land has been created by construction of a confined dredge spoil disposal facility. The Oshawa Second Marsh is a large estuarine wetland next to the more exposed McLaughlin Bay. From Darlington Provincial Park, the shoreline rises to bluffs 12 metres (40 feet) high, which occasionally "slump" toward the lake. Darlington Generating Station, built partly on reclaimed land, employs massive armourstone revetments across its extensive shoreline.

At Raby Head, the bluffs are some 12 metres (40 feet) high, descending to a small coastal wetland just west of a large cement company dock, where a 32-hectare (79-acre) lakefill structure projects 675 metres (738 yards) into the lake.

Continuing east, the shoreline is a series of 10-metre (33-foot) bluffs, cut by creeks with small estuarine marshes behind sand and gravel baymouth bars. The estuaries at Port Darlington and Bond Head have been partially dredged for marinas and the baymouth bars are cut by entrance groynes. Still farther east, the pattern is repeated, with some bluffs reaching as high as 20 metres (66 feet); vegetation there suggests a lower rate of erosion. The area behind the bluffs is almost entirely agricultural.

SIGNIFICANCE OF SHORELINE MODIFICATION

The Commission's interim reports acknowledge that lakefilling and human alterations of the shore have provided substantial benefits to the region: Ontario Place, Harbourfront, and Bluffers Marina, for example, were constructed on lakefill and have improved the social, cultural, and economic life of the community. These and other projects have expanded the land base; improved public access and amenities such as parks, beaches, and boat-mooring capacity; and/or increased fish and wildlife habitat.

Tommy Thompson Park, located on the five-kilometre (three-mile) spit at the foot of Leslie Street, demonstrates some of the benefits of lakefill, both planned and accidental. Planned benefits include extensive boat mooring capacity, and facilities for sailboards, dinghy sailing, rowing, and canoeing in the sheltered waters of the Outer Harbour, in the lee of the spit. The spontaneous emergence of grasses, herbs, shrubs, and trees provides exceptional habitat for a variety of birds and animals, an urban wilderness of amazing variety. The shallow, sheltered cells within the park provide fish with refuge from the periodic cold-water upwellings that occur, with deadly consequences, along much of the Lake Ontario shore. As a result, populations of perch, pumpkinseed, and pike have expanded rapidly.

Public access to the shoreline has been enhanced by the artificial headlands at Humber Bay East and Bluffer's Park, and elsewhere thousands enjoy picnicking, walking, and other types of recreation. Groynes and other forms of shoreline erosion control have created new beaches near Oakville and various other places where people can view the lake and enjoy the heat of the summer sun. Homes and properties along the Scarborough Bluffs, among other areas, were saved by measures to halt or

delay erosion. As well, commerce has bene-
fited from lakefilling: thousands of new boat
berths have supported the boat building
and service industry. Sport fishing, mainly
salmon charters and private boats from facilities at Port Credit, Bluffers, and other new
marinas, brings millions of dollars in revenue
to the region. Extensive condominium,
tourism, and commercial facilities stand
on land created by lakefilling.

There has been another benefit,
particularly to the downtown waterfront
area of Metro Toronto: the lake has been
a convenient, inexpensive repository for
large volumes of material excavated from
downtown construction sites.

These benefits extract a price, however,
as described in *Shoreline Regeneration*:

Much of the exca-
vated material used
for lakefill was con-
taminated with
lead, other heavy
metals, and organic
materials that
found their way
into the lake sediments and the food
chain. This [fill] material, combined
with the much larger sources of pollution, the sewage treatment plants,
storm sewers, and urban rivers, has
degraded the water quality of the
shore. The combined impact of urban
development — filling wetlands and
river estuaries, and armouring for
erosion control, in addition to vast
quantities of silt released from lakefill
sites — has damaged much of the
natural habitat both above and below
the water line.

The Commission's Shoreline
Regeneration Work Group found that the

environmental price was higher than
necessary, and sometimes outweighed
apparent benefits. In this respect, the Work
Group agreed with the position taken by
many critics of lakefill who made submissions to the Royal Commission during
public hearings.

SHORELINE
REGENERATION ISSUES

Concerns about the negative effects of
shoreline modification give rise to several
issues, including:

- the environmental effects of lakefill
  structures and erosion control
  measures, including cumulative effects
  of many activities, loss or damage to
  both aquatic and
  terrestrial habitat,
  obstruction of sand
  movement, elimina-
  tion of traditional
  sources of sediment
  through shoreline
  armouring, and accel-
  erated erosion in other places;

- the degree to which current guidelines
  and control procedures for materials
  for lakefilling ensure safety;

- lack of standards for lakefilling
  methods and structural designs;

- disposal of the waste materials from
  construction and excavation, including
  that judged not suitable for lakefill;

- changes in economic opportunities,
  and the wisdom of spending public
  money to protect private and public
  land through armouring — as
  opposed to acquiring — hazard lands;

- similarly, constructing artificial headlands for private boat clubs; and

*The lake has been a convenient,
inexpensive repository for large volumes
of material excavated from downtown
construction sites.*

- the impact of shoreline modification on aesthetics, access, vistas, and recreation.

These concerns should be considered in the context of general apprehension about the safety of Lake Ontario as a source of drinking and bathing water. The preceding chapter of this report describes Lake Ontario's condition and the impact of pollution, even from sources far from the Greater Toronto bioregion's shoreline; it also examines efforts by the International Joint Commission, the Metro Toronto RAP, and other groups to address these problems.

The contaminated sediments, overloaded sewage plant, or toxic pollutants from the Niagara River and elsewhere will take considerable time to correct. Lakefilling, however, is a discretionary activity and can be stopped as a pollution source tomorrow — if we choose to do so. There are choices of methods and materials, as well as of locations at which lakefilling would be allowed.

IMPACT OF LAKEFILL STRUCTURES AND EROSION CONTROL MEASURES

Artificial headlands — peninsulas created by lakefilling to shelter boat basins — have become common on the shore of the Greater Toronto bioregion. They have created negative impact on the environment in four ways:

- materials used for fill have contributed to contamination and turbidity of the water;
- structures have blocked the lake's ability to rinse its shoreline;

Major Waterfront Concern

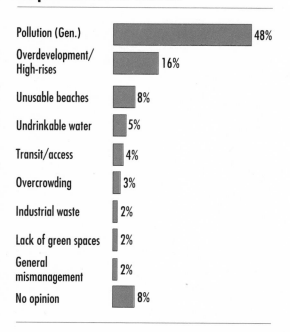

Pollution (Gen.)	48%
Overdevelopment/ High-rises	16%
Unusable beaches	8%
Undrinkable water	5%
Transit/access	4%
Overcrowding	3%
Industrial waste	2%
Lack of green spaces	2%
General mismanagement	2%
No opinion	8%

Pollution is considered the waterfront's major issue by the respondents.

Source: Environics Poll. 1991.

We are a species that, through its intelligence, has exceeded its biological constraints but in the process lost its sense of place in the biosphere. Convinced of our knowledge and ability to control nature, we exploit the very life-support systems of the planet in the name of short-term comfort and economic profit. Wilderness is disappearing throughout the world so quickly that each remaining untouched area becomes that much more rare and precious.

Suzuki, D. 1989. *Carmanah: Artistic Visions of an ancient rainforest.* Vancouver: Western Canada Wilderness Committee.

- transport of sand along the waterfront has been limited; and
- aquatic habitat has been destroyed.

Loss of shallow lake bottom for breeding and feeding at the site reduces habitat, while large amounts of sediment — material that blocks the light and blankets the lake bed — is lost during construction, thus imposing further, indirect harm. In a deep, dark, silt-covered environment, few aquatic species flourish. Light is essential to the growth of some plant organisms that fuel the aquatic food chain. High turbidity results in altered and reduced biotic life and spawning capacity, in the zone that could be most productive.

Embayments and boat basins in artificial headlands, which provide shelter from cold-water upwelling in the exposed lake, can be a positive factor in aquatic habitat. Above the water line, the natural growth of plants, shrubs, and trees on lakefill and erosion control projects have provided new habitat for a wide variety of birds and animals. These benefits would be much more valuable, however, if this attractive environment were not so contaminated.

The new headlands, which have extended as far as five kilometres (3 miles) into the lake, are a significant barrier to longshore movement by waves and current. As a result, suspended and floating materials are trapped and deposited nearby, where they create various pollution problems.

Erosion control embraces a variety of materials applied to the shore to slow or stop the loss of land by wave action. They include vertical steel pilings, concrete walls, large quarry stones (armourstone), construction rubble, and old tires. MTRCA has undertaken massive erosion control measures at the foot of the Scarborough Bluffs and erosion control efforts by individuals and agencies are estimated to cover as much as 70 per cent of the shore from Burlington to Scarborough.

In addition to habitat loss, erosion control impounds the sediment that would normally drift along the shore, renew beaches, and repair storm damage done to sand and gravel bars that are essential to protecting estuarine marshes. Further, the structures may change wave patterns and accelerate erosion elsewhere on the shoreline.

CUMULATIVE EFFECTS

As the Shoreline Regeneration Work Group observed:

> It became evident that many larger problems along the waterfront were not the result of one horrendous event but, rather, the cumulative effect of many acts or interventions. Treating each project in isolation from the rest of the shore was a common cause of significant degradation.

The tendency to treat lakefill and erosion control projects singly is understandable, when each is proposed at a different time, has a different set of characteristics and location, and is subject to decisions by different municipalities and agencies. Nonetheless, they are not independent, and their combined impact will, at some point, exceed the carrying capacity of the shore.

The impact of one artificial headland may be acceptable; but there are now eight new headlands, with many more planned. At some point, the shoreline circulation of water may be so impeded that it creates a regional cesspool.

Similarly, it would be hard to prove that 100 metres (110 yards) of armoured

House atop eroded Scarborough Bluffs

shore have starved any beaches or eliminated a significant amount of shallow-water
aquatic habitat. However, 50,000 metres
(31 miles) of armoured shore is another
matter. It is estimated that 90 per cent of
aquatic life depends on the shallow nearshore zone that is destroyed by many forms
of erosion control. Losing such large areas
leads to reduced food supply and spawning
capacity. As discussed previously, shoreline
modification damages habitat, but that is
partially offset by some benefits. Clearly,
the important issue is how to alter practices
and technology so that they have a positive
overall effect on habitat.

Loss of habitat, combined with other
stresses such as contaminants and the
presence of exotic species like the lamprey
eel, has placed great stress on aquatic life
forms. Along the Greater Toronto shore,

the number of types of fish, which are an
indicator of the health of aquatic ecosystems, has already decreased from 50 to
approximately 25 and, in some areas, is as
low as 11.

Cumulative effects — the combination
of various stresses over time — is a difficult
but important issue in evaluating the present and future health of the region's aquatic
ecosystem.

SAFETY OF CURRENT GUIDELINES AND CONTROL

Materials for open water disposal —
lakefilling — are controlled according
to a system defined by the Ministry of the
Environment, using maximum levels of contaminants set out as "Sediment Guidelines".
In the Metro area, the control system is
operated for MOE by the Metropolitan

Toronto and Region Conservation Authority. MTRCA samples soil in large construction sites, and accepts or rejects fill from them, based on the results of its tests of contents. In the past, trucks were sampled when they arrived at the lakefill site, but results were not available until days after the sampling. MTRCA records show that some material used in lakefill (25 per cent in 1989, 15 per cent in 1990) was contaminated beyond the levels suggested by the existing MOE sediment guidelines.

The Royal Commission was given persuasive evidence, based on MOE research, showing that toxic materials moved from contaminated sediments to nearby plants and fish. Aquatic life accumulates some of the contaminants and introduces them, in concentrated form, to the food chain. This pattern has raised public and regulatory concern.

Established in 1976, current MOE sediment guidelines consider a very limited range of toxic contaminants to establish nominally safe levels in materials for open water disposal. Many toxic substances are omitted. Recent work on contaminants in the 1976 list has shown that some are higher than the "no-effect level", that is, the greatest concentration that showed no measurable effects when tested on indicator species. Considering this new information, the 1976 guidelines can no longer be relied on to define concentrations that are not harmful.

STANDARDS FOR MARINE CONSTRUCTION

There are no standards or codes to define what level of storms artificial headlands must be able to withstand, what water levels they must attain or even how fill must be controlled to avoid pollution and turbidity. Without such minimum standards, it is not surprising that minimum initial cost can

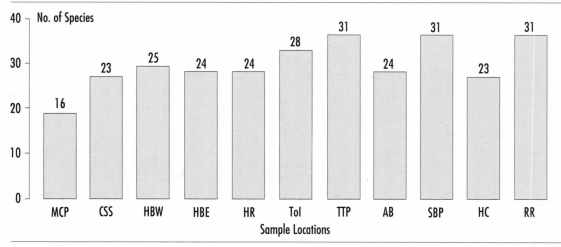

Figure 4.1   Number of fish species found — Toronto waterfront fish collections, 1989

Notes:
MCP: Marie Curtis Park
CSS: Colonel Samuel Smith
HBW: Humber Bay West
HBE: Humber Bay East
HR: Humber River
Tol: Toronto Islands
TTP: Tommy Thompson Park
AB: Ashbridge's Bay
SBP: Scarborough Bluffer's Park
HC: Highland Creek
RR: Rouge River

Source: Buchanan, I.D. 1991. *Presentation for the Royal Commission on the Future of the Toronto Waterfront.* Maple: Ontario. Ministry of Natural Resources.

become the governing factor on deciding how to construct these headlands. Operators may dump soft loose fill into open water, and leave such material exposed to waves and current. As a result, substantial quantities of fill escape, create turbidity, and mix with the water along the Greater Toronto shoreline.

Precisely how much material is lost during construction of lakefill projects is not known. However, the Shoreline Regeneration Work Group estimated that it is between one and ten per cent of material deposited annually. One per cent might be achieved with very tight control. Ten-per-cent fill loss could be expected with year-round filling at an unprotected site, plus additional loss due to a major storm. Current practice is believed to fall about mid-way between these extremes. Figure 4.2 compares suspended solids contributed by lakefill along the Metro waterfront during a typical year with the other major pollutant

Figure 4.2 Metropolitan Toronto waterfront pollution sources

Suspended Solids

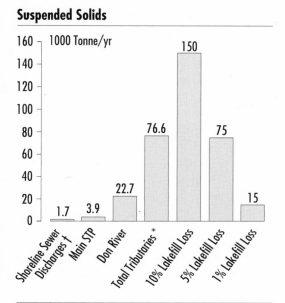

Lead

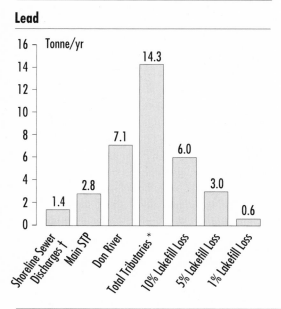

Copper

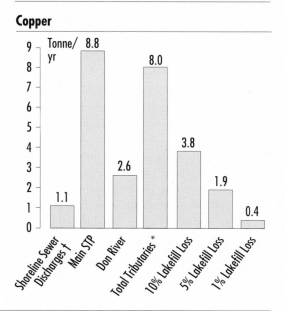

Notes:

† Input from storm and combined sewers discharging on Lake Ontario shoreline.

* Tributaries include Etobicoke Creek, Mimico Creek, Humber River, Don River, Highland Creek, Rouge River.

Source: Metro Toronto Remedial Action Plan, 1988. *Environmental conditions and problem definition.* Toronto: Metro Toronto Remedial Action Plan.

MARCH OF THE MOTORIZED MASTODONS

Each morning, an elephantine procession emerges from the depths of downtown construction sites: a herd of dusty dump trucks struggles to the street level, then lumbers through the canyons between office towers toward the lakeshore. Brakes squealing, engines snorting, the vehicles rumble through intersections, harassed by taxis, cycle couriers, and pedestrians preoccupied with the day's work ahead. The trucks bear a massive burden of rubble and soil extracted from the foundations of large buildings, to make way for parking, passageways, and the subterranean shops of downtown Toronto. Their destination is the dusty peninsula near the mouth of the Don River.

South of the flaking concrete pillars that support the aging expressway, the loaded trucks gain speed and momentum, surging toward the open spit. There, freed of traffic, stoplights, and human obstacles, they stampede the length of the peninsula, a swirl of dust and gulls rising in the eddies behind their bulky frames. At the water's edge, they grind to a stop, turn, and await a turn to dump their burden of rock and soil. One by one, each struggles to the bank, arches its back, and relieves itself at the water's edge. Most of the material hangs on the banks or slides below the surface, while some dances away, suspended in the wavy turbulence, to be deposited far along the shore.

This pattern will be repeated more than a thousand times a week — nearly sixty thousand times a year. The land area expands and the water surface contracts in a ritual that has continued and accelerated for the last century.

sources, including tributaries and sewage treatment plants (STPs).

Not only is lakefilling a very significant contributor to suspended solids and water turbidity in the region, those effects are increased dramatically when construction practices allow a greater proportion of fill to escape.

Given that some lakefill is contaminated and that some of it escapes, fill contributes copper and lead contamination to water in the region. However, even at the highest percentage loss, lakefill ranks well behind other sources (see Figure 4.2).

To summarize, in light of new information, current guidelines for fill sediments are inadequate: the control system allows some material exceeding guidelines to be deposited, and lack of codes permits construction methods which result in large amounts of fill mixing freely with water along the shore.

Furthermore, lakefill projects contribute indirectly to shore contamination. As a result of wave action, sediments and nearshore waters naturally progress along an exposed shore; unobstructed they disperse widely, taking with them any attached contaminants from partially treated sewage, storm water or other sources. At an artificial barrier like that at Humber Bay East (lakefill), sediment is trapped and deposited; the result is a contaminant sink, often accompanied by foul odours and floating debris.

DISPOSAL OF WASTE MATERIALS FROM CONSTRUCTION

Earlier it was mentioned that lakefill was considered an inexpensive and convenient waste disposal arrangement. The practice has been a particularly prevalent on the Metropolitan Toronto's downtown waterfront, where land values are extremely high. These high values preclude disposal on-site, and the need for large underground parking facilities dictates that a great deal of material must be excavated at each location.

While the average annual amount of fill is immense, it varies from year to year, depending on the amount of construction activity. Estimates of volume from 1984 to the year 2000 were prepared by Environmental Applications Limited for the Ministry of the Environment; they projected average annual volume of 1,050 tonnes (1,155 tons) — the contents of roughly 60,000 dump trucks per year.

But how will Toronto dispose of up to 60,000 dump-truck loads of waste if lakefill is banned, or restricted by tighter standards? While relatively low levels of contaminants in this material mean that it should not be mixed with water or otherwise introduced to the food chain, most of the fill does not require the control provided in sanitary landfill. The most critical issues for MOE and the construction industry are how to classify, and where to deposit, material unsuitable for lakefill.

ECONOMIC ISSUES

Everyone receives some form of personal benefit from the expenditure of public funds: motorists drive on public highways; pedestrians stroll in public parks. However, when shoreline modifications are carried out with public funds, personal benefits at public expense can become an issue.

Constructing artificial headlands that protect and house private boat clubs is a case in point: the appropriateness of using public funds to build sheltered harbours for private clubs surrounded by chain link fences that deny public access is questionable. Although everyone may enter the public park, only a select group may enter the grounds of a private club.

Another issue arises from publicly funded erosion control measures undertaken to protect private property. Those who benefit from erosion control are easily identified, but the consequences of such activity are hard to predict: whose property

A downtown Toronto construction site

163

will suffer from accelerated erosion as a consequence of the initial measures? Whose beach will no longer receive the sand that is the owner's riparian right? Having used public money to protect one property, how does the government refuse to safeguard another one, nearby, particularly if there is a link between one government erosion control structure and the subsequent complaint?

Alternatives to shoreline armouring include purchasing hazard lands, a strategy that may prove less costly and improve public access. In addition, expanded public ownership of nearshore hazard lands can increase opportunities for natural links between stream valleys.

There are many ways in which shoreline regeneration can contribute to the economic vigour of the waterfront: a waterfront free of debris and sewage is a more attractive place for tourism, conventions, and recreation. The more attractive the setting, the more tourist dollars available and the more sales of nearby commercial establishments.

Real estate and housing on a cleaner, greener waterfront could meet shelter needs while, at the same time, providing amenities that bring a higher return. Cleaner water, restored fish habitat, and boat-launching facilities built on lakefill may increase boat-chartering and related service industries. The point is that all these economic opportunities depend on the basic resource — healthy water and waterfront ecosystems. The question is how to expand and enhance these opportunities.

AESTHETICS, ACCESS, AND RECREATION

Some shoreline issues are difficult to express in economic terms; they are generally those that fall in the broad categories: aesthetic aspects, access, and recreation.

AESTHETICS

Aesthetic considerations include:

- variety in landscaping techniques for parks and public open space;
- protection of open-water views;
- incompatible development on or next to fill;
- odour and appearance problems arising from debris trapped in embayments;
- protection of natural shoreline features such as beaches and bluffs; and
- protection of built heritage and connections with the past.

Traditional management and landscaping of public lands limit habitats. Variety in landscaping, that is, providing areas with native wild grasses, flowering plants, shrubs, and trees, as well as formal park settings, will increase diversity of habitat and species.

Unobstructed open-water vistas are among the most valued amenities on the waterfront. Proposals for lakefilling that would block those views, or that would support towering waterfront developments, represent a threat to those values and a challenge to planning waterfront areas. Protecting shoreline views involves paying attention to the height and location of buildings, and the design of programs for tree-planting on public land.

Incompatible developments — parking lots or busy marinas next to quiet residential areas, structures that trap debris or contaminated water — can degrade the value of both public and private waterfront land. Planning must consider adjacent land uses.

The variety of the bioregion's shoreline is one of its important assets. Bluffs, such as those in Scarborough, depend on erosion of the base to maintain their steep face; therefore, erosion control at the base, and normal wearing away of the cap, will eventually eliminate the sharp slope that gives the area its character. As mentioned earlier, armourstone at the water's edge impounds the sediment that would normally move downshore to renew the natural beaches that the public values highly. We cannot stop erosion and retain its benefits, any more than we can "eat our cake and have it too".

Certain shoreline modification activities may conflict with the public need to retain connections with the built heritage and the past. For example, lakefill has reduced the Harbour Commissioners' building from being what it once was in Toronto — a striking waterfront welcome to the City — to just another inland office. Fort York, which once commanded the harbour, lies hidden behind approximately 800 metres (0.5 mile) of fill and structures, its role, purpose, and location equally obscured; the visitor may find it difficult to

comprehend that this fort was once central to the defense of Upper Canada. Achieving progress without compromising our connection to the past is another challenge for shoreline regeneration.

ACCESS

Accessibility is an important factor in enhancing the public value of the waterfront, but must be achieved in a way that is fair to landowners and shows due consideration for the many other demands on the public purse. Some public utilities need special security and some other land should be set aside for use as sanctuary and natural areas. Transportation corridors parallel to the shore, such as the railways and expressways, provide barriers to recreational access. A lakeshore that is hidden behind a wall of industrial, public or private fences provides few public benefits. The issue is how to provide for a continuous waterfront trail at or near the shore, and access to the water at reasonable intervals, while achieving

Desired Waterfront Development Objectives

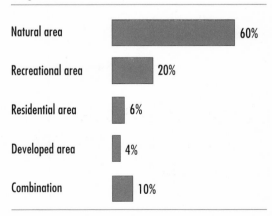

Nearly two-thirds of the respondents would like to have more natural areas on the waterfront.

Source: Environics Poll. 1991.

fairness to existing landowners, and costs that are affordable.

RECREATION

Many forms of recreation, both active and passive, can and should be enjoyed along the shore: active pursuits include cycling, running, fishing, power-boating, sailing, swimming, and rowing. Less vigorous activities include picnicking, walking, birdwatching, sunbathing, photographing, and simply observing the passing scene.

While these pastimes are among the most valuable to the community, they can create conflicts, both among activities and with other values on the shore. For example, some residents of the shore object to the traffic and noise created in their neighbourhoods by visitors to aquatic parks like Bluffer's; birdwatchers object to motorized invasion of natural areas.

Regenerating the shoreline with lake-fill can increase the types of recreational opportunities available, by creating new land at a cost of construction that is one-fifth to one-tenth that of acquisition. The environmental costs vary with the lakefill site and construction methods but must be added for fair comparison with acquisition of existing land. An ecosystem approach to land-use planning must balance and allocate the benefits, while minimizing the conflicts — a process that includes many issues that must be considered.

HOW HAS SHORELINE MODIFICATION CAUSED PROBLEMS?

The Royal Commission heard considerable testimony that shoreline modifications are part of the problem of shoreline degradation. There has been significant evidence

Lakefront Promenade Marina, Mississauga

Map 4.1: Lake Ontario northern shoreline

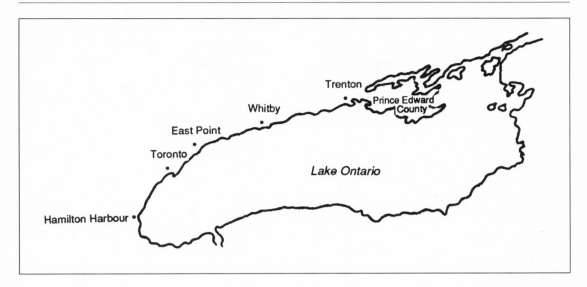

that they can also be part of the solution but, before that can happen, the root causes of past difficulties must be identified.

Collectively, we are fouling our own nest and acting against our own best interests. To the best of our knowledge, no person or group sets out to destroy natural habitat, drive away species, or close the beaches of the Greater Toronto bioregion. These consequences are the result of accident or neglect, the unplanned consequence of millions of independent actions, all focused on another goal — whether that goal is to protect property from erosion or to construct boat berths and parks for public use.

Damage occurs because of the way projects, including shoreline modification, are evaluated: each is considered individually by persons or agencies looking at one aspect, whether that is road connections or hazard land protection. They are sometimes considered solely on the basis of economic feasibility, and from a narrow local viewpoint, without much regard for other developments elsewhere. Given that the most

serious problem is the lack of broad responsibility, the Shoreline Regeneration Work Group attempted to establish who was in charge, and found that:

> . . . the Lake Ontario shoreline in the GTB comes under the jurisdiction of 11 local municipalities, five conservation authorities, four regional governments, at least six federal and provincial ministries, several Crown corporations, and two harbour commissions.

As a result of the profusion of responsible agencies, governments, and boards, some projects — such as the construction of a dock projecting into the lake — receive detailed scrutiny from all three levels of government. Obviously the multijurisdictional approach results in a patchwork quilt of regulations rather than a comprehensive approach to setting and achieving goals for developing and protecting the shore.

With so many levels, departments, ministries, and special purpose bodies, it is difficult to find one that is clearly in charge.

It is not surprising that, with no co-ordination, there is no ecosystem approach to the evaluation of various projects, or the whole shoreline of the Greater Toronto bioregion. Nor is it possible to evaluate cumulative or incremental effects of a project or series of projects, because there is no estimate of the carrying capacity of the shore. While there are plans for segments of the shore, there is little progress toward comprehensive ecosystem rehabilitation, and so the losses are legion and the gains are few.

Failure to consider coastal processes, that is, erosion and deposition of sediment as a result of the action of wind and waves, is another concern in lakeshore planning. The littoral cell, a section of shore where barriers restrict the longshore movement of sediment so that very little is gained or lost, provides a minimum physical unit. The barriers which limit movement may be natural, like the Toronto Islands, or artificial, like the Leslie Street Spit. Since a littoral cell contains the physical movement of sand, it can provide a basis for planning boundaries, although the exact cell boundary is sometimes difficult to determine, and subject to change due to new structures and physical changes on the shore.

A shoreline where the general movement of sediment is in one direction may consist of a chain of sub-cells. Within the Greater Toronto bioregion, longshore movement is westbound from East Point in Scarborough to the mouth of Hamilton Harbour. Between East Point and Whitby, very little material is produced, and direction of movement varies. Sediment movement is generally eastward from Whitby to Prince Edward County.

Coastal processes cannot be considered properly when evaluated by a municipality or conservation authority whose view is limited to a segment of a littoral cell. For example, an artificial headland created in Mississauga can affect the Halton shore by blocking the movement of littoral sand to the west. The same headland can impair the quality of water drawn into Mississauga because of obstruction of contaminants moving east from the rivers and sewage treatment plants of Metropolitan Toronto.

> *Coastal processes cannot be considered properly when evaluated by a municipality or conservation authority whose view is limited to a segment of a littoral cell.*

Planning a shoreline embracing one or more complete littoral cells is consistent with an ecosystem approach, and is not a new idea. Recognizing the problems inherent in a piecemeal approach, the three conservation authorities with responsibility for the littoral cell in the eastern part of the Greater Toronto bioregion conducted a combined study. In 1990, Sandwell Swan Wooster Inc., consulting engineers, submitted a report titled *Lake Ontario Shoreline Management Plan* to the Central Lake Ontario, Ganaraska Region, and Lower Trent Region conservation authorities. This plan had a logical planning envelope, and a consistent approach to hazard land management and protection of environmentally sensitive areas. Many issues of concern in the Greater Toronto bioregion were raised, such as policies for shoreline erosion control and fill and construction guidelines.

In summary, the damage to the shoreline environment is not deliberate, but happens as the unplanned consequence of pursuing other goals. The provincial ministries of the Environment and Natural Resources and the federal Department of Fisheries and Oceans have an interest in protecting the shore: they are trying to minimize the damage, but there is a lack of co-ordination, no overall plan, and no one agency or body with a mandate to improve the shoreline. No one has estimated the carrying capacity so that cumulative effects can be controlled or been given a mandate to establish or enforce codes or standards for marine construction. It is not surprising, therefore, that most incremental changes have degraded the natural environment and reduced its potential benefits for the residents and economy of the region.

WHY SHOULD WE BE CONCERNED?

A healthy shoreline is a priceless asset for the Greater Toronto bioregion: it offers drinkable water, recreation, rest, and solace at the doorstep of millions, and is an exciting stimulant for commerce, tourism, and the economy. It is worth defending, and it is not yet too late to do so.

Much of the shoreline east of Scarborough remains in a relatively healthy state, and adequately maintaining it will require wisdom and fortitude, but little money. The most significant parts of the remaining shoreline west of Scarborough can be protected or restored.

The Greater Toronto bioregion is expecting a large increase in population and density; people, industry, and other activity will substantially increase strains on the waterfront and its natural systems. Some

will collapse. This, given existing and persistent environmental degradation, suggests that positive measures must be taken soon to preserve the benefits we enjoy today.

WHAT IS THE PROBLEM?

While there is a great deal of planning along the waterfront of the Greater Toronto bioregion, there has been little progress toward effective shoreline regeneration.

One problem is the general lack of a co-ordinated, ecosystem approach to planning. Municipal waterfront plans are usually based on boundaries without an ecosystem rationale, leaving each municipality vulnerable to the actions of its neighbours. A related problem is the inability to consider cumulative environmental effects, because planning is done for a portion of a natural system.

Resolving intra-municipal planning issues is a responsibility of the provincial government. In some cases, federal agencies are involved as well. Many of these agencies have specialized interests such as "protect the environment", "expand the housing supply", and "enhance transportation" without much incentive to work together. Given the specialized viewpoints, complicated planning issues, and lack of agreed goals, objectives, and timetables, endless review and delay is the common result. The waterfront is plagued by jurisdictional gridlock.

WHAT CAN BE DONE?

Effective co-ordination is the missing element. A mechanism is needed to integrate special interests, establish goals and timetables, strike balanced decisions, negotiate compromises, and thereby break the gridlock. Based on a review of experience in other jurisdictions, and the situation within the Greater Toronto bioregion, the Commission has concluded that a co-ordinated shoreline regeneration plan would provide the required mechanism.

If it is to bring about shoreline regeneration, this plan must contain three elements:

- a co-ordinating agency with the mandate, will, and skill to involve all responsible parties in planning and acting on shoreline regeneration;
- positive goals and objectives for protecting and regenerating the shore, as well as co-ordinated action to achieve those goals and objectives; and
- constraints on certain development activities in order to ensure a healthy, resilient, productive shoreline with increased aesthetic, social, and economic value to the community.

A co-ordinating agency with the mandate, will, and skills needed to improve the situation will be able to bring the interested municipalities and agencies together, and to facilitate agreement on goals, principles, and timetables for the plan area. In order to encourage integration of the various interests, the co-ordinating agency will need a mandate to act as the primary negotiator for the province in arbitrating disagreements.

The Greater Toronto bioregion has unique advantages, but is not alone in facing a maze of waterfront jurisdictions: in the United States, for example, the San Francisco Bay Conservation and Development Commission has 13 counties and cities working co-operatively to protect common resource. On a broader scale, the government of the United States, through

the Coastal Zone Management Act (CZMA), has applied constraints and incentives to create partnerships to protect the Great Lakes.

In Canada, the Fraser River Estuary Management Plan (FREMP) involves approximately 60 agencies, including six Native bands, two harbour commissions, the federal and provincial governments, and all area municipalities. In each case, a co-ordinating agency was created to bring them all together to protect and develop the waterfront resource.

The Greater Toronto bioregion's need for such a co-ordinating agency was recognized by the Shoreline Regeneration Work Group which, in its report to the Royal Commission, said that the Waterfront Regeneration Trust recommended in *Watershed* could be:

> . . . a valuable vehicle for shoreline regeneration; it should pursue only those shoreline modifications that meet ecological criteria and ensure that newly created lands remain in public ownership for the benefit of future generations.

DESIRABLE CHARACTERISTICS OF A SHORELINE REGENERATION PLAN

Protecting and restoring the shoreline in keeping with the nine regeneration principles described in Chapter 1 will require some limitations on how and where development may proceed. Such constraints could be established using a readily understood control pattern — such as maps with "red" zones for the most restrictive natural or historical areas; "orange" zones for areas in which moderate constraints are necessary; and "green" zones to identify the most flexible areas. Certain areas, in the "red" zones, will be too important to the goals of public access, habitat protection or enhancement to allow construction, erosion control or lakefilling.

The plan should emphasize such opportunities as initiatives that increase access, tourism, boating, walking, swimming, wildlife, fishing, trail hiking, and greenways. Increasing these opportunities can be an important tool in reducing conflicts between uses, as well as stresses on existing facilities.

The plan should not attempt to establish all social, commercial, transportation, and other goals and objectives for the shoreline: other plans and mechanisms, such as those being undertaken by regional and area municipalities, address such needs. However, the Shoreline Regeneration Plan will provide enhanced opportunities for social and commercial development, and should be integrated with those other plans.

There are other characteristics that would contribute substantially to a successful plan; they include:

- an overall "red" designation for the shoreline, until the plan identifies discrete areas, as an incentive for stakeholders to participate in, negotiate, and complete the plan;
- a clearly defined, efficient approval and control process (one-wicket application);
- a consultative approach to developing and administering the plan, including provision for regular public input and review;
- adequate resources for agencies responsible for developing and implementing the plan; and

- powers adequate for protecting natural areas and enforcing any restrictions required by the plan.

Defining the boundaries for the plan is important. An ecosystem approach suggests that the planning envelope should have a natural system rationale. On land, watersheds normally provide the logical dimensions. In the case of the waterfront, a large littoral cell or a combination of cells would provide a reasonable unit. There is some uncertainty as to the precise limits of these cells along the Greater Toronto waterfront and cell definition should be an early priority for planning. Population density and development pressure provides another basis for giving priority to certain areas. A plan for the shore between Burlington Bay and the Trent River would capture a substantial combination of littoral cells embracing the whole Greater Toronto bioregion, as well as an area under significant pressure for change.

IMPLEMENTING THE PLAN

The following recommendations are designed to implement a Shoreline

Whether they begin with the policies and programs of the state, in the head offices of large corporations, in the workplace, or at someone's kitchen table, the end result of sustainable development must be the creation of sustainable communities.

Wismer, S. 1990.: 8 "Assessing sustainable development in an urban context.". In *Ethical dimensions of sustainable development and urbanization: seminar papers.* Winnipeg: Institute of Urban Studies.

Regeneration Plan and to deal with existing or future problems that could affect the efficiency and effectiveness of that plan.

In order to implement the Shoreline Regeneration Plan, co-operation is needed from all levels of government. Such a partnership approach, which recognizes constraints and provides incentives but does not remove authority and responsibility, is the most effective approach to planning on the waterfront.

Success will depend on the incentives provided by a process that both safeguards environmental and public values, and streamlines the approvals required. The framework for ecosystem-based planning described in Chapter 2 should be examined as a possible model. Having satisfied themselves with the rigour of the ecosystem planning process, the federal and Ontario agencies responsible for approvals should be prepared to co-operate with timetables.

For example, proposals that conform to the plan could receive "credits" toward completion of any environmental assessment required.

Further, there must be rewards and incentives to negotiate the shoreline plan, and to support its implementation. The most important incentive for municipalities and conservation agencies would be breaking the jurisdictional "log-jam", and predictable, steady progress of plans and projects through provincial agencies, once those plans comply with the agreed plan.

RECOMMENDATION

25. The Royal Commission recommends that the Province of Ontario ensure preparation of a Shoreline Regeneration Plan to protect and regenerate the shoreline of the Greater Toronto bioregion, employing an ecosystem

Fishing in the fog, Darlington

approach. This plan should be developed with the full participation of relevant departments of the governments of Canada and Ontario, as well as those of affected regions, area municipalities, conservation authorities, the private sector, non-governmental groups, and the public. It should emphasize:

- protection of remaining natural areas;
- rehabilitation of degraded areas;
- a mechanism for considering cumulative environmental effects; and
- improvement of access and recreational opportunities.

Any shoreline plan should have the benefit of expertise in the affected community; therefore, before a plan proceeds, interested groups and individuals should have the opportunity to comment on and improve the ideas advanced by the Royal Commission and its work groups. Such input would allow the shoreline planning process to proceed with the support of improved community confidence and focus.

RECOMMENDATION

26. The Royal Commission recommends that as early as possible in the process, the Province ensure public consultation, including public hearings, to permit interested parties and the public to respond to recommendations on shoreline regeneration, made in the Commission's *Watershed* and *Shoreline Regeneration* documents, as well as in this final report.

It is important to prevent construction of major new projects without the benefit of the shoreline plan, because these may create unnecessary harm and foreclose options for future benefits.

RECOMMENDATION

27. The Royal Commission recommends that the Province place a moratorium on approval of all major new lakefill and shoreline erosion control projects, pending approval of a Shoreline Regeneration Plan.

Notwithstanding the need for a moratorium, some small projects might have no material influence on the plan, or there might be demonstration projects that could provide valuable insights and other benefits without compromising the integrity of the plan. The criteria for "small" and "demonstration" should be determined very early, to avoid uncertainty.

RECOMMENDATION

28. The Royal Commission recommends that criteria, performance standards, and procedures be established for small or demonstration projects that

The old way of doing things has proven hollow and sometimes quite destructive, though we have not yet learned the rules for the new ways of doing things, so we are in the age of in-between.

Morris, D. 1990. "The ecological city as a self-reliant city." In *Green cities: ecologically-sound approaches to urban space.* Montreal: Black Rose Books.

> **T**he social, economic and ecological forces that shape the city are completely interlocked in the world that we experience. Neither our institutions nor the structure of our systems of governance reflect this reality, nor do they respect the logic of the interdependent systems that they represent.
>
> Jacobs, P. 1991. *Sustainable urban development.* Montreal: Third Summit of the World's Cities.

could be undertaken without compromising the integrity of the Shoreline Regeneration Plan.

BEFORE THE SHORELINE REGENERATION PLAN IS COMPLETE

An effective shoreline plan, efficiently administered, is essential to the long-term health of the waterfront. While development and agreement on the plan may take several years, some matters merit immediate action. It is proposed that the Ministry of the Environment prepare up-to-date sediment standards for open-water disposal and construction standards for lakefilling, to be applied to completing current work as well as any small or demonstration projects. In addition, consideration can proceed on finding alternative means of dealing with materials produced by construction, as well as creation of greenways and the Waterfront Trail.

Lakefilling is discretionary activity. Given the link established between sediment contaminants and uptake by plants and fish in the aquatic food chain, it seems reasonable to avoid knowingly and voluntarily damaging aquatic ecosystems and the quality of our drinking and bathing water.

RECOMMENDATION

29. The Royal Commission recommends that the Province adopt new sediment guidelines for open-water disposal; these should reflect the latest scientific studies, and should establish contaminant limits at levels that will protect aquatic ecosystems.

Appropriate sediment standards are one step in protecting the quality of water on the shore; applying such standards effectively, using a quality assurance system, is the important second step. This is essential, particularly in view of the Commission's information that, in the past, 15 to 25 per cent of material deposited at lakefill did not meet existing sediment standards.

RECOMMENDATION

30. The Royal Commission recommends that the provincial Ministry of the Environment and the Metropolitan Toronto and Region Conservation Authority review the quality assurance system used to monitor and control the quality of materials accepted for lakefill and that all necessary improvements be made to improve its effectiveness.

There are several codes and standards governing house construction, but none for massive lakefill structures that may contain large quantities of contaminated sediments. Considering that some of Ontario's engineers and engineering firms are known and respected worldwide, it is clear that we have the expertise needed to set appropriate standards and practices that will ensure the safety of the public and the natural environment.

RECOMMENDATION

31. The Royal Commission recommends that the federal and provincial governments consult with marine construction engineers, academics, and experts with relevant information, regarding practical codes and standards applicable to lakefill and erosion control structures. Possible topics include standards related to the range of water levels, intensity of storms, allowable fill loss, turbidity, and any other issues connected to public safety, public property, and aquatic habitat.

As soon as new and tighter MOE draft sediment guidelines are applied, a great deal of slightly contaminated material would be rejected as lakefill. The precise volume is unknown, but is estimated to be at least half of all material currently being accepted. This means that, once construction activity recovers from the recession, as many as 1,000 truckloads per week would require new disposal sites. In the past, this material was accepted at the Leslie Street Spit for less than $100 per load. Even at current rates (more than $1,000 per load), this material would not be welcome at sanitary landfill sites, because capacity is limited. Furthermore, the degree of contamination on most loads is low enough that disposal in licensed sanitary fill sites is not necessary. Obviously, a practical alternative is needed.

RECOMMENDATION

32. The Royal Commission recommends that the Ministry of the Environment create a new "restricted fill" waste classification for excavated soil that is unsuitable for open water disposal, but does not require the degree of control imposed for sanitary landfill. Moreover, the MOE should actively assist in identifying and licensing suitable sites.

The classic "3 Rs" approach to any waste problem — reduce, reuse, recycle — can be applied to construction excavation wastes.

Reducing the amount of excavate produced by deep excavations for parking lots can be achieved by building above-ground parking garages, reducing the number of parking spaces required below buildings, and increasing public transit capacity. This excavate is the material that is most often used in lakefill.

Other considerations such as aesthetics, safety, security, and the very high value of downtown land will dominate decisions about parking. But, because excavation is typically less than five per cent of a building's cost, and the cost of new transit would dwarf even the recently inflated price of landfill disposal, the requirement for underground parking is unlikely to change quickly.

Recycling is a practical approach for some bricks and broken concrete, but these materials represent a small proportion of overall construction waste.

Reuse offers some very interesting options. If the material is regarded as a resource, rather than a problem, there are possibly some positive ways of employing it. For example, small amounts could be utilized to landscape nearby grounds, in order to provide contour and texture. Further away, they could be used in noise berms and toboggan or ski hills. On a still larger scale, millions of cubic metres could raise the elevation of industrial lands currently under redevelopment in downtown Toronto, such as the Railway Lands, Port Industrial Area, Garrison Common, and Ataratiri.

The Commission has been advised that, assuming that contaminated soils below can be sealed properly, large amounts of material could be utilized in these ways. Benefits would include raising some lands above the floodplain of the Don River, achieving pleasing slopes and contours, "hiding" expressways and rail corridors in newly created ravines, and improving sound buffers and general drainage. It has been estimated that, in downtown Toronto, as much as 12 million cubic metres (15 cubic million yards) could be diverted from waste disposal sites — an amount that would exceed the projected production of excavated soils over the next decade.

RECOMMENDATION

33. The Royal Commission recommends that the possibility of using excavated material be evaluated in the preparation of plans and proposals for redeveloping downtown Toronto sites, such as Garrison Common, the Railway Lands, the Port Industrial Area, and Ataratiri.

WATERFRONT GREENWAY AND TRAIL

Although a Waterfront Greenway and Trail should be part of the Shoreline Regeneration Plan, there is no need to wait for the plan before encouraging initiatives that will help regenerate the terrestrial edge of the shore and make it more accessible. Parts of the Waterfront Trail exist, and further development is under way. The greenway concept can help create the natural network that will encourage more species at the waterfront. Greenways and shoreline regeneration initiatives are highly complementary. (See next chapter for an extensive examination of the greenway concept.)

RECOMMENDATION

34. The Royal Commission recommends that the Waterfront Greenway and Trail be integrated into the proposed Shoreline Regeneration Plan for the Greater Toronto bioregion, and that work should proceed while the plan is being prepared, providing that it does not compromise the plan's integrity.

CHAPTER 5: GREENWAYS

We face a more crowded future: urban planners tell us that the population of the Greater Toronto Area will swell from the current four million to nearly six million three decades from now. Development in the cities will become denser, even as the urban edge moves ever outwards. We will spend more than $75 billion on new roads, sewers, water, schools, hospitals, and other infrastructure — just to keep up with demand. Under the relentless pressures of urbanization, it may become increasingly difficult for most people to find a quiet refuge, an unpolluted stream, a place to walk among the trees.

But not only the human habitat is at risk: the rich mix of wild plants and animals with which we share the bioregion are in even more jeopardy. Among the 1,400 species of wild plants in the bioregion, for example, 140 are already limited to a single known location. More than 100 wild species are classed as provincially rare. Streams that leave the Oak Ridges Moraine as cool, clean homes for aristocratic brook trout arrive at the waterfront choked with filth.

Shaping our future to meet the needs of a burgeoning human population and a vulnerable ecosystem is an extraordinary challenge. One of the most promising tools for meeting that challenge is the concept of greenways: corridors of protected greenspace throughout the cities and beyond, into the countryside. Greenways do not pit humankind against nature; rather they serve the needs of both, protecting the quality of the natural environment while providing recreation and quiet places close to home.

The idea behind greenways is elegantly simple: link existing green spaces to create interconnected corridors, thereby increasing their usefulness for both people and wildlife. A system of greenways fits neatly in the nine principles put forward by the Commission in its interim report *Watershed* (1990); it proposed that the waterfront be clean, green, useable, diverse, open, accessible, connected, affordable, and attractive.

The greenway concept is gaining prominence, in part because there is a lack of funding for acquiring traditional parklands. Moreover, large blocks of natural landscape close to the urban mosaic are becoming increasingly scarce, and increasingly expensive. Greenways offer opportunities to provide equally good or better recreational

Oakville waterfront

opportunities, as well as vital ecological benefits, at a much lower cost.

Examining the role of greenways in the bioregion builds on the earlier work done by the Commission and others. In its *Watershed* report, the Commission proposed a system of trails along the waterfront, up the associated river valleys, and along the Oak Ridges Moraine. This trail system, buttressed by corridors of green space, would "cast a green net over the Greater Toronto Area, making the public open spaces far more accessible and attractive". The Commission also noted the need for special attention to ecological corridors, particularly along the river valleys that intersect with urban areas.

In her response to the Commission's recommendations, the provincial Minister of the Environment, the Honourable Ruth Grier, endorsed the concept of a Waterfront Trail, and said that it

> will become the Greenway that ties the Greater Toronto Area together from Burlington to Newcastle. . . . the highest land use for all public lands along the water's edge. . . . much more than a four-foot strip of asphalt.

The Province subsequently sponsored a study on optimum and interim routes outside Metro Toronto, released in April 1991 as *The Waterfront Trail: First Steps from Concept to Reality* (Reid et al. 1991). This report confirmed the feasibility of a trail alignment, and noted that a Waterfront Trail will link together some 34 major parks, 74 small waterfront parks and promenades, 40 significant natural habitats, and 25 marinas. It gave further support to the idea of the waterfront as a greenway, recommending that eight new "green nodes" be acquired, and that links incorporate a corridor of greenspace.

In June 1991, a new public group, Citizens for a Lakeshore Greenway (CFLAG), was formed to support the concept of a waterfront trail. Clearly, its members also envision the links along the waterfront as "more than a four-foot strip of asphalt".

This evolution in emphasis, from recreational trail to greenway, prompted the Commission to examine more closely the concept of greenways, and how they might fit within the sphere of ecosystem planning. What we discovered was a planning approach that is rapidly gaining favour across North America and has considerable potential for application within the bioregion and across Ontario.

The term "greenway" is relatively new, although the ideas it embodies have been around for some time. The first modern use, in the 1960s, is credited to planner and author William H. Whyte. It combines the syllable "green" from the British term greenbelt, and "way" from the American term parkway. Appropriately, greenways themselves also connect the ideas behind the British and American words and the result is a system of protected linear corridors of open space, managed for conservation and recreation purposes.

The essence of greenways is connections — not simply connecting recreational areas through trails, but connecting wildlife habitats to each other, human communities to other human communities, city to country, people to nature.

The essence of greenways is connections — not simply connecting recreational areas through trails, but connecting wildlife habitats to each other, human communities to other human communities, city to country, people to nature.

This emphasis on links contrasts with the traditional approach to conservation of open space and natural areas, which stresses purchasing blocks of parkland, large and small, often isolated in a sea of surrounding development. While such parks are vital for conserving habitat and for recreation, their value could be greatly enhanced by creating green links among them. In fact, the existing parks and natural areas in the Greater Toronto bioregion are the basic building blocks of a greenway system. These parcels, often termed "greenlands", include wetlands and woodlots, Environmentally Sensitive Areas, and Areas of Natural and Scientific Interest (ANSIs).

While it is important to define these and other aspects of a greenway, it is just as important to recognize how greenways differ from the more limited concept of trail systems, with which they are often confused. A trail right-of-way may be little wider than a sidewalk, but a greenway is a continuous corridor of natural vegetation and open spaces. Greenways may vary dramatically from each other in width, depending on landscape opportunities and on the character of the natural landscape, but those ecological elements are always present. A trail is usually — but not always — part of a greenway. In areas of ecological sensitivity, or on private lands within a greenway, a continuous trail may not be possible.

Most greenways created recently are those in and near American cities, but Ontario has several good examples of

greenways. One of the best is along the
Niagara Escarpment, a prominent landform
feature that snakes across southern Ontario
for 725 kilometres (450 miles) from Niagara
Falls to the Bruce Peninsula. Under the
Niagara Escarpment Planning and Development Act, a special Commission is charged
with the responsibility of "maintaining the
Escarpment and land in its vicinity substantially as a continuous natural environment".

This Niagara Escarpment Commission
(NEC) administers an environmentally
based plan, which limits development of private lands to that consistent with protection
of the ecological, recreational, and visual
qualities of the escarpment. A system of more
than 100 public parks is complemented by
the links of the Bruce Trail, which was
created by a private association. More
than 1.3 million visitors use the Bruce
Trail annually, including 50,000 who stay
overnight. As the lands adjacent to this
escarpment corridor become increasingly
developed, the value of its network of greenways and associated open spaces grows.

A second Ontario greenway is the
result of work in and near Ottawa, carried
out by the National Capital Commission
(NCC), which has been involved for several
decades in creating greenbelts and linked
bicycle and pedestrian trails. The trail
system includes loop routes along the
Ottawa Greenbelt, in Gatineau Park, and
along four major water courses. Currently

130 kilometres (81 miles) in length, the system has a variety of surfaces, and is heavily
used in all seasons. Development of the
NCC system has involved strong central
planning and considerable public expenditure; the result contributes greatly to the
high quality of life in the Ottawa-Hull
region.

There are more than 500 greenways in
the United States, many of them small-scale.
However, the Bay and Ridge trails around
the City of San Francisco are substantial
twin greenways, each about 640 kilometres
(398 miles) long. The Bay Trail greenway
is being created by the Association of Bay
Governments, with funding from a variety
of public and private sources. Planning and
implementation of the Ridge Trail is carried
out by a special council, including citizens'
groups, municipalities, and various agencies.
Municipalities along the trail provide funding for their trail sections, assisted by private
grants and donations.

A similar public-private partnership is
at work in Oregon to sponsor creation of
the Willamette River Greenway, which runs
through nine counties and 19 municipalities.
Under a State Greenway Law, municipalities
are required to adopt plans and ordinances
to protect greenway lands, and to take
responsibility for managing greenway lands
within their jurisdiction.

Some municipalities have established
greenway advisory committees, made up of
local citizens, to provide planning advice
and seek input from other citizens and
special-interest groups.

One clear lesson from the American
experience: their greenways' success does
not flow from massive public expenditures,
but rather from a clear vision of the opportunities they offer, and from strong individual

and public commitment to that vision. Creating a greenway can foster a strong sense of pride and accomplishment within a community, and help local people focus more clearly on the kind of place they want to leave to their children.

THE BENEFITS OF GREENWAYS

If in some ways greenways are old ideas dressed up in new clothing, in other ways they represent the forefront of ecological and economic thinking. Implicit in the concept is the recognition of an overlapping matrix of benefits and values. Few greenways, taken individually, will bring all of the benefits described in this chapter. But, as an interconnected system looked at from a regional perspective, in the same way that a network of roads might be evaluated, the benefits of greenways are striking. In a landscape rapidly filling with humankind's infrastructure, greenways provide the natural infrastructure vital to an environmentally sustainable region.

GREENWAYS ARE ECOLOGICAL CONNECTORS

Diversity is one of the fundamental underpinnings of natural systems, providing the abundance of different plants and animals that make them function. The importance of diversity has been recognized, among other places, in the proposed *Wild Life Strategy for Ontario* (Ontario Wild Life Working Group 1991), which ranks the conservation of biodiversity as a primary goal. As well as protecting the integrity of the ecosystem, a diverse mix of species enhances the potential for human interaction with wildlife and other elements of the natural landscape.

As agriculture and urbanization increasingly fragment natural habitats, the diversity of wild species declines sharply. In effect, the remaining bits and pieces become islands of habitat, isolated in a sea of farmland and suburbs. A major factor in the declining diversity within them is that they are unconnected to other green areas.

In even a completely natural setting, stresses — natural fluctuations in weather and food supplies, for example — can temporarily reduce or wipe out some species. Added to these natural fluctuations are the urban pressures of pollution, disturbance, and predation by cats and dogs. The small size of many habitat remnants makes them especially vulnerable to these stresses, and means that some species (e.g., those that require interior forest conditions) cannot be sustained. Severing habitat connections can be lethal for species that use different parts of the environment at various life stages, such as salamanders that breed in ponds but live mostly in forests.

Many species have an innate ability to disperse to escape the effects of these fluctuations or to recolonize once habitat conditions improve. In an urban setting, however, that natural dispersal process is often deadly, the results visible as road kills on almost any highway. Recolonization of isolated islands of habitat, especially by animals, is almost

> *Creating a greenway can foster a strong sense of pride and accomplishment within a community, and help local people focus more clearly on the kind of place they want to leave to their children.*

impossible: when a species is eliminated from its island from whatever cause, it is likely gone for good.

In order to counteract forces that reduce biodiversity, it is vital to maintain and expand natural links among habitat islands. Within the bioregion, greenway corridors along valleys are among the most significant connectors and also provide passageways for migrating birds and butterflies. Improved waterfront connectors could also do a great deal to stem the impoverishment of such isolated habitats as Mississauga's Rattray Marsh.

Re-creating the natural links to these remnant habitats, which were severed as the result of inadequate planning in the past, can help restore their natural balance. These habitat links must be carefully designed because the same stresses that affect habitat islands are at play in narrow greenway corridors. Greenway planners must ensure that habitat links do not become wildlife deathtraps, and must realize that the design of a greenway has a major effect on the species mix that can use it. While there is still more to be learned in this field, the design principles for an area-wide natural heritage system, produced by the Ministry of Natural Resources in April 1991, provide a useful starting point.

In the bioregion's more rural parts, the degree of habitat fragmentation is generally less pronounced, and the effect on wildlife populations is less noticeable. However, in the longer term, the near-urban forces of aggregate extraction, estate housing, roadways, and utility corridors will lead to the same kinds of stresses. Rural communities have the opportunity, in advance, to lay out greenway systems that will protect the integrity of their ecosystem, rather than piecing together remnants of the urbanizing process later.

Forks of the Credit Provincial Park near Cataract in Caledon: part of the Bruce Trail

While greenway connectors are essential in the landscape, they are not a substitute for other forms of sound planning. Environmentally Sensitive Areas, wetlands, and other greenlands have been identified across the bioregion, some of which do not fit logically in a greenway system. Nonetheless, these should be protected, particularly where they are known to shelter rare species or to provide other vital ecological functions.

Greenways are one tool in the package of sound planning processes, but certainly not the only one. Other issues such as agricultural land preservation and countryside management demand ongoing attention outside the context of greenways.

GREENWAYS ENHANCE WATER QUALITY

The degradation of water quality in the bioregion is not simply the result of point sources, such as sewage treatment plants and factories. Equally important are the multitude of small sources of pollution: eroding streambanks and construction projects, stormwater run-off from streets and parking lots, pesticide and fertilizer residues from lawns, golf courses, and farmland. Greenways, particularly those along stream valleys and wetlands, can help filter and remove these diffuse pollutants, protecting downstream water quality.

Greenways carry out this cleansing function in a variety of ways: vegetated buffers along waterways slow the flow of incoming water, trapping sediments and attached pollutants. Excess nutrients are soaked up by floodplains and wetlands vegetation and eventually are incorporated into the soil. Vegetated banks reduce erosion, by shielding the soil from the impact of falling rain and by binding the soil in the root system.

In an urban context, greenways can also provide a suitable location for facilities that enhance water quality, such as stormwater detention ponds and wetlands. Properly designed, these features could also be used to improve wildlife habitats and recreational access.

Most greenways include wooded areas, especially along valleylands. Even the shade provided by these woods can be a benefit to water quality: it reduces the photosynthetic process (which requires sunlight) in the stream, thereby reducing the growth of undesirable algae. Shaded waters remain cooler in summer, improving the habitat for fish and other aquatic creatures, and

Rural communities have the opportunity, in advance, to lay out greenway systems that will protect the integrity of their ecosystem, rather than piecing together remnants of the urbanizing process later.

increasing the water's capacity to hold dissolved oxygen.

In the Greater Toronto bioregion, the Oak Ridges Moraine has been identified as a major recharge area for groundwater, and as a source for more than 30 major watercourses. The water quality in the upper sections of these streams is excellent, because of the high baseflow contribution from the moraine. To maintain water quality in these streams, and to protect the associated cold-water fishery, it is vital to safeguard the moraine. The Province has recognized this need by expressing a Provincial Interest in the Oak Ridges Moraine, issuing interim guidelines for planning decisions, and initiating a two-year study to produce a long-term strategy for the moraine.

Maintaining vegetation in key recharge and source areas along the moraine, as part of a greenway system, should be an integral part of that protection. Unless the moraine itself is healthy enough to provide a strong flow of cool water to the bioregion's streams, it will be impossible to restore water quality in their lower reaches.

Even the best greenway system can be overwhelmed by uncontrolled stormwater flows, excessive nutrients, and other pollutants: while greenways can play an important role in improving water quality, they can do so only in concert with other pollution control measures. Therefore, they should be a central part of water quality restoration plans, but cannot be used as a substitute for other measures.

GREENWAYS PROVIDE RECREATION OPPORTUNITIES CLOSE TO HOME

As part of the background report, *A Green Strategy for the Greater Toronto Waterfront* (Reid, Lockhart, and Woodburn 1990), the Commission examined trends affecting participation in recreation. Among the more significant:

- a dramatic increase in population to be served, especially on the fringes of the metropolitan area;
- free time being spent closer to home, bringing increasing demands on near-urban facilities;
- increasing interest in the environment and out-of-doors, physical and emotional well-being, and spontaneous rather than structured recreation activities;
- a rapidly aging population, which will probably lead to increases in the demand for golf, bicycling, walking, and similar outdoor pursuits; and
- strong public support for linked parks and trail systems, and for preservation of natural areas.

Recognizing these trends, as well as evidence of high use of existing cycling and walking trails, the Metropolitan Toronto and Region Conservation Authority has called for a system of river valley and moraine trails as part of its Greenspace Strategy. In his report, *Space for All: Options for a Greater Toronto Area Greenlands Strategy,* former MPP Ron Kanter (1990) also recommended "a series of regional trail systems". The Royal Commission's

Figure 5.1 Greenways bring people to the water's edge

interim report, *Watershed*, echoed those recommendations.

Several conclusions can be drawn from the Commission's background studies and from deputations made at its hearings. First, the value of trail systems is enhanced by increasing their length and interconnectedness. Second, trails are more attractive and more likely to be well-used when they are set in a corridor of greenspace. Third, the increasing time pressures being felt by working people mean that most trails must be immediately accessible, so that recreational use can be integrated into modern lifestyles. Trails that can be used easily as a route to the corner store, or to commute to work or school, will rapidly become part of community life.

Therefore, in a network of greenways, several distinct trail types should be recognized:

- long-distance trail networks, such as those proposed along the moraine, the waterfront, and the major river valleys, will attract users from across the bioregion and beyond who will devote a day, a weekend or a short vacation to the greenway as a destination;
- near-urban greenway trails, on the other hand, are more likely to be used on a regular basis by people from the surrounding neighbourhoods. On American greenways, 75 to 80 per cent of recreational users are people who live within an eight-kilometre (five-mile) range of the amenity.

Clearly, as well as the major regional greenways, it is important to create local links into adjacent communities, so that greenways are accessible and useable. These

Most Important Current Waterfront Use

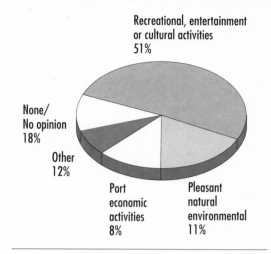

Half of the respondents consider recreation, entertainment or cultural activities to be the most important current use of the waterfront.

Source: Environics Poll. 1991.

local links might follow tributary streams, or utility corridors, abandoned rail lines or even quiet streets.

The character of local links should be more community-oriented, designed for an evening stroll rather than an all-day cycling trip. While these links are particularly important as part of the urban fabric, they are also an asset in rural communities, especially in those where there has been considerable non-farm residential development.

Greenways located close to home are accessible to all income groups, particularly those who cannot afford the cost of a weekend cottage. To the greatest extent possible, urban greenways should be accessible by public transit, to ensure they remain affordable to all citizens, and to minimize environmental costs associated with car use.

In some cases, development of heavily used recreational trails will conflict with the ecological functions of greenways. Where such incompatibility arises, the greenway may have to be widened or altered in some other way to allow trails to be routed around wetlands or other sensitive natural environments. Throughout the greenway system, careful design is needed to ensure that recreational uses do not impose unacceptable levels of stress on vulnerable natural areas.

Other design considerations might involve separating recreational uses, so that heavy cycling, for example, does not pose a danger to walkers, or so that horseback riders can use appropriate trails. Users' safety and the security of adjacent communities are also major concerns and must be addressed in the design of greenways and trails. Especially within urban areas, trails should be designed and patrolled where necessary, so that all users feel physically secure: encouraging frequent use will help maintain safety.

In some places, the popularity of greenways as destinations for visitors and tourists may raise conflicts with local users and this, too, must be considered during design. Particularly in rural municipalities, adequate facilities such as washrooms and parking lots to handle peak periods is essential. Designating suitable parks as recreation nodes is one way of providing these facilities and directing access and levels of use along the greenway.

GREENWAYS BRING ECONOMIC BENEFITS TO COMMUNITIES

Greenways make good economic sense. Living and working in or near a greenway can enhance the economic prospects of existing businesses and create opportunities for new ventures.

A report by the U.S. National Parks Service (1990), *Economic Impacts of Protecting Rivers, Trails, and Greenway Corridors*, cites examples from across that country of documented increases in property values adjacent to protected greenways. Increases in property values range from five to 32 per cent, particularly near greenways that highlight open space rather than highly developed facilities. Increased local tax revenues, and increased commercial activity in selected areas in greenways (food concessions, bicycle rentals, etc.) have also been widely reported. Related tourism developments, such as nearby overnight accommodation and restaurants, can also benefit from a greenway system. The San Antonio Riverwalk, for example, is considered the second most important tourist attraction in the State of Texas. In Ontario, the Bruce Trail has been estimated to have a direct economic impact on the province's economy of at least $30 million per year, even though the trail corridor is mostly through natural landscapes.

Perhaps more significant than these direct economic effects is the overall impact on a community's image. Greenway projects have been used as a spur for urban redevelopment, prompting private investment in adjacent areas. Their presence through the heart of the city is used aggressively by such places as Sacramento, California to attract new business.

> *Throughout the greenway system, careful design is needed to ensure that recreational uses do not impose unacceptable levels of stress on vulnerable natural areas.*

Given that corporations increasingly cite an area's "quality of life" as a major factor in location decisions, the clean, green, accessible image of greenways is a strong attraction.

They make economic sense on the expenditure side as well because they take advantage of what we already have — hundreds of parks and open-space areas, large and small, along the waterfront and in the valley systems. In some areas, the Humber River for example, the foresight of conservation authorities and municipalities has provided major blocks of public lands along the valley. Linking these together to create a continuous greenway will enhance their use and value, bringing a greater return on past investments.

Greenways are able to take advantage of linear features that do not attract other economic activities — floodplains, abandoned rail lines, and utility rights-of-way, for example. With vision and forethought, greenways can convert low-value, often derelict, remnants of the urban landscape into environmental and economic assets.

In his book, *Greenways for America*, Charles Little (1990) argues that public expenditures on greenways are justified for yet another reason. He refers to the advantages of "edge effect", noting that a long thin greenway looks much the same from the edge as a wooded park that might be a kilometre wide. The linear greenway, therefore, provides a great deal more *apparent* open space from the same acreage. According to Little's calculations, "for every dollar of tax money spent on the traditional blob park, you can get the same edge effect (assuming an equal price per acre) with an expenditure of 18 cents for a greenway".

GREENWAYS MAKE MORE LIVEABLE COMMUNITIES

Over the past several years, the Province has been examining various options for accommodating future growth in the bioregion, through the *Greater Toronto Area Urban Structure Concepts Study* (IBI Group et al. 1990) and other mechanisms. The bioregion currently supports about 40 per cent of Ontario's population on less than one per cent of its land base. This concentration is expected to continue into the foreseeable future, with about six million residents by the year 2021. Continued low-density urban sprawl along the fringes of the city to accommodate this increased population would have undesirable environmental and social effects. Considerable attention, therefore, is being focused on how to concentrate growth into smaller urban areas with a greater emphasis on mass transit.

Greenways can contribute in a very positive way to making such future communities more attractive and liveable. A green infrastructure throughout the city will soften the effects of urban concentration, and provide relief from the stresses of urban life. Corridors of green will replenish oxygen in city air, and help buffer noise and traffic. Urban greenways can be designed to separate communities visually, to help define neighbourhoods at a human scale.

In a practical sense, extended greenways will link the city to the countryside, through trails that provide opportunities for extended off-street travel. Such on-the-ground links can do a great deal to promote mutual respect and understanding between urban and rural residents, and to show urbanites what is happening on the city fringes. In many places, greenway trails can become an alternative and efficient means of commuting to work, reducing pressure on road and transit systems. Nearby greenways can become resources for educators, fitness classes, and community groups.

Woven into the urban fabric, they help promote human health, both physical and emotional. In a more compact urban form, where there are fewer opportunities for individual residents to have their own private bit of green backyard, greenways can become a kind of community common, where people renew their contacts with nature.

This contact is vital to remind an increasingly urban population that the bioregion sustains us all. We need reminders, too, that the bioregion involves species other than our own, and habitats more complex than the concrete and brick structures that house us. In an informal sense at least, greenways and other green spaces are vital building blocks for the environmental education of this generation and of those yet to come.

In a more compact urban form, where there are fewer opportunities for individual residents to have their own private bit of green backyard, greenways can become a kind of community common, where people renew their contacts with nature.

GREENWAYS HELP TO STRENGTHEN COMMUNITIES

Characteristically, there is a high degree of community involvement in the creation of greenways. By combining public dollars and volunteer expertise and labour with private investment, establishing a greenway can bring out the best in a community. The U.S. President's Commission on Americans Outdoors, reporting in 1987, said that, among the major goals of greenways, one was to build partnerships among private enterprise, landowners, and local governments and groups, as well as to encourage local pride. Those partnerships, feeding on the success of greenway projects, can spill over into other aspects of community life.

In the words of Charles Little (1990), "To make a greenway. . . is to make a community."

GREENWAYS PROVIDE LINKS AMONG EXISTING PROGRAMS

One of the difficulties facing both urban and rural communities is the confusing and sometimes contradictory array of agencies and programs created by all levels of government. Establishing greenway strategies, involving many agencies and citizen groups, provides a mechanism to integrate these programs for at least the key natural corridors. Of necessity, the process will help agencies document existing public lands and resources, identify gaps and opportunities, and build partnerships necessary to carry out a greenway strategy. This process can and should lead to a more cohesive approach to the waterfront, the major valleys, and the Oak Ridges Moraine.

Developing a greenway strategy should not become just another process, in addition to existing programs for wetlands, ANSIs, floodplains, and the like. Rather, it should be a means of integrating these programs at the community level, and reinforcing them where appropriate.

Such integration can lead to a new appreciation of opportunities for conservation

Members of Citizens for a Lakeshore Greenway (CFLAG)

and recreation. In the Town of Caledon, for example, background work undertaken for the Royal Commission brought together, for the first time, maps of public lands owned by a variety of agencies, and sparked recognition of possibilities for greenway links.

STRUCTURING A GREENWAY SYSTEM

The major elements of a greenway system in the Greater Toronto bioregion can be defined in two tiers: arterial greenways that establish an interconnected framework across the region, and local connectors in each community.

Along the Lake Ontario waterfront, the Province has already developed specific proposals for arterial greenway development, anchored by the Waterfront Trail. The Niagara Escarpment Plan and Bruce Trail provide an existing greenway along the western boundary of the bioregion. Provincial studies currently under way will help define a ridge-top greenway along the Oak Ridges Moraine in the Greater Toronto Area.

Other arterial greenways most logically follow river valleys, which are well defined in at least their downstream sections. In some of these valleys, such as the Credit, the Humber, the Rouge, and Duffin Creek, significant stretches of public land have already been acquired by conservation authorities, municipalities, and other public agencies.

In addition to these arterial greenways, a network of locally based connecting links should be developed, based on local planning and priorities. In some cases, these connectors can tie into community parks or tributary valleys. They may provide cross-connections between valley greenlands to allow recreational loops by using utility corridors, abandoned rail lines, and parkway belt lands. Especially in the area's eastern sections, the ridges and slopes associated with the Lake Iroquois shoreline (which roughly parallels the existing shore) also provide opportunities for creating links between valleys.

The nature of greenway systems will vary considerably between urban and rural parts of the Greater Toronto bioregion. In urban sections, the width of potential greenways is usually already defined by the presence of residential or industrial developments on either side. Greenway corridors, even those on floodplains, may be threatened by proposals for roadway or utility uses, unless they are protected by strong policies.

Recreational use of greenway trails will be heavy, and public ownership of core greenway lands is likely to be necessary. In some circumstances, however, it would make sense to include a band of existing or proposed development within the greenway. This zone could be recognized in planning documents as requiring special policies to minimize conflicts with the ecological, aesthetic, and recreational values of the greenway. In many places, these private lands could help to buffer the core of the greenway from adjacent urban uses.

Potential greenways should be examined not only in the context of a regional network, but also as a component of overall rural planning, to address the conservation of a living, functional countryside in the shadow of the city.

The boundaries of greenways in rural areas are more difficult to define, and the need to create greenways may seem less immediate. It is there, however, that vital opportunities exist to help shape the future form and quality of the bioregion. Ecological arguments for greenways should play a major role in defining rural greenways, particularly the need to protect downstream water quality. Private lands in wider greenways in rural areas can continue to support compatible uses such as agriculture, small hamlets, and scattered estate development. Potential greenways should be examined not only in the context of a regional network, but also as a component of overall rural planning, to address the conservation of a living, functional countryside in the shadow of the city.

Several beginnings have already been made. For example, a greenlands strategy has been developed by the Region of Halton (1990), in conjunction with local municipalities and conservation authorities. It recognizes the significance of a linked system, and proposes a series of implementation steps related to policy formulation: a regional parks system, land acquisition, property tax incentives, and tree-cutting by-laws. More recently, the Town of King has proposed to establish a Greenways Advisory Committee to draw up plans for a municipal greenway system. An MTRCA proposed program would establish a 900-kilometre (560-mile) inter-regional trail system that could form a basis for greenways.

This evidence of local interest should be matched by provincial support and

Map 5.1 Greenways and trails concept for the Greater Toronto bioregion

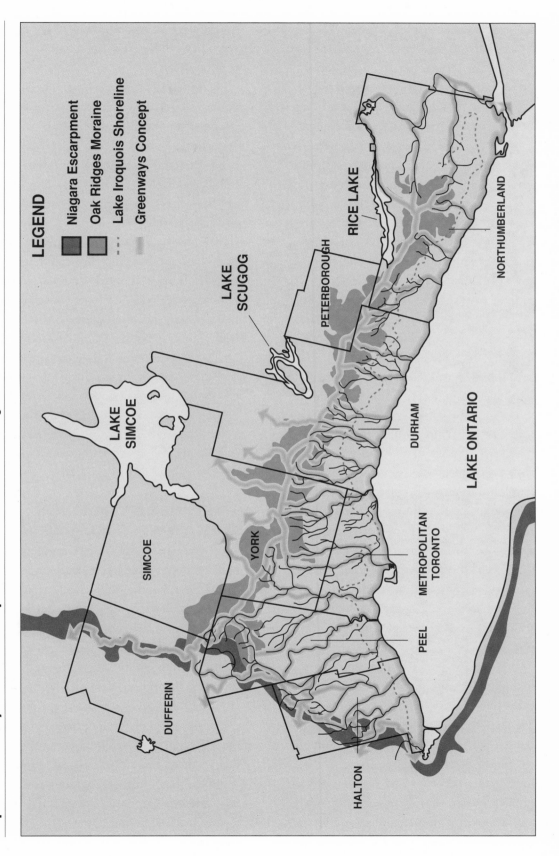

LEGEND

- Niagara Escarpment
- Oak Ridges Moraine
- Lake Iroquois Shoreline
- Greenways Concept

LAKE SIMCOE

LAKE SCUGOG

RICE LAKE

SIMCOE

DUFFERIN

YORK

PETERBOROUGH

NORTHUMBERLAND

HALTON

PEEL

METROPOLITAN TORONTO

DURHAM

LAKE ONTARIO

assistance. Because arterial greenways can be expected to serve users from across the Greater Toronto bioregion and beyond, provincial involvement in setting a policy framework, design standards, and funding is necessary and appropriate. Local connectors are oriented more towards local use and can be left more readily to the community. However, provincial support and encouragement (for example, through the community assistance programs of the Ministry of Tourism and Recreation) may also be justified — a recognition of the benefits of their proximity to local residents, and of their contribution to the overall system.

While greenways should make maximum use of existing public lands in these corridors, not all lands in greenways need to be publicly owned. For example, lands with particular biological or visual significance might often be better protected in sympathetic private hands, with public access restricted. A range of alternative techniques, such as conservation easements, can be employed to provide long-term protection of specific features, without buying land outright. Municipal planning powers, together with more comprehensive regulatory powers for conservation authorities, could be employed to ensure that any development in designated greenways is compatible in scale, location, and design with greenway purposes.

This vision of creating greenways includes all existing public lands, such as those owned by Ontario Hydro and other agencies, to form the core of a greenway system. For example, on the 133 kilometres (83 miles) of proposed waterfront greenway outside Metro Toronto, 37 per cent is now publicly owned (mostly by conservation authorities and municipalities) and is

accessible, with an additional 17 per cent owned by other public agencies but not currently accessible.

Added to all greenways will be lands dedicated during development of adjacent properties, and lands purchased by public agencies for such related projects as flood protection and shoreline stabilization. Public acquisition of key properties may be necessary in crucial locations, particularly to establish public access links.

Enlisting the support and involvement of the development industry could bring significant benefits to the greenway system. For example, local developers have been major supporters of establishing the Georgian Trail between Collingwood and Meaford, because the trail makes adjacent residential developments more attractive. For the same reason, developers in the bioregion may find that a greenway in the neighbourhood, perhaps using some of their lands, becomes a selling point for their projects.

IMPLEMENTING GREENWAY PLANS

The detailed planning for greenways, and the steps needed to make them reality, cannot be carried out effectively by any single agency. Rather, implementation should involve provincial agencies, conservation authorities, regional and municipal governments, private non-profit groups, and landowners acting on the basis of a common vision of the greenway system to be created.

Successful experience elsewhere shows that developing this vision must strongly involve the community at its grass roots. In the context of the bioregion, it is vital to have a strong emphasis on watersheds as a planning level for greenways.

In the State of Maryland, a special Greenways Commission appointed by the Governor in 1990 examined greenway benefits and opportunities, and urged the state and local governments to "embark on a bold adventure . . . pioneering a statewide greenway network". The Maryland study (Maryland Greenways Commission 1990) did not call for new greenway legislation, but proposed better use of the existing complement of tools available. Ontario needs a similar call to action, along with a package of provincial incentives to catch the interest of landowners and municipalities.

Given their current land holdings, their watershed orientation, their regulatory powers, and their position as a partnership between the Province and municipalities, conservation authorities must be important players in a greenway system. Citizen groups, including such groups as Citizens for a Lakeshore Greenway, Action to Restore a Clean Humber, Save the Rouge Valley System, and Friends of the Credit River Valley, must also play a part. Other co-ordinating bodies such as the Don Watershed Task Force, being established by MTRCA, can also play a central role. However, if the full range of resources and public enthusiasm for greenways is to be captured, we believe a co-operative approach, rather than a single agency, is required.

The active involvement of municipalities in creating greenways has particular potential: as the level of government closest to the people, municipalities can be expected to represent local interests in greenway design, and to ensure that greenways are responsive to local needs. Through their planning powers and recreation programs, municipalities also have many opportunities to help make greenways a reality. If initiatives are viewed as simply another program of the conservation authority, or of the Province, they will fall far short of their potential. Municipalities must become full partners and, in some cases, they should become the leading partners in creating greenways.

Across the bioregion, mechanisms for implementing the greenway system will differ. Its three major components — the waterfront, the Oak Ridges Moraine, and valleyland and community connectors — can be examined individually.

THE WATERFRONT GREENWAY

The Province has accepted responsibility for co-ordinating a waterfront greenway and establishing trails; to do so, it will have to co-ordinate intergovernmental policies and programs along the waterfront, and manage provincial lands, assets, and information resources. This will guarantee a strong continuing provincial presence along the waterfront, an area where creating some greenway links will be particularly challenging.

In carrying out this work, the Province may wish to develop Partnership Agreements with municipalities, conservation

The planning of a greenway begins with the commitment of a group of people. Energy is more important, at this point, than financial resources, and enthusiasm is more important than expertise.

Howe, L. 1987. *Keeping our garden state green: a local government guide for greenway and open space planning.* New Jersey: New Jersey Department of Environmental Protection.

authorities, and others. Progress will be monitored, and no doubt encouraged, by a new non-profit group, Citizens for a Lakeshore Greenway.

Development of the waterfront greenway will be assisted by the 1991 study carried out for the Province, *The Waterfront Trail: First Steps from Concept to Reality* (Reid et al.), which recommends optimum and interim routes for the Waterfront Trail outside Metro Toronto, and also identifies certain additional lands to be used for a greenway. The report notes that, while a substantial amount of the shoreline is now in public hands, significant stretches are privately owned, with varying opportunities for ecological restoration and public access in future. In September 1991, Metro announced the formation of a Working Committee to oversee completion of a Lakeside Trail in the municipality, which will complement the provincial work already done.

In the previous chapter, preparation of an integrated plan for the bioregion's shoreline is recommended as part of shoreline regeneration. This plan will address such issues as future lakefill management and protection of significant natural habitats. Because these elements and the objectives of a waterfront greenway overlap, and because future land acquisition and related shoreline protection activities will provide opportunities for trail and greenway links, such a plan should incorporate greenway design.

RECOMMENDATIONS

35. The Royal Commission recommends that the proposed shoreline regeneration plan for the Greater Toronto bioregion include basic design and policy for a waterfront greenway, and

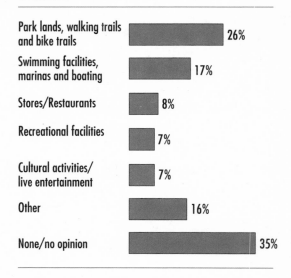

Type of New Waterfront Facilities Wanted

Facility	Percentage
Park lands, walking trails and bike trails	26%
Swimming facilities, marinas and boating	17%
Stores/Restaurants	8%
Recreational facilities	7%
Cultural activities/ live entertainment	7%
Other	16%
None/no opinion	35%

More than a quarter of the respondents favour more park lands, walking trails, and bike trails along the waterfront.

Source: Environics Poll. 1991.

provide for ongoing consultation with affected municipalities, conservation authorities, other agencies, and citizens' groups.

36. The Royal Commission further recommends that a waterfront greenway be of sufficient scope to incorporate the recommended interim and optimum routes for the Waterfront Trail. Policies for public lands along the waterfront should reflect the Province's assertion that the Waterfront Trail will be "the highest land use for all public lands along the water's edge". Policies should be developed for private lands in the greenway to encourage landowner participation in ecological restoration. In some cases, such as major blocks of private waterfront lands, negotiated public access should be sought. In

THE LYNDE VALLEY AND OTHER GREENWAYS IN THE TOWN OF WHITBY

Three major greenway components cross the Town of Whitby: the waterfront, the Oak Ridges Moraine, and the twin branches of Lynde Creek. There are several other significant local greenway opportunities along the east-west ridge created by the shoreline of prehistoric Lake Iroquois, as well as along several streams that rise from this landform feature.

Map 5.2 Town of Whitby: potential greenways

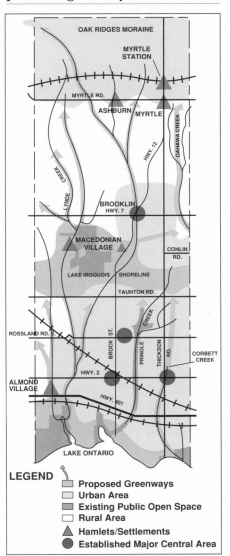

LEGEND

- Proposed Greenways
- Urban Area
- Existing Public Open Space
- Rural Area
- ▲ Hamlets/Settlements
- ● Established Major Central Area

Approximately 70 per cent of Whitby's shoreline, including several important wetlands, is publicly owned. A shoreline management study sponsored by the Central Lake Ontario Conservation Authority (CLOCA) recommended development setbacks along the entire shore, related to erosion rates. These setbacks, combined with the Town's planning policies, should result in a permanent open-space corridor along most of the shore. A recent provincial study, *The Waterfront Trail: First Steps from Concept to Reality* (Reid et al. 1991), recommended that a larger block of parkland be acquired on Thickson's Point, which provides sweeping vistas along the shore. Whitby has recommended that a large regionally significant open-space area be created south of Highway 401, between the Lynde Shores Conservation Area and Ajax.

On the other hand, there is currently no public parkland in the Whitby section of the Oak Ridges Moraine, which runs across the northern section of the town. Developing east-west greenway links along the moraine, either in Whitby or in neighbouring Scugog Township, should be a high priority.

CLOCA owns two major nodal parks in the Lynde Creek Valley: the 176-hectare (435-acre) Lynde Shores Conservation Area at the creek mouth, and the 269-hectare (665-acre) Heber Down Conservation Area just north of Taunton Road. The Town of Whitby has secured extensive portions of the valleyland system south of Heber Down Conservation Area through dedication of land as subdivisions were being developed.

North of Heber Down, where there is less immediate urban pressure, the valleylands are likely to remain in private hands for some time, and a regulatory framework to protect the natural continuity of the valleys will be essential. Landowner agreements to encourage habitat improvement and to negotiate trail corridors would be useful there. North of Myrtle Road, greenways from the east and west branches could be merged to create a single corridor north to Chalk Lake (in Scugog Township), Lynde Creek's major source.

There are a number of unopened road allowances in Whitby's rural areas. These should be considered as possible interim — or, in some cases, permanent — links in the greenway system. Within the wooded and environmentally sensitive areas along the pre-historic Lake Iroquois shoreline, there are opportunities to create east-west links across Whitby and into the neighbouring municipalities. Existing Ontario Hydro and Northern Gas rights-of-way could provide potential greenway links.

The Town has acquired most of the Pringle Creek Valley between Taunton Road and its mouth; it would be useful to extend this greenway north to link with the Lake Iroquois shoreline. The majority of the Lynde Valley system up to Rossland Road is also publicly owned. Further east, the Corbett Creek Valley could provide another greenway link. The recently adopted Region of Durham Official Plan and the Whitby Official Plan Review include a major open-space corridor between Whitby and Ajax.

Like many waterfront municipalities, Whitby has made considerable progress in securing linked open-space corridors in its more urban areas. Developing a greenway system in the rural countryside to the north will require partnerships with a variety of private landowners, and with existing commercial users such as the owners of golf courses, tree nurseries, and ski resorts.

One of the five development principles established as part of the Whitby Official Plan Review process — establishing and maintaining linked systems — provides a policy framework for a greenway system. With the participation of CLOCA, other government agencies, and community groups, the Town of Whitby appears to have a strong basis for future greenway development.

all cases of new development along the waterfront, provision for a public trail alignment should be required.

37. The Province of Ontario should maintain a resource centre and technical assistance service on greenways, land trusts, and other conservation mechanisms, available to any agency or citizens' group in the bioregion.

THE OAK RIDGES MORAINE

In June 1991, the Province released Implementation Guidelines on the Provincial Interest in the Oak Ridges Moraine Area. These are intended to control development activities in the Moraine while a two-year planning study, including extensive citizen involvement, takes place.

In October 1991, a founding committee was established for a non-profit organization dedicated to developing an Oak Ridges Moraine trail system. Preliminary work on trail routes has been carried out by MTRCA, and further investigation of trail options is under way by the Province. An equestrian trail, most of it located along roadways, has been in existence since 1975.

These activities suggest growing recognition of the ecological and recreational values of the moraine as an interconnected unit. The Implementation Guidelines recognize the importance of "stream corridors and other linear natural features which may serve as passageways for animal movement", and require the maintenance of "the health and functionality of natural corridors". It would appear to be a short step further to recognizing the potential of connected linear features in the moraine as a greenway system.

One of the moraine's striking elements is its similarity to the Niagara Escarpment. In both cases, a linear landform feature and associated natural landscapes are the focus of attention. In both cases, water quality in streams is a major concern. In both cases, threats to future integrity of the natural landform involve urban and scattered residential development, aggregate extraction, and intensive recreational developments such as golf courses. In both cases, the features of interest cut across many jurisdictions, with the Province involved to ensure that provincial interests are protected (see also Chapter 2).

Recognizing east-west elements of the moraine as greenways faces several key challenges. First, the amount of existing development, both agricultural and urban-related, in the moraine area means that a greenway there must incorporate cultural landscapes

as well as natural ones. Second, the moraine currently has only a few nodes of public lands, without extended parklands to act as a spine for conservation and recreation uses. Third — and unlike the Niagara Escarpment, which usually has a sharply defined cliff as its centrepiece — the moraine landform is relatively diffuse.

These challenges do not lessen the need for effective conservation of the moraine's natural functions; if anything, they strengthen the case for provincial involvement. They also demand new and innovative approaches, to join the needs of a working landscape, in large part privately owned, with the ecosystem imperative that must guide land use there. Therefore, a system of ridge-top and valley greenways, designed to strengthen ecological and recreational links, should be a key element of future planning for the moraine.

RECOMMENDATION

38. The Royal Commission recommends that the Oak Ridges Moraine Technical Working Committee incorporate the concept of greenways, as part of an ecosystem planning framework, into the planning exercise currently under way, and address the need for east-west links along the length of the moraine, and for continuity of an open landscape character.

VALLEYLAND AND COMMUNITY CONNECTOR GREENWAYS

Implementing a greenway system in the bioregion's valleylands and communities means finding a balance between an ecosystem-based, cross-jurisdictional system, and the desire for a grass-roots, community-based approach. Sorting out who does what may require a fair measure of co-operation, as well as a degree of provincial supervision and co-ordination. In many cases, citizens' groups with an interest in greenway benefits can lead the way, helping to define which institutional arrangements will work best for their community.

A logical starting point for most valley-land greenways is the watershed. Some watersheds cross many municipal jurisdictions, as in the case of the Don, or have valleys that form municipal boundaries, as in parts of the Rouge, the Humber, and several other rivers. In such cases, leadership for a connected greenway system will likely come from either the conservation authority or citizens' groups. In other cases, such as Whitby, most of the watershed is in one municipality, which may want to take the opportunity to create a greenway system. Elsewhere, the Town of Caledon has potential greenways related to the Niagara Escarpment, the moraine, the Credit and Humber valleys, all inside its boundaries. It would seem sensible for the Town to play a key role in integrating greenways into its jurisdiction.

In each watershed or municipal unit, the most important step is to develop a co-operative mechanism to create and implement a common greenway vision. This might be called a Community Greenways Alliance, and should include representation from:

- local municipal planning and parks/recreation departments;
- the regional municipal planning department (and parks department, if there is one);
- the local conservation authority;
- any provincial or federal agencies with land holdings or programs in the greenway area;
- local or regionally based environmental and recreation interest groups (hiking or cycling groups, naturalist clubs, land trusts, etc.);
- local community development groups (service clubs, business groups, etc.); and
- major private landowners or developers.

These suggestions for representation on greenway committees are not meant to be exclusive: for example, if a particular greenway incorporated a number of structures of historic or architectural interest, a representative from the local architectural conservation advisory committee (LACAC) would be appropriate. If the potential greenway included considerable farmland, a representative of the agricultural community should be present at the table.

These alliances have four goals:

- to develop a community greenway strategy, incorporating both arterial greenways and local connector links;
- to recommend an implementation plan for the various elements of the strategy;
- to co-ordinate specific mandates and tasks among various agencies and groups, and to build appropriate partnerships; and
- to monitor progress on implementation, and set priorities for further action.

Each alliance should be assisted by a staff person, who would report to it but could receive administrative support from

POTENTIAL GREENWAYS IN THE TOWN OF CALEDON

The Town of Caledon, in the northwestern section of the Greater Toronto biore-gion, is situated at the intersection of four provincially significant greenway corridors: the Niagara Escarpment, the Oak Ridges Moraine, the Credit Valley, and the Humber Valley. While the Caledon area does not have a major urban centre, Bolton, Caledon, Caledon East, and a half-dozen hamlets are experiencing considerable growth. Largely because of its scenic landscape, Caledon is under tremendous pressure to develop rural estates.

Land use in a band along the Niagara Escarpment is controlled by the provincially appointed Niagara Escarpment Commission, which has a mandate to maintain the natural environment and open landscape. Public lands along this landform are included in six escarpment parks, linked by the Bruce Trail. The trail was created and is managed by a private non-profit association but, through the escarpment parks program, receives some funding for land acquisition, in order to secure a permanent route.

The Metropolitan Toronto and Region Conservation Authority (MTRCA) has acquired a great deal of land in the Humber Valley between Bolton and Mono Mills. Three large nodal parks along this valley — the Albion Hills, Palgrave, and Glen Haffey conservation areas — are located in the Oak Ridges Moraine. MTRCA has proposed development of a Humber Valley trail, which would have to be linked to other greenway features throughout the valley. The Humber Heritage Committee, a group representing the watershed municipalities, is attempting to have the Humber designated as a Canadian Heritage River. Another citizens' organization, Action to Restore a Clean Humber (ARCH), is also active in issues affecting the watershed.

The Credit Valley Conservation Authority (CVCA) has assembled several strategic open- space nodes along the river, in the vicinity of Terra Cotta, Inglewood, Belfountain, Alton, and Caledon Lake. In addition, the Ministry of Natural Resources operates the Forks of the Credit Provincial Park near Cataract. A program to develop a continuous trail system along the Credit River from Lake Ontario to Orangeville was initiated by the Town of Caledon and supported by all government agencies. CVCA recently agreed to co-ordinate preparation of a concept plan for this continuous pathway system. A non-profit group, Friends of the Credit River Valley, will assist and support this project.

Caledon has been fortunate in its ability to develop east-west links along the Niagara Escarpment and Oak Ridges Moraine, which actually overlap in Caledon and have been connected by a number of conservation areas and the Bruce Trail. The Town recently purchased a former CN Rail corridor, which cuts diagonally across the full width of the municipality, and is being developed as a passive trail for non-motorized activities. This strategic corridor links many historic hamlets in the Caledon area, and provides a direct connection between the Credit and Humber valleys, the Niagara Escarpment, and the Oak Ridges Moraine.

The Great Pine Ridge equestrian trail is a connection to eastern portions of the moraine and other trail links, running east along the moraine, have been proposed by

Map 5.3 Town of Caledon: potential greenways

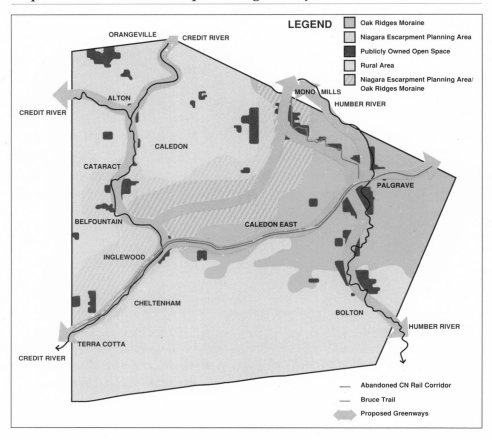

LEGEND

Oak Ridges Moraine
Niagara Escarpment Planning Area
Publicly Owned Open Space
Rural Area
Niagara Escarpment Planning Area/ Oak Ridges Moraine

— Abandoned CN Rail Corridor
— Bruce Trail
➤ Proposed Greenways

MTRCA and the Oak Ridges Moraine Planning Committee. In October 1991, a public meeting was held to discuss establishing an Oak Ridges Moraine Trail Association.

The Caledon Official Plan dates from 1976 and is currently undergoing a major review. Given the significant existing and potential greenway network in Caledon and the number of agencies and citizens' groups involved, the Town has an opportunity to build on its accomplishments and forge an extensive and fully integrated greenway system. By building community support and enlisting the co-operation of private landowners, effective ecological and recreational links can be achieved between existing public lands.

any one of the agencies involved. The work of the alliances would also be assisted by provincial policy support, technical advice, and financial assistance.

As part of developing a strategy, the alliance would consult with the community, using public meetings and other forums. The alliance's recommendations would guide relevant agencies in their greenway-related activities, as well as building a consensus for greenway development. The completed greenway strategy would become a part of the municipal Official Plan and other related documents (such as recreation Master Plans). The plan would be designed as an integrated part of community planning, rather than being viewed as external to the life of the community. It would clearly spell out responsibilities for implementation, with leadership roles to be determined through local negotiation.

A greenway strategy should bring together the needs, resources, and aspirations of the community, as well as the abilities and interests of various groups and agencies. Among its elements should be:

- an analysis of ecological resources (natural areas, watercourses, significant groundwater areas, etc.) to identify significant green nodes and connecting corridors;
- identification of existing and potential recreational attractions, trails, and other connectors;
- an inventory of existing public lands, as well as of properties slated for public acquisition, and opportunities for securing other high-priority lands;
- an analysis of visual corridors, to protect the scenic quality and appeal of proposed greenways, and to provide community separation where that is appropriate;
- integration of significant heritage elements;
- management guidelines for public lands and for compatible private land uses such as agriculture, etc.;
- identification of opportunities for compatible economic development in or adjacent to greenways;
- guidelines for the safety and security of greenway users and adjacent

landowners, and for insurance coverage where necessary;
- strategies for enhancing ecological and recreational connecting links where that is appropriate; and
- a list of priorities necessary to create or complete greenways, as well as proposed mechanisms and responsibilities for undertaking those actions.

Community greenway alliances would not disband once their strategies were completed and accepted. Rather, they would continue to co-ordinate implementation and management activities. For example, they could play a role in programming greenway uses, to ensure these continue to be valued by the community. They could work to create partnerships for specific projects, monitor progress, and address problems as they occur. Their most important ongoing role would be to ensure that greenway strategies are not simply put on a shelf, but form a guide for a wide range of concrete actions.

RECOMMENDATIONS

39. The Royal Commission recommends that provincial and local agencies encourage and support creation of community greenway alliances at the watershed or municipal level, as appropriate. Regional interest groups such as Citizens for a Lakeshore Greenway, Friends of the Credit River Valley, Action to Restore a Clean Humber, and Save the Oak Ridges Moraine should be closely involved in defining the most logical units for these alliances.

40. The Royal Commission further recommends that in developing community

greenway strategies, alliances pay particular heed to the need to:

- build municipal and other bodies' commitment to the greenway concept;
- create links compatible with an overall greenway system for the bioregion;
- give priority to protection of ecological systems, while providing informal recreation opportunities close to home;
- create mechanisms to effectively involve private landowners and developers.

41. Community greenway strategies should focus on creating a common vision, a community consensus, and a community commitment to work toward implementing that vision. In developing greenways, communities should take advantage of considerable valleylands that are already publicly held.

42. Community greenway strategies should include creation of continuous arterial greenways in the following valleys:

> Grindstone Creek
> Bronte Creek
> Sixteen Mile Creek
> Credit River
> Humber River
> Don River
> Rouge River
> Duffin Creek
> Lynde Creek
> Oshawa Creek
> Bowmanville Creek
> Wilmot Creek

> Ganaraska River
> Cobourg Brook
> Shelter Valley Brook

THE PROVINCIAL ROLE IN CREATING GREENWAYS

Speaking in the Legislature on 17 December 1990, the Honourable Ruth Grier, Ontario's Minister of the Environment, said:

> Our clear endorsement of Mr. Crombie's principles should be viewed by municipalities and the community as a ringing endorsement of the ecosystem approach to planning as well as to the underlying values of the Commission report. . . . We intend to use those nine principles as a guide, not only for the waterfront, but to move beyond the waterfront — to the GTA urban structure process.

Provincial support and assistance in creating greenways should be a central component in carrying out this commitment. The Province should require that greenways be considered an integral part of the infrastructure of municipalities in the future; when land-use planners talk about infrastructure needs, they should also be talking about greenways with the same emphasis as they give roads, sewers, electricity, and other essential services.

Several forms of provincial involvement in creating greenways are needed:

- legislative and policy backing, for provincial agencies, conservation authorities, and municipalities;
- direct involvement in implementation in selected areas, particularly along

the waterfront and on the Oak Ridges Moraine;

- technical assistance on greenway design and implementation, in support of community activities;
- financial commitment for planning activities, priority land acquisition, and trail development and maintenance; and
- broad co-ordination of a greenway system throughout the bioregion.

One of the key questions about the provincial role is whether a comprehensive new greenways act is required; while such legislation would symbolize provincial commitment to the concept, this Commission does not believe it is a prerequisite to action at this point. However, several amendments to existing legislation are required, to strengthen tools for creating greenways.

It is more important, in the Commission's view, for the Province to create incentives for creating greenways. These can be viewed in two packages: those that encourage municipalities and other agencies to take part in greenway planning and implementation; and those that secure participation by private owners of land in greenways.

Many of the incentives proposed in Ron Kanter's 1990 report, *Space for All: Options for a Greater Toronto Area Greenlands Strategy*, can be applied to greenways. For instance, the proposals for a five-year, $100-million acquisition fund and for a Greenlands Foundation warrant further consideration.

In general, public acquisition of land should be considered a last resort in securing greenways. However, there will be instances, particularly where vital connectors for trails or other public access are required, in which no other means are likely to succeed. Without some form of significant provincial funding, a program of greenways in the bioregion would be crippled from the start.

Rather than simply allocating a set amount from the Consolidated Revenue Fund, however, there may be alternate, more effective means of providing funding. In the same way that a special tire tax is now collected to fund environmentally sound tire disposal, a designated tax source tied to land development could be used to create greenways and, thereby, contribute to environmental health.

When land-use planners talk about infrastructure needs, they should also be talking about greenways with the same emphasis as they give roads, sewers, electricity, and other essential services.

Some American states levy a greenway surcharge on the Land Transfer Tax; typically in the one-to two-per-cent range, it has the advantage of producing added revenues when development activities are at their peak, and when funding for protecting greenways is most needed.

Given the emphasis on community involvement in greenways, it would seem entirely consistent to provide funding assistance for acquisition on a matching, rather than a full-cost, basis. Again, experience in such American states as New Hampshire provides some interesting possibilities. Rather than providing a set rate of matching funding, they allow local agencies to "bid" for funding, based on the ability of the to pay, the priority given to the project, the

> **G**reenways . . . have the potential to
> be this country's most important land-
> based effort for conservation and
> recreation in the next several decades
> . . . . They can . . . give pride of accom-
> plishment and responsibility to millions
> of people in every community. They
> can protect vital water, fish, wildlife,
> and recreation resources as integral
> parts of the growth of cities and
> communities. And, if greenways truly
> capture the imagination and boldness
> of the American spirit, they could
> eventually form the corridors that con-
> nect open spaces, parks, forests, and
> deserts — and Americans — from sea
> to shining sea.
>
> President's Commission on Americans Outdoors. 1987.
> *Americans outdoors: the legacy, the challenge.*Washington, D.C.:
> Island Press.

ability to attract matching funds, and
other factors.

If a landowner agrees to sell below
full market value, the donated value can
be used as part of the local matching
funds, as can the value of lands or con-
servtion easements donated elsewhere in
the local system. This flexibility greatly
increases incentives for local creativity, and
maximizes the value received for each
public dollar.

Administering grants and other incentive programs could be carried out by an
appointed Greenways/Greenlands Foundation, which could also act as an agent of the
Crown to receive donations. One model for
this foundation is the British Countryside
Commission, a highly successful agency
that collaborates with others to benefit
the countryside. Among other things, the

Countryside Commission carries out
research on landscape change and leisure
patterns, and on new approaches to the care
and enjoyment of the landscape. It works
with planning authorities, provides technical advice, and offers grants to landowners
and agencies for conservation and public
access projects. While it places great emphasis on partnerships, it does not own or
manage land directly.

Given its current initiatives, the
Province is already strongly involved in
creating greenways along the waterfront
and in the Oak Ridges Moraine and Niagara
Escarpment areas. Elsewhere in the bioregion and in other parts of Ontario, the
Province should act as catalyst and suppor-
ter of local actions, and as a partner in
providing new tools and funding support
for establishing greenways.

RECOMMENDATIONS

43. The Royal Commission recommends
that the Province give high priority
to introducing a legislative package
as follows:

- amendments to the relevant
  sections of the Conservation
  Authorities Act to clarify the
  mandate of conservation authorities to undertake environmental
  protection and recreation
  activities related to greenways;
- amendments to the Planning Act
  to require that, in the case of
  development, valleylands, wetlands, and other significant natural environments be dedicated
  to a public agency, or protected
  in private hands through such

Meewasin Valley Trail, Saskatoon

permanent mechanisms as conservation easements; this would be in addition to lands dedicated for park purposes;

- introduction of enabling legislation to permit municipalities, conservation authorities, and non-profit conservation organizations to hold conservation easements, so that local bodies can use this important conservation technique.

44. The Royal Commission further recommends that, under the Planning Act, the Province prepare a policy regarding the incorporation of greenway strategies into municipal Official Plans, and define the elements to be included in a greenway strategy.

45. The Province should establish a greenways/trails unit in the appropriate ministry to co-ordinate policies, programs, and activities across Ontario, and to act as a source of technical assistance and advice for local jurisdictions.

THE ROLE OF THE FEDERAL GOVERNMENT

While most activities related to greenways involve provincial or municipal agencies, there are several ways in which the federal government can play a supportive role: for example, it could make a statement of support for partnership arrangements involving federal lands or could formalize the process for disposing of abandoned rail rights-of-way which, in some cases, could provide important recreational links.

At present, once a railway line has been abandoned, federal authorities have no jurisdiction over the property, which reverts to the railway. The railway may then sell rights-of-way in parcels, as it sees fit, or retain them for real estate development (obviously the most profitable course in urban centres).

The federal government can also use its taxing powers to encourage private landowners to participate in greenways. While it is likely that, over time, some public-spirited landowners may be willing to donate lands for greenways, a donation of real property to the Crown or to a non-profit charity is a "deemed disposition" for tax purposes: the donor may be liable for significant capital gains taxes, although he has donated his property for public benefit.

The inequity of this situation has been recognized in cases where cultural artifacts are donated, through the Cultural Property Import and Export Act , which exempts them from being considered capital gains in the donor's income. Designated non-federal institutions are also allowed to issue charitable receipts equivalent to those for gifts to the Crown, which can provide a tax advantage to the donor. Similar treatment is needed for those who donate natural lands or interests in lands. Otherwise, the painting of a natural landscape could be more favourably treated than a gift of the land itself.

RECOMMENDATIONS

46. The Royal Commission recommends that the Government of Canada encourage its departments and agencies to co-operate, in any feasible way, in establishing greenways involving federal lands.

47. The Royal Commission further recommends that the federal government, in co-operation with the provinces and the railways, seek to establish adequate formal procedures for disposing of rail rights-of-way after they have been abandoned, so that they can be acquired or retained for future use as a greenway corridor, if any level of government deems that use desirable.

48. The federal government should introduce appropriate legislation or amendments to permit significant lands, or interests in lands, to be donated to qualified organizations without triggering capital gains assessments, and to permit the use of a tax credit up to the full value of the donation.

CHAPTER 6:
WINTER WATERFRONT

The greenway system proposed in the previous chapter offers opportunities for more people to enjoy the waterfront. Those who currently visit it in the colder months know how beautiful the shoreline is, year-round. However, most people assume that high-quality outdoor waterfront experiences in the Greater Toronto bioregion occur only during the summer months. Therefore, it is useful to examine the potential of the waterfront and river valleys to create different but equally memorable experiences in the colder months, from mid-September to mid-May. Harbourfront and the City of Toronto's eastern beaches offer examples of waterfront areas already well-used throughout the year.

In April 1990, the Board of Trade of Metropolitan Toronto suggested to the Royal Commission that a study be undertaken to "explore the possibilities of more wintertime recreational and entertainment activities along the central waterfront." As a result, the Commission organized a work group comprising representatives from local and regional agencies, including the Board of Trade, to examine ways of enhancing outdoor use, and to prepare a report on the matter. The *Winter Waterfront* working paper was released by the Commission in December 1991 as a contribution to enhancing year-round waterfront use in Metropolitan Toronto.

The Greater Toronto waterfront is more than 175 kilometres (109 miles) long, encompassing an impressive variety of places — from peaceful natural wilderness areas to towering residential condominiums adjacent to highways and commercial/tourist facilities. From Burlington Bay to the Trent River, there is a great deal of potential to improve year-round waterfront use, at low cost.

From Burlington Bay to the Trent River, there is a great deal of potential to improve year-round waterfront use, at low cost.

ENHANCING WINTER WATERFRONT USE

Emerging development of a greenway system will increase year-round use of the Greater Toronto waterfront. Municipalities and conservation authorities would benefit from sharing pertinent information and participating in joint waterfront user studies. Municipalities could also contribute by adopting and implementing policies that achieve six major goals:

- providing year-round access;
- ameliorating outdoor climate;
- providing facilities to accommodate year-round activities;
- increasing year-round opportunities for contact with nature;
- enhancing user safety; and
- improving winter events and programming.

PROVIDING YEAR-ROUND ACCESS

Accessibility to recreational areas is a key element in enhancing year-round use. The variety of walkways, ranging from the broad promenades at Toronto's Harbour-front to the modest paths and nature trails in Mississauga's Rattray Marsh or the Rouge River Valley in Scarborough, reflect the diversity of the bioregion's waterfront and river valleys; this should be retained, but connections between the various amenities should be made more comfortable.

The proposed greenway system would accommodate pedestrians and cyclists and would provide continuous access to water-front promenades, parks, open spaces, and links to adjacent areas. The system should be safe and comfortable, connecting water-front areas and the river valleys. The route of the waterfront greenway should be evaluated according to its ability to offer year-round use to pedestrians, cyclists, and others, including seniors and the physically challenged, and recognizing that some portions might be only seasonally accessible. Washrooms and

food concessions should also be provided at appropriate nodal points and should be open to the public, as much as possible throughout the year. Frequent year-round public transit service to the waterfront, with shelters designed to be comfortable in the colder months, would also encourage use.

Waterfront Visits

Summer Visits

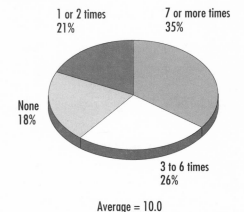

Average = 10.0

Winter Visits

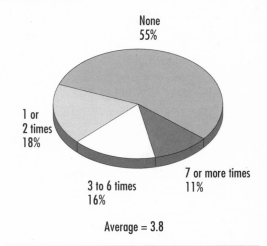

Average = 3.8

The respondents visit the waterfront on average ten times in the summer and four times in the winter.

Source: Environics Poll. 1991.

Parking along the waterfront should be integrated into the surrounding environment; limited amounts should be carefully located along the waterfront, accommodating those who cannot walk long distances and enjoy visiting the waterfront, and those who enjoy viewing the lake from within a parked car.

AMELIORATING OUTDOOR CLIMATE

The climate of the Greater Toronto bioregion waterfront area is affected by the Great Lakes, which tend to make average winter temperatures three celsius degrees warmer and summer temperatures about one and-a-half degrees cooler than in the hinterland. In winter months, the influence of the lakes causes constant freezing and thawing periods, often making weather unpredictable and the use of outdoor spaces sporadic.

The prevailing mean daily wind direction for the Toronto region shifts according to the season: in winter it is from the west about 50 per cent of the time. In spring, prevailing winds come from the west only four per cent of the time, and 42 per cent from the northeast. In summer, the prevailing winds are from the southwest 61 per cent of the time, while in autumn they come from the west/northwest almost half the time.

Some northern cities with colder climates provide year-round facilities, but the challenge in cities such as Toronto, where weather is less predictable, is to use the urban design process to ameliorate wind conditions and maximize access to the sun: year-round facilities requiring substantial financial investment are not always necessary.

There are two basic ways of reducing wind velocity in a specific site: by planting vegetation or building structures such as berms, walls, and screens. Berms, combined with trees and shrubs, provide effective year-round windscreening, the degree of effectiveness varying with the porosity of the plantings. For example, very dense evergreens achieve a strong reduction (about 80 per cent) in wind speed and force but such reductions can be sustained only for short distances (about the equivalent of five tree heights), because of the return flow of deflected air to the ground. Less dense planting reduces the sheltering effect but increases the range at which it is effective.

The relationship between microclimate and use of the outdoor environment during colder months has been studied in various places. For example, Scandinavian studies show that, on days when the temperature is as low as 10 celsius degrees but there is no wind, people will feel comfortable even without heavy clothing and will make use of outdoor open space.

A recent research study concluded that Toronto's microclimate could be moderated by providing shelter against the wind, thereby extending comfortable outdoor use by approximately 56 additional days a year — an extension of park use of almost 50 per cent over the existing 18-week base season. (See Figure 6.1.) Because ambient temperatures in March, April, and May are often below the human comfort level of 10 degrees celsius, but sunlight and the length of days are increasing, techniques that offer site-specific shelter from the wind and that capture the sun in strategic spaces could increase temperatures and encourage use of these areas.

Temperatures in October and November are still in the outdoor comfort range but the effect of wet, windy weather on people needs to be addressed, if comfortable levels of outdoor use are to be achieved.

Studies examining the effects of built forms on sun and wind conditions and on pedestrians at street level have been done locally and in other parts of the world. San

Francisco recently developed and adopted solar access and wind comfort standards for modifying building forms, heights, densities, and setbacks to ensure that developments do not put open-space pedestrian environments in shadow and do not generate a wind tunnel effect.

In response to massive development that reduced usable open space in San Francisco's downtown and on its waterfront, voters approved referendum "Proposition K" in 1984; it requires that access to sun be protected in all public parks and open spaces under the jurisdiction of the Parks and Recreation Department, from one hour after sunrise to one hour before sunset throughout the year. Following the referendum,

Figure 6.1   Increasing year-round use of parks by removing wind chill effects

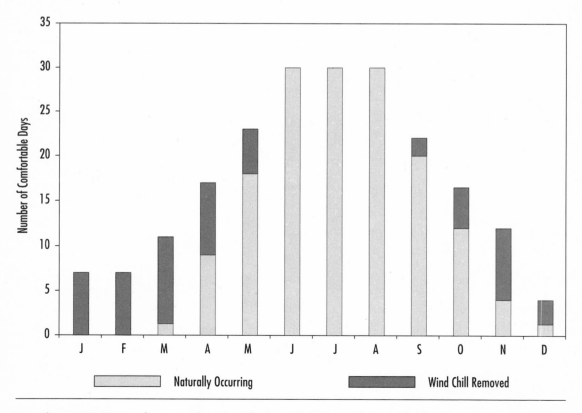

Source: Klinger, X. 1991. *Winter waterfront: year-round use in Metropolitan Toronto.* Working papers of the Canadian Waterfront Resource Centre, no. 9. Toronto: Royal Commission on the Future of the Toronto Waterfront.

several related amendments about access to sun on sidewalks and other open spaces have also been adopted.

Guidelines for controlling windiness in public open spaces in Toronto's Central Area were developed in 1974 but have not been adopted as part of its Official Plan. Currently, developers are encouraged to assess a project's impact on the microclimate of surrounding areas but — because proposals are tested for wind effects only in the final stage of the planning approvals process — are seldom required to make changes.

A 1991 study undertaken for the City of Toronto as part of Cityplan '91 examined and analysed the effect of buildings on wind conditions at street level and the combined effect of sun and wind conditions on pedestrian comfort. It recommended establishing procedures and standards for preserving access to sunlight on Central Area sidewalks, parks, and open spaces, and confirmed that sun and wind conditions are critical to outdoor uses, particularly in spring and fall. The report also suggested further studies to establish performance standards that will protect pedestrians from possible high winds resulting from future development such as those proposed for the Railway Lands.

Microclimate improvements in built forms, such as courtyards and wind-screening buildings, have been demonstrated in several Scandinavian projects. Studies show that courtyard use may be extended by about six weeks, most notably in spring, by applying the 10 degrees celsius comfort criterion. This microclimate improvement was achieved by applying urban design guidelines for each residential block — building heights are gradually increased from two stories at the southern edge of the

Modest sunpocket at High Park in Toronto

courtyard to six storeys at the northern edge to screen out prevailing cold winds while allowing for maximum solar penetration.

Although appropriate authorities have a general understanding of the benefits of improving outdoor comfort levels, more appropriate policies, standards, and guidelines could be developed and implemented. For example, wind comfort and sun access standards would be helpful in developing all publicly accessible urban promenades, open spaces, and parks on the waterfront. Related guidelines could include the design of sitting areas and walkways located in areas protected from winter winds, sheltered to maintain views.

When building heights are routinely increased . . . the shadow impacts are greatly increased. For those on the receiving end the change is not one of degree; it may be absolute. They had sun; now they have none . . . Sunlight should be a right, not an amenity that is nice to have.

Whyte, W. H. 1988. *City: rediscovering the centre.* New York: Doubleday Anchor Books.

Windgate of Main Street Mall in Buffalo, New York

Sunpockets can also be created in appropriate locations along the waterfront to encourage outdoor use in the off-season. These are a site-specific tool that can ensure solar access — semi-enclosed seating areas with direct sunshine access, protected from winds. They can be created using landscaping or other screening methods and are particularly desirable on the waterfront, where they can block the wind and provide vistas and views to the open water.

Walls and windgates should also be considered as wind protectors at promenade or park entrances and along roads. Windgates could be made of transparent materials, similar to those proposed as protection for walking areas in the City of Buffalo. Combined with vines and other plantings, they could become attractive sculptural elements and park landmarks.

PROVIDING FACILITIES TO ACCOMMODATE YEAR-ROUND ACTIVITIES

Available information on summer use indicates that walking, sitting, and enjoying nature are the most popular activities on the waterfront. Limited available data indicate that these activities, in addition to others such as skating, remain the most popular outdoor waterfront activities in the colder months.

Cold, snow, and ice tend to hinder outdoor recreational use in winter months, especially on the waterfront. To capitalize on investments and increase use, existing and future recreational and sports facilities on the waterfront should be re-examined, looking for ways to maximize year-round use. For example, the courts used for tennis in summer could be used for skating in winter, while swimming pools could be converted for year-round use: uncovered in summer, enclosed in winter.

Improvements to waterfront facilities should be based on the interests and needs of both local and regional users, determined through surveys if necessary. Public consultation would also help determine which areas are more likely to be used throughout the colder months, and warrant immediate attention. Special emphasis should be placed on the needs of the elderly, physically challenged, women, children, teenagers, families, and ethnic communities.

The length of recreational outings in cold weather will depend, in part, on air temperatures and the degree of protection from the wind. As a rule of thumb, people will walk for approximately ten minutes in winter before they need to warm up, with seniors and children more susceptible to cold. Walks and visits tend to be much shorter than in the summer, depending on the attractions and on available facilities such as washrooms, sheltered seating areas, and food outlets. Further studies of behavioural patterns of various user groups are required to pinpoint the length of travel time and average duration of a winter waterfront visit.

Locating facilities at selected nodal points along walkways would increase use and promote longer visits. Shelters from wind, rain, and snow, that still allow enjoyment of lake views, would also encourage prolonged visits to the waterfront as the weather gets cooler. Strategic locations for shelters include places where visitors linger or sit, such as look-out points and along walkways; these could be designed in combination with food concessions and washrooms.

Existing facilities in park areas could be modified to function throughout the year. For example, gazebos could be adapted

Waterfront Activities

Summer Activities

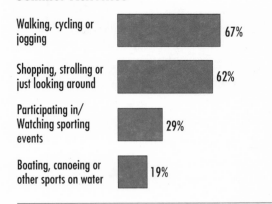

Winter Activities

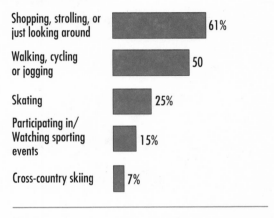

Participation in summer and winter waterfront activities by the respondents.

Source: Environics Poll. 1991.

with temporary enclosures such as transparent or glass panels and could even be equipped with stoves and wood to warm those who use the area for prolonged visits.

There is a general lack of seating in urbanized waterfront areas and parks. To foster year-round use, seating capacity standards and guidelines should be developed and applied for areas including parks and promenades. A lot of existing seating is unusable in winter: concrete benches and steps are too cold, and seats in the shade, exposed to wind or covered with snow are rarely used.

Where it is appropriate, and especially where access to sun is limited in peak use periods, consideration should be given to movable seating. Movable chairs and benches allow users to take maximum advantage of sun and shade conditions. Moreover, flexible seating arrangements provide opportunities for both privacy and social interaction: Paris, New York, London, and Stockholm provide movable seats in many of their parks, and some — like the little chairs in the Luxembourg Gardens — have become park trademarks.

Vandalism and theft are often given as reasons for not providing movable chairs. However, this runs contrary to the experience at New York's Metropolitan Museum of Art,

which provides 200 movable chairs along its front steps, and leaves them out 24 hours a day, seven days a week. The Met found that it is less costly to replace stolen chairs than to pay for storage each night.

INCREASING OPPORTUNITIES FOR CONTACT WITH NATURE

One natural attraction of the outdoors is its seasonally changing moods; many places appeal to people because of natural features: a relaxing fall walk to view the changing colours; a family outing to learn about plants and animals on a wildlife reserve or conservation area; a spectacular view of the bluffs.

Sometimes what is a magnificent view in winter can be undistinguished in summer — a snow-covered landscape, for example.

Movable chairs in Luxembourg Gardens, Paris

Seasonal opportunities along the waterfront could offer the chance to:

- observe birds and butterflies along their migratory flight paths in spring and fall;
- follow winter animal tracks in the snow;
- observe and feed winter waterfowl;
- view the frozen lake and sculptured icy waves in winter;
- observe trees and shrubs, with their interesting bark, branch patterns, and clinging berries in winter; and
- appreciate the seasonal experiences of silence and the smell of melting snow in the winter, changing colours in the fall, warm spring breezes, and the softness of summer days.

Low sun angles and long shadows in winter present opportunities to exploit the intricacies of gates, trellises, sculptures, and plantings to create imaginative winter landscapes and enhance outdoor spaces.

Fragrant and tactile gardens would also offer those with impaired vision or limited mobility special opportunities for enjoying nature year-round. Only a few waterfront sites, such as the Royal Botanical Gardens in Burlington and the Rosetta McClain Gardens in Scarborough, currently do so.

Vistas should be developed with consideration given to seasonal weather, ambient light, and colour. Care should be taken to ensure that structures such as windgates and windscreens do not impair these views. Low angles of sun and long shadows in winter present opportunities to exploit the intricacies of gates, trellises, sculptures, and plantings designed to create imaginative winter landscapes and enhance outdoor spaces. Lighting,

ice, and the kinetic energy of wind can also be combined to devise intricate seasonal sculptures. Other ideas include using lake water to create fountains, cascades, ponds, and channels that could be artificially frozen to create skating and hockey areas.

Year-round nature interpretation centres should be provided in selected regional parks where natural areas, woodlands, marshes, and wetlands constitute a significant proportion of parkland. Nature trails should include sheltered areas for observing and describing natural species, habitats, and geological formations. Special winter outdoor educational programs for children could be developed and would include games, nature hikes or exploration tours, bird-watching, and animal tracking.

ENHANCING USER SAFETY

Given that the presence of people makes a place feel safe, the greater the number at a particular area of the waterfront, the safer they all feel. The safer they feel, the more inclined they are to continue visiting an area — an important factor, especially during colder seasons when fewer people use the waterfront and there are fewer hours of daylight.

The proposed greenway could make access to parts of the waterfront safer and more comfortable by adding connections from the city to the water, from downtown offices to waterfront parks, and from neighbourhoods to the water's edge, during the winter months.

In designing safe and comfortable recreational areas and pathways, consideration should be given to the change in level of usage and its effect on safety. The configuration and types of vegetation, proper lighting, effective signage, and seasonal wind and ice conditions should be considered and, where possible, bad-weather hazards should be ameliorated and safety improved.

Carefully sited built forms and well-designed facilities, complemented by events staged on the waterfront, could draw large crowds, increasing perceptions of the area as being safe.

IMPROVING WINTER EVENTS AND PROGRAMMING

Special outdoor events and festival programming at the waterfront have so far focused on the summer season, while unpredictable changes in climate and increased temperatures have made it difficult to stage traditional outdoor events in winter. Local cities have sponsored winter festivals and events that failed because they were planned for cold, snowy conditions that did not materialize.

In order to increase seasonal tourism and recreation, emphasis should be given to events and activities that do not depend on ice and snow. Entertainment should be used as a means of promoting the waterfront's unique attributes: Christmas tree decorating, bonfires, and winter-adapted summer sports such as camping, marathons, triathlons, and canoeing could form the basis for successful festivals. Planning for such events should take into account the needs of nearby communities, especially in regard to potential traffic, parking, and other issues.

Efforts should also be made to facilitate the development of community-based annual outdoor/indoor events.

During the colder months in Toronto, special waterfront events are often held indoors in selected locations such as Harbourfront, Ontario Place, and Exhibition Place. Harbourfront's York Quay in Toronto is a good example of a popular site for recreational and educational water-related activities in the summer and skating and other uses in the winter. Further north, Nathan Phillips Square is used as a venue for numerous promotional events, such as fund-raising campaigns and art exhibitions. The square is a breathing space in front of Toronto's City Hall, with a park-like atmosphere in summer that appeals to hundreds of people who sit and eat their lunch or simply relax in the sun. At other times of the year, the reflecting pool becomes a skating rink, while nearby concessions serve the public. Popular outdoor activities such as pleasure skating should continue to be accommodated along the waterfront.

For more than 35 years, Québec City has had an annual winter carnival, 11 days in February filled with outdoor activities such as skating along 3.8 kilometres (2 miles) of the St. Charles River, a perilous canoe race in the half-frozen St. Lawrence River, a snow sculpture contest, and horseback riding. There are also many indoor events, including a beach party, an exotic hair-styling and make-up competition, a fashion show featuring Canadian designers, and a casino night.

Ottawa has its own February event, the 10-day Winterlude Festival. Activities include such adaptations of summer sports as snow-golfing and a triathlon that comprises skating, skiing, and running. Among other events is a 160-kilometre (100-mile) Canadian ski marathon, which receives more than 1,000 entries each year.

Other North American cities also mount special winter activities: Easton, Maryland, hosts a Waterfowl Festival in mid-November to celebrate waterfowl conservation. The International Eelpout Festival in Walker, Minnesota, held in mid-February, began as a spoof on all the north woods fishing contests and a celebration for those who had survived the "worst" of winter, but is now enormously popular and draws thousands of fishers. In Fond du Lac, Wisconsin, the "Spectacle of the Geese" each September celebrates the migration of Canada geese to the marshes, with sunrise and sunset viewing tours and paddlewheel boat excursions to see fall colours. The success of these events does not depend on snowfall or very cold temperatures, and similar activities may be well-suited to southern Ontario's climate, the joy of winter being celebrated whatever the weather.

In winter, the city's cultural life is at its peak, with theatres, concert halls, restaurants, and cafés alive with people. However, if urban promenades, parks, and open spaces had a higher level of comfort, some of those activities could be brought outdoors. If the Greater Toronto bioregion is to develop further as a tourist area during the colder months, there must be better attempts to promote outdoor winter opportunities on the waterfront, linked to the river valleys, as well as to the unique setting, culture, and history of the shoreline.

OPPORTUNITIES FOR MAXIMIZING YEAR-ROUND USE

It is not feasible nor necessary to "winterize" the entire Greater Toronto bioregion waterfront. Rather, appropriate waterfront nodes should be selected as potential sites for year-round use and for staging winter events and festivals of a regional, national, and even international scale. These sites should be connected to the greenway and year-round public transit should be encouraged.

It is not feasible nor necessary to "winterize" the entire Greater Toronto bioregion waterfront. Rather, nodes for year-round use and for staging winter events and festivals should be selected and connected to the greenway.

The waterfront from Burlington Bay to the Trent River has a number of successful recreational areas, although primarily in the summer months, and they are the nodes with the most potential for year-round use. Many of them could be improved with vegetation barriers or shelters, at little cost to managing agencies, but with the promise of increased use and added revenue.

Four such recreational nodes in the Region of Halton, each adding to the diversity of the regional waterfront, are as follows:

- Spencer Smith Park, on the Burlington waterfront, is a well-used facility in summer for boat-launching and passive recreational activities; its location, immediately adjacent to the downtown area, gives it tremendous potential for year-round use.
- The Oakville and Bronte Harbour areas in the Town of Oakville could

also be winterized at little cost and indoor club facilities could support outdoor recreational uses. Catering to the boating community, the regional facilities serve boaters, most of them in the western part of the Greater Toronto bioregion.

- Coronation Park in the Town of Oakville is one of the larger active waterfront parks, attracting many families. Amenities include summer weekend concerts and children's play equipment. As in the case of many local waterfront parks, the most popular winter activities here are walking and viewing.

Mississauga, the only Region of Peel municipality adjacent to Lake Ontario, has a variety of recreational waterfront uses:

- Jack Darling Memorial Park, between the Rattray Marsh nature preserve and forests and ravines in privately owned Lorne Park Estates, provides waterfront recreation and is surrounded by complementary uses. Seasonal park facilities could be extended to support added outdoor winter activities as well as the tobogganing that is now popular in the winter.
- To the east, the Port Credit Harbour area south of Mississauga's downtown houses one of the largest fresh-water marinas in North America. Although much of the harbour is currently publicly owned, it is leased to private operators, which limits public access. City proposals to revitalize the area and increase public access could increase the harbour's year-round potential. Adjacent indoor recreational facilities

at J. C. Saddington Park would also serve to enhance year-round use.

- Canada Post's site on the waterfront offers significant long-term potential for mixed uses, including year-round recreational facilities, particularly if some existing buildings can be adapted.

Metropolitan Toronto also has a number of diverse waterfront nodes with great potential for year-round use:

- Etobicoke's motel strip/Humber Bay Park area is the subject of ongoing review. Future development plans will likely include extensive residential and retail areas, creation of wetlands, and educational and recreational facilities. A proposed community park and supporting amenities are intended to accommodate major events and festivals. Humber Bay Park East is already well-used during the summer months; improvements could greatly enhance comfort and safety in the park, bringing in more regional park users during the colder months.
- Harbourfront and Garrison Common attract visitors regionally, nationally, and internationally. Harbourfront currently provides the most extensive year-round programming and entertainment along the Greater Toronto bioregion waterfront. The majority of off-season events are held indoors, although winter programs organized around the skating rink are very popular. If future public and private open spaces are designed for year-round use, there will be opportunities to expand events outdoors.

WINTER IN HUMBER BAY PARK

Etobicoke's Humber Bay parks east and west are well-used during the summer, but would benefit further from winter facilities and programming. Proposed redevelopment along the nearby motel strip may substantially boost demand for park use throughout the year. Thoughtful and low-cost improvements to existing facilities could result in high quality recreation for an increasing number of winter visitors.

The parks already have good road access and abundant parking, but public transit connections and facilities must be improved; building shelters for and servicing of both parks by TTC buses would increase accessibility. An existing proposal for relocating the nearby GO station may result in improved regional transit access.

Park vegetation is predominantly deciduous, which often means a bleak winter landscape; planting coniferous trees and shrubs would create a more attractive environment, provide wildlife habitat, and improve the microclimate. Metro's parks department has already begun planting native species in Humber Bay Park East. Extending wetlands on both sides of the fishing pier would promote wildlife diversity. The shoreline is the most desireable area for walking and sitting, but is exposed directly to winter winds; planting trees along the south and east shorelines of both parks would provide wind-screening.

Well-defined walking and bicycling paths exist throughout Humber Bay Park East, but not in Humber Bay Park West. The trail network — separated from roadways — should be expanded throughout the site and along the shoreline to maximize views to the lake. The trail should connect both parks via a bridge over Mimico Creek and extend north along the banks of the creek. Major walkways should be constructed using heat-absorbing surface materials, which would make winter maintenance easier.

Seating should be increased in both parks, especially in Humber Bay Park East, which attracts more people. Skating and winter bird-watching along Mimico Creek and nearby natural areas could be enhanced if resting areas were provided in landscaped outdoor sunpockets. A gazebo-type shelter adjacent to the canal would benefit both pedestrians and skaters.

There are no food concessions open permanently to the public, although mobile ones cater to park users occasionally on summer days. In winter, mobile vendors could provide visitors with hot chocolate while they walked or skated. An existing comfort station in Humber Bay Park East could be enlarged to house a café/restaurant and horticultural display. Signs at all park entrances should give people information about year-round facilities.

The reduced number of park visitors during the winter season increases the risk of assault. Landscaping should reinforce safety, without detracting from the natural setting. Year-round food concessions would create a permanent presence in the park; pedestrian lighting and visitor information kiosks at park entrances would also create a safer environment.

Improvements now and in the future will attract more visitors; as the number of people using the Humber Bay parks increases, so will opportunities for expanding winter facilities and programming.

Source: Klinger, X. Winter waterfront: year-round use in Metropolitan Toronto. *1991. Working papers of the Canadian Waterfront Resource Centre, no. 9. Toronto: Royal Commission on the Future of the Toronto Waterfront.*

Figure 6.2   Winter waterfront case study: proposed improvements for Humber Bay Park

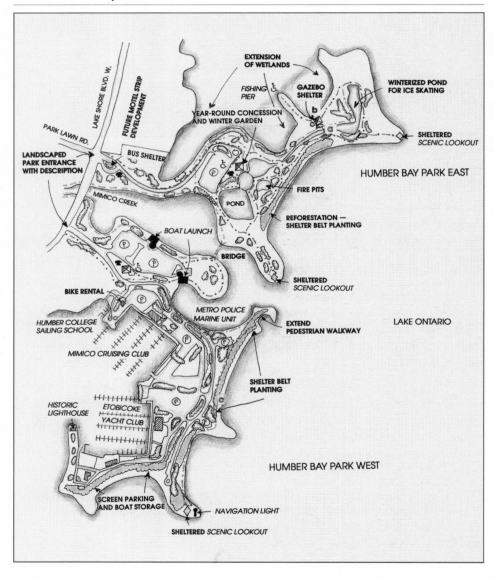

People promenading along Toronto's Harbourfront in March

The Preliminary Master Plan for Garrison Common (Berridge Lewinberg Greenberg et al. 1991) examines year-round use in the area. Right now, outdoor spaces are used primarily during the summer, while design and programming ignore the possibility of year-round utilization. Winter climatic conditions here are harsh and open spaces would have to be modified to provide an acceptable microclimate.

- The park on the Toronto Islands is currently used year-round, as a major regional public place that accommodates millions of visitors, primarily during the summer season. With a few low-cost, key modifications, it could be made more comfortable, attractive, and accessible in the colder seasons. The feasibility of the present location of the Ferry Terminal should also be reviewed for potential as a year-round operation.

The Islands already have a good vegetation base, including evergreen trees planted in the past five years. Additional planting would help to screen open spaces currently exposed to strong winds. Overall, in fact, winterization would require relatively little additional investment. Winter programming would also help to increase the number of park users.

- The Guild Inn and Guildwood Park in Scarborough are already used year-round. The hotel is privately operated, while the park, including an extensive collection of architectural artifacts, is operated by Metro and is open to the public. The park is especially beautiful in winter, when it can be viewed against a serene background of snow, evergreens, and the lake. Future redevelopment plans for the Guild Inn should maintain the site's existing scale and character and enhance year-round use.

While portions of the Durham waterfront are not yet fully developed, there could be recreational waterfront nodes in the future, providing opportunities for developing year-round use. Of those already developed, the key nodes on the Lake Ontario shoreline that have potential for year-round enhancement are as follows:

- The Petticoat Creek Conservation Area, in Pickering, surrounded by residential homes, currently operates seasonally and caters primarily to families; adding indoor recreational facilities would probably mean year-round use of the area.
- The Lynde Shores Conservation Area in Whitby is well-known as a place for viewing wildlife in the spring and autumn months, with boardwalks and viewing facilities. Both the Lynde Creek and Cranberry marshes provide excellent habitat for nesting birds. Summer activities at the conservation area include picnicking, fishing, and canoeing while winter-time users include participants in scheduled events such

as winter bird-feeder tours and skating on the Lynde Creek Marsh — one of the area's most popular outdoor winter activities. Future improvements could include an interpretive centre with improved indoor washroom facilities.
- The harbour area in the City of Oshawa is currently being studied with respect to its future uses. It has potential to be developed for uses including recreational with year-round facilities.
- Darlington Provincial Park in the Town of Newcastle is a haven for rugged outdoor types — camping and fishing are most popular in this passive and active park. Other waterfront areas along the Newcastle shoreline have yet to be developed for recreational or other uses. In planning for these sites, consideration should be given to building form and design and to recreational facilities that promote use throughout the year.

STEPS TO WINTERIZATION

Local and regional waterfront planning policies and practices should recognize the potential for enhancing outdoor recreational use in the colder months. Municipalities should undertake user surveys, and adopt and implement appropriate policies after public consultation, and with the co-operation of relevant governments, agencies, and special-purpose bodies. Standards and guidelines for sun access and wind comfort levels should be developed and enforced, requiring studies of wind impact, sun access, and other relevant factors before issuing project approvals. These studies should include assurances that there will be no detrimental change in wind patterns, velocities, and turbulence at the sites in question. Wind testing of proposed projects should also be conducted by the proponents early in the approvals process and be taken into account in planning and urban design decisions.

Proposed developments for areas in which wind speeds already exceed acceptable comfort levels should aim to reduce these speeds. New promenades, open spaces or park sites in development or redevelopment projects along the waterfront should be located to minimize wind effects. As it is neither possible nor desirable to screen all areas of the waterfront from adverse winds, each site should be assessed on its need and potential for modification based on the existing microclimate, present and future uses, and adjacent development.

Surveys of both existing and proposed sites that would be affected by future development or redevelopment should be conducted to determine whether there is a need for site-specific guidelines covering building location, height, and form to avoid overshadowing. Modifications to built form should be required if proposed projects would create extensive overshadowing.

RECOMMENDATIONS

49. The Royal Commission recommends that local and regional municipalities across the Greater Toronto bioregion waterfront review their Official Plans and relevant supporting documents to incorporate policies that encourage year-round recreational use of the waterfront, particularly in the colder months.

50. The Commission further recommends that local municipalities prepare and promote design guidelines that encourage landowners and developers to enhance pedestrian microclimate conditions. Factors such as wind impact and sun access should be considered in deciding whether the location and mass of a building are appropriate.

51. Because not all areas of the waterfront are suited to year-round use, local and regional municipalities should work with agencies and the public to define priority recreational waterfront nodes for winterization; decisions should be based on user needs, the facilities available, and the potential to expand programming.

HEALING AN

URBAN WATERSHED:

THE STORY

OF THE DON

The stream that once gurgled through cool forests and flashed with salmon is a storm sewer today. It is fed by filthy water flushed off the city's pavements and by the effluent of a sewage treatment plant. Much of what was once a lovely valley is now a transportation corridor and a repository for road salt, dirty snow, and illegally dumped garbage. The river's lower stretch is strait-jacketed in steel and concrete, while chain-link fences discourage strolls along its degraded banks. Long gone is its natural mouth, an expansive delta that once teemed with life. Instead, a contorted right-angle turn and a tangle of expressways and railway tracks mark the river's entrance into the lake.

But with help, this sad watershed can regenerate, creating healthier human communities as it does so.

The existing mouth of the Don

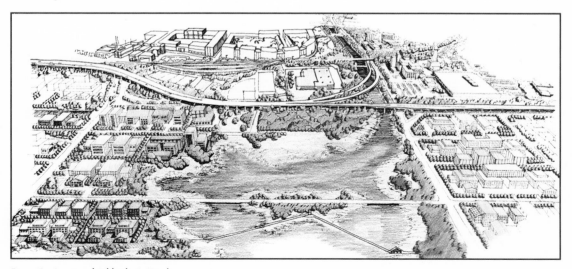

Figure 1   A restored Ashbridge's Marsh

The Don River runs through the heart of Toronto. The Don is similar to most of the urban rivers of North America. Everywhere, city building, industrial development, and suburban sprawl have left a legacy of lost woods, wildlife, and countryside, poisoning the natural environment on which our cities and our own health depend.

systems is a newer and harder task. Yet the Don is not a disgrace throughout. Some headwater streams still trickle through shady woods, the river's entire length is a migratory corridor for birds and other wildlife, and ducks paddle in the oily waters of its mouth. Such signs of life — to be found, if one only looks, along most urban rivers — give

A pond at the source of the Don

But Toronto's Don watershed has many friends, advocates with a vision for restoring it. They are residents who live nearby, from the headwaters to the mouth 38 kilometres (23.6 miles) to the south. They are schoolchildren attuned to the environment, and seniors who remember the valley in better days. They are naturalists, scientists, planners, and engineers whose expertise is needed to heal the Don. All of them are focusing on the Don because, of Metro's several rivers, it is the most degraded, accounting for much of the chemical, heavy metal, and nutrient pollution in Toronto's harbour. For Torontonians, this river has become a symbol of environmental neglect.

People know how to preserve pristine natural places, but restoring degraded natural

the Don's advocates hope. They attest to nature's own powerful, regenerative life force. Restoring a natural system means working with, not against, such natural processes; it means nature becomes a priority in making planning decisions. For a watershed, it means healing the whole, not just some of its parts.

LINKS TO THE PAST: THE NATURAL HISTORY OF THE DON

The Don River is one of the 60 rivers and major streams in the Greater Toronto bioregion that flow south from the Oak Ridges Moraine into Lake Ontario. This whole watershed is part of the Great Lakes

Keating Channel; mouth of Don. Inset: Mark Wilson, chair of, and Michael Hough, consultant to, the Task Force to Bring Back the Don, explain their ideas for the regeneration of the river to Prince Charles during his 1991 visit to Toronto.

Basin, the most massive concentration of fresh water in the world and home to 35 million people. Air, water, nutrients, and, alas, pollutants cycle repeatedly through the whole basin. That is why restoring the Don will not only improve Toronto's local environment, it will help heal the Great Lakes ecosystem of which it is a part.

In assisting the Don to regenerate, it is necessary to seek connections, not just with other parts of the larger bioregion, but with the watershed's past — its origins and functions in the natural system before the arrival of the first European settlers.

At various times, the Toronto area was covered with shallow seas, glaciers thousands of metres thick, and freshwater lakes and rivers that had basins larger than those of today. Different plants and animals have inhabited the area, responding to changes in climate and land migration routes. Each left its own signature of sedimentary deposits and fossils in the geological record.

Toronto's bedrock was laid down 450 million years ago in the Ordovician period as sediments in shallow seas. These solidified into the blue-grey shale of the Georgian Bay formation. Geologists have found evidence of ancient rivers that once cut through this bedrock, but the Don and its sister rivers in the Toronto area are much younger.

During the Pleistocene epoch, which began one million years ago, three successive waves of glaciation buried the bedrock beneath thick glacial till. The Don was born at the end of that time, only 13,000 years ago. The alternating freezing and thawing of two glacial lobes north of Toronto squeezed a porous, water-filled ridge of glacial debris between them — the Oak Ridges Moraine. As the glaciers retreated, streams began flowing south from the moraine, cutting valleys through the glacial drift. The Don has not reached bedrock yet.

In their early days, the two streams that form the modern Don River's east and west

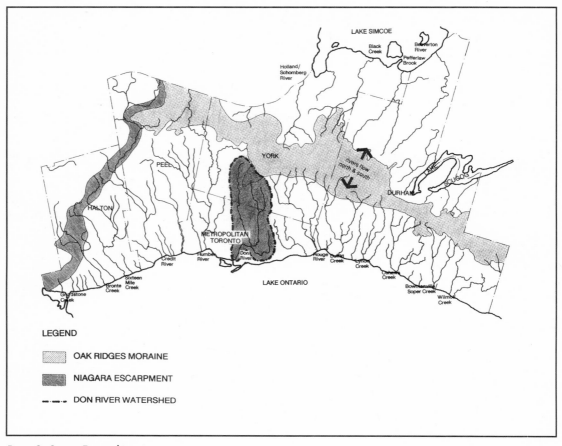

Figure 2 *Greater Toronto bioregion*

branches ended several kilometres north of
the present mouth (Figure 4) at the shores of
Lake Iroquois, formed from glacial meltwa-
ter, which was larger than its successor body
of water, Lake Ontario. Wave action and
westward shoreline currents built up a sandy
baymouth bar where the young east and

west Don entered Lake Iroquois; sands, silts,
and clays were deposited in a protected
lagoon behind the bar.

As the glaciers continued melting,
the land began slowly lifting up, and the
St. Lawrence channel, previously blocked with
ice, opened up. Gradually, Lake Iroquois

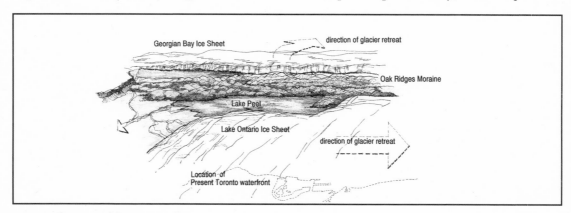

Figure 3 *The retreat of the Wisconsin glaciers*

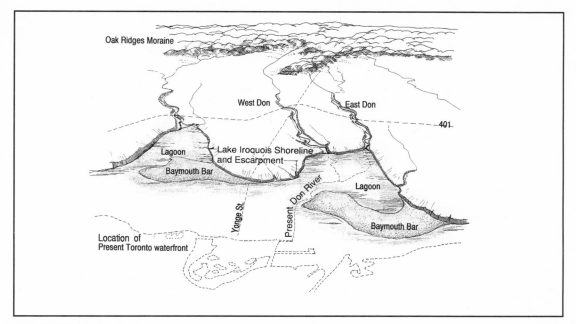

Figure 4   Lake Iroquois shoreline

shrank to become Lake Ontario, leaving behind its old delta at the river's sharp westward bend south of the forks, which was quarried for sand thousands of years later. The old shoreline is the distinct escarpment that extends across Toronto, forming the hill at Yonge Street and St. Clair Avenue and the ridge on which Casa Loma sits.

Now the Don flowed as one river out of its old lagoon and south across the flat sediments of what had been Lake Iroquois. As it entered Lake Ontario, the process of building a baymouth bar and backshore lagoon was repeated, forming the harbour islands spit and a protected lagoon known as Ashbridge's Marsh (Figure 5).

Just as global climate change drove glaciation, the changes in local temperature and precipitation determined which plants and animals could live here. During the three glaciations of the Pleistocene epoch, temperatures ranged from six degrees celsius lower to three degrees celsius higher than our present temperatures.

Perhaps the most renowned Pleistocene geological site in North America is in the Don Valley. The north face of the old brickworks quarry (Figure 6) exposes a rich fossil

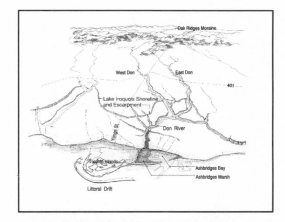

Figure 5   The Don Valley before European settlement

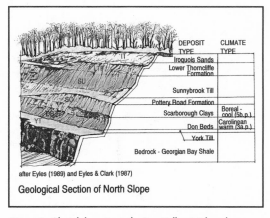

Figure 6   Glacial deposits at the Don Valley Brickworks

sandwich that records astonishing swings in habitat long before the Don's birth. It took only a few thousand years for a cool, northern boreal forest habitat to give way to a warmer Carolinian forest with more southerly plants including sycamore, holly, and grape, and such animals as giant beaver and bison.

But climate does not account entirely for habitat: a snapshot taken of the Don watershed just a few hundred years ago, before European colonization, would reveal healthy, varied, interconnected habitats created by local microclimates, soil types, and the river's action. On the slopes of the moraine, sugar maples and oaks shaded headwater tributaries, an

Natural Habitats of the Don Valley

Upland forest

Marshes along the river

River valley woods

inviting habitat for brook trout. Downstream, one would have found a lowland forest of willow and Manitoba maple in the floodplain, and oak, beech, basswood, maple, and almost pure stands of white pine on the valley slopes, attracting birds and mammals. The northern limits of the oak-dominated Carolinian forest reached the old Lake Iroquois shoreline, and the vast, fertile marshes near the river's mouth connected land and lake, sheltered nurseries for fish and other wildlife, and were home and stopping place to many kinds of fish, amphibians, and birds — including ducks, waders, geese, and mergansers.

Archaeological and early historical records show that natives who inhabited the region almost from the Don's inception lived gently on the land. They harvested wild rice, caught fish and turtles from the marshes, speared salmon from canoes in the river, planted corn on the tableland, trapped animals for food and clothing, and traversed the area on narrow walking trails for hunting, seasonal migrations, and trading. Although life was often hard for the people, the natural system was robust and healthy then, when so few people lived in the watershed, compared to today.

EARLY COLONIAL HISTORY

When Europeans came to the New World, they brought with them an attitude toward nature radically different from that of the native peoples. To the newcomers, nature was less a home than a resource for commerce and, later, an unruly force to be controlled.

The French came first, mapping the Don watershed as early as 1688, but largely ignoring it in their fur-trading operations. Next came the British, who established a

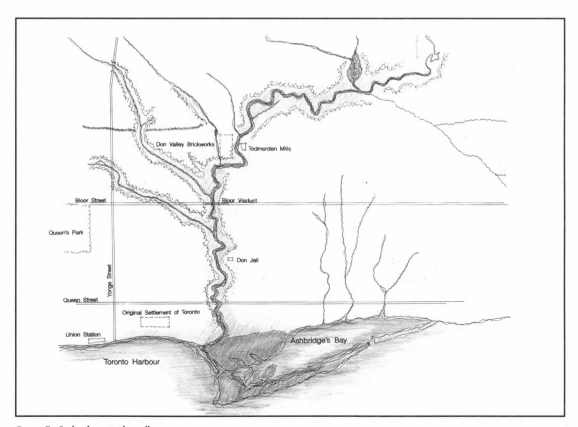

Figure 7   Early places in the valley

military garrison west of the Don, and called it York. But the Don's fate was sealed in 1787, when the British bought the "Toronto Purchase" — the Don watershed — from the Mississauga Indians for the equivalent of £1,700 in cash and goods.

Surveyors laid out a city plan for the future capital of Upper Canada with streets and lots for future homes and shops — a geometric grid branded artificially onto the landscape. City blocks were drawn on top of creeks, which were later buried. Such is the legacy of most North American cities of the 18th and 19th centuries.

Elizabeth Simcoe, wife of Upper Canada's first Lieutenant Governor, loved the valley and river her husband had named the Don, after a river back home in England. (The Indians had called it Necheng-qua-kekonk, meaning perhaps "back-burnt lands" or "woods and wetlands".) When the Simcoe family boated upstream soon after their arrival in 1793, the city was so new that only one residence had been built on the planned lots. Mrs. Simcoe wrote enthusiastically of the valley's forests and grand outlooks, of the Indians spearing salmon at night. She saw to it that the family's summer home, a wooden Grecian temple, which she called Castle Frank after her ailing son, was built on a promontory a few kilometres up the river. Mrs. Simcoe's diary and watercolours of the valley have made her the patron saint of today's advocates of the Don River.

Elizabeth Simcoe

Castle Frank

FIGHTING THE RIVER

Most settlers were too busy taming the wilderness to appreciate the Don River as a place of beauty and recreation: they used it for transportation, and harnessed its energy, building mills for lumber, flour, wool, and paper along its main trunk and tributaries. They farmed its floodplain and fished it for salmon and trout. They mined the old baymouth bar for sand, and baked the clay south of the forks into the bricks that were Toronto's favourite building material for more than half a century. In less than 150 years, the settlers cleared the lower valley almost entirely of trees. The watershed was a vast resource, its apparent purpose being to provide sustenance and raw materials for the young, growing city.

The settlers also viewed the river as a nuisance, a threat, and an obstacle. Floods regularly swept away mills and bridges. The Don was a barrier to the city's eastward expansion. The huge marsh at Ashbridge's Bay — its waters fouled by human and cattle wastes — was reviled as an unhealthy swamp. Habitat destruction was well under way. In the 1860s, the salmon finally stopped spawning in the Don, and the only brook trout in the headwaters today are escapees from the Ministry of Natural Resources' hatchery.

In the late 19th century, engineers set out to tame the river and, by the end of the century, they had strapped the meandering lower Don into a five-kilometre (3-mile) linear canal. Bridges would now be more secure and the railway north of the waterfront could be easily built along its edge. In the years after 1912, the Ashbridge's Bay marshes were filled in to create the port lands, the most massive engineering project on the continent in its time, forcing the Don into a right-angle exit into the harbour.

Figure 8   The lower Don before and after channelling

Filling in Ashbridge's Marsh

An early flood on the Don

Forks of the Don today

But, despite the constraints, the Don continued doing what rivers naturally do. Deprived of its delta, it dumped thousands of tonnes of silt in its lower reach — which has necessitated an expensive dredging annually ever since. With its lowland forests and most of its marshes gone and its flow swollen by urban run-off from the storm sewers, it flooded more devastatingly than ever before. In 1954, Hurricane Hazel, the worst storm on record, ripped out bridges and buildings along the Don and Humber rivers, and claimed 84 lives.

A 19th-century Torontonian would hardly recognize the Don watershed of the late 20th century. It is difficult for seniors to see in today's urbanized area the wild valley they once enjoyed for hiking, fishing, and swimming. Construction in the 1950s of the Don Valley Expressway and the Bayview Extension turned what had been a corridor for wildlife into one for cars. Not only has traffic radically changed the area's character, but pollution from road salt, lead, and oil seeping off the expressway, and snow dumps in the valley continue to degrade habitats.

Each decade of the 20th century has seen thousands more hectares of countryside paved over by development until, today, the watershed is 70-percent urbanized and houses 800,000 people. Much of the remaining countryside is owned by developers.

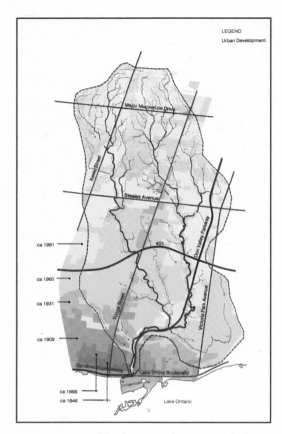

Figure 9   History of development in the Don Watershed

THE DON TODAY

Healing a damaged watershed is a great challenge. First, it requires changing the attitude that nature is merely a resource to be used, and abused, by human beings. That kind of "old-think" — clear the woodlands, fill the marshes, pave over the countryside, and treat streams as storm sewers — is still pervasive. It is our most environmentally damaging inheritance.

Nowhere is that attitude more prevalent than in the Don's sensitive headwaters, today the most threatened portion of the river, where many square kilometres of countryside have already succumbed to tract housing, monster homes, industries, shopping malls, and parking lots.

The cumulative effect of development has a major impact on ecological health. Silt from construction pours into streams, suffocating life and clogging the river's mouth far downstream. Untreated stormwater from completed developments worsens flooding and further poisons habitats. In the Don watershed, a total of 1,185 storm-sewer outfalls discharge directly into the river and its tributaries. Ninety-five per cent of the Don's pollution originates north of the City of Toronto.

As the source of many rivers, the Oak Ridges Moraine is of special concern. Uncontrolled development there threatens highly vulnerable habitats. It acts as a cap on the land, reducing the amount of precipitation that recharges aquifers. And, because the

Development continues in the headwaters

moraine is so porous, it also threatens the aquifers with pollution. One moraine site that should be monitored closely is the Keele Valley Landfill, the third largest garbage dump on the continent. While engineers insist that there is no leakage through the site's clay liners, what will happen 50 or 100 years from now?

Although the Don's biggest polluter is urban run-off (carrying lead, oil, salt, animal feces, garden and park chemicals, and whatever residents pour down the storm drains), raw human sewage, and industrial wastes also continue to foul the river. Although work to disconnect them continues, 30 combined sewers in Toronto and East York discharge untreated human waste directly into the Don after heavy rainfalls. So do an unknown number of illegal cross-connections between sanitary and storm sewers. And, while it is now illegal for industries to discharge polluted wastewater directly into watercourses, many companies send their wastes to the North Toronto Sewage Treatment Plant, the daily effluent of which accounts for a quarter of the Don's downstream volume. The plant, built in 1927 and upgraded very little since then, is ill-equipped to handle metals and organic chemicals.

Throughout, the valley is a repository for harmful substances. Golf courses and parks may appear benign uses of floodplain land, but the tons of herbicides, pesticides, and fertilizers needed to maintain their 1950s style manicured look run right into the river. Public works departments store road salt, PCBs, and polluted snow in the valley.

The lower Don, the part most residents and tourists see, suffers from channelization, a sterile mouth, buried tributaries, and the entire river's accumulated pollution. Expressways, railways, and chain-link fences discourage public access. Downtown neighbourhoods symbolically turn their backs on the river: most buildings don't even have windows on the valley side.

Vignettes of the Valley

Golf course under construction

Keele Valley Landfill

The Ross Lord Dam and reservoir

Restricted access — lower Don

Expressways at the river's mouth

Nonetheless, there is cause for hope. The Don's water quality is actually better now than it was 40 or 50 years ago, when industries discharged directly into it and paint factories often turned the Don into a flowing rainbow of colours. At that time, dozens of small, overloaded sewage treatment plants sent their smelly brew into the river. Once, when Princess Margaret visited Toronto, the City had perfume poured into the Don, to mask its stench.

Because many citizens now view the watershed as a place in its own right, a precious stretch of nature in the city, there is even more cause for hope. Rejecting the old attitude of the valley as a "resource", they are fighting insensitive development and protesting unsound environmental policies at all levels of government. Activist citizens' groups from all parts of the valley — from Save the Oak Ridges Moraine (STORM) at the river's source, to the Task Force to Bring Back the Don in the city core — are banding together, determined to heal the watershed.

A NEW VISION FOR THE VALLEY

The Nature of Restoration

A healthy city depends on a healthy environment: you can't have one without the other. In order to help a watershed regenerate into a healthy natural system, people must treat nature with respect. Connections to the natural and cultural past must be maintained — for example, by protecting remnant woodlands and retaining historical links. Sometimes healing requires intervention to create the conditions for nature's own regeneration. It certainly means that the health of the environment must have a higher priority in planning decisions than short-term human gains.

In the following pages, the guidelines for regenerating the watershed are based on the principles of ecosystem planning as defined in Part I of this report. Although our focus on the Don Valley, "clean, green, useable, diverse, open, accessible, connected, affordable, and attractive" can be applied to regenerating any urban watershed.

The guidelines are not listed in sequence: they must be implemented together. For, as the American ecologist Barry Commoner has said, "Everything connects to everything else". Taken as a whole, the guidelines treat the entire watershed, although quite different approaches are often needed in different areas: the urban core, the suburbs, and the remaining natural or agricultural areas. They require a new way of thinking: the old dichotomies of city and country, urban and natural, people and nature disappear because, in an urban watershed, the human and natural communities are one.

Allowing nature to regenerate

Preserving historical links

Preserving natural remnants

REGENERATION GUIDELINES

One: Protect Natural and Cultural Features

Moraines, aquifers, and natural springs are the watershed's ultimate source of cool, pure water, and should be sacrosanct. Wetlands are not undeveloped land waiting for fill; they control flooding, absorb pollutants, release purified water to groundwater and streams, and are havens for birds and other wildlife. Woodlands, too, recharge groundwater and create wildlife habitats. Trees cool streams, maintaining aquatic habitats, absorb carbon dioxide, and release oxygen into the air. Healthy tributary streams, valuable in their own right, also contribute to watershed health downstream. Historical farms and mills connect us to our human past, while farm hedgerows and fencelines have become important links for wildlife migration. Old industrial buildings need protection too:

often, they are where artists work and new businesses begin.

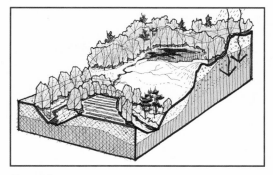

Figure 10

Two: Let Topography and Countryside Define Urban Form

Urban sprawl has imposed a sameness over the North American landscape, despoiling natural habitats, destroying the working countryside, and obliterating any local sense of place with monotonous tracts of housing and shopping malls. While population increases close to economically thriving cities are probably inevitable, alternatives to conventional development can actually enhance environmental health. No tract developments should be allowed on headwater moraines and other sensitive groundwater recharge zones. Instead, increases in population can be accommodated by building in established town centres, where municipal services already exist.

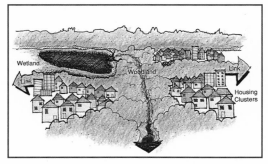

Figure 11

In upland areas of the watershed, medium- to high-density developments should be clustered on the least sensitive land, preserving river valleys and ravines, wetlands, woodlots, hillocks, and farms. This is not only aesthetically pleasing: it maintains the open natural and farmland areas that attract people to the countryside, and protects streams and healthy, diverse habitats for native plants and animals.

Three: Ensure That Development Enhances Environmental Health

Development can no longer be tolerated as an inevitable despoliation of nature and countryside; rivers and streams can no longer be used as ready-made storm sewers. New development should be seen as an opportunity to improve stream health, and to strengthen existing green corridors. It should adhere to a policy of zero increases in pollution siltation and run-off. No silt during construction or increases in stormwater afterwards should discharge into streams. Wetlands should be protected, restored or created to help treat run-off biologically and, wherever possible and if groundwater is not at risk, stormwater should be directed into the ground. In existing urban areas, the storm sewers that discharge into streams should be gradually replaced by biological treatment wherever possible. A network of storage ponds and wetlands on available floodplain land could treat stormwater while creating new wildlife habitats.

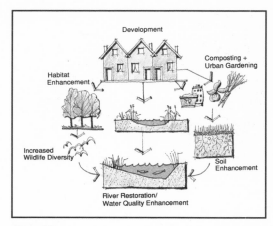

Figure 12

Four: Intensify and Diversify Development

Conventional suburbs waste space. Land in the headwaters region of the watershed can be saved if development intensifies in existing suburbs and the urban core. Housing, shops, and small clean industries can infill parking lots, and apartments can be built over the stores in low-rise commercial strips. In the downtown core, unused industrial land can be transformed into small, intimate neighbourhoods of medium- and high-density housing, if the soil is safe or can be decontaminated. In many cases, relaxing zoning regulations encourages homeowners to create basement apartments, split large homes

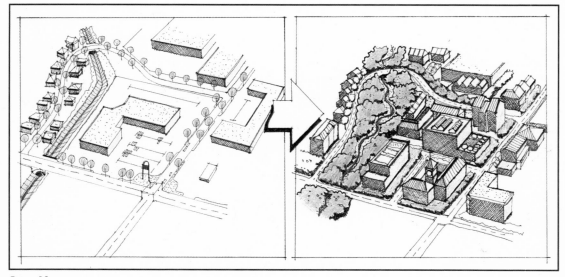

Figure 13

into several units or build "granny houses" in backyards. Such measures use land responsibly and help create diverse, interesting neighbourhoods while, at the same time, streams and ravines are protected and railway and electrical rights-of-way are enhanced as wildlife corridors and walking trails.

Five: Maintain Rural Traditions

When farmland is lost to urbanization and exotic horticultural species replace native plant communities, the city loses its connection to its rural base. The healthy, diverse urban communities of the future will maintain family farms, market gardens, and rural-based industries at the city's edges, as European cities have done for centuries. Where farmland has been sold, the "waste space" in new industrial developments can be returned to agriculture, boosting rural employment and creating a new living and working environment in the countryside.

Zoning regulations in suburbs and the urban core should encourage vegetable gardening, a productive practice that was popular, especially during World War II, and is being revived by immigrant families. Rooftop and backyard gardens, composting, and community gardens on floodplain or unused industrial land connect the city to sustainable rural traditions. The health of the watershed only improves when "users" become "stewards".

Figure 14

Six: Work with Nature

Nature has great restorative powers; even quite degraded parts of a watershed can return to a state of health if natural regeneration is allowed to take place. That sometimes means fencing off an eroded stream bank to keep people, dogs, and livestock out for a while. It always means working to eliminate harmful substances that pollute natural habitats. The watershed can benefit if parks and private property, including the edges of golf fairways, are allowed to naturalize, rather than continuously being subjected to expensive and polluting maintenance.

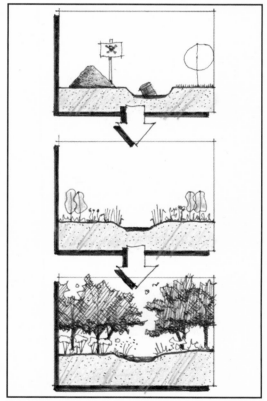

Figure 15

Minimal intervention is often necessary in places that might otherwise take decades to restore themselves, or where major human changes have made natural regeneration impossible. Planting native trees and shrubs to enhance a green corridor or stabilize a stream bank, creating wetlands to improve water quality, and stocking a newly restored stream with native fish help nature's own healing. It is sometimes necessary to reverse past engineering: redirecting storm-sewer outfalls, restoring a buried stream, removing artificially channelled banks, or re-creating a natural delta. Engineering must be the minimum possible, small in scale, and it must work with, never against, the processes of nature.

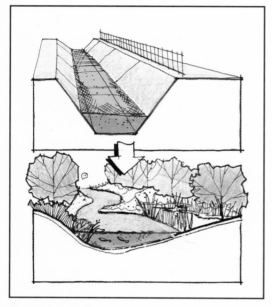

Figure 16

Seven: Encourage Watershed Consciousness

The desire to restore an urban watershed originates with the people who live there, who want healthy natural places in and near the city. When planners become involved, there is an opportunity for citizens and experts to work closely together. Neighbourhoods can initiate local stream rehabilitations, naturalized plantings, and ravine clean-ups. This happens when people have an investment in the health of their own local area, and is encouraged when authorities ensure easy and safe access to ravines and river valleys.

Community groups can also serve as watchdogs, reporting spills and nature vandalism. All citizens should understand the effects of household and garden chemicals

on local watercourses. And since a watershed must be healed as a whole, new mechanisms must be found to protect, plan, and restore beyond the boundaries of local jurisdictions: to create stewardship programs with private landowners, provide shared funding, and help citizens' groups co-ordinate throughout the watershed.

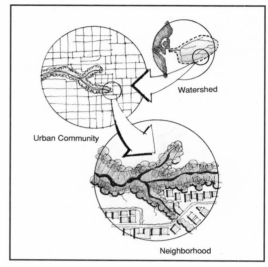

Figure 17

APPLYING REGENERATION TO THE DON

In the coming decades, population pressures on the Don watershed will grow. No one wants the entire valley to look like the city core, or believes that what remains of the countryside should be paved with suburbs. To protect the health of the natural system and the human communities that are part of it, all further human change to the watershed must be directed towards improving the environmental health of the river system.

Protecting the Oak Ridges Moraine and its agricultural slopes is crucial to the future of the Don. Not only is the moraine the source of many of southern Ontario's rivers, it is a rare and beautiful area enjoyed by hikers, school groups, and naturalists from every part of the Greater Toronto bioregion.

Farmland in the headwaters

This Commission supports the efforts of the joint citizens' and provincial government planning committee to devise strategies that will protect the entire moraine. Taking inventories of its habitats and aquifers; assessing the cumulative ill effects of development, gravel extraction, roads, and sewers; and creating a greenway along its entire length are important. The most effective protection measure would be to accommodate population growth only in existing towns, where municipal services already exist. Development on the moraine countryside, if allowed at all, should be severely restricted.

If the current rate at which development is gobbling up farmland continues, Toronto will soon be severed from its rural base. It is time to consider direct aid to farmers — whether in the form of land-stewardship programs, conservation deeds to farm certain lands in perpetuity, land-banking for future agricultural needs, or tax relief — which will keep farming and rural-based industries viable at the city's edge. Limited development in the agricultural uplands must then fit into and enhance working farms.

Countryside can be protected by building more living and working space in existing suburbs, the urban core, and under-used industrial areas. This also helps create more diverse and interesting human communities. Throughout the watershed, stormwater management must be radically changed, so that it will enhance, rather than destroy, aquatic habitats. And in the urban core, as well as intensifying neighbourhoods, a dramatic plan to give the Don back its natural mouth would regenerate the lower river and the Toronto waterfront for wildlife and people alike.

In this section, seven regeneration guidelines are applied throughout the Don watershed, with different emphases for the countryside, the suburbs, and the urban core. Although we still need to learn a great deal about restoring natural systems, we know that we cannot continue doing things in the old way.

THE COUNTRYSIDE

Conventional tract suburbs in the Don's headwaters have already steamrolled over many rural and village scenes (Figure 18). Headwater streams are especially sensitive: often little more than braided rivulets, their health depends on the shade and water-retaining ability of woodlands. Conventional development, as illustrated in Figure 19, consumes far too much land. In the landscape shown in Figure 20, development can protect natural features, as well as the farm and village, simply by concentrating growth within the town by creating higher storey build-up and infilling with housing and shops. When a clear edge is kept between town and country, malls, commercial strips, and conventional housing tracts do not spill over the countryside: residents can then enjoy both the livelier village and the more serene countryside. Topography and cultural features define the urban form; rural traditions are maintained; streams and woodlands are protected.

When new development is allowed in the upper watershed, it might best be clustered as villages that fit unobtrusively

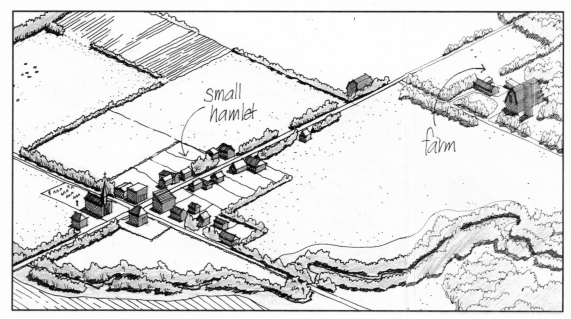

Figure 18   Traditional rural village in the moraine

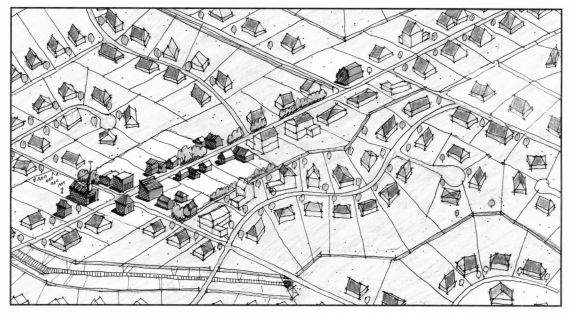

Figure 19   Village and farmland obliterated by conventional development

into the natural system and landscape as shown in Figure 21. Increasing housing densities, by permitting multi-storey houses, duplexes, and triplexes, and by decreasing the private space around them, protects countryside. Streets should be narrow to cut both traffic speed and waste space. Grouping commercial shops at corners fosters a sense of neighbourhood, and encouraging market gardens brings rural practices into the new village. Farm hedgerows, fencelines, and old railroad tracks should be conserved as wildlife corridors and paths for people. Taking these steps enables the human community to become part of the countryside, neither dominating nor degrading it.

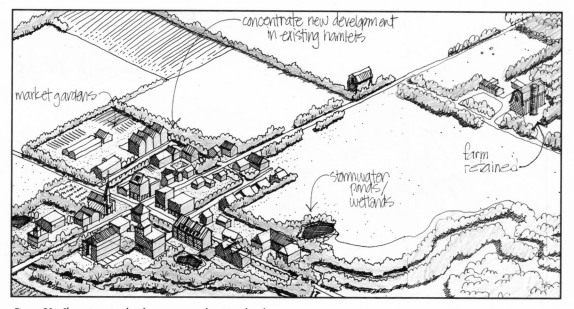

Figure 20   Clustering new development around existing hamlet

Figure 21   Mixed use in new residential areas

EXISTING SUBURBS

A home in the suburbs, the North American dream of the 1950s and 1960s, is beyond our environmental means today. Car-dominated, low-density living consumes too much land and energy for transportation. The expanses of lawns around buildings waste space and energy, and add to the watershed's burden of chemicals. As well, the hectares of wide roads, driveways, parking lots, and malls squander space and make polluted urban run-off a problem of major proportions.

But existing suburban development (Figure 22) could accommodate many more people, protecting countryside elsewhere. Furthermore, diversifying housing and land use can create far more interesting communities (Figure 23). In the suburbs today, many people, especially in immigrant families, want to change their property in ways that contribute to a healthier environment.

Homeowners should be allowed to create basement apartments, split large homes into duplexes and triplexes, add extensions, in-fill townhouses in side yards, or build granny flats in backyards or over garages. In addition, energy-consuming lawns can be converted into more productive organic vegetable and flower gardens.

At the same time, narrowing the typical suburb's wide streets would create more shared neighbourhood space, with wider sidewalks and more trees to provide a shady and pleasant street environment.

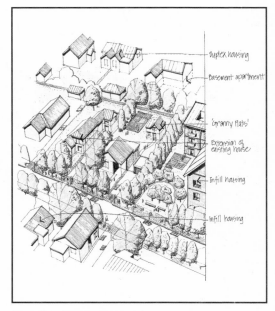

Figure 23   Alternative potential

INDUSTRIAL/COMMERCIAL DEVELOPMENT

Other than outmoded zoning regulations, there is no reason why clean industrial sites should not include housing and shops. When people live close to where they work and shop, walking and bicycling replace polluting commuting by car, and real communities can spring up — a far cry from separate bedroom suburbs, shopping malls, and sterile industrial parks. Turning some

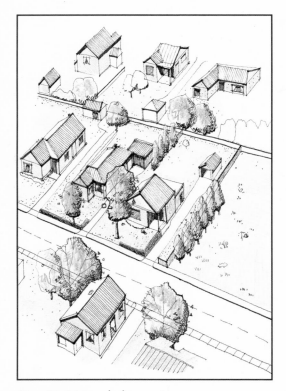

Figure 22   Existing suburb

land back to agricultural use as private or community gardens, and transforming industrial flat roofs into vegetable gardens or rooftop wetlands can enliven and diversify healthy communities even further. Here again, intensifying industrial sites, whether in the city's core or at the outskirts, reduces population pressures on the countryside.

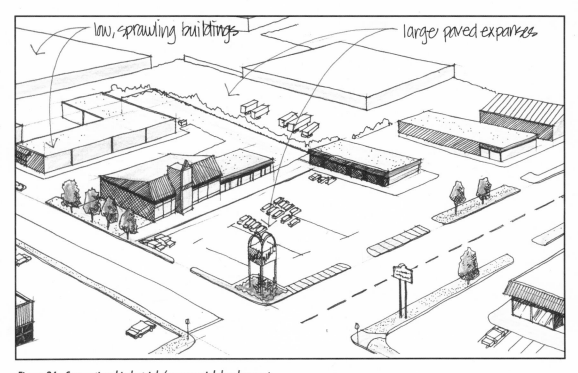

Figure 24   Conventional industrial / commercial development

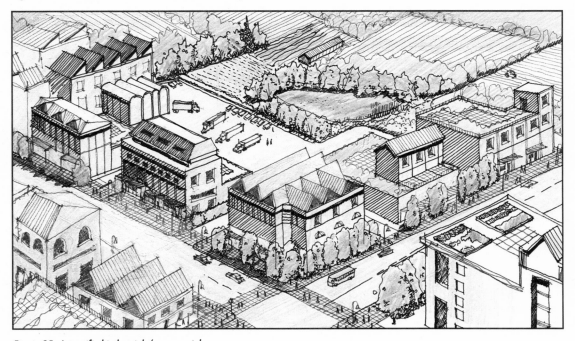

Figure 25   Intensified industrial / commercial

AN ECOSYSTEM APPROACH TO DEVELOPMENT

Figure 26 is a picture of a typical scene in the upper Don watershed: farm fields, interspersed with hedgerows and hillocks, nestle near a branching, wooded stream. But developers have bought the land from farmers, and the town council has approved a zoning change that will bring in far more tax revenue than farming ever did.

Soon, bulldozers and graders will scrape off the topsoil, remove trees and hillocks, and grade the former fertile farmland to a sterile, monotonous, easy-to-build-on level plain. Any wetlands, too, will be routinely filled. During development, which may last up to four years, the headwater stream will be subject to massive siltation and erosion. Eventually, it may be channelled in concrete.

The developer will put in the typical infrastructure: hard-surfaced graded roads, gutters, storm sewers, and lines for gas, water, and sanitary sewage. He will then sell parcels of prepared land to other companies, which will erect large, low-density offices and industrial plants, and pave over several hectares for parking lots — similar to those nearby. Most of the unpaved land will be turned into lawns dotted with non-native "lollipop trees" (Figure 27).

But, with some imagination and sensitivity to natural systems, this development could protect and fit into the countryside and its habitats. Tighter, higher-density mixed development could edge the site, preserving the stream and its treed banks as the natural centre and human focus (Figure 28). Woodlands, hillocks, some farm fields and buildings, and any wetlands could be conserved. Rather than destroying the stream, urban run-off could be directed into ponds and new wetlands.

Such a development follows all the guidelines of regeneration: it protects nature and countryside; its form adheres to local topography by clustering on the least sensitive land; and it enhances environmental health. The development is dense and diverse (with mixed industrial, commercial,

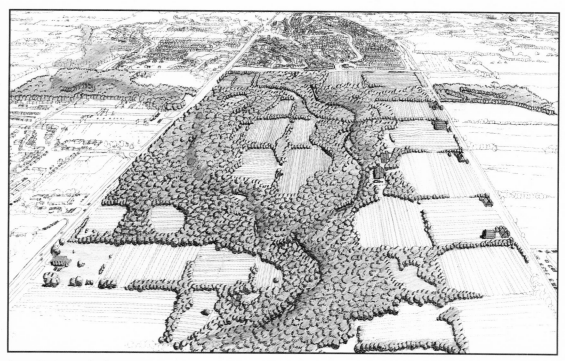

Figure 26 Existing landscape patterns

and residential buildings), and maintains rural traditions by protecting farmland and incorporating land-based industries. Throughout, it works with — rather than against — nature. The people who live in it cannot help but develop a watershed consciousness. Given the rate at which urbanization is steamrolling countryside in the Don watershed, it is crucial that developments follow this new pattern.

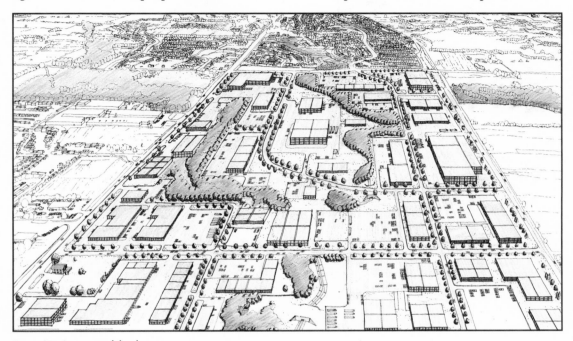

Figure 27   Conventional development

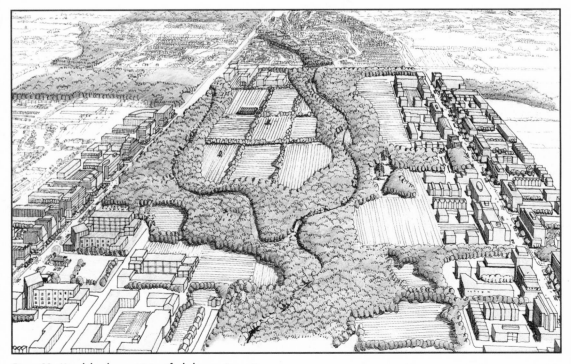

Figure 28   Mixed development intensified along major routes

STORMWATER MANAGEMENT: OLD HABITS, NEW SOLUTIONS

The most effective way to help aquatic habitats regenerate would be to make radical changes to the conventional system for handling stormwater. In the Don, stormwater — urban run-off — discharging directly into the river is the main cause of the river's pollution and its peak high and low flows, both of which degrade habitats severely. Stormwater damage is ubiquitous in the watershed, in new developments, existing suburbs, and the urban core.

The concrete and steel infrastructure of gutters, drains, catchbasins, and underground storm pipes rushes polluted water off city pavements as rapidly as possible and into rivers, streams or lakes. Designed for the safety and comfort of urban residents, the system keeps feet dry and prevents standing water that could freeze to slick ice. Untreated run-off water carries with it oil, lead, salts, fertilizers, herbicides, pesticides, decaying leaves, animal feces — plus whatever people pour down the storm drains — straight into rivers and streams.

Sudden, excess stormwater pouring into the river causes rapid high flows and dangerous flash floods. Ironically, the water moves so efficiently out to the lake that, in dry periods, there is little reserve; streams dry up, levels in the lower Don fall, and the river becomes sluggish. The extremes of floods and low flows — added to the pollutants in the run-off — wipe out habitats for fish, turtles, and amphibians. Small wonder that only four small hardy fish species survive in the Don.

A typical storm-sewer outfall

In order to keep it from harming the natural system, before it reaches watercourses, all stormwater could be treated in the same way as sanitary sewage, an extremely expensive undertaking. Better still, all substances polluting stormwater could be stopped at source. That would mean finding safe alternatives for road salt, prohibiting the use of chemicals on parklands, golf courses, and gardens, discouraging the use of cars, and fining residents who operate leaky cars, dump toxins in storm drains, and ignore stoop-and-scoop laws.

In addition, adjustments could be made to the conventional storm-sewer system itself, using such methods as regulating its flow during storms, creating detention areas or gradually replacing the hard, impervious surfaces of storm pipes, sidewalks, parking lot surfaces, and gutters with porous materials.

While such measures should be considered seriously, there are other ways to work with nature and ensure that stormwater helps enhance the health of rivers and streams.

Wetlands provide wildlife habitats and also cleanse water effectively: such plants as bulrushes absorb pollutants. Throughout the watershed, every opportunity to create marshes and wetlands should be welcomed. Even in the urban core, there is often space to move stormwater outflows away from stream and river banks to create small, narrow wetlands farther back. In addition, ditches can replace hard pavements along expressways and major roads, allowing run-off water to simply be absorbed into the ground. In such conditions, wetland plants often move in and find a home. Finally, reforestation — aside from the other benefits trees confer — helps the soil throughout the watershed retain and cleanse water naturally.

Rather than being seen as a waste to be gotten rid of quickly, stormwater, handled according to regeneration principles, becomes a means of creating diverse and beautiful places. In urban areas, they profit the human community as well as enhancing the natural one.

Figure 29   Wetland vegetation for stormwater treatment and habitat enhancement

LOWER DON DELTA

Conventional development of port lands tends to create dreary, sterile industrial parks dotted with horticultural plantings — places that are welcoming neither to wildlife nor to people. But applying regeneration guidelines can revolutionize the look and function of port lands: historical and natural features can be protected, and development can be intensified to leave extensive naturalized greenspace. A 1991 plan by the City of Toronto's Task Force to Bring Back the Don would work dramatically with nature, helping the river once more create a natural, marshland delta on the port lands site itself.

In the 1990 *Watershed* report, the Commission recommended that green industries and parkland be established on the existing East Bayfront/Port Industrial Area, which is the old, filled Ashbridge's Marsh.

According to the Task Force's plan, the river would meander through a 50.6 hectares (125-acre) regenerating marsh, emptying into the shipping channel to the south, with office buildings and clean industries clustered on either side. Compared to conventional port land development, this is an exciting prospect (see contrasting views, Figures 30 and 31).

The Task Force believes that encouraging the Don to regenerate a marshland delta, which engineers removed 80 years ago, would help re-establish a wildlife corridor between the Don Valley and the Leslie Street Spit (home and resting place to hundreds of waterfowl and other birds); recreate a healthy delta habitat for fish, amphibians, birds, and other wildlife; and create a large naturalized greenspace at the Toronto waterfront for city dwellers to enjoy. The long-abused river would end its journey as a river should, with the dignity of a natural mouth.

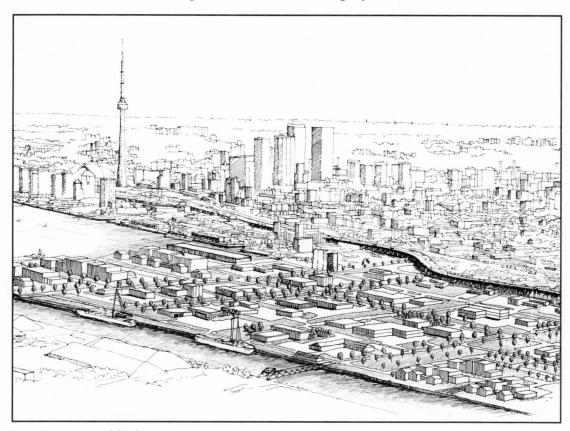

Figure 30 Conventional development

The Task Force planning team is now examining detailed technical requirements for achieving the delta vision. The strategy would integrate hydrology, biology, engineering, and environmental planning to restore, rather than control, nature — to work with, rather than against, natural processes.

For like all rivers, the Don "wants" to build up a delta. Every year, the Toronto Harbour Commissioners dredge 100,000 cubic metres (3,531,467 cubic feet) of silt to prevent silting and keep the Keating Channel open. With a delta marsh, the need for that $600,000 annual effort would be greatly reduced: instead — by diking and controlling where the delta forms — the Don would be allowed to create the marsh, and would fill in the Keating Channel and, by this one significant change, would alter the situation upriver.

This vision for the Don would transform Toronto's waterfront. It would make the river the focus of the city, rather than a sewer to be ignored. The Task Force's plan is long-term and the group proposes that, in the 20 to 40 years needed to carry it out, a research and education station be established in the port lands to study the natural processes of delta and marsh generation.

LOWER DON ROSEDALE FLATS

During its natural evolution, as the glaciers melted and the waters of Lake Iroquois finally fell, the Don River snaked slowly across the exposed flat lake bed, creating a huge delta of wetlands, ponds, and lagoons on its way (Figure 4). That is why the flat, channelled lower Don fills with silt today: it is still "trying" to form its old delta.

Simply allowing that to happen would obliterate much of the city's infrastructure that now hems in the lower part of the river.

Figure 31 Alternative development

Initial studies by the Task Force suggest that the river's gradient must be made steeper so that it provides the extra energy needed to pull the Don's silt out to a delta in the port lands. A two- to three-metre weir at the Rosedale Flats just north of Gerrard Street would do just that — a case in which nature can regenerate itself only with human intervention. Because of massive past engineering changes to the Don, some restorative work will now be needed to bring the lower watershed back to health and to approximate its former natural state.

Building a weir at Rosedale Flats would act like a beaver dam, creating behind it a headpond that would fill with sediments and create opportunities for varied bottomland habitats of meadow, wetland and woodland. Ponds and wetlands would help regulate flooding, wildlife would return, and people could enjoy renewed recreation opportunities.

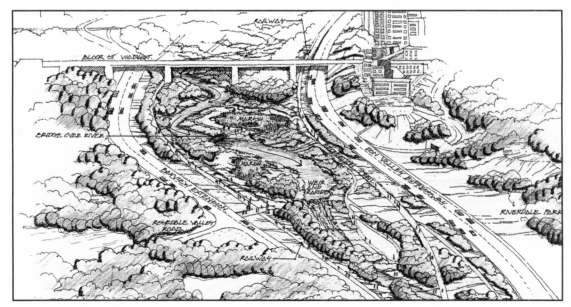

Figure 32   Lower Don Rosedale Flats

LOWER DON CHANNEL

It is difficult to naturalize a linear, channelled river like the Don between Rosedale and the proposed new delta. The City found it challenging just to find space for a cycling and walking trail there two years ago. Because the railroad tracks, expressways, and steel and concrete banks that hem in the lower Don seem to be here to stay, this highly urbanized stretch might better be treated more formally, as an attractive riverside park.

As part of the delta restoration, the Don Task Force suggests pools and rapids every hundred metres or so in the Don. They would help maintain the river's new and steeper gradient, and provide upstream access for fish. Fast-growing, water-loving willows and poplars could be planted on the almost treeless banks; their shade, as well as falling leaves and insects, would improve fish habitats and food sources. But, most important, the degraded lower Don would become a "people place" with welcoming shade trees, the pleasant sounds of a more natural river, and spots to sit and watch ducks paddling and fish circling in the pools.

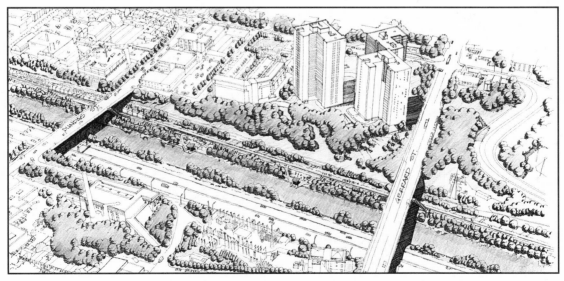

Figure 33 Lower Don Channel

ACCESS AND RECREATION

The Don watershed is a dramatic network of branching green valleys and ravines in one of North America's largest urban centres. Through regeneration, it can again become a healthy home and migration corridor for wildlife. It can become a haven for people too, maintaining vital connections with nature and offering respite from the pressures of the city within the city itself. The mobilizing force for restoration is access. The more people who enjoy the valley, even in its present state, the greater the groundswell for its healing.

What better way to encourage a watershed consciousness than to link up existing

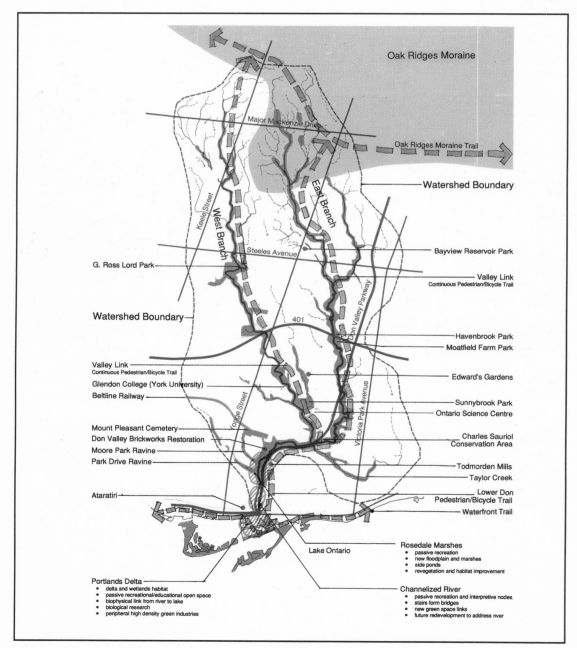

Figure 34   Connecting the watershed

trails — such as the lower Don bicycle path and the nature trail through the Charles Sauriol Conservation Reserve — through the whole watershed? That, in turn, would link the Martin Goodman Trail along the lakeshore with the proposed greenway on the Oak Ridges Moraine. Ever since the City opened a path on the lower Don — especially since an access stairway was built at Riverdale Park — dozens of cyclists, joggers, bird-watchers, and people just out for a stroll enjoy the lower valley every weekend.

Apart from any recreational or spiritual uses it may provide human beings, the Don watershed is valuable in its own right as a natural system. Nonetheless, because people are now an inextricable part of the natural system, the point is to heal the watershed for all. The Don's advocates hope that, someday, when the foxes, turtles, and maybe even salmon return, children will be able to splash in the Don's swimming holes again.

THOUGHTS ON ACHIEVING THE VISION

How do 800,000 people in seven municipal jurisdictions, with bureaucrats from several different provincial and federal ministries — plus troops of interested planners, politicians, naturalists, biologists, engineers, landscape architects, and lawyers — achieve a vision as far-reaching as restoration of a watershed?

One way not to achieve the vision is for each city and town in the watershed to continue acting on its own. What may benefit one local municipality may harm the entire watershed as well as local natural areas.

A further recipe for failure is to allow the vision to slip out of the hands of citizens and become the sole property of experts.

Dictating regeneration from above — by governments and their consultants — almost guarantees the loss of public support and stifles valuable initiatives. Neighbourhood and citizens' groups already practise restoration locally: planting trees, cleaning up ravines, and acting as watchdogs to stop chemical spills and vandalism of nature. They must become part of a co-ordinated process for watershed regeneration.

PART III:
PLACES

This part of the final report of the Royal Commission is an appreciation of the waterfront as a place and as a series of places. Moving across the bioregion, from Burlington Bay in the west to the Trent River in the east, it offers comments about the Commission's experience of the diverse places on the waterfront.

While those who live, work, and play in these places probably have a deeper appreciation of their attributes, in this section the Commission attempts to define the public values and objectives for each place along the waterfront, as well as recommending strategies for the future.

The kinds of places we create and evolve — the buildings we allow to be built; the way we treat our rivers, roads, wastes, trees, and water; the care and attention we pay to our offices, schools, factories, restaurants, recreational facilities, monuments, and places of worship — measure who we are and what is important to us.

In his excellent book, *The Experience of Place* (1990), author Tony Hiss captures the importance place has in the ordinary, day-to-day experiences of people.

We all react to the places where we live and work, in ways we scarcely notice or that are only now becoming known to us. Ever-accelerating changes in most people's day-to-day circumstances are helping us, prodding us, sometimes forcing us, to learn that our ordinary surroundings, built and natural alike, have an incredible and continuing effect on the way we feel and act, and on our health and intelligence. These places have an impact on our sense of ourself, our sense of safety, the kind of work we get done, the ways we interact with other people, even our ability to function as citizens in a democracy. In short, the place where we spend our time affects the people we are and can become.

As places around us change — both the communities that shelter us and the larger regions that support them — we all undergo changes inside.

> *The kinds of places we create and evolve tell us who we are and what is important to us.*

Toronto, cityview in the evening

This means that whatever we experience in a place is both a serious environmental issue and a deeply personal one. Our relationship with the places we know and meet up with — where you are right now; and where you've been earlier today; and wherever you'll be in another few hours — is a close bond, intricate in nature, and not abstract, not remote at all. It's enveloping, almost a continuum with all we see and think. And the danger we are now beginning to see is that whenever we make changes in our surroundings, we can all too easily short-change ourselves by cutting ourselves off from some of the sights, or sounds, the shapes or textures or other information from a

Most and Least Desired Types of Waterfront Development

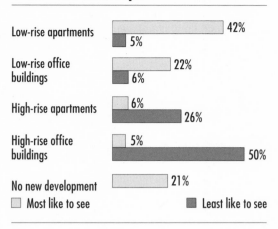

	Most like to see	Least like to see
Low-rise apartments	42%	5%
Low-rise office buildings	22%	6%
High-rise apartments	6%	26%
High-rise office buildings	5%	50%
No new development	21%	

When asked to consider different development options for the waterfront, respondents favoured low rise over high rise development.

Source: Environics Poll. 1991.

place that have helped mold our understanding and are now necessary for us to thrive.

When people speak about vivid experiences of place, they are often referring to fond memories or magical moments; the waterfront offers many of these. Stand at the foot of Grindstone Creek and see the densely treed slopes rise steeply on either side of the water; glance across Humber Bay from the eastern shore of Etobicoke and see the distant gleaming towers of downtown Toronto shining in the sun; watch children play in Ajax's Rotary Park with the rushes and shrubs of Duffin Creek in the background; walk on Scarborough's bluffs and look out over the lake — these are experiences to savour and remember for a lifetime.

Sometimes, however, people's most unforgettable experiences are of places that have been damaged and diminished over time. Absorb and survive the assault on all the senses when walking down York Street under the rail viaduct and the Gardiner across Lake Shore Boulevard, past the parking lots to reach the water's edge; fight the down-draft winds hurling down the sides and around the corners of the new high-rises along Toronto's Central Waterfront on a windy day; find an historic vista across the bay, one that has brightened the daily lives of many, but is now being appropriated for the benefit of a few hundred — these experiences remind us that we need to safeguard, repair, and enrich the places our heritage has lent to us so that we can enjoy them before we pass them on to others.

Many of the places surveyed here are in transition: sometimes that transition is measured and gentle, while nonetheless important, while in others, change is fundamental and magnificent in its impact. In all of these places, we have the opportunity not to "short-change" either our heritage or our future.

CHAPTER 7:
HALTON

The Halton waterfront comprises some 33 kilometres (20 miles) of Lake Ontario shoreline, and 5 kilometres (3 miles) along Burlington Bay/Hamilton Harbour. The regional waterfront includes the local waterfronts of Oakville and Burlington and stretches from Joshua Creek west to Grindstone Creek, where the waterfront meets the Niagara Escarpment. A significant number of watercourses enter the lake through deeply incised valleys, the most prominent being Bronte Creek (Twelve Mile Creek) and Sixteen Mile Creek, both in Oakville.

The waterfront area was the first to be settled, both in Oakville and in Burlington. Consequently, the area has more historical diversity in the age of its buildings and built forms and in the maturity of vegetation than can be found in more inland areas.

Across Burlington Bay, the stark Stelco and Dofasco steelworks in Hamilton contrast with waterfront residential estates, golf course lands, and the lush greenery of the Burlington side. La Salle Park on the Burlington waterfront, but owned by the City of Hamilton, is named after the French explorer who set out from Montreal in 1669

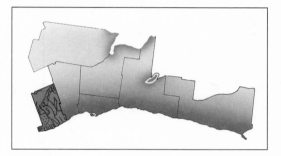

to find a way to the southern sea. His party reached Burlington Bay and, after landing at what is now the park site, continued inland to the Seneca Indian hamlet of Tinaouataoua, near present-day Westover, before returning to Montreal. It was only 13 years later that La Salle completed exploration of the Mississippi River and reached its mouth.

St. Luke's Church in Burlington, built in 1834, still retains its unbroken view of Lake Ontario from the main south door. For almost 160 years, this narrow strip of tree-lined lawn — 20 metres by 160 metres (66 by 525 feet), extending from the lake to Ontario Street, and originally without streets crossing it — has been known as Church Avenue. This green lane provides a visual connection to the lake and is part of the

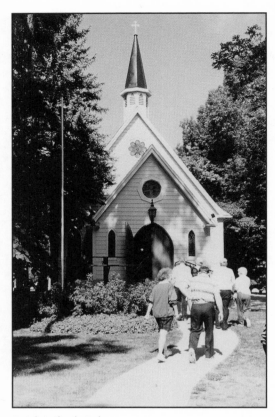

St. Luke's Church, Burlington

In October 1990 the City of Burlington purchased the 5.6-hectare (14-acre) McNichol estate at the mouth of Shoreacres Creek. The City will preserve the McNichol house, dating back to the 1930's, and will retain the eight-acre creek valley in its natural state. Plans for the approximately 2.4 hectares (6 acres) of tableland overlooking Lake Ontario have not yet been made.

The Town of Oakville also offers a variety of waterfront vistas. On the eastern part of the Oakville waterfront, Gairloch Gardens stretch from Lakeshore Road south to the lake. The gardens are a highly mani-cured formal park with rose beds, decorative landscaping, flagstone walkways, and an armourstone shoreline. The land was bequeathed by James Gairdner to the Town of Oakville in 1971 so that the public could enjoy the beautiful lakefront setting at the mouth of Morrison Creek, where numerous ducks and geese make their home. The existing stucco dwelling has been converted to a gallery and artists' studio operated by the Oakville Art Gallery. This park is a favourite for wedding photos which, because of demand during the spring and summer, have to be scheduled months ahead.

In western Oakville, the Lakeshore Road bridge over Bronte Creek offers a number of views: looking toward the lake, you can see the inner harbour, the river-mouth, and the new Bronte Outer Harbour. Beyond the breakwalls of the outer har-bour, which is nearing completion, is Lake Ontario. Connecting the two harbours is a public boardwalk along the edge of the river, extending along the lake frontage. Upstream from the Bronte bridge is a large lagoon and cattail marsh; a new eight-storey condominium building wraps partially around the eastern edge of the marsh

property given to the Church of England by Joseph Brant, chief of the Six Nations.

Spencer Smith Park, gently sloping to the lake, presents an inviting vista of Lake Ontario and the Niagara Peninsula. On a clear day, the CN Tower is visible in the east. The view of the lake, from the lower end of Brant Street, is an invitation to take a break from work and to contemplate the magic of land meeting open water. A children's play area, recently added at the western edge of the park away from the water's edge, enables parents to enjoy the waterfront view while youngsters are busy.

The extreme western end of Spencer Smith Park is the former site of the Brant Inn which, from 1920 to the mid-1960s, hosted the big jazz and swing bands, and saw the beginnings of rock and roll.

before the marsh merges with the heavily vegetated slopes of the creek valley.

In contrast to other parts of Lake Ontario in the Greater Toronto region, the Halton waterfront has no overwhelming environmental problems. However, the adjoining Hamilton Harbour has been identified by the International Joint Commission (IJC) as one of 42 Areas of Concern in the Great Lakes. Significant progress has been made on the Hamilton Harbour Remedial Action Plan (RAP), and improvements to water quality in Hamilton Harbour have resulted from actions by the responsible parties, principally the steel companies and sewage treatment plant operators.

The dominant image of the Halton waterfront, encompassing both the Burlington and the Oakville waterfront areas, is one of suburban, maturing residential communities. It has the highest average household income of any region's waterfront in the Greater Toronto Area, the highest proportion of residents engaged in managerial and professional occupations, and a pattern of dispersed housing and employment that makes people strongly dependent on automobiles. The region's waterfront area also has below-average housing opportunities for households of moderate and lower income.

Employment opportunities are concentrated at the edges of the Halton waterfront, with heavy industry on the western Hamilton side and the high-growth service and office sectors in Mississauga and Metro Toronto, on the eastern side of Halton. The two edges are connected by the Queen Elizabeth Way, the Lakeshore GO Transit commuter route, and the CN Rail line. Adjacent to the transportation corridor is a growing band of mixed industrial

The McNichol Estate at the mouth of Shoreacres Creek, purchased by the City of Burlington, 1990

and commercial buildings, the most significant of which is still the Ford assembly plant in Oakville, built in 1953.

The limited number of waterfront industrial uses, such as the Shell oil refinery and test track, are gradually being displaced by more intensive residential development. The extensive environmental clean-up required prior to redevelopment of the Shell lands is nearing completion.

1981 and 1986, its waterfront-area population actually declined by three per cent to 43,500 persons, as household size decreased. In fact, this area has the lowest proportion of children and the highest proportion of seniors on the Greater Toronto region waterfront. Housing ownership is increasing in this area, which is likely to continue to accommodate residential development once the economy improves. Almost 1,500 units

On the Burlington waterfront

Residential estates, with large formal grounds, form a significant portion of the lakefront uses south of Lakeshore Road. Development north of Lakeshore Road is also predominantly suburban residential with newer developments further inland.

Almost 37 per cent of Burlington's population live in waterfront communities. While the population of the City of Burlington increased marginally between

of medium or high density housing are either approved or in process.

As part of its Official Plan review, the City of Burlington commissioned a Gallup Community Attitude Survey; it found that 78 per cent of City residents say there is a need to provide a wider range of housing prices throughout the City. A further 61 per cent want more land used for multiple unit housing and smaller homes in new development areas. While not specific to waterfront areas, these results show general support for a broader mix of household incomes and diversity of housing types in new waterfront residential developments.

The Oakville waterfront, with a population of nearly 30,000, has approximately 34 per cent of the Town's population. This waterfront area has the highest concentration of single detached homes, the highest proportion of residents in managerial and professional jobs, and the highest average household incomes on the Greater Toronto region waterfront.

As might be expected, the Oakville waterfront has a low proportion of residents with housing affordability problems and a low incidence of overcrowded dwelling units. There is a low proportion of young adults (aged 20 to 34) on the Oakville waterfront probably because of the limited opportunities for those people who need rental or affordable housing.

The Oakville waterfront area also has the highest proportion of GO Transit use (13 percent of work trips) of any local waterfront area in the Greater Toronto region. This reflects the proximity of the Lakeshore GO train route and the high proportion of residents working in Metro Toronto.

WATERSHED UPDATE

In its 1990 *Watershed* report, the Royal Commission made two recommendations regarding the Halton waterfront. First, as requested by Halton Region, Burlington, and Oakville, it urged the Province to declare a Provincial Interest in the Halton waterfront. Second, the Commission recommended that the Province negotiate a Waterfront Partnership Agreement with the Region of Halton, as well as with other levels of government and their agencies. The purpose of these recommendations was to create a more open and accessible waterfront, as well as stronger connections with the creeks and river valley systems.

Subsequently, the Region of Halton, the Halton Region Conservation Authority, the Town of Oakville, the City of Burlington, and Ontario Hydro, acting independently, have endorsed the *Watershed* recommendations.

While no Provincial Interest was declared, the Province has endorsed the principle of Waterfront Partnership Agreements. The region and local municipalities have begun to respond to some of the issues identified as a basis for negotiations, including:

- reviewing the (1982) Halton Waterfront Plan's conformity to the nine waterfront principles, as part of the Halton Region Official Plan Review;
- helping identify interim and preferred waterfront trail routes in the provincially initiated waterfront trail study;
- identifying opportunities to maintain and create green corridors as described in the 1990 planning document, *A Greenlands Strategy for Halton*, with strengthened policies to be included in the Halton Official Plan Review;
- preparing to add, as part of the Burlington Official Plan Review, a Council-approved policy requiring that the water's edge to be dedicated for public use whenever redevelopment takes place; and
- reconsidering the Region of Halton's residential designation of 4.2 hectares (10.3 acres) of waterfront, known as the Shell House lands, prior to

approving the 511 hectare (1,263 acre) Burloak Secondary Plan.

TOWARDS A GREEN NET

The Waterfront Trail should be a major pedestrian and bicycle link in an integrated greenway system. (See Chapter 5 on Greenways for further information.) The Burlington waterfront encompasses both Lake Ontario and Burlington Bay portions of the Waterfront Trail. One of the fundamental trail planning questions in this area is how to ensure greenway connections to the Hamilton waterfront, to the Niagara Escarpment and to the existing Bruce Trail.

Map 7.1 shows part of the Burlington Bay waterfront greenway and trail. In this context, the existing trails, landscaped grounds, and strategic location of the Royal Botanical Gardens (RBG) offer an immense resource. The gardens front on Cootes Paradise and Grindstone Creek, and the RBG is prepared to participate in developing an integrated trail system for the area. The objective would be to connect five basic elements: the RBG lands, the Grindstone Creek valley, the Niagara Escarpment, the environmentally sensitive Cootes Paradise wetlands, and the western edge of Burlington Bay. This would greatly enhance public access and use, while maintaining the environmental integrity of each of these significant natural areas.

On the Lake Ontario side, the three-kilometre (two-mile) long Burlington Waterfront Park, from the Spencer Smith

Map 7.1   The waterfront trail, Burlington

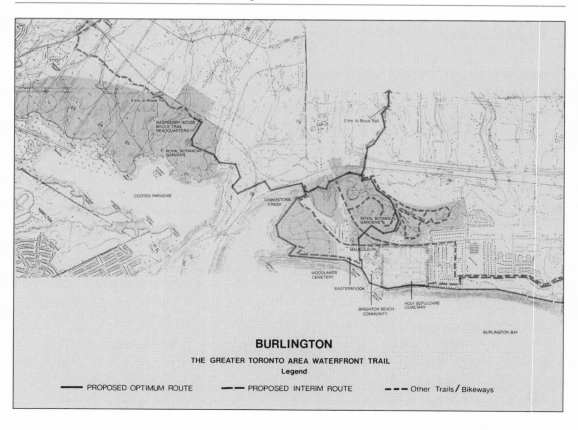

BURLINGTON
THE GREATER TORONTO AREA WATERFRONT TRAIL
Legend

—— PROPOSED OPTIMUM ROUTE   — — PROPOSED INTERIM ROUTE   – – – Other Trails / Bikeways

Park headland to the Hamilton Harbour canal, is publicly owned. This continuous park is the result of long-term co-operation among the Halton Region Conservation Authority, the City of Burlington, the region, and the Province of Ontario. In the summer of 1991 a bike trail was established on the former CN Rail bed adjoining the Beach Strip. Burlington opened the Beach Strip proper to full public use, including supervised swimming and beach programs, and general recreation. During the summer, approximately 24,500 persons used the park. The beach was "posted" as unsafe for swimming on 12 days because of poor water quality; but was nevertheless open for swimming 82 percent of time.

The Breezeway link, which would connect Hamilton's Confederation Park to the Burlington Beach waterfront, was proposed in the 1987 Hamilton Beach Concept Plan and approved by both the City of Hamilton and the Hamilton Region Conservation Authority. However, the more recent draft Hamilton Beach Neighbourhood Plan (1991) proposes local modifications to the original plan and, in its current state, appears to reduce both public waterfront access and local and regional waterfront recreational potential. In particular, the Breezeway link appears to have been removed and more restrictive access to the waterfront proposed. Clearly, there is a need to reconcile local and regional waterfront uses: the fact that the Breezeway link is proposed for the western edge of the Greater Toronto waterfront offers both continuity with the Waterfront Trail and a unique

One of the goals in Burlington is to connect five areas of natural significance, greatly enhancing public access and use while maintaining the environmental integrity of each natural site.

opportunity to strengthen the Hamilton Beach community.

According to the 1991 provincial study, *The Waterfront Trail: First Steps from Concept to Reality* (Reid et al.), only about eight per cent of Burlington's shoreline has an existing waterfront trail located on the optimal route. In contrast, about 20 per cent of Oakville's waterfront has an existing trail along the optimal route — outside of Metro Toronto, the highest proportion of any local municipality in the Greater Toronto region. Local waterfront planning policies make the difference: while Oakville requires that a 15-metre (50-foot) strip be dedicated to the town when waterfront redevelopment takes place, the City of Burlington has no such requirement.

In March 1990, the Region of Halton, in concert with its local municipalities and conservation authorities, submitted *A Greenlands Strategy for Halton* to then-MPP Ron Kanter's (1990) study, *Space for All: Options for a Greater Toronto Area Greenlands Strategy*. In general, that document takes a watershed approach, recognizing the interconnections between the Niagara Escarpment, the river valleys, and the waterfront. Although short on specifics, Halton's submission clearly acknowledges the multiple roles that green space can play in a regional framework. The Halton Greenlands Strategy objectives include:

- protecting the diversity of fauna and flora, ecosystems, communities, and landform of Halton;

- maintaining the water quality and natural flow regulation of rivers and streams within Halton;
- providing expanded opportunities for a variety of public outdoor recreation activities near urban settings;
- contributing to a continuous natural open space system to provide visual separation of communities and to provide continuous corridors between ecosystems; and
- protecting significant scenic and cultural landscapes, including archaeological resources.

The Halton Parkway Belt Review Committee has since recommended that Sixteen Mile Creek be included in the Parkway Belt designation in order to preserve major green space. The Committee's recommendations have not yet been heard by Regional Council and a provincial amendment would be needed to the Parkway Belt West Plan, if those recommendations were to take effect.

The Parkway Belt Plan is a corridor plan for major infrastructure (e.g., roads and utilities) and open space (e.g., urban separators and natural corridors). While not explicitly acknowledged as a potential tool in the Halton Greenlands Strategy, the Parkway Belt designation could provide additional protection for valleylands and the adjacent tableland edges, involving the provincial government in the approvals process as soon as a development application is submitted.

WATERFRONT PLANNING POLICIES

The 1982 Halton Waterfront Plan recognized the need to identify nodes of intensive public use through a series of major regional waterfront parks at intervals along the entire Halton waterfront; and to provide access links between them on existing and proposed public lands and roadways. In the words of the Halton plan,

> The concept excludes a waterfront strip along the entire shoreline, as previously envisioned in the Halton-Wentworth Waterfront Study, and instead provides a nodal rather than linear pattern of open space areas.

However, local municipalities have considerable discretion in interpreting the regional plan and articulating local waterfront policies.

As noted previously, Burlington is in the process of reviewing its Official Plan and intends to develop waterfront policies as part of that review process. The review will include a reappraisal of extensive lakefilling proposals for the vicinity of the downtown waterfront. In the interim, the municipality is proceeding on a site-by-site basis to ensure that waterfront public access is obtained whenever there is development of waterfront lands.

A Gallup Community Attitude Survey commissioned by the municipality as part of its Official Plan Review found that 82 per cent of the City's residents felt that it should give high priority to increasing public access to the waterfront. Moreover, 96 per cent of residents felt that new waterfront development should not obstruct views of the lake or public access to it.

The Town of Oakville's long-time planning policy has been to require, as a condition of development approval, dedication of a 15-metre (50-foot) strip along the water's edge whenever waterfront redevelopment occurs. This strip, along with required shoreline stabilization, ensures an incremental extension of public access to the water's edge. In comparison, the City of Burlington has no such requirement. The result, as noted earlier, is evident in the amount of land accumulated over time for public access.

The Town of Oakville's public access policy, consistently applied since the mid-1970s, has shown great foresight and has been of substantial long-term benefit to citizens. It can also delay recognition of new opportunities. For example, the Burloak Secondary Plan (1991, formerly Shell Lands Secondary Plan) involves redevelopment of 511 hectares (1,262 acres), including the 4.2-hectare (10.3-acre) lakefront Shell House lands. The Town is currently seeking only a 15-metre (50-foot) wide public access strip, if and when the lakefront Shell House lands are redeveloped.

The Plan also proposes two new residential neighbourhoods with a planned population of 7,500 persons. New light industry and a business park proposed for the northern portion are expected to add an eventual 14,000 to 16,000 jobs.

The Shell House lands represent a unique opportunity to acquire several hectares for a waterfront park, as part of the largest secondary plan along the entire Greater Toronto waterfront. These lands also adjoin the proposed Burloak Park, where extensive lakefilling is proposed. Designating the Shell House lands as public open space would expand public waterfront access using the existing land base while reducing, to some extent, the need for 9.4 hectares (23 acres) of lakefill at Burloak.

The provincially initiated waterfront trail study, *The Waterfront Trail: First Steps from Concept to Reality* (Reid et al. 1991), identified the Shell House lands as the first of eight priority candidates for "green nodes" along the trail.

The waterfront Shell House lands; part of the Burloak Secondary Plan

> **U**rban development strategies and
> the forms that we impart to the urban
> landscape must reflect our commit-
> ment to conserving, developing, and
> sustaining urban places of quality while
> satisfying a broad range of bio-physical
> and cultural needs; those that are func-
> tional and those that are symbolic;
> and those that tap our individual and
> collective imagination.
>
> Jacobs, P. 1991. *Sustainable urban development*, Montreal:
> Third Summit of the World's Major Cities.

PLANNING INITIATIVES

Halton Region is drafting a new Official Plan, with strengthened environmental and waterfront policies, scheduled to be completed in mid-1992. As part of its Official Plan Review, in January 1991 the Region of Halton issued a draft report, Land Stewardship and Healthy Communities: A Vision for the 90's and Beyond, which sets out values and directions for changes to the Plan. It presents a clear and concise summary of proposed changes, as well as the reasoning behind the proposals. In terms of the natural environment, it proposes a Greenlands System

> . . . to provide a single framework for the protection of the natural environment while at the same time affording the opportunity for the public to appreciate and learn from the ecosystem.

Clearly, the region is now moving beyond formulating ideas to implementing them.

Overall, there are also significant opportunities to create and enhance the public use and enjoyment of the Halton waterfront. At various times, the local waterfront municipalities, regional municipality,

and conservation authority have demonstrated leadership and foresight on waterfront-related issues. They have tended to operate within a broad collaborative framework or loose partnership. A renewed commitment to ensuring long-term public benefits from both private and public waterfront projects and to a greater recognition of new opportunities that can bring net environmental gains would be benificial to everyone.

RECOMMENDATIONS

52. The Royal Commission recommends that Halton Region, the Town of Oakville, the City of Burlington, and the Halton Region Conservation Authority (HRCA) continue to review relevant documents including official plans and any waterfront-specific plans to ensure that they incorporate an ecosystem approach and the nine waterfront principles described in Part I.

53. Further, the Commission recommends that Halton Region, the Town of Oakville, the City of Burlington, and the HRCA participate in preparing the proposed shoreline regeneration plan, including the waterfront greenway and trail, and ensure that any other plans for waterfront areas are reviewed and/or developed in this context.

54. The Province should negotiate a Waterfront Partnership Agreement or agreements with the Region of Halton, as well as with other levels of government and their agencies, and, where it is appropriate, with the

private sector. The agreement should use the Halton Waterfront Plan as the basis for negotiations, and should consider the following issues:

- confirmation of agency roles in implementing the plan, with Halton Region as the leading co-ordinating agency;
- expanding the ability of the Halton Region Conservation Authority to regulate valleyland development, based on ecological and recreational objectives and on planning for protection from floods and erosion;
- implementing interim and preferred routes for the Waterfront Trail in Halton, as well as developing mechanisms to establish the trail;
- making arrangements to transfer federal and provincial Crown lands and waterlots to local public agencies, at nominal cost, where they are needed for public access and use;
- relocating the Ministry of Transportation work yards from Burlington Beach to allow redevelopment of the present site;
- exploring the most feasible means of removing Ontario Hydro's existing electrical transmission lines from Burlington Beach;
- identifying opportunities and plans to maintain or create green corridors up the valleys of Grindstone Creek, Bronte Creek, Fourteen Mile Creek, and Sixteen Mile Creek, and to preserve and enhance natural habitats at creek mouths such as those at Fourteen Mile and Shoreacres creeks;
- reviewing, within the current City and Regional Official Plan reviews, the City of Burlington's current policy of not requiring dedication of the water's edge for public use as part of redevelopment activities; and
- financial arrangements under which the federal, provincial, local, and regional governments, and the private sector, would participate in the development of the proposed Great Lakes Science Centre, as a means of educating the public about the historical, environmental, recreational, and economic importance of Great Lakes rehabilitation.

55. The Commission recommends that Halton Region, the Town of Oakville, the City of Burlington, and the HRCA re-examine the proposed Waterfront Urban designation of the waterfront Shell House lands and the design of the proposed Burloak lakefill park in the Draft Burloak Secondary Plan. The municipalities, in co-operation with the Province and Shell Canada Ltd., should also recognize the opportunity to make the Shell House lands public open space.

56. The City of Hamilton, Hamilton Region Conservation Authority, and Hamilton-Wentworth Region should review the Hamilton Beach Neighbourhood Plan and the approved

Hamilton Beach Concept Plan to ensure linkages to the Waterfront Greenway and Trail and other trail systems. This review should evaluate whether the potential for the Breezeway link, public access, and local and regional waterfront recreation are adversely affected by the Neighbourhood Plan. If they are, local and regional uses should be reconciled.

57. Halton Region and the provincial government should provide additional protection to the Sixteen Mile Creek valleylands and adjacent tableland edges; this could be done by designating these features as Parkway Belt Open Space in the Parkway Belt West Plan and providing generous building setbacks for adjoining new development.

CHAPTER 8:
MISSISSAUGA

The City of Mississauga is the only local municipality within Peel Region which is located on the Lake Ontario waterfront.

The Mississauga waterfront stretches 15 kilometres (9 miles) along the lake, approximately from Joshua Creek east to Etobicoke Creek. Its major natural features are the Rattray Marsh at the mouth of Sheridan Creek and the Credit River, the lower course of which is entirely within the City of Mississauga. In addition, a number of smaller creeks enter the lake at various points along the waterfront.

The waterfront contains a mix of shoreline uses including parks, industries, utilities, and residential neighbourhoods. The proportion of shoreline devoted to each use is approximately as follows: public parks, 33 per cent; industrial, 21 per cent; utilities and residential, 23 per cent each. Approximately two-thirds of the Mississauga shoreline is protected by armourstone and other erosion control measures.

The Mississauga waterfront includes two major lakefill projects undertaken by the Credit Valley Conservation Authority (CVCA), at J. C. Saddington Park and

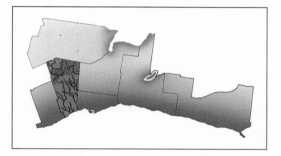

Lakefront Promenade Park. The latter, which was officially opened in May 1991, includes an extensive boat basin with a public marina as well as an area for the relocated Credit Valley Yacht Club.

The City of Mississauga lies on the doorstep of the Lake Ontario salmon fishery and bills itself as the "Salmon Capital of the World". In addition to providing recreation for anglers, sport fishing has contributed to the local economy of Port Credit and adjoining harbour areas. The cumulative impact of Mississauga's lakefilling proposals could include diminished cold-water fish habitat, particularly in the nearshore forage and nursery areas, as well as silting of nearshore spawning beds.

The Mississauga waterfront has a mix of land uses and a broad range of images:

from the abundant life of the Rattray Marsh to the Lakeview Thermal Generating Station's four stacks, or the "four sisters".

The natural features of our landscape often conceal their own history: looking at Rattray Marsh, for example, may lead us to assume that we have always protected its natural beauty, its diverse flora and fauna, its uniqueness. In fact, the fight to save the existing part of the marsh spanned 16 years, from 1959 to 1975.

If some people loved its natural state, there were others who wished to develop Rattray Marsh as a site for luxury homes, replete with yacht basin and marina. In 1965 the township's engineer announced that the marsh was not worth saving because run-off water quality would become so poor that the marsh would degenerate into a "stinking mess". Early in 1967, the fight seemed lost. Bulldozers moved in to begin Phase 1 of the Rattray Park Estates. As a personal protest, a neighbourhood boy

stood in front of a bulldozer to block its path. He was not successful in stopping Phase 1, but in the next four years citizens redoubled their efforts to save the remaining marsh. In 1971 the CVCA purchased 9.7 hectares (24 acres) of the marsh, the site of a proposed marina.

In the spring of 1973 help came from an unexpected source: Lake Ontario rose to its highest level in more than 20 years, flooding the other low-lying Rattray lands. Citizen action — combined with nature, and the timely introduction of fill regulations — made the developer decide to sell the remaining 23 hectares (57 acres). These lands were acquired by the CVCA and, in 1975, the marsh and buffer land was opened to the public as the Rattray Marsh Conservation Area. It exists today because people persevered and acted in consort with nature, rather than against it.

If Rattray Marsh is nature's jewel, the "four sisters" of the Lakeview Thermal

Rattray Marsh today

278

Generating Station are a landmark of a different order. These tall stacks, fronting Lake Ontario, are a beacon to sailors and boaters and, when viewed from the water, are a welcome sight: the circular tapered towers are somewhat majestic and contrast sharply with the boxy structure of the generating plant itself. Moreover, they represent industry, jobs, and the utilitarian parts of the waterfront; and are the most prominent feature of the Mississauga waterfront skyline.

Between the marsh and the stacks, at the mouth of the Credit River, lies the Port Credit community and harbour. The village of Port Credit, on the river's west bank, is part of the original settlement, established in 1843. The attractive, small neighbourhood of cottage-style homes may be designated a Heritage Conservation District. The Port Credit downtown, on the east bank of the river, dates back about 150 years.

The Port Credit Harbour Marina at the mouth of the Credit River comprises 21 hectares (51 acres) of land and water, and is one of the largest fresh-water marinas (1,000 berths) in North America. Two rubble and armourstone breakwaters and a sunken freighter protect the harbour. The marina and much of the rivermouth are under federal ownership and leased to private operators and yacht clubs, resulting in restricted public access. Mississauga's *Port Credit Harbour and Waterfront Concept* (Hough Stansbury and Woodland et al. 1987) proposes an ambitious revitalization of the area.

The Mississauga waterfront area, as the Commission has defined it, extends from the lakefront to the Canadian National (CN) railway tracks, which are located north of Lakeshore Road. This area includes communities that either have a waterfront orientation or have the potential for one.

The Draft Mississauga Waterfront Plan uses the south side of Lakeshore Road as its northern boundary. Although it is quite wide, Lakeshore Road does not represent a major physical barrier to the movement of people along or into the waterfront area. Waterfronts are a significant public amenity serving a variety of interests that are both local and regional. Consequently, proximity to the waterfront generally means use by members of nearby communities.

The Mississauga waterfront has a number of community characteristics that distinguish it from other waterfront areas. The housing stock has the lowest proportion of single detached dwellings of any region's waterfront, the highest proportion of high-rise apartment dwellings, and the third-highest proportion of rented dwellings of any local waterfront in the Greater Toronto region. (Most high-rise buildings are north of Lakeshore Road, not on the water's edge.) Between 1981 and 1986, the population of the Mississauga waterfront area grew by a moderate 4.4 per cent to about 375,000 people. In order to meet the community's housing needs, construction of a broader range of housing types and tenures should be encouraged. Rental and social housing targets should be included in waterfront Secondary Plans and residential developments should be designed with

The Port Credit Harbour Marina at the mouth of the Credit River comprises 21 hectares of land and water, and is one of the largest fresh-water marinas (1,000 berths) in North America.

particular attention to affordable housing and meeting the housing needs of families with children. In addition, the waterfront rental stock should be protected and improved, to preserve mixed-income waterfront neighbourhoods.

The Mississsauga waterfront is a diverse suburban area that includes a broad range of housing types and tenures, despite the limited variety built over the past decade. Unlike the waterfronts of Burlington and Oakville, Mississauga's includes a substantial amount of rental housing, particularly in high-rise apartments, most of which were constructed before the 1980s. Average annual row housing and apartment construction activity on the waterfront has been relatively low since 1980, because of the limited number of waterfront area sites. Waterfront multiple-unit housing completions averaged 60 units per year, almost 60 per cent of them condominiums, between 1981 and 1988. While waterfront housing starts have doubled since 1986, 95 per cent of them are condominiums; no assisted housing or private rental starts have taken place in the waterfront area since 1985.

Affordability is less of a problem in the Mississauga waterfront area than on the Greater Toronto region's waterfront as a whole because of the range of housing opportunities in the waterfront area, particularly its large existing stock of modestly priced rental accommodation.

There is no clear distinction between the occupations of residents on the waterfront and of the region as a whole. However, while waterfront residents have the same occupation patterns as those in the region, they have lower average household incomes and represent a higher proportion of low-income households. The similarity in

Lakeside Park, Mississauga

occupations, but substantial differences in income, are explained by the higher proportion of both older rental housing and younger adults (aged 20 to 34) in the waterfront area.

People on the Mississauga waterfront are slightly less dependent on the automobile than are those from other suburban waterfront areas: GO Transit accounts for 10 per cent of all work trips from the Mississauga waterfront, the highest of any region, while local transit use accounts for an additional 5 percent. This greater use of transit is the result of both the sizable number of moderate-income households and the better public transit availability, particularly the Lakeshore GO Transit route for commuters.

In 1987 — the most recent year for which there are data — there were approximately 12,800 jobs in the Mississauga waterfront area, almost 53 per cent of which were in the retail, service, and construction sectors, with 47 per cent in manufacturing and wholesaling. Between 1983 and 1987, waterfront area employment in the retail, service, and construction sectors grew by 21 per cent, while manufacturing and wholesaling increased by only two per cent.

WATERSHED UPDATE

In its *Watershed* report of August 1990, the Royal Commission made two recommendations concerning the Mississauga waterfront. First, in accordance with a request by the City of Mississauga, it recommended that the Province declare a Provincial Interest in the Mississauga waterfront, and, second, it recommended that the Province negotiate a Waterfront Partnership Agreement with the City of Mississauga and other relevant agencies. These recommendations focused on creating an open and accessible waterfront, protecting and enhancing natural areas, and site specific redevelopment.

The Region of Peel in October 1990 adopted the following resolution as its response to the Commission's report:

> . . . that the principles contained in the report titled *Watershed* be encompassed into the review of the draft Regional Official Plan forming the basis for the development of a regional green-space framework that incorporates, among other things, river valleys, the Niagara Escarpment, the Oak Ridges Moraine, the Mississauga waterfront and other environmentally sensitive features.

In December 1990, the Province of Ontario endorsed the Commission's nine waterfront principles; agreed that a Waterfront Trail should be established; and supported the concept of Waterfront Partnership Agreements, identifying Mississauga as one of two priority municipalities for such agreements.

The City of Mississauga continues to work on the Mississauga Waterfront Plan and has invited the Royal Commission and others to comment on its draft document. In addition, it is still pursuing those priority items identified through its waterfront planning process and contained as major elements of the proposed Partnership Agreement.

In late 1990 the City expanded its existing Lakeside Park by acquiring the westerly 5.3 hectares (13 acres) of the former National Sewer Pipe Property from Petro Canada. In addition, the municipality has co-operated in identifying interim and preferred waterfront trail routes, which are to be incorporated in the Mississauga Waterfront Plan.

In the past year, there has also been action on the highest-priority land acquisition identified in the draft plan. At the invitation of the Mayor of Mississauga, the Royal Commission encouraged continued negotiations by the City, Province, Metro Toronto, Peel Region, and MTRCA regarding acquisition of the Canada Post site (formerly Canadian Arsenals property). Agreement would see the MTRCA acquiring 14.7 hectares (36.3 acres) of land south of Lakeshore Road, adjacent to the existing Marie Curtis Park, for waterfront park purposes.

Ontario Hydro responded positively to *Watershed*. In addition to supporting planning that is consistent with the ecosystem approach, Hydro recognizes the importance of the waterfront to the community and will continue to cooperate with provincial and local authorities in providing access to their lands, where space, safety and security considerations can be met.

The Petro Canada refinery, Mississauga waterfront

WATERFRONT PLANNING POLICIES

In the absence of relevant provincial policies or guidelines and specific regional official plan policies, the Mississauga Official Plan, drafted in 1976 and approved in 1981, is the only planning instrument for the waterfront. Mississauga's Waterfront Plan, when approved, will lead to changes to the Official Plan, and will consequently become the major document guiding development of the waterfront.

The Waterfront Plan, begun in March 1988, is currently in draft form; the planning process is intended to result in a comprehensive plan for the entire Mississauga waterfront, changes to the Official Plan, and amendments to waterfront Secondary Plans. The plan proposes development concepts for the waterfront that are to be achieved over the next 30 years.

Thus far, several waterfront planning documents have been released as background studies to the final proposed plan. The documents, *Fundamentals, Vision 2020,* and *Implementation,* were released for public review in June 1990, and the results of the review process were consolidated in the *Draft Mississauga Waterfront Plan: Results of Agency Review and Public Consultation* (1991).

Fundamentals sets out 60 waterfront planning principles; identifies associated issues; and applies various sets of principles to specific waterfront properties. *Vision 2020,* the draft waterfront plan, begins by exploring the planning context and existing conditions of the waterfront, and then sets out general concepts for waterfront planning and an analysis of waterfront issues.

The *Vision* document contains a site-by-site plan of the waterfront, analyzing constraints and opportunities, and proposing strategies for each site. Readers are referred to the *Implementation* document for matters of policy or guidelines. That paper was not complete at the time of the Commission's review, but it is likely to provide a clearer set of waterfront policies and further guidance on lakefilling and urban design issues.

As *Vision 2020* notes:

In some respects, this Plan should be considered a work in progress until the relevant investigations by other agencies are concluded and any resulting provincial and federal interests defined and policies established.

The openness and flexibility of that comment is an acknowledgement that the Mississauga Waterfront Plan is being prepared while the work of the Royal Commission and other agencies has not been concluded. The draft plan, and its policies and guidelines, will likely be refined to reflect the ongoing work by the City of Mississauga and other organizations.

The Draft Mississauga Waterfront Plan begins by accepting the fundamental direction of the *Waterfront Plan for the Metropolitan Toronto Planning Area* (Proctor Redfern Bousfield and Bacon Consultants 1967), a document never formally adopted by Metro but implemented over the last 20 years. The 1967 Plan included the Mississauga waterfront, and proposed extensive lake-filling in Metro's portion of the waterfront, but said there was a lack of available and suitable material for a similar scheme for Mississauga. *Vision 2020* further notes that:

Notwithstanding current concerns about the environmental and social impacts associated with lakefill, the potential benefits of extending the land base as proposed by the 1967 Metro Waterfront Plan are equally valid today.

The two major components of the draft plan are lakefilling, for a variety of purposes, and waterfront access including acquisition of public land and establishment of a trail system. It proposes approximately 70 hectares (170 acres) of lakefilling in a series of projects across the Mississauga waterfront. These will be subject to further refinement as environmental imperatives are more fully considered. In addition, *Vision 2020* sets out three planning concepts for the waterfront — that it be green, clean, and accessible — which are among the Royal Commission's nine principles.

The Royal Commission, in its review of the Draft Mississauga Waterfront Plan and supporting documents, is strongly supportive of the consultative approach adopted by the City. The Commission has also suggested that they reconsider waterfront principles and environmental imperatives, including proposed lakefilling.

The *Results of Agency Review and Public Consultation* document proposes that the *Fundamentals* report not constitute a component of the final Plan. However, the review and consultation process confirmed widespread support for the 60 principles articulated in *Fundamentals*. The Commission is of the opinion that a condensed set of core principles should be an integral component of the plan, and the basis for developing a clear set of waterfront policies.

The Draft Mississauga Waterfront Plan would be further improved if it explicitly adopted the ecosystem approach, and included all nine waterfront principles, as recommended by the Commission's *Watershed* report, and later adopted by Peel Regional Council. Elements of the ecosystem approach and several waterfront principles are already included in the draft plan.

The draft waterfront plan has two elements directly related to the environment: lakefill proposals and landward environmental issues on the waterfront. A 1991 Environics poll conducted for the Royal Commission found that, of all residents in the Greater Toronto Area (GTA), those in Mississauga were most likely to feel that environmental protection should be the greatest influence in any GTA development strategy.

The plan proposes that lakefill be used extensively in order to create a chain of islands and to extend the land base into the lake by constructing artificial headlands and marinas. However, there appears to be little consideration given to the cumulative environmental effects of these proposals.

There are several potential concerns with the lakefill component of the draft plan. First, it may draw attention from planning opportunities for waterfront recreation, amenities, natural areas, and development on existing lands.

Second, the difficult environmental issues regarding lakefill, a central focus of the plan, are not made clear. Rather, the plan gives the impression that its impact on the environment and its cumulative effects have been fully considered, with only engineering concerns to be resolved. No reference is made to any extensive environmental analysis that might have taken place before the lakefill proposals were made. In addition, the goals to be achieved by the lakefill proposals in terms of fish

St. Lawrence Cement pier on the Mississauga waterfront

and aquatic habitat, public access, etc. are not clear.

Third, the lakefill proposals are subject to approval by the provincial and federal governments, respectively the owners of the lakebed and the managers of fisheries and navigable waters. Consequently, the lakefill proposals are at this stage only conceptual.

Chapter 4 of this report, "Shoreline", contains recommendations for a Shoreline Regeneration Plan within which various proposals could be assessed. The study will be helpful to the City in this regard.

Mississauga independently commissioned a consultant's report concerning *Guidelines for Shoreline Regeneration Relating to Fish Habitat and Water Quality*. It recommends initial modifications to the draft waterfront plan's lakefill proposals including the elimination of two proposed islands and the reduction in the size of the larger "Salmon Island". Additional changes will result from more detailed assessments of the lakefill proposals.

While the draft plan mentions such issues as site decommissioning, habitat restoration, naturalization, and stormwater management in waterfront areas, it does not yet provide sufficient strategic guidance for addressing these issues.

As noted in the plan, site decommissioning and soils clean-up at the former Canadian Arsenals site and at the Texaco site are important, with implications for the future use of these lands and for other waterfront properties. Habitat restoration includes compensation for aquatic habitat diminished by lakefill and renaturalization of creek mouths and valleylands. Naturalization itself becomes an issue in the draft plan, which proposes modifying both the shoreline and coastal processes in order to enhance nature (e.g., "correcting" the lack of a wetland at the creek mouth); but it does not analyse possible adverse effects. Stormwater management relates to the creation of hard surfaces (e.g., parking lots and roads) near the water's edge, storm run-off, and the locations of outfalls for storm and combined storm/sanitary sewers. The Commission expects that these issues will be more fully addressed as the draft plan moves through the planning process and as implementation strategies are developed.

The Draft Mississauga Waterfront Plan notes that half of the 14 utilities and industries situated on the waterfront require access to Lake Ontario for water intake, discharge or shipping; however, none requires exclusive use of the shoreline. In addition, three of the 14 sites no longer support active industrial enterprises (the National Sewer Pipe East, Texaco Canada South, and St. Lawrence Starch properties).

Planning for the future should take advantage of opportunities as they become available. In particular, there are significant land-based opportunities offered by three non-active industrial sites that together make up 10 percent of Mississauga's total shoreline, as well as by recently acquired public lands and acquisitions in process.

WATERFRONT GREENWAY AND TRAIL

The City of Mississauga places importance on public access to the waterfront, as noted in their draft Waterfront Plan. Their proposals are consistent with the Royal Commission's recommendations in Chapter 5, "Greenways", which further discusses public access to the shore and the river valleys in the Greater Toronto bioregion.

As a result of consultation between the City of Mississauga and the Ontario Ministry of the Environment, a tentative agreement has been reached to locate part of the Waterfront Trail on the water's edge of the Lakeview Pollution Control Plant, eliminating the need for a "lakefill trail link" around that site. The trail will connect to adjacent lands including Ontario Hydro's Lakeview Generating Station. Mississauga hopes to begin work on the first phase of the Waterfront Trail, between Marie Curtis Park and Lakefront Promenade Park, in 1992, based on design work begun in 1991.

The Waterfront Trail will connect a series of nodal parks, ranging in scale and function from local neighbourhood parks to regional facilities. The "linked-nodal" strategy for waterfront public access and use is implicit in the draft plan. However, it is equally important to connect the Waterfront Trail to more inland locations, which will require special attention to the use of river valleys and floodplain lands, as well as public rights-of-way and road allowances. Such links to the waterfront are essential to enhanced access and should be identified in the plan. There should also be concerted regional action to protect the environmental integrity of natural features and ensure that a greenlands strategy becomes an integral component of future planning and development.

PLANNING INITIATIVES

Peel Region was formally incorporated in 1974 but still lacks an approved Official Plan; a draft plan prepared in 1988 was not approved by the Regional Council. As a result, development is guided by a patchwork of local Official Plans with no clear, region-wide strategy to protect and enhance natural features of either regional or inter-regional significance. These features include the waterfront, the river valleys, and the Oak Ridges Moraine.

Regional participation in waterfront planning and development has been limited to approval of, and financial contributions to, the waterfront development program of the Credit Valley Conservation Authority (CVCA). There has been a lack of effective action on regional planning issues. A greenlands strategy for Peel in the regional Official Plan would effectively address environmental and human settlement issues. In particular, such a strategy should link the waterfront to the river valleys and headwaters, simultaneously increasing public use and enjoyment, and protecting the environmental integrity of each element.

The CVCA is proposing a new set of policies to protect watercourses and valleylands in the Credit River watershed. In 1988, the Authority commissioned a water management strategy study, which predicted dire consequences for the watershed if new methods are not found to deal with development. Typical of most watersheds in the bioregion, the approach to flooding and erosion problems had been oriented to "engineering", including the channelling of streams and constructing rip-rap and concrete banks. As a result, fish and wildlife habitat were lost and watercourses and valleys degraded.

The new approach is designed to work with nature and to accept a certain level of erosion as part of natural processes. New policies are designed to avoid future erosion problems by keeping new development far from valley edges and by including water management as a basic at the beginning of the development review process.

The valleyland protection policy was approved in principle by the CVCA in October 1991 and is being circulated for comment prior to being finalized.

RECOMMENDATIONS

58. The Royal Commission recommends that the City of Mississauga, the Region of Peel and the Credit Valley Conservation Authority continue to review relevant documents including their official plans and waterfront-specific plans to ensure they incorporate the ecosystem approach and the nine waterfront principles described in Part I.

59. The Commission further recommends that the City of Mississauga, the Region of Peel and the Credit Valley Conservation Authority participate in preparing the proposed shoreline regeneration plan, including the waterfront greenway and trail, and ensure that any other plans for waterfront areas are reviewed and/or developed in this context. Specifically, the proposed lakefill and shoreline modification components of the Mississauga Waterfront Plan should be analysed in the context of the shoreline regeneration plan prior to being approved.

60. As part of the approval process for the Mississauga Waterfront Plan, the Province should negotiate a Waterfront Partnership Agreement or agreements with the City of Mississauga, the Credit Valley Conservation Authority, the Region of Peel, the federal government, and other appropriate agencies

and private-sector interests. This agreement should be based, in large part, on the waterfront plan currently being prepared and on the Port Credit Harbour Master Plan, and other relevant documents. Among other things, the agreement should consider:

- designating which agencies will implement such an agreement, with the City of Mississauga in the lead co-ordinating role;
- incorporating the results of the approved Mississauga Waterfront Plan into the Official Plan and Secondary Plans;
- implementing preferred and interim routes for the Waterfront Trail, including negotiating public walkways and bicycle paths across Ontario Hydro lands and properties with water and sewer facilities;
- establishing suitable mechanisms to permit redevelopment of the Port Credit Harbour; and
- finalizing transfer of the Canadian Arsenals property from Canada Post Corporation to MTRCA, so that it can be managed as parkland.

CHAPTER 9:
ETOBICOKE

The City of Etobicoke waterfront is approximately 9.7 kilometres (6 miles long) stretching along the Lake Ontario shoreline from Etobicoke Creek east to the Humber River. Etobicoke Creek forms a major part of the City's western boundary with Mississauga, while the Humber is its eastern boundary with the City of Toronto. The only major watercourse inside the Etobicoke municipal boundaries is Mimico Creek; there are, however, several small feeder streams to the Humber River and Etobicoke Creek, and a significant portion of the west branch of the Humber River, all wholly within the municipality.

The waterfront area comprises parts of the former villages of Mimico, New Toronto, and Long Branch, which were amalgamated with Etobicoke in 1967. The Lake Shore Boulevard commercial strip ties together these formerly separate municipalities, and provides employment and services to their waterfront neighbourhoods. Manufacturing and industries are located north of Lake Shore Boulevard.

The neighbourhoods include the modest single-family homes and small-scale apartment buildings of Long Branch and

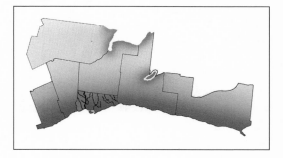

New Toronto, as well as the more intensely developed Mimico apartment strip. The former Lakeshore Psychiatric Hospital site, with its historic quadrangle of residential buildings, its clock tower and landscaped grounds sloping gently to the water's edge, provides a large window to the lake in the central part of the Etobicoke waterfront.

Lake Shore Boulevard, west of Royal York Road, is a continuum composed mostly of low-rise streetfront retail and commercial buildings interspersed with newer, modest-scale developments. The wide expanse of Lake Shore Boulevard, with its ample on-street parking, streetcar service, and broad sidewalks, creates a neighbourhood feel reinforced by the vibrant mixed-income community that surrounds it.

Until the mid-'80s, the Etobicoke waterfront had a stable population of about 40,000 residents and little new development. The area had one of the broadest mixes of income groups on the Greater Toronto waterfront. Almost 45 per cent of the waterfront housing stock was in walk-up apartments and 63 per cent of the total stock was rental. As a result, this waterfront area had the lowest average household income on the Metro Toronto waterfront, and the lowest proportion of residents engaged in managerial and professional occupations.

Major parts of the Etobicoke water-front area are in transition: in part, the substantial loss of manufacturing jobs results from firms shifting production to other locations so as to take advantage of the increased land values at their Etobicoke sites. Industrial closings have been accompanied by a large number of proposals for high-density residential development. The area is tending to shift from an open, inclusive community of mixed incomes and jobs to isolated new developments that capitalize on waterfront locations. Recent waterfront housing activity includes a very high proportion of condominiums, with major new residential developments being planned and proposed.

From 1981 to 1988, housing completions on the waterfront were relatively low: only 400 units were added. These were balanced among ownership, assisted, and rental housing and reinforced the mix of tenures in the community. Recent housing starts since 1986 have shown a dramatic change: almost 2,000 dwelling units have been started. The Etobicoke waterfront has more housing units in the development approval process than any other area on the Greater Toronto waterfront. Of the more than 10,800 dwelling units with development applications either approved or in process, all but 100 are high-density.

There have been equally dramatic changes in employment: in the 1980s, more than 2,200 full-time manufacturing jobs were lost (a 33-per-cent decline). In fact, the Etobicoke waterfront accounts for almost all the loss of full-time manufacturing jobs on the Metro waterfront, and it is the only area with a net loss in total full-time employ-ment (–six per cent). In 1990, the Etobicoke waterfront lost a further 800 full-time manufacturing jobs (–17 per cent) and total employment declined by an additional 3.5 per cent.

Thus far, new developments on the Etobicoke waterfront are located east of Royal York Road in the Mimico section of the waterfront, where the differences in scale and form between new and old are striking. Essentially, new waterfront devel-opment has been exclusive water's-edge condominiums catering to upscale adult lifestyles. Moreover, these developments are self-contained — closed and insular vertical communities that appear to exist in isolation while exploiting the uniqueness of their waterfront locations and views of the lake.

In the words of a recent advertisement for the Grand Harbour development:

> In days past harbours filled with the rich rewards of international trade brought prosperity to the world's great cities. Today waterfronts are the exclusive reserve of the world's most elegant residences. Presenting the homes of Grand Harbour, traditionally styled resi-dences with exquisite site details and finishes crafted from brick, slate and

stone. Strategically located on Toronto's waterfront. Traditional Waterfront Residences From $349,000 To Over $2,000,000.

Large portions of the Etobicoke lakefront have been altered from their natural state by major lakefills. Humber Bay Park East and Humber Bay Park West now flank the mouth of Mimico Creek and together comprise about 65 hectares (161 acres) of lakefill. Colonel Samuel Smith Park, at the southern extreme of the former Lakeshore Psychiatric Hospital site, now extends into the lake and displaces approximately 19 hectares (47 acres) of water surface.

New lakefill proposals include 12 hectares (30 acres) immediately west of the mouth of Etobicoke Creek, at Marie Curtis Park, to create an artificial boat basin.

An additional 3.7 hectares (9 acres) of lakefill are proposed to smooth out the shoreline at the motel strip and provide a minimum 50-metre (164-foot) wide public amenity strip. (The existing shoreline consists of unregulated lakefill dumped primarily during the 1950s, which has created an unnatural and irregular edge of indenttions and protrusions.) As part of the motel strip redevelopment, fill is to be placed in embayments at Humber Bay Park East to raise the lakebed and create a wetland as a demonstration area for stormwater management.

The entire Humber Bay has been identified as part of Metro's waterfront Area of Concern by the International Joint Commission, as the result of contaminants in the aquatic sediments; metals and organics in the water and biota; and

Etobicoke Creek, Marie Curtis Park

Painted turtles

elevated levels of nutrients and bacteria. (See Chapter 3 for a more detailed discussion of Areas of Concern in the Great Lakes.) Efforts to clean up the waterfront will be meaningless unless significant sources of upstream pollution and sedimentation are controlled effectively. The recently formed group, Action to Restore a Clean Humber (1989), has been a strong voice of reason and should be given a prominent place at any round table dealing with the Humber River watershed.

Water quality in Humber Bay is generally poor because of pollution entering from the Humber River, Mimico Creek, and the Humber Sewage Treatment Plant. Furthermore, the bay is sheltered from the main-lake circulation currents and has been described as a "bathymetric trap", in which most of the sediments discharged into it accumulate and remain relatively undisturbed. An area of sediment, described by the Ministry of the Environment as "highly contaminated", extends south of the motel strip as much as three kilometres (2 miles) into the bay.

WATERSHED UPDATE

In its 1989 Interim Report the Royal Commission recommended that:

The heritage values of the Lakeshore Psychiatric Hospital and associated grounds should be preserved by using the site for compatible institutional, cultural, and recreational purposes.

The Ministry of Government Services' current development proposal for housing on the Humber College site and adaptive reuse of the hospital buildings for college purposes is generally consistent with this recommendation.

In *Watershed* (1990), the Royal Commission made three recommendations concerning the Etobicoke waterfront:

- that the Province declare a Provincial Interest in the Etobicoke waterfront area and its immediate hinterland;
- that the Province, Etobicoke, and Metro Toronto jointly undertake strategic planning for the waterfront

area, culminating in a comprehensive waterfront plan and a consolidated waterfront component to the Official Plan; and

- that the Province, in order to protect the integrity of these planning studies, impose a moratorium on development in the waterfront area until a comprehensive waterfront plan and changes to the Official Plan are adopted.

The recommendations were a response to two factors: the Etobicoke planning approach of approving site-specific development applications and narrow area-specific secondary plans without a clear planning strategy and public objectives for the waterfront; second, the magnitude of development, either conditionally approved, in process or proposed, that would, in total, add as many as 12,000 high-density dwelling units and 251,000 square metres (2,701,741 square feet) of non-residential space in the waterfront area.

In its December 1990 response, the provincial government noted that:

... Etobicoke, Metro and the Province will be working co-operatively to ensure that there is a comprehensive planning framework for new development in South Etobicoke, culminating in modification to the Etobicoke Official Plan, plus other implementation measures. The three levels of government have agreed on a program that includes extensive community consultation.

In April 1991, the *Lakeshore Overview Study South Etobicoke: Draft Report* (Butler Group), jointly initiated by the Province, Metropolitan Toronto, and Etobicoke, was completed; it provides a partial basis for a comprehensive waterfront plan. It also indicates that some progress has been made toward creating a waterfront planning policy that is closer to the nine principles recommended in Watershed.

WATERFRONT GREENWAY AND TRAIL

The bases of a "green net" for Etobicoke are its waterfront and river valleys. A significant trail system already exists up the Humber River Valley, and there are beginnings of a similar trail up Etobicoke Creek. These valleylands along with those of Mimico Creek, should be linked to the waterfront in an integrated greenway trail system that both provides public access and protects the environmental integrity of natural features and the tableland edges.

The Etobicoke section of the Metropolitan Toronto waterfront offers significant potential for a waterfront trail because nine local parks and five regional parks already exist along the shoreline. In some sections, because of residential development along the water's edge, the trail route will likely have to follow the first road inland from the lake. However, there are substantial sections where a water's-edge route is possible. Perhaps the greatest potential is from the western entrance to the boat basin of Humber Bay Park West to the Humber River, including the Mimico apartment strip.

In the Mimico apartment strip, parts of the trail and greenway currently exist in a series of unconnected waterfront parks. The strip itself consists mainly of low- and medium-rise rental apartment buildings on the south side of Lake Shore Boulevard, most on long, narrow lots running down to the lake. The unconnected local waterfront parks in the area include:

- Norris Crescent Park at the foot of Douglas Boulevard over to Summerhill Road, with approximately 200 metres (656 feet) of lake frontage and extending 25 to 90 metres (82 to 295 feet) inland;
- Amos Waites Park and Swimming Pool at the foot of Mimico Avenue, comprising about 140 metres (459 feet) of lakefront (including the former Sikh Temple lands) and extending 80 metres (262 feet) inland;
- Superior Park, at the foot of Superior Avenue, encompassing about 50 metres (164 feet) of lakefront and 100 metres (328 feet) inland.

The City of Etobicoke's 1983 *Mimico Study,* under review by Council, recognized the potential for a linear waterfront park and boardwalk in the area. What is needed to link the existing parks is to negotiate public easements in perpetuity over the intervening privately owned waterfront land, and to extend public use over the public portions of filled waterlots.

The Mimico apartment strip represents an opportunity to work with both rental property owners and tenants to achieve waterfront access that will benefit all parties. While this is not current practice in Etobicoke, the apartment strip could be used as a pilot project for working out easement agreements that could be applied there and elsewhere. Strategies for the negotiation of public easements are discussed more fully in Chapter 5, "Greenways".

The Grand Harbour and Marina Del Ray developments, immediately east of the apartment strip, have a 15-metre (50-foot) waterfront promenade, with pathways at the property edges, constructed as a condition of development. Since the mid-1980's Etobicoke has had an informal policy of requiring dedication and construction of such public access strips as part of waterfront development. The adjoining Humber Bay Park West and Humber Bay Park East constructed by the Metropolitan Toronto and Region Conservation Authority provide for public access, except in those areas leased to yacht clubs.

Further east is the Motel Strip Secondary Plan Area. As a condition of redevelopment, the developers will be required to pay for a Waterfront Public Amenity Strip having a minimum width of 50 metres (164 feet). In the main, it is to be constructed from lakefill and will smooth out the undulating shoreline (itself the result of unregulated dumping of fill); it will also widen the development area so that a grid street pattern can be provided. The resulting public road network will provide both public access to the amenity strip and public parking.

The adjoining Palace Pier development, to the east, has both a local park and a water's-edge public walkway that can be linked to the Waterfront Public Amenity Strip. The second phase of the Palace Pier development, at the entrance of the Humber River, has a six-metre (20-foot) wide water's-edge accessway that, in future, can be linked to trails going up the Humber River Valley.

WATERFRONT PLANNING POLICIES

Commenting on Etobicoke waterfront planning policies, *Watershed* noted:

Changing values, such as the upsurge in environmental consciousness and the

Humber Bay Parks west and east

concern about the quality of life in an intensely urbanized setting, appear to have caught decision-makers unaware. It is not that the City is without plans but, rather, that the plans to which it has committed itself, and those it is contemplating, may not have been formulated on the basis of an integrated and comprehensive approach. Public concerns about the barrier effect of high-density development at the water's edge, about waterfront access and the cumulative impact of lakefilling, have not yet been fully resolved. Instead, decision-makers in the City have been quick to support development applications and to grant high densities, because they view the waterfront area as stagnating and in need of revitalization.

Normally, Secondary Plans are built on policies and strategies found in Official Plans. However, Etobicoke's existing Official Plan and its proposed Official Plan Update

do not treat the waterfront as an area requiring a special planning strategy. Due to the absence of a clear planning strategy, both Secondary Plans and site-specific applications lack strategic guidance and public objectives. This lack of clear direction is of particular concern given the densities permitted or proposed on major sections of the Etobicoke waterfront.

There are three plans related to the Etobicoke waterfront. First, the 1991 *Lakeshore Overview Study South Etobicoke: Draft Report* has been the major initiative toward a comprehensive plan for the waterfront area. Second, the *Motel Strip Secondary Plan* (approved by Etobicoke Council February 1988 and revised May 1990) is the only secondary plan approved by Council for any portion of the Etobicoke waterfront; it has been subject to a number of further changes during the life of the Royal Commission. Third, there is a Park Master Plan for the Colonel Sam Smith Waterfront Area approved by the Environmental Assessment Board.

LAKESHORE OVERVIEW STUDY SOUTH ETOBICOKE: DRAFT REPORT

The *Lakeshore Overview Study South Etobicoke: Draft Report* was initiated by the Province of Ontario, Metro Toronto, and the City of Etobicoke to assess the cumulative impact of development applications in the South Etobicoke waterfront area and outline a planning framework.

This framework accommodates residential intensification along Lake Shore Boulevard with sections widened to suit the approved and in-process development applications, in the "Mainstreet Activity Area". In addition, an industrial-based Secondary Plan is proposed for the New Toronto area.

The development applications in the Mainstreet Activity Area include: the Long Branch Village lands, comprising 11.7 hectares (29 acres); the Lakeshore Psychiatric/Humber College redevelopment, 25 hectares (62 acres) in size; the 8.1-hectare (20-acre) Goodyear/Daniels site; the motel strip of 20 hectares (49 acres) of land and water; the McGuinness site, 6.2 hectares (15 acres); as well as lands adjoining Park Lawn Road.

The Mainstreet area would be divided into two Secondary Plan areas: the Mainstreet Lakeshore Secondary Plan Area and the Park Lawn/Lakeshore Secondary Centre Planning Area. Significant portions of the Etobicoke waterfront area and of the water's edge are excluded from these two proposed Secondary Plan areas.

The *Lakeshore Overview Study South Etobicoke: Draft Report* recommended that:

- a survey of community livability be considered;

- there be comprehensive planning and modifications to the new Official Plan as soon as possible;
- these modifications include revised Secondary Plan areas and incorporation of the Royal Commission's nine waterfront principles;
- a study be made of the existing industrial areas south of the CNR line, to provide for industrial revitalization and stability;
- the City of Etobicoke complete the Master Parks Plan and integrate its recommendations into future Secondary Plans; and
- a Human Services Needs Assessment Study be undertaken and applications for redevelopment include a social impact study.

The Overview Study has yet to be fully considered by any level of government, and consequently its recommendations have not been accepted to date. In the meantime, individual development applications and area-specific secondary plans continue to weave their way through the approval process.

At the same time as the Overview Study was being completed, the Ontario Municipal Board (OMB) began hearings concerning the Daniels Group's redevelopment of the former Goodyear Tire plant site. The OMB decision of 13 August 1991 confirmed the Daniels Group's Lakeshore Village Development, which comprises over 1,700 dwelling units, as well as industrial and commercial space, on 8.1 hectares (20 acres) of land. Building heights will range from four to 14 storeys and the development is to proceed in two phases, the second phase to depend on the availability of schools and community facilities and services.

On 1 November 1991 the 6.2-hectare (15 acres) redevelopment of the former McGuinness Distillery site was referred to the Ontario Municipal Board (OMB) as a site-specific amendment to the Etobicoke Official Plan.

On 21 October 1991, the City of Etobicoke asked staff to prepare a draft Secondary Plan for the proposed Park Lawn Road/Lake Shore Boulevard Secondary Plan Area (also known as the Secondary Centre) — to include both the motel strip and the former McGuinness Distillery site. The OMB began hearings on the Motel Strip Secondary Plan on 1 October 1991. Consequently, issues dealing with the motel strip are being debated prior to policies being established for the larger Secondary Centre area.

Just as there is currently no planning framework for the Secondary Centre area, which is a part of the waterfront, there is no comprehensive plan that sets out a clear strategy and public objectives for the Etobicoke waterfront. Such a waterfront plan is needed, as both a framework for assessing major development applications and a context for securing public values and setting Secondary Plan objectives.

THE MOTEL STRIP SECONDARY PLAN

In 1988, a 20-hectare (50-acre) Motel Secondary Plan was approved by Etobicoke Council. The Plan called for 2,700 dwelling units base on a comprehensive land assembly of the site. (This was consistent with a Provincial Cabinet decision in 1977.)

In August 1988, citizens' concerns about the proposed motel strip developments and the proposed lakefilling led them to request that the Secondary Plan Area be designated under the Environmental Assessment Act. The Minister of the Environment decided not to subject any part of the redevelopment to such a review under the Act. Instead, the Province declared a Provincial Interest in the motel strip and instituted an Environmental Management Master Plan (EMMP)/Public Amenity Scheme process within the context of the Planning Act. This process is intended to bridge the gap between environmental and planning concerns.

The EMMP study was designed to address concerns about both lakefilling and urban design, while the densities assigned in the proposed Secondary Plan were outside its terms of reference. The study took place over just three months and proposed three elements: a deflector arm (to deflect water pollution from the development area and to create a sheltered mooring basin); shoreline lakefill to create a public amenity strip; and urban design guidelines to ensure that built form relationships would be subject to some type of review.

The Minister of the Environment subsequently announced that the proposed deflector arm, if it was to proceed, would be subject to a separate environmental assessment. The deflector arm represents 5.1 hectares (13 acres) of lakefill, while the other components are shoreline smoothing combined with a public amenity strip of 3.7 hectares (9 acres) and marshes, for stormwater management, which cover 6.5 hectares (16 acres).

The shoreline smoothing would help the lake flush the shore; however, the deflector arm could potentially reduce flushing and create a relatively stagnant embayment.

Although it is recognized as being subject to a separate environmental assessment, the arm is included in the revised Motel Strip Secondary Plan.

The EMMP process has helped clarify the public amenity area in the motel strip, but it does not provide a comprehensive approach to lakefill or other environmental matters; nor does it adequately address urban design and density considerations.

The Secondary Plan was revised in May 1990 — in part, to reflect the results of the provincially initiated Environmental Management Master Plan/Public Amenity Scheme for the area. The proposed waterfront public amenity strip in the revised plan was widened from the initial minimum of 15 metres (50 feet) to 50 to 80 metres (164 to 262 feet), predominantly through proposed shoreline lakefill.

Furthermore, the revised plan allowed incremental development of the waterfront public amenity area — which means that the entire public amenity strip need not be established at one time. The revised plan also dropped the requirement that the McLaughlin portion be comprehensively assembled as a condition for permitting development of the 2,700 units, allows a reduction in the amount of parkland that must be dedicated and off-site development of affordable housing, and would permit designation of a school site only if the form and occupancy of developments warrant it.

DIAMOND SCHMITT URBAN DESIGN STUDY

After the Royal Commission's *Watershed* report was released, the Ontario Ministry of Municipal Affairs hired the firm of Diamond Schmitt Architects to consider urban design and density for the motel strip, within the broad framework of the Commission's nine waterfront principles. Having declared a Provincial Interest in the motel strip, the Province asked Diamond Schmitt to provide guidance regarding built form, public access, and public use in the area.

The study, undertaken over eight months, was released for public review in June 1991 (A. J. Diamond Donald Schmitt and Company). It began by setting out neighbourhood planning objectives and principles, to be followed in controlling built form in the Secondary Plan Area. The study then further developed the neighbourhood objectives and principles in terms of a possible grid street pattern; open space lay-out, including a central park; land use; built form; parking and sun/shade and view studies.

The built form objective was to distribute the mass of buildings in such a manner that a livable, open and publicly accessible community would result. Assuming 2,721 dwelling units at a density of 3.3 times net lot area, the Diamond Schmitt study recommends that low-scale four-storey structures be built immediately north of the waterfront public amenity strip and Lakeside Drive because, given the orientation of the site, high structures near the lake edge would have shaded the entire waterfront park in the afternoons. Buildings of eight storeys were to predominate along Lake Shore Boulevard, with an intermediate zone of six storeys between them and the shorter buildings. The result would be a "stepped" development, in which four-storey structures adjoin the water's-edge public amenity strip, progressing to six storeys in the middle of the development, and eight storeys along most of the Lake Shore Boulevard frontage. At the northeastern Lake Shore Boulevard frontage the structures would rise to a maximum of 15 storeys.

The sun/shade studies in the Diamond Schmitt report are shown for the existing development applications and the 2,700 dwelling units with a floor space index of 3.3. They indicate clearly that, using the stated neighbourhood development principles, any net floor space with an index of more than 3.3 would result in diminished daylight on the public roadways, sidewalks, parks, and interior courtyards of buildings.

KIRKLAND URBAN DESIGN REPORT

After the Diamond Schmitt report was released, the City of Etobicoke hired the Kirkland Partnership (1991) to advise it and, later, to prepare an Urban Design Supplement to the *Etobicoke Motel Strip Secondary Plan.* The consultants were instructed to use the Secondary Plan's density of 4.0 times net lot area in developing guidelines.

On 7 October 1991, shortly after the OMB began hearings on the amended Motel Strip Secondary Plan, Etobicoke Council endorsed a revised Secondary Plan. Using a 4.0 times density, the urban design supplement to the plan allows maximum building heights of 10 storeys on the first blocks inland from the waterfront public amenity area and 15 storeys on the second blocks, which front Lake Shore Boulevard. In addition, a maximum building height of 20 storeys would be permitted at the Lake Shore Boulevard frontage of the Camrost lands.

On 21 October 1991, Etobicoke Council approved additional changes to the proposed motel strip plan that was before the OMB. There were three types of modifications. First, Council recognized that the need for a school site or sites should ultimately be determined by boards of education and, if they were required, they should be accommodated in the Secondary Plan Area. Second, Council provided a planning rationale for the location of two 25-storey buildings on the Camrost site, claiming that it would create a "central gateway . . . in a distinctive landmark built form". Curiously, the proposed buildings exceed the guidelines Council had approved only two weeks earlier. Moreover, additional modifications were made to the site-specific development policies for the Camrost lands. Third, the implementation of the built form guidelines was relaxed so that they would apply in general intent and variations could be permitted by Council.

On 17 December 1991 the City of Etobicoke presented the OMB with further revisions to the plan, including removal of the deflector arm. There appear to be an added number of unresolved issues which the Ontario Municipal Board may consider in the course of its review. They include: the water's-edge location; density transfers from water to land; ultimate densities (including bonuses and the treatment of seniors' units); the adequacy of built form guidelines in relation to detailed sun/shade studies and neighbourhood objectives; affordable housing; and implementation mechanisms for the plan. In its deliberations, the OMB will also have to bear in mind the Province of Ontario's Declaration of Provincial Interest in the motel strip.

The lack of a comprehensive Etobicoke waterfront plan, as noted earlier, is a major impediment in assessing the public values and objectives for the motel strip, and for assessing the secondary plan itself. The

Royal Commission believes that it is important to recognize how much is at stake. As explained in the following chapter on the Central Waterfront of Greater Toronto, the entire eastern part of Etobicoke, including the motel strip, is part of Humber Bay. It is in the public interest to ensure that plans, decisions, and developments take this broader context into full account.

THE COLONEL SAMUEL SMITH WATERFRONT AREA

In 1978 the Metro Toronto and Region Conservation Authority (MTRCA) prepared a park Master Plan for the Colonel Samuel Smith Waterfront Area, covering the area south of Lake Shore Boulevard, between 23rd and 13th streets. The plan provides for a multi-service park, including moorings for 335 boats and a boat basin to be constructed through substantial lakefilling. It includes park uses on parts of lands owned by the Metro Works Department, Humber College, and on the Lakeshore Psychiatric Hospital site.

In approving the Colonel Samuel Smith Master Plan in 1980, the Environmental Assessment Board summarized the undertaking:

> The Colonel Sam Bois Smith Waterfront Area will provide 70.5 acres of recreational/educational park space on the Etobicoke waterfront . . . 48.5 acres of the park would consist of landfill extending approximately 1,500 feet into Lake Ontario. . . . The components of the park would include an artificial swimming lake, mooring facilities for boats, an amphitheatre, environmental gardens and educational display areas, a fitness trail, sunbathing beaches, and passive areas for picnicking and viewing,

for both local and regional visitors of all ages (Ontario. Environmental Assessment Board 1980).

The proposed park, shown in Map 9.1, is intended to serve both local and regional needs and, in part, address a critical shortage of public park space in the South Etobicoke area.

Since the original approval was given, there have been several changes to the geographic limits covered by the proposal, including the removal of approximately 6 hectares (15 acres) of Humber College and Metro Works Department lands and the addition of 13 hectares (32 acres) of the psychiatric hospital site, which were purchased from the Ministry of Government Services (MGS). The Ministry of the Environment's Environmental Assessment Branch has yet to consider the impact of these changes on the delivery of other public elements contained in the approved Master Plan. Substantial lakefilling, completed in 1990, created the headland and boat basin.

The only element of the Master Plan that has proceeded to date is a Boating Federation Concept Plan providing for an eventual 500 boating slips and adjoining parking for 500 cars. Phase 1 of the proposal provides for 250 moorings and associated waterfront parking to be completed in 1992. The latter is to be used exclusively by federation members for their cars and for winter storage of boats.

There is no indication of the timing of delivery, location, and funding of most of the public elements in the approved 1980 park Master Plan. However, the waterfront/fitness trail is to be in place within three years and there are to be passive areas available for picnicking and viewing.

Map 9.1 Colonel Samuel Smith Waterfront Area Master Plan — 1980

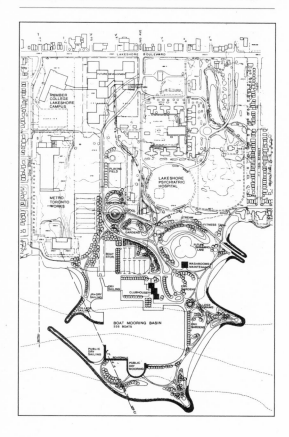

MTRCA acknowledges the lack of certainty regarding delivery of these public elements.

The success of the park and planning for its public elements is linked to integrated planning for the proposed MGS/Humber College development and the proposed expansion of the R. L. Clark Filtration Plant.

On 27 November 1991, the provincial government announced that as compensation for a settlement of the Toronto Islands issue, about 9 hectares (23 acres) of the MGS/Humber College development would be made available as additional parkland to Metro Toronto and Etobicoke, leaving about 15 hectares (39 acres) for redevelopment.

The provincial decision, added to MTRCA's purchase of surplus Lakeshore Psychiatric Hospital lands, means that the overall land base of the park will be bigger than originally planned. Therefore, while the planning context has shifted, there would appear to be sufficient lands to incorporate the public elements and it may be possible to ensure that they are delivered, especially if all parties are prepared to work together.

RECOMMENDATIONS

61. The Royal Commission recommends that the City of Etobicoke, the Regional Municipality of Metropolitan Toronto and the Metropolitan Toronto and Region Conservation Authority (MTRCA) continue to review relevant documents including official plans and waterfront-specific plans to ensure that they incorporate an ecosystem approach and the nine waterfront principles described in Part I.

62. The Commission further recommends that the City of Etobicoke, Metropolitan Toronto and the MTRCA participate in preparing the proposed shoreline regeneration plan, including the waterfront greenway and trail, and ensure that any other plans for waterfront areas are reviewed and/or developed in that context.

63. The City of Etobicoke, Metropolitan Toronto, and the Province, in partnership with the lakeshore community, should jointly implement the following recommendations of the *Lakeshore*

Overview Study South Etobicoke and of
the Royal Commission:

- to prepare a comprehensive
  Waterfront Plan for the Etobicoke
  waterfront area and modify both
  the Official Plan (to create a consolidated waterfront component)
  and Secondary Plans;
- to enhance comprehensive planning in South Etobicoke's waterfront area by:
  - preparing and approving a
    New Toronto Industrial
    Secondary Plan and a study of
    industrial revitalization and
    stability in the broader area
    south of the CNR tracks;
  - adopting two additional
    secondary planning areas (the
    Mainstreet Lakeshore and the
    Park Lawn Road/Lake Shore
    Boulevard Secondary Centre
    Planning Areas); and
  - preparing long-term imple-
    mentation strategies including
    a Parks Master Plan, Human
    Services Plan, Metropolitan
    Waterfront Plan, and inte-
    grating the recommendations
    of those plans into Secondary
    Plans.

64. The Metropolitan Toronto and Region
Conservation Authority should undertake a public review to update the
approved 1980 Colonel Samuel Smith
Park Master Plan.

CHAPTER 10:
THE CENTRAL WATERFRONT

This chapter deals with the bioregion's Central Waterfront and its three bays: Humber, Toronto, and Ashbridge's. Two rivers — the Humber and the Don — empty into this part of the waterfront. South and east of Toronto Bay, separating it from Ashbridge's Bay (or what little remains of it), stretches the Leslie Street Spit which, with the Toronto Islands, forms a southern ring around Toronto Harbour. On the landward side, the Central Waterfront stretches east from Park Lawn Road to Woodbine Avenue, while on the north lies the escarpment carved by the shoreline of ancient Lake Iroquois.

The Central Waterfront embraces parts of the waterfronts of two cities: Etobicoke (at its eastern end), and Toronto (as far as the Beach). This area, home of indigenous peoples before European exploration and settlement began, the meeting place where ancient trails joined, and the trading place where indigenous and other peoples have traditionally traded goods and services, is the cradle of our modern region.

It is also the central part of an area identified by the International Joint Commission as one of the hot spots around

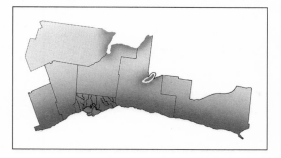

Lake Ontario, with clean-up problems as complex and difficult as any in the Great Lakes. In addition, it is the area on the entire waterfront in which the greatest change is occurring. Almost all the places along this waterfront are in a state of transition, which raises major issues but also produces major opportunities — opportunities to regenerate the environment, reconnect the waterfront to the river valleys and the cities to their waterfront, and stimulate economic recovery.

This is the part of the waterfront where the Government of Ontario first made significant interventions, signalling the emerging importance of waterfront issues in the Province. The Provincial commitment to making substantive changes in the way the waterfront is redeveloped can be found in three moves: the declaration of a Provincial Interest in the Etobicoke motel strip and in the East Bayfront/Port Industrial Area; and the ministerial zoning order freezing development on the Harbourfront and Stadium Road lands until redevelopment plans met the test of public values and objectives, including public access to the waterfront.

As then-Premier David Peterson and Cabinet Minister John Sweeney explained when announcing these actions, the Province wanted to ensure the integrity of the Royal Commission's work and provide an appropriate opportunity for formulating policies and plans.

In October 1989, the provincial and federal governments asked the Royal Commission to carry out an in-depth environmental audit of the East Bayfront/ Port Industrial Area. In December 1990 the provincial Minister of the Environment asked the Commission to study the feasibility of relocating the Gardiner Expressway, and to examine the possibility of pooling lands and integrating future plans for the Canadian National Exhibition, Ontario Place, Fort York, and HMCS York. Among them, these three studies cover the most important issues on the waterfront: environment, transportation, and land use.

In response, the Royal Commission organized intergovernmental steering committees and work groups, and contracted consultants who have a wide variety of disciplines, skills, and experience, to research the issues and formulate policy, planning, and program recommendations. The Commission also consulted the private sector (business and labour), neighbourhood, environmental, and other community groups, and members of the general public to obtain their views of the problems and opportunities.

The results of these collaborative efforts were published in four background reports (No. 10, *Environment in Transition: A Report on Phase I of an Environmental Audit of Toronto's East Bayfront and Port Industrial Area* (RCFTW 1990); No. 11, Pathways: *Towards an Ecosystem Approach: A Report of Phases I and II of an Environmental Audit of Toronto's East Bayfront and Port Industrial Area* (Barrett and Kidd 1991); No. 14, *Garrison Common Preliminary Master Plan* (Berridge Lewinberg Greenberg et al. 1991); and No. 15, *Toronto Central Waterfront Transportation Corridor Study* (IBI Group et al. 1991)) and, in addition, 12 working papers and an in-depth technical report.

All work was based on the ecosystem approach. A common thread running through every piece was that, because the Central Waterfront has the greatest pressures, problems, and opportunities, regeneration of that area, more than of any other part of the regional waterfront, requires integrated planning.

Balancing and integrating these issues is difficult but necessary. The best example of doing that can be found in the Royal

Commission's last background report, *Toronto Central Waterfront Transportation Corridor Study*. It is based on the Commission's earlier work, reflecting what had been learned about environmental issues during the environmental audit of the East Bayfront, and applying the understanding of place-making that had been developed as part of the Garrison Common Preliminary Master Plan. In its turn, the corridor study gave those involved an opportunity to apply the ecosystem approach to resolving transportation issues, as well as the challenge of integrated environment, land use, and transportation planning.

Therefore, this chapter begins with an essay that follows "*Watershed* Update", which summarizes the process and findings of the transportation corridor study, describes how governments could move toward integrating the elements of the ecosystem, and proposes a Stage I program designed to reach that goal.

This is followed by a survey of various places in transition, starting with Humber Bay, the western gateway to the Central Waterfront, and concluding with the Lower Don Lands at the eastern end. There is no reason to comment at length on those waterfront places — Swansea, High Park, Parkdale, the Toronto Islands, and the Beach — that have important qualities of their own but are not in serious or significant transition. Obviously, the Commission recognizes their values, and urges that these be maintained.

For the purposes of this analysis, the Commission classifies the places along the waterfront according to a combination of natural, cultural, and/or functional characteristics. The transitional processes affecting them have been operating for at least 20 years. All these areas have smaller sub-places,

districts or neighbourhoods within them, each with its own characteristics and functions as part of the greater whole. They are discussed in the following order:

Humber Bay:
> eastern Etobicoke
> Humber bridges
> Swansea
> High Park
> Sunnyside
> Parkdale

Garrison Common:
> Ontario Place
> Exhibition Place
> HMCS York and
>   Coronation Park
> Fort York
> Northern Industrial Area
> Niagara neighbourhood
> Fleet Street
> Lower Bathurst

Toronto Bay:
> Railway Lands (CityPlace,
>   Central Park and
>   Southtown)
> Harbourfront
> Toronto Island Airport
> Union Station, and Bayfront

Lower Don Lands:
> East Bayfront
> Ataratiri Lands
> Gooderham and Worts
> Lower Don Industrial Area
> Port of Toronto
> Cherry Beach
> Leslie Street Spit (Tommy
>   Thompson Park)
> Ashbridge's Bay

Map 10.1 Central Waterfront

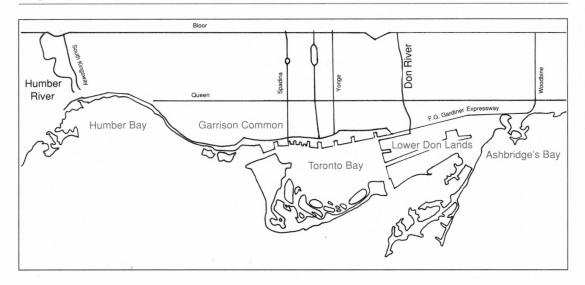

There is remarkable diversity within and among the different places along the waterfront. It must be recognized and sustained. At the same time, there is the potential to integrate the area's natural and cultural environments with transportation functions and land use in a way that connects the various places along the waterfront, links the waterfront to the hinterland, and attaches the central waterfront to the region.

At present, proponents of plans for the various places bump into one another as they try to move through the maze of approval processes, an intra- and intergovernmental gridlock. None, however, can move alone. Matters along the waterfront are complex and linked to each other. Progress in shaping and improving the waterfront, regenerating the environment, and reviving the region's economy requires consensus about its future and the various places along it.

Technology makes a good servant but a bad master.
— Jacques Ellul

Co-ordinated action plans and partnerships, which are also needed, are discussed in Part IV.

WATERSHED UPDATE

In its *Watershed* report, the Commission described the Gardiner/Lakeshore Corridor as the central fact of the Central Waterfront, and noted that:

Depending on the decision made about its future, the people of Greater Toronto will have an excellent waterfront — or they will not. The waterfront will be integrated into downtown Toronto — or it will remain essentially separate from it.

The combination of the elevated portion of the Gardiner Expressway, Lake Shore Boulevard underneath it, and the rail corridor beside it has created a physical, visual, and psychological barrier to the Central Waterfront.

It is a constant source of noise and air pollution, a hostile, dirty environment for thousands of people who walk under it daily, and a barrier to thousands of others who risk life and limb to get across or around it. The Gardiner/ Lakeshore is not only a road; it is a structure. As it processes traffic, it stunts land use; meant to move us along, it limits our opportunities.

The Commission has concluded that the elevated portion of the Gardiner Expressway is incompatible with the fundamental environmental and land-use objectives in the Central Waterfront.

With respect to the rail corridor the Commission concluded that:

As it crosses over major north-south arteries such as York, Bay, and Yonge streets, the rail corridor is a major barrier between the City and the waterfront, visually and in day-to-day pedestrian use. The effect can be greatly reduced by such changes as glass partitions between the sidewalk and road traffic, improved lighting, and possibly opening up retail outlets along the sidewalks under the rail corridor.

The length of the underpass and its barrier effect will be substantially reduced when the rail corridor is narrowed in preparation for redeveloping the Railway Lands.

Pedestrian walkways and amenities could be greatly improved south of the railway corridor, as suggested by the Gardiner/Lakeshore Task Force, which proposed tree-lined, widened sidewalks and improved pedestrian crossings to recreate Lower Yonge as an urban street, rather than an expressway ramp.

Another promising possibility would be to deck over the rail corridor in the central area, to allow pedestrian access between the City and the waterfront, in conjunction with a newly created plaza and park, which would have harbour vistas.

THE PROVINCIAL RESPONSE

In December 1990, in response to these comments, the Province of Ontario asked the Royal Commission, in consultation with the Ministry of Transportation and Metropolitan Toronto, to address the feasibility of relocating the Gardiner Expressway.

SETTING UP THE STUDY

In early 1991, in order to reconcile transportation functions with environmental regeneration and evolving land uses along the Central Waterfront, the Royal

Creating sustainable urban transport systems that meet people's needs equitably and that foster a healthy environment requires putting the automobile back into its useful place as a servant. With a shift in priorities, cars can be part of a broad, balanced system in which public transport, cycling, and walking are all viable options. Neither the exploding Cairos and Delhis nor the relatively stabilized New Yorks and Londons can sustain future growth in automobile use.

Lowe, M. D. 1991. "Rethinking urban transport." In *State of the world 1991*. Washington, D.C.: Worldwatch Institute.

Commission — with the active participation of the Province, Metropolitan Toronto, the City of Toronto, and the federal government — contracted with a consulting team comprising 11 different firms and individuals to undertake a major study.

The team that was assembled included a broad range of skills and expertise in a variety of disciplines: environmental science, landscape architecture, urban and regional planning, land use and land development, transportation and civil engineering, economics, and finance. A steering committee was organized, composed of senior officials from all four levels of government and the special-purpose bodies concerned; in addition, a work group of technical specialists from Metropolitan Toronto, the City, and the Province was established to provide overall direction and technical advice and support for the study.

The terms of reference specified an integrated ecosystem approach, one that brings together environmental, land-use, transportation, and economic considerations, and asked the team to take a long-term (20- to 30-year) planning perspective.

The team was also asked to consider the Gardiner/Lakeshore in the light of three objectives:

- to improve the Central Waterfront, recognizing its strategic importance as a place, as well as a corridor, in the context of the Greater Toronto bioregion (GTB);
- to improve the relationship and links between the GTB, the central city, and the waterfront, and;
- within the context of the first two objectives, to improve the overall transportation system to and through the Central Waterfront.

Map 10.2   Regional context

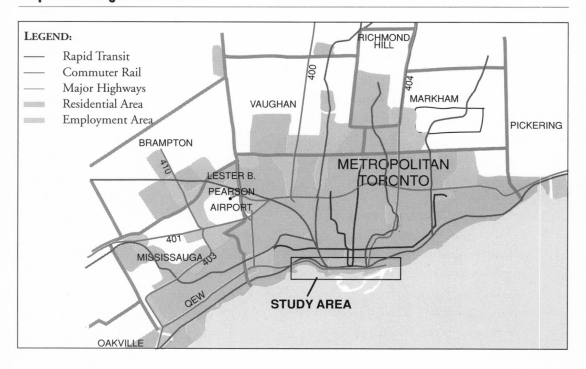

The primary geographical focus of the study was the Central Waterfront: i.e., stretching from Park Lawn in the west to Woodbine in the east, Queen Street in the north and the water's edge to the south. However, the study also examined the Central Waterfront in the context of a Toronto's Central Area: from Bathurst Street to the Don River, and from Lake Ontario to the CP Rail tracks north of Dupont Street. Considerable thought was also given to the full regional context and functions: to the area beyond Metropolitan Toronto, as well as the implications for all of Metro of changes to the Central Waterfront.

SUMMARY OF THE STUDY FINDINGS

The study was completed in November 1991, and the results published in two documents: Publication No. 15, *The Toronto Central Waterfront Transportation Corridor Study* (IBI Group et al. 1991), and a detailed 450-page technical report. In a sense, the study belies its name: while it establishes the fact that the role of the Gardiner/Lakeshore is diminishing in the overall regional transportation system, it does more than that. The study also offers new insights on future environmental conditions; green infrastructure; the strategic value of place-making on the Central Waterfront, supported by a major housing program and transit expansion; the need for consolidated capital budgets among participating governments; and the role of the private sector. It came to the conclusion that:

1. It is both feasible and desirable to relocate and redesign the expressway and Lake Shore Boulevard, as part of an integrated and phased plan to improve the Central Waterfront.

2. Green infrastructure (parks, open space, and waterfront trail links) and other environmental infrastructure are needed as a priority in regenerating the waterfront.

3. Regionally, workplaces and living places must be integrated, in order to reduce sprawl, improve the regional urban structure, contribute to regional environmental goals, reduce dependence on the automobile, and moderate the pressure of commuter traffic on the Central Waterfront and the central area.

4. There are major opportunities for place-making and community-building on the Central Waterfront.

5. A substantial and sustained long-term housing program would be a catalyst for doing so.

6. There is a need to maintain and extend a connected arterial road system to support the regional economy.

7. A "civilized" street system should be designed as the armature around which places, community, and green infrastructure can be organized in the Central Waterfront.

8. There is an urgent need to expand the transit system as a means of linking the region and the centre and of providing freedom of movement and circulation within the centre.

9. If the necessary critical mass of private and public investment is to be created, integrated approval processes, consolidated capital budgets, and timely decision-making are vital.

10. The framework and conditions for private-sector involvement should be established, in order to fully exploit its enterprise, initiative, and capability for investment and creativity.

11. The first stage of the suggested implementation program in the study offers opportunities for public/private sector co-operation and action.

These matters, which are part of the summary that comprises the rest of this chapter, are covered in greater detail in *The Toronto Central Waterfront Transportation Corridor Study*; readers who are particularly interested in this aspect of the waterfront should read it in conjunction with this part of the final report.

THE REGIONAL CONTEXT

The consultants first examined the relationships between the Central Waterfront, the Central Area, and the region in the light of economic trends, population growth, and changing land uses since the Second World War. This included the migration of heavy industry from the centre to the suburbs, the accompanying changes in rail and road systems, office and commercial growth in the Central Area and in the regional centres, and the residential growth of suburbs.

Toronto's Central Waterfront has undergone economic changes similar to those in other major metropolitan areas: at the end of World War II, Canada was the world's fourth-largest manufacturing country. While manufacturing has continued to be of basic importance to Canada's economy in the years since then, its relative significance has declined and its nature has changed as other nations have developed their own capabilities and Canada's service economy has grown.

During the war and for some years following it, Toronto's Central Area and parts of South Etobicoke and Scarborough, as well as areas north of what is now Metropolitan Toronto, contained perhaps the single largest concentration of manufacturing capability in Canada. This important sector was supported by the massive road-building program of the 1950s and 1960s which included, among other important links, the Gardiner Expressway, the Don Valley Parkway, and Highway 401.

However, as the metropolitan region grew, land values in the Central Area increased dramatically and so did intensification of land uses in the Central Area and Central Waterfront. As early as the 1960s, and in the face of these trends and the resultant increases in road traffic and congestion, heavy industries started to migrate from their original, central locations to suburban sites where land values were lower, modern one- or two-storey facilities could be constructed economically, and adjacent freeways provided greatly improved access for increasingly important truck traffic.

Thirty years ago CN Rail also decided to transfer its rail freight operations from the Central Area to the suburbs. It built a by-pass freight rail line (the York and Halton subdivisions just north of Metro's boundary), and constructed major new freight yards adjacent to that line. Similarly, CP Rail created a major new freight classification yard at Agincourt and moved its freight operations from the centre, while continuing to use its Galt, North Toronto, and Belleville subdivisions (which pass through midtown Metropolitan Toronto) as its main freight line. The railways were responding to the same economic forces and the centrifugal migration of their major industrial customers: it was efficient and economic to build the extensive new classification yards on suburban land, which was also well served by highways for truck interchange movement, and to free up more valuable downtown land for other, more intensive, urban uses.

The railways' move also freed up significant capacity on the "spider's web" of radial rail lines converging on Union Station, allowing the Province of Ontario to introduce commuter rail service, initially on the Lake Shore West and Lake Shore East lines, in 1967.

The major concentrations of heavy industry, as well as of other industrial activities, are now in the outer reaches of Metropolitan Toronto (e.g., towards Pearson International Airport and in northeast Scarborough) and beyond (in Oakville, north Mississauga, Brampton/Bramalea, Vaughan, Markham, Pickering, Ajax, Oshawa, etc.). While some of these

municipalities had substantial industrial activity during and following the War, all have benefitted economically from the industrial exodus from central Toronto, and have experienced related residential growth.

During the 1960s and early 1970s, most of the remaining underdeveloped land in Metropolitan Toronto was covered, and there has been dramatic population growth in the outer regional municipalities (Peel, Durham, York, and Halton) in the past two decades.

As documented in the 1990 *Greater Toronto Area Urban Structure Concepts Study* (IBI Group et al.), earlier suburban residential development in Metropolitan Toronto was relatively compact and occurred in the context of a well-developed urban transit system. Until very recently, by contrast,

Map 10.3 Major existing industrial areas, freight rail, and highway facilities

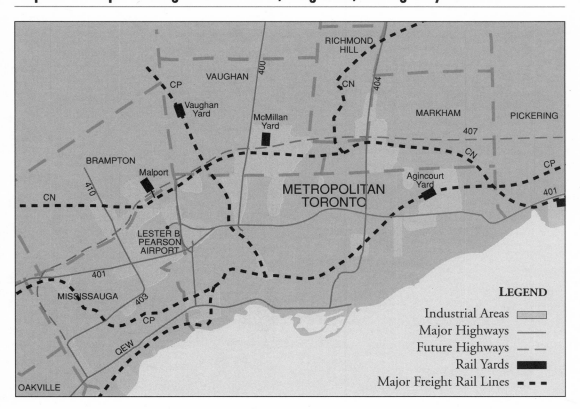

development in the outer regions tended to be at lower densities, without the benefit of extensive urban transit services, and it created extensive auto-dependent areas surrounding Metropolitan Toronto. These trends added greatly to the pressure for cross-boundary commuting trips to jobs within Metropolitan Toronto, a large majority of which are by automobile.

As these regional changes were going on, a trend developed on the Central Waterfront for more intense and specialized land uses, utilizing the hundreds of hectares of prime land vacated by industrial and rail activities. Obvious examples include the expanding financial service industry, manifested in the office buildings of major international and national financial institutions in Toronto's central core. Office, retail, and trade activities also expanded and intensified greatly in the Central Area, as well as in other city centres (e.g., North York, Scarborough, Mississauga) in keeping with the Metropolitan Toronto Official Plan, the Official Plans of adjacent municipalities, and provincial policies.

In recent years, total office/commercial growth in the regional centres and throughout the region rivalled that of the Central Area in absolute terms; but the Central Area remains an order of magnitude greater in size, diversity, and critical importance than any others. While continuing growth is anticipated in all these centres, it is expected that the Central Area will remain paramount in the region and will continue as a major financial centre in the global markets of the next century. In addition, the Central Waterfront has become the focal point for Toronto's important international tourism, trade, and convention industries and associated recreational areas and facilities.

While there has been a tendency to move heavy manufacturing and related warehousing to the suburbs, there has been significant growth in a wide variety of light industrial activities, sometimes referred to as urban industrial, which are thriving in the shoulder areas adjacent to the financial core. These activities, many of which are directly related to office/commercial activities but cannot support premium rents, include the burgeoning information industry (computer systems, data processing centres, word processing, software development, communications) and media industries (e.g., publishing, film, music, visual art) that have expanded in their own right and in support of other commercial activities.

Such urban industrial activities tend to be "at home" in medium-rise (four- to eight-storey) buildings located on urban streets, and have naturally congregated in buildings in the shoulder areas surrounding the financial core. Accordingly, these areas have been transformed in both occupying uses and physical rehabilitation, particularly during the past two decades.

Beginning in the 1970s, and especially after the OPEC cartel crisis, the suburban dream began to crumble as gas prices rose. At first, those who already lived downtown simply stayed put; later, people who had moved out began to move back in. In doing so, they were renewing a Toronto tradition

> *The Central Area will remain paramount in the region and will continue as a major financial centre in the global markets of the next century.*

Many buildings that housed industry have been converted for office and retail use

— maintaining the downtown as a place, not just for the very rich and the very poor, but for middle-class families.

POPULATION, EMPLOYMENT, AND TRAVEL PROJECTIONS

Having considered the past and present regional context, the team examined the projections of the Central Area's share of population and employment projections to the year 2021, as well as forecasts of travel demand; on that basis it assumed a total regional population of 6 million people with a total employment of 3.4 million.

To evaluate the implications of the relationship between place of work and place of residence, including various degrees of compactness, five land-use scenarios were developed, representing a range of future possibilities for the region. These were used as a basis for estimating travel demand to the year 2021.

In four scenarios, the 2021 population in Metropolitan Toronto was 2.8 million, and in the fifth 3.2 million, while in all five scenarios, Metro's 2021 job total was assumed to be 1.9 million.

The 2021 Central Area resident population in the scenarios ranges from 235,000 people to 405,000, compared with the 1986 level of 133,000 people. Future employment there ranges from 571,000 to 617,000 jobs by 2021, relative to the 1986 level of 429,000 jobs. The higher number of people, compared with the number of jobs, reflects policies of the City of Toronto and Metro and is consistent with the 1989-1990 provincial long-term forecasts for the Greater Toronto region.

The projections and scenarios were used throughout the study as a basis for considering the implications of growth for environmental conditions, place-making, and transportation requirements.

ENVIRONMENTAL CONDITIONS

The environmental conditions of Toronto's Central Waterfront have always been dynamic, responding to changes in climate; forces of glaciation; the power of wind and waves; and, more recently, human activities.

For thousands of years, aboriginal people travelled the rivers — trading, fishing, and hunting. For them, "Toronto" meant a "meeting place" at a natural lakeside landing. Few in number, the Indians lived lightly on the land: they made trails in the forests, cut timber for shelter and firewood, hunted and fished for food, and planted crops on small clearings above the valleys.

With the arrival of European settlers in the 18th century, the environment began to change dramatically. As described in Chapter 4, the waterfront was soon modified to provide piers for the boats and ships that were the primary means of transportation. Large quantities of stone were removed from nearshore waters for ballast and building. The land base was extended by lakefilling: almost all the land south of Front Street was once part of the lake; the vast Ashbridge's Bay marshes at the mouth of the Don River became a new port and industrial area. The ponds and creeks of High Park were severed from Lake Ontario, first by railway lines, and then by lakefill at Humber Bay, where a breakwater was built to protect the newly created beaches from wave action and to establish sheltered water for boating.

Humber and Toronto bays quickly became repositories for the wastes of the growing population: first for raw sewage and industrial effluents, later for waste that had undergone varying degrees of treatment. Today, stormwater and treated sewage from three treatment plants pollute the Humber and Don rivers and the lake; this is still one of the most serious environmental problems in the Central Waterfront (see Chapter 3).

If Elizabeth Simcoe, wife of Upper Canada's first lieutenant governor and a diarist who faithfully recorded her impressions of Upper Canada, could visit the Central Waterfront today, she would find little to remind her of the wetlands, sand spits, clear rivers, creeks, and forests she enjoyed nearly two hundred years ago. In their place, she would find the manicured lawns of the Western Beaches, the asphalt of the CNE, the built landscape of Harbourfront, the lower Don in its concrete channel, the vacant lots and old industrial buildings of the Port District.

There are only small, fragmented patches of good-quality natural habitat remaining in the marshes of the lower Humber River, High Park, the Toronto Islands, and the Cherry Beach area. But pehaps Mrs. Simcoe would be pleasantly surprised to explore the Leslie Street Spit — a headland created by lakefill — where she would find many of the plants and animals that once lived all across the waterfront. A victim of malaria ("the shaking ague"),

Painting of the Town of York, 1803

Map 10.4   Storm outlets and combined sewer overflows

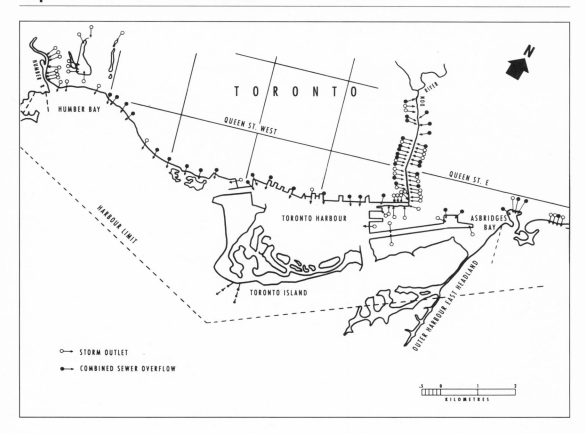

she would certainly enjoy the decline in mosquitoes!

Typical of most towns and cities, Toronto tended to ignore the floodplains of its rivers as it grew along their fertile valleys. Hurricane Hazel, which swept through this area in 1954, wreaked havoc across the city, destroying lives and property, especially in the Humber watershed. In the aftermath, authorities moved to keep many river valleys free of development, to avoid future trage-dies. However, some older areas of the City, particularly in the Central Waterfront, still sit in the floodplain of the Don River.

The microclimate of the Central Waterfront is affected by both the city and by the lake. All cities affect their climatic con-ditions: vehicles and the heating/cooling systems of buildings create excess heat; built form creates shade and changes wind patterns and speeds; and pollution in the air reduces the intensity of solar radiation. Combined with these factors, the Central Waterfront is influenced by weather patterns associated with the lake: wind, fog, and the moderating effects of the water on temperatures.

Air quality in the Central Waterfront generally meets health-related guidelines, except that there are often high levels of ground-level ozone during spring and summer; there are high levels of nitrogen dioxides, carbon monoxide, volatile organic compounds, and dust near the transporta-tion corridor.

In the past decade, pollution from all sources except vehicle emissions has been

Map 10.5 Habitats

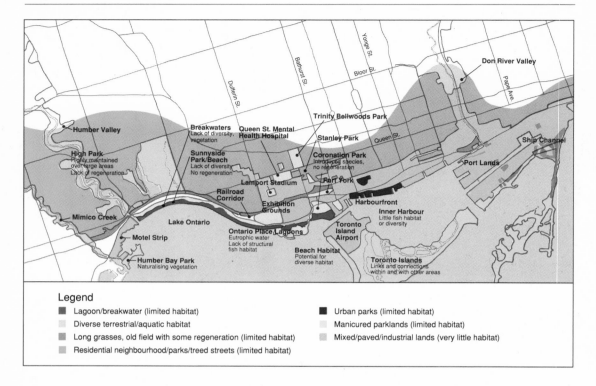

Yonge St.

Don River Valley

Bathurst St.

Bloor St.

Papa Ave.

Dufferin St.

Trinity Bellwoods Park

Ship Channel

Humber Valley

Breakwaters
Lack of diversity,
vegetation

**Queen St. Mental
Health Hospital**

Stanley Park

Queen St.

High Park
Highly maintained
over-large areas
Lack of regeneration

**Sunnyside
Park/Beach**
Lack of diversity
No regeneration

Coronation Park
Introduced species,
no regeneration

Port Lands

Lamport Stadium

Fort York

**Railroad
Corridor**

Harbourfront

Mimico Creek

Lake Ontario

**Exhibition
Grounds**

Inner Harbour
Little fish habitat
or diversity

Lamport Stadium

Motel Strip

Ontario Place/Lagoons
Eutrophic water
Lack of structural
fish habitat

**Toronto
Island
Airport**

Humber Bay Park
Naturalising vegetation

Beach Habitat
Potential for
diverse habitat

Toronto Islands
Links and connections
within and with other areas

Legend

- ◼ Lagoon/breakwater (limited habitat)
- ◻ Diverse terrestrial/aquatic habitat
- ◼ Long grasses, old field with some regeneration (limited habitat)
- ◼ Residential neighbourhood/parks/treed streets (limited habitat)
- ◼ Urban parks (limited habitat)
- ◻ Manicured parklands (limited habitat)
- ◻ Mixed/paved/industrial lands (very little habitat)

---

reduced in the City of Toronto. Although advances in technology could be expected to reduce automobile emissions in the future, the *Toronto Central Waterfront Transportation Corridor Study* concluded that benefits in terms of overall air quality may be minimal:

> . . . over the next 30 years, technological developments may make possible substantial reductions in energy consumption and/or vehicular emission per vehicle-kilometre, but absolute reductions in energy consumption and the impact on the environment would require greatly improved transit and changes to land use/urban structure. These will be needed in order to reduce average trip lengths, encourage transit use, and motivate behavioural change to divert discretionary travel from cars to transit, cycling, and walking. Stabilization or

reduction of vehicle-kilometres of auto travel will be required if we are to achieve the significant reductions in automobile energy consumption and emissions made possible by technological developments.

Air pollutants from industrial activities also cause concern locally; in the Port Industrial Area, for example, high levels of dust and odour create unpleasant conditions and sometimes affect nearby residential neighbourhoods (such as parts of South Riverdale).

Transportation is also the greatest source of noise in the Central Waterfront: traffic on the Gardiner/Lakeshore, trains and shunting yards, aircraft at the Toronto Island Airport — all are major contributors. Residential communities on the Toronto Islands and at Harbourfront have been particularly affected by aircraft noise. Buildings in the St. Lawrence neighbourhood were designed without open windows and balconies facing the Gardiner/Lakeshore/ railway corridor.

The Ataratiri and East Bayfront/Port Industrial areas are also subjected to high noise levels from the transportation corridors, which may restrict the form and design of any residential buildings there.

Lakefilling and former industrial activities have left a legacy of contaminated soils and groundwater in much of the Central Waterfront, particularly Ataratiri, the Railway Lands, and the East Bayfront/Port Industrial Area. In many places, toxic metals, oil and grease, and complex organic chemicals are found at levels that may have harmful effects on people, other animals or plants.

The costs of cleaning up — which must be done if these lands are to be kept in productive use — are uncertain because of a lack of knowledge on several fronts: the full nature and extent of the problem; standards to which the soil must be cleaned; and the best methods of treatment. There are many methods, of varying cost and effectiveness, so that not even experts can say with certainty what should be done and how much it will cost.

The uncertainties and the possible liabilities have caused almost all parties — owners, investors, lenders, and governments — to hesitate. For its part, the banking industry has identified the problem as the biggest single domestic issue facing Canadian banks in the 1990s. To avoid potential liability, which could exceed the value of assets, banks are simply refusing to extend credit to business facilities that show signs of pollution. However, the problem cannot be ignored; nor should we allow it to bring clean-up to a grinding halt.

The built environment of the Central Waterfront is a mixture of old and new,

from the historic Gooderham and Worts distillery to the high-rise condominiums of Harbourfront. Although much of the heritage on this part of the waterfront has already been lost to redevelopment, enough remains to retain a sense of history — if changes are approached thoughtfully.

Although every one of the Commission's studies in the Central Waterfront focused on environmental conditions, the environment of the East Bayfront/Port Industrial Area was studied in greatest depth. The environmental audit of that area is relevant to the rest of the Central Waterfront in two respects: first, many of the audit's findings and recommendations are appropriate to other places along the waterfront. Second, the audit process is applicable to future studies elsewhere. (A description of the audit results is included in the Lower Don Lands section of this chapter.)

Having reviewed past, present, and possible future environmental conditions (air, water, soil quality, and other factors) along the Central Waterfront, the *Toronto Central Waterfront Transportation Corridor Study* concluded that:

Urbanization processes in the Central Waterfront have degraded both terrestrial and aquatic habitats resulting in a poor environment for wildlife and for human activity. The ongoing transition of the Central Waterfront from largely industrial and related transportation uses to a more diverse and urban place — and the fact that hundreds of hectares are currently vacant or underutilized and waiting for the second half of the transition to occur — provides this generation of Torontonians with a unique opportunity to improve the area's natural and physical environment

— first in terms of creating a "green infrastructure" of open spaces, parks, and links and then in terms of other aspects of environmental quality.

The study sees green infrastructure as an essential element of urban infrastructure, as important as — some would say more important than — streets and utilities. "Green" is shorthand for natural and pedestrian spaces of many kinds, from plazas and streets to public gardens and urban wilderness. The arrangement and proportion of paving, structures, and plantings vary, but green infrastructure has certain common characteristics: it provides a useable, diverse, open, accessible, connected, safe, and attractive environment for people outdoors, whether they are walking, running, playing, sitting, lounging or using wheelchairs, bicycles, or roller skates.

The reviews of environmental conditions undertaken for the Transportation Corridor Study and the Environmental Audit of the East Bayfront/Port Industrial Area provided an understanding of the requirements for green infrastructure and environmental regeneration in this area. For example, it became apparent that plans and programs in the Central Waterfront should:

- take into account current and future pollution levels and noise from all sources;
- include measures to improve the quality of water, soils, and air;
- ensure that studies are conducted to assess levels of toxic contaminants in air; assess air quality in the vicinity of the Gardiner/Lakeshore Corridor; undertake further air modelling in the area; and assess noise levels in the area;

- ensure that there is an adequate buffer between industry and utilities, including the Main Sewage Treatment Plant, and any sensitive uses in the area;
- include consultation with emergency response departments on access, hazardous material use and storage, and availability of hospital and other emergency services;
- increase the diversity and connectedness of parks and other open spaces;
- ensure that future recreation in, and access to, open spaces in the area strikes a balance between the needs of people and those of wildlife;
- increase the diversity and quality of terrestrial and aquatic habitats;
- maintain and enhance the diversity and distinctiveness of places in the Central Waterfront, and, through integration and reuse, keep as much as possible of the area's industrial and natural heritage; and
- protect and enhance vistas.

PLACE AND CORRIDOR

The central theme of the *Toronto Central Waterfront Transportation Corridor Study* is the balance between place and corridor within this regional and environmental framework.

As used in the study, "place" is shorthand for a habitable place, a memorable place, one that can be occupied comfortably by people on foot or seated, to linger and appreciate, a place which can and should be clean, green, useable, diverse, connected, and beautiful. In short, a pleasant and accessible place. It is a suitable and desireable place in which to work, live, and play — a place that can be developed economically.

The term "corridor" is used as shorthand for a passageway for high-speed and efficient movement, the primary purpose of which is the easy flow of powered vehicles and where people on foot or bicycle or in a wheelchair are unwelcome and unsafe. The corridor may contain different modes of transport: rail, road, transit, etc. If the transport is by automobile, the corridor usually connotes an expressway, highways, regional or arterial roads — through routes, as opposed to main, local or neighbourhood streets that rank lower in the road hierarchy.

Many main or neighbourhood streets in Toronto accommodate movement and, in a sense quite different from that meant in the study, can be described as corridors. But a street's place-making — its social — attributes are dominant. If done well, the social or place-making element gives main and neighbourhood streets a civilized quality. However, there is a limit to their capacity to perform this function if they are made to carry too much traffic.

The central theme of the study is the balance between place and corridor.

Protecting Toronto's neighbourhoods from corridor traffic has channelled vehicles to fewer and fewer free-flowing corridors, and these, having surpassed their social carrying capacity as places, have now reached their transportation carrying capacity as corridors. The primary vehicular conduit serving the downtown is the Gardiner/Lakeshore couplet.

To varying degrees, it compromises the habitability of all the places it goes through, but it does so most severely between the downtown and Toronto Bay.

The balance of place-making and corridor-making design criteria will have to shift in favour of the former if this central piece of the waterfront is to become truly habitable, an integral part of the downtown.

PLACE-MAKING

For the past several decades our regional community has been playing out two urban development themes. The first has been continued urban sprawl, designed around the auto as the dominating factor, augmented by single-use zoning, which was originally intended to separate unhealthy industrial workplaces from residential areas. It is characterized by free-standing houses, separated workplaces, and shopping centres linked by vast networks of roads. This form has been immensely popular, space-consuming, and, it is now apparent, very expensive in land, money, environmental health, and travelling time.

The second theme is becoming increasingly evident here, as in other parts of the world: it features closer integration of workplaces and living places, more compact mixed-use zoning interspersed with larger green spaces, a greater role for transit, and less reliance on cars. This composite model for development has begun to take hold in Toronto's Central Area, and is showing signs of acceptance elsewhere. All the Commission's studies, including the *Central Waterfront Transportation Corridor Study*, reinforced the need for a greater emphasis on the second model.

A significant portion of the study dealt with the ingredients of place-making, the changes and planning approaches necessary for a more habitable central waterfront. It pointed out that there is a unique opportunity to make the waterfront memorable, as the result of the regional shift in heavy industrial and related transportation uses from the city core to the periphery. Making the waterfront a better place will not only be of benefit locally, but will help the city and region as a whole. This offers a chance to create an extensive green infrastructure, a better quality of urban development, and economic growth in the City's Central Area, which is otherwise constrained for space.

The study showed that a quantity of new housing is particularly important; it will reduce pressures for more long-distance commuting; create a livelier, more diverse, and safer place day and night throughout the week; and reduce the tendency to destroy outlying countryside.

The presence of people who live on or close to the waterfront in well-designed communities is the best way to ensure the vitality of the Central Waterfront, assure public security and safety, and encourage the fullest use of waterfront amenities.

The study envisages a range of neighbourhoods (and supporting community facilities), with a wide mix of different housing types and tenures, and a population that is socio-economically reflective of the region: all income groups, all ages, all family types, including childless couples, singles, and people who are able-bodied as well as those who are handicapped.

Given the Central Area's dominance as the region's workplace, with its current surplus of office capacity, more emphasis on housing and community development will help to redress the balance and integrate workplace and living place there.

In order to understand the full scope as well as the impediments to place-making there, and to explore the regional effects, the team studied each of the places along the Central Waterfront. They also analysed the emerging land-use trends, including land prices and related economic considerations.

It became clear that there is sufficient land capacity — some 300 hectares (750 acres) — to accommodate most or all of the expected increase in the Central Area population, projected at between 100,000 and 270,000 people. Furthermore, it is also obvious that jobs, housing, and related community facilities on the waterfront could co-exist in mixed-use developments.

The analysis showed that at normal Central Area densities and at the rate projected in Cityplan '91 (3,500 housing units per annum), one year's production of housing would consume about 16 hectares (40 acres) of Central Waterfront land (rather than the 280 hectares (700 acres) that suburban densities would consume).

It also showed that increasing the ratio of population to employment in the Central Area, and creating a more compact urban structure in the Greater Toronto region, would reduce increased demand for travel into the centre, by as much as 50 per cent.

But the analysis showed that if place-making in the Central Waterfront is to be done well, the barrier and environmental effects of the Gardiner/Lakeshore and the rail corridor would have to be eliminated or substantially reduced; the green infrastructure would have to be installed; and the City's normal "neighbourhood-friendly" street grid would have to be extended wherever possible south of Front Street to the water, where it does not now exist.

This more interconnected, multi-use, civilized street network would have to be developed as the armature around which housing, mixed-use development, and a green infrastructure could be created.

It is also obvious that jobs, housing, and related community facilities on the waterfront could co-exist in mixed-use developments.

THE CARRYING CAPACITY OF CITY STREETS

As development in the region around Toronto spreads, it becomes increasingly obvious that the Central Area road network is limited: untold acres of land in outer municipalities have been dedicated to road networks that, increasingly each year, feed traffic that winds up on the Central Area's fixed amount of roadway. Moves to make this central road network operate more efficiently lead inevitably to road designs that only increase traffic flow, and that do so at the expense of the pedestrian environment and the sense of the street as a habitable public place.

A neighbourhood street can be wonderful: the public domain that serves as a means of address to the houses along it, a space in which neighbours meet and children play, where trees grow, and from which services of all kinds are supplied. A main street can be equally enjoyable: diverse and active, organizing elements that serve the local community, it offers shopping, commerce, entertainment, and the company of others.

Such main streets frame public space. While they permit traffic movement, they have a finite carrying capacity which, if exceeded, changes them from being attractive to becoming dreary stretches that serve

Map 10.6 Emerging urban intensities in the Central Waterfront

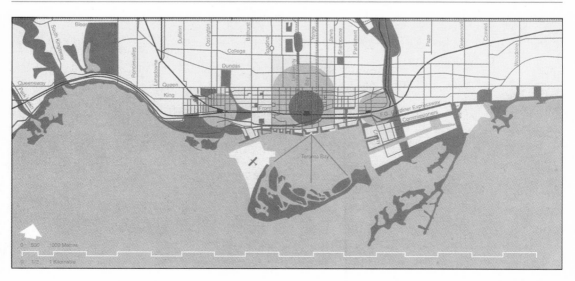

only vehicles going to and from somewhere else. In the shorthand of the *Central Waterfront Transportation Corridor Study*, they become corridors dedicated to or dominated by traffic, rather than public places.

The turning point or threshold at which place-making dominates corridor-making can be called the social, as opposed to transportation, carrying capacity of the street. While not usually expressed that way, the fact that liveable streets have a carrying capacity is well-known to residents of Toronto's neighbourhoods. They have successfully insisted that traffic flow remain below this threshold — a major reason that Toronto's neighbourhoods work so well.

The team suggested that the street system in the Central Waterfront be designed to meet standards that limit — and, if necessary, reduce — the quantity of commuter traffic to fit a street's social carrying capacity;

necessary transportation capacity would be made up by improved public transit service.

THE CENTRAL WATERFRONT AS A CORRIDOR

The Central Waterfront is also a strategic corridor for moving people and goods to, from, and through the Central Area. Road, rail, marine, and air transportation facilities are all part of the Central Waterfront's role as corridor.

The major rail facility is the Lakeshore Corridor, which stretches across the Central Waterfront, and is joined by lines from the Don River corridor in the east and the northwest corridor in the west. GO Transit provides rail commuter services on seven radial lines that converge along these corridors to arrive at Union Station, while VIA provides rail service to other cities and provinces.

A friendly street, Markham Street, Toronto

A rail freight spur runs south from the rail corridor to the East Bayfront/Port Industrial Area, connecting there to a number of freight spurs. Most of the other rail freight lines that served industries in the Central Waterfront have followed the exodus of industrial customers.

The other significant transportation facility on the Central Waterfront is the Gardiner Expressway/Lake Shore Boulevard, which also cut across the waterfront as far east as Woodbine Avenue. This part of the waterfront is also served by arterial and local roads that form a network that is sparser south of Front Street than the more closely spaced urban streets north of it; that reflects the industrial and institutional uses that predominated south of the rail corridor during most of the past century.

The team studied the use of the corridor over the past 15 years (and, in one case, the past 30 years) by analysing traffic volumes and movements in a number of categories (truck, automobile, transit, and person), including origins and destinations. The analysis was based on data supplied by Metropolitan Toronto, the City, the Province, the TTC, and GO Transit. It included traffic counts for the peak morning hour (7:45 a.m. to 8:45 a.m.), the peak morning three-hour period (7:00 a.m. to 10:00 a.m.) and the 12-hour daily period (6:30 a.m. to 6:30 p.m.), as well as origin and destination surveys. (The team was not able to obtain comparable vehicular traffic data for the full 24-hour period.) As already mentioned, the team developed travel demand projections to the year 2021, based on population, employment, and land-use scenarios.

When combined with the land-use analysis, the traffic analysis showed clearly that the Central Waterfront is in transition, not only as a place but as a corridor. In particular, its corridor function is undergoing modal change to a degree that has hitherto escaped notice, and the projections indicate that changes are permanent and must be taken into account if the waterfront's full potential is to be achieved. The following is a description of the directions and the trends of the modal changes.

GOODS MOVEMENTS

Depending on the time of day, these make up between 10 and 15 per cent of the road traffic in the corridor; over the past 15 years, the number of trucks on roads in the corridor increased slightly (by three to five per cent) but there was a significant decline (by more than 70 per cent from 870 to 210 peak-hour trips) in the number of heavy trucks (those having three or more axles), which was offset by an increase of 70 to 85 per cent (from 880 to 1,630 peak-hour trips) in the number of more mobile light trucks.

PERSON TRAVEL

According to the Transportation Tomorrow Survey (TTS), in 1986 in the Greater Toronto region (extended to include Hamilton-Wentworth), there were almost two million trips during the morning peak period (trips starting between 6:00 a.m. and 8:49 a.m.); some 318,000, or 16 per cent, were destined for Toronto's Central Area. Of the 318,000, approximately 36,000 were from the Central Area, 218,000 from the remainder of Metro, and the rest from regions outside Metro.

The TTS revealed that about 65 per cent of the total a.m. peak period travel in the Greater Toronto region was by private car; 25 per cent by public transit; and the remaining 10 per cent by foot, bicycle or other means. However, of trips to the Central Area, only 36 per cent were by automobile whereas 58 per cent were by public transit, and the rest by other modes.

About 40 per cent of trips in the Central Area itself were by other modes: walking — 36 per cent; cycling — two per cent; and taxi/motorcycle — two per cent; while 34 per cent was by public transit and 26 per cent by automobile. The survey showed that walking is the most common mode for trips within the Central Area.

Using information from the Toronto Transit Commission to supplement these data, it was possible to examine trends as far back as 1960; since that time, there has been a tendency for the total person trips entering the Central Area in the a.m. peak period to increase, while the number of persons entering in automobiles has actually declined slightly.

According to Metropolitan Toronto's traffic counts, between 1975 and 1990 the number of vehicles travelling into the Central Waterfront was virtually stable in the a.m. peak hour; increased slightly in the a.m. peak period (by six per cent); and rose somewhat more in the 12-hour daily period (by 15 per cent). This suggests that the road network in the waterfront corridor has been operating at near-capacity since 1975, restricting increases in vehicular traffic during the peak periods. The more significant growth in the 12-hour vehicle traffic may reflect a spread in the a.m. and p.m. peak periods in the waterfront corridor.

There were similar traffic trends on the Gardiner Expressway/Lake Shore Boulevard facility: between 1975 and 1990,

auto traffic on the Gardiner/Lakeshore grew two per cent (from 10,580 to 10,780 vehicles) in the a.m. peak hour; five per cent (from 27,500 to 28,900) in the a.m. peak three hours, and 17 per cent (from 75,200 to 87,600) in the 12-hour daytime period.

In those same years, however, auto occupancy in the a.m. peak period declined from 1.31 persons per car to 1.22: in other words, the same number of vehicles were carrying seven per cent fewer people in 1990 than they carried in 1975.

Person trips into the waterfront corridor had a very different growth pattern, growing substantially in all three periods: by 32 per cent in the a.m. peak hour, 28 per cent in the a.m. peak period, and 22 per cent in the 12-hour daytime period. These figures also show that, in contrast to the surface transit and automobile traffic trends, the concentration of total person trips into the Central Waterfront during the morning peak hour and the peak three-hour period actually increased.

With the exception of the 12-hour period, in which auto person trips grew discernibly, the growth in person trips in the 15 years under study was due mainly to growth in the number of persons carried by GO Transit commuter rail services, which increased 259 per cent (from 10,000 to 36,190) passengers in the a.m. peak three-hour period. However, between 1975 and 1990, the number of persons entering the Central Waterfront by other forms of public transit declined in all three periods. (This occurred despite an increase in the number of persons travelling by transit into the entire Central Area.)

The study team estimated that the number of persons entering the Central

The central waterfront viewed from the east

Waterfront could grow from about 46,900 in the peak hour in 1990 to between 79,200 and 111,000 in 2021 (an increase of between 69 and 137 per cent). This is a range of about 32,000 to 64,000 additional trips per hour, with the lower end corresponding to scenarios with relatively more housing in the Central Area and the higher end corresponding to scenarios with relatively less housing there.

PEDESTRIAN AND CYCLE TRAFFIC

Unfortunately, statistics on volumes of pedestrian and cycle traffic in the Central Waterfront and adjacent areas are not collected in as much detail as those for vehicular travel by road and transit. However, the 1986 Transportation Tomorrow Study revealed that, during the a.m. peak three hours, about 12,600 or 36 per cent of total person trips made entirely within the Central Area were pedestrian trips. This was the most-used method of travel for trips within the Central Area, more than the number of transit trips within the area, and almost half again as high as the number of auto trips. There were only 870 peak-period cycle trips, about two per cent of the total.

THE DIMINISHING ROLE OF THE GARDINER

The Gardiner Expressway, designed and built in phases between the mid-1950s and the mid-'60s in what was then a largely industrial area, serves a dual function: it is an efficient route for moving goods, in particular by heavy trucks going between the Port area, industrial sections of southern Etobicoke, and other industrial parts of the Central Area; and it offers a radial route for truck and automobile traffic entering the

CARS AND OUR QUALITY OF LIFE

At about the time the first automobiles appeared, the horse-and-buggy industry confidently predicted that their number would be limited by the chauffeurs who could be trained to drive them. How right they were: today hundreds of millions of drivers around the world sit behind the wheels of 400 million cars, an eight-fold increase since 1950.

This tremendous growth reflects the obvious improvements cars have made to the quality of people's lives. They offer convenience, flexibility, comfort, privacy, speed, and independence. They have altered our very perceptions of time and space: we speak not of the distance to another place, but of the time it takes to arrive there by car. We think of places being nearby that, a century ago, involved arduous overnight journeys. And for many people today, there are no alternative modes of transportation.

Despite these positive benefits, however, cars contribute to the deteriorating health of our planet and erode the quality of life in urban centres in many ways. They consume roads, resources, and — increasingly — the environment.

Cars are the biggest single source of the greenhouse gases that threaten global climatic patterns. Even "clean" cars produce nearly two and half kilograms of carbon dioxide for each litre (20 pounds per gallon) of gas used. Other gases released from the end of a tailpipe include nitrogen oxides, volatile organic compounds, hydrocarbons, carbon monoxide, and suspended particulates.

In addition to their greenhouse effect, these emissions contribute to acid rain, reduce crop yields, and affect human health. For example, by inhibiting the photosynthesis process, accumulations of ground-level ozone, which are produced when nitrogen oxides and hydrocarbons react in sunlight, reduce crop production. The Ontario Ministry of the Environment estimates that meeting ozone standards could increase crop production in Ontario by an average of $39 million per year (in 1986-87 dollars).

Our excessive dependence on the automobile has affected our quality of life by encouraging the separation of work, recreation, home, and shopping. "The great emancipator" has given us long commutes and daily traffic chaos, and increased stress levels. It has affected the form and structure of our cities by eating up at least a third of the land for roads, parking lots, and other elements of car infrastructure.

There is a wide range of strategies to reduce the cumulative effects of individual car use. Technical improvements such as alternative automobile fuels, and cleaner and more efficient vehicles, are among the first steps. However, to deal with such problems as congestion, we must move beyond technical solutions towards innovative transportation management policies in which cars complement other forms of transportation. Finally, distances between daily destinations must be reduced so that biking, walking, and transit are feasible and enjoyable alternatives to the car.

Sources: Carson, P. and J. Moulden. 1991. *Green is gold: business talking to business about the environmental revolution.* Toronto: Harpercollins Publishers; Pearson, R. G. and J. A. Donnan. 1989. "Impact of ozone exposure on vegetation in Ontario". In *Proceedings environmental research: 1989 technology transfer conference.* Toronto: Ontario. Ministry of the Environment; Renner, M. 1988. *Rethinking the role of the automobile.* Washington, D.C.: Worldwatch Institute; Schaeffer, R. 1990. "Car sick". *Greenpeace* 14.

Central Area from west and east, as well as being a through connection to and from the lower end of the Don Valley Parkway. Much of the expressway is elevated; in the central and eastern portions, Lake Shore Boulevard runs underneath it at grade.

A 1986 survey of Gardiner Expressway users, carried out by the City of Toronto, showed that about 22 per cent of those coming from the west between 7:00 a.m. and 9:00 a.m., and 39 per cent of a much smaller volume from the east (about 1,100 to 1,200 vehicles per hour in each direction), were through traffic.

In terms of truck traffic, totals for both light and heavy trucks on the Gardiner/Lakeshore facility grew by eight to 12 per cent in the 15 years from 1975 to 1990. Specific heavy/light truck counts for the Gardiner/Lakeshore were not available, but the trends are probably consistent with those for the Central Waterfront mentioned earlier: heavy truck traffic declined while light truck traffic increased.

Based on the downward trend in heavy truck traffic in the Central Waterfront as a whole, it can be argued that one of the original purposes of the Gardiner Expressway — carrying heavy truck traffic in a largely industrial area — has been significantly decreased because of economic and land-use changes described earlier.

The other major purpose of the expressway — as a radial commuter route for trips from outside Metro Toronto and within Metro to the Central Area — has continued, but is declining, relatively and absolutely. Its role as a commuter route has diminished compared to that of its major competitor, GO Transit. While the number of a.m. peak-hour person trips to the Central Area, using the Gardiner Expressway, declined

from about 10,500 to 8,000 between 1975 and 1990, the number carried by GO Transit increased from about 6,800 to about 21,600, and in 1991 increased further to about 26,000.

In relative terms, the proportion of total person trips carried by the Gardiner Expressway to the Central Area declined between 1975 and 1990: from 8.4 per cent to 5.4 per cent of the total during the a.m. peak hour; from 10.4 per cent to 6.9 per cent during the a.m. peak three hours; and from 13 per cent to 10 per cent of the total during the 12 hours between 6:30 a.m. and 6:30 p.m.

In absolute terms, reflecting the reduction in average vehicle occupancy, the number of persons carried by auto on the expressway also declined in the same period: by 24 per cent in the a.m. peak hour; by 21 per cent in the peak three hours; and by four per cent in the 12 hours from 6:30 a.m. to 6:30 p.m.

Approximately one-third of commuting trips crossing the Metro boundary are destined for the Central Area, with the rest going elsewhere in Metropolitan Toronto. In particular, there is strong pressure for automobile commuting to the Central Area, from Peel and Halton, with less pressure from Durham in the east; these trips rely heavily on the Queen Elizabeth Way/Gardiner Expressway from the west and the Don Valley Parkway from the east and northeast. GO Transit serves the same commuter market and has captured an increasing share of it as rail service improved while roads became increasingly congested.

In summary: while the Gardiner Expressway continues to be used as a through route, its role as a heavy truck carrier and a commuter route is declining in both relative and absolute terms, as the result of a

Barriers to the waterfront

variety of factors. Among the most basic are economic forces and land-use changes that encouraged heavy industry to move to the suburbs and the resultant decline in heavy truck trips on the Gardiner. Furthermore, car occupancy levels have declined; increasingly, peak-period operations are limited by the expressway's capacity; and GO Transit patronage has expanded substantially.

While there has been growing pressure to use the expressway as a commuting route and for light trucks serving the Central Area, commuter traffic is being taken over increasingly by GO Transit and related TTC services.

In the same period, the physical and fiscal impracticality of expanding road capacity into and through the Central Area has resulted in specific City of Toronto, Metropolitan Toronto, and provincial policies to serve growth by expanding transit rather than building more roads. This is reflected in the relatively static number of auto trips entering the Central Waterfront in the a.m. peak period in the past 15 years, while the number of transit passengers (particularly of GO Transit) has increased.

Considering changes in the use made of the expressway, and recognizing that it is a barrier to the waterfront — particularly in the central section between Jarvis and Bathurst streets — this is the time to examine the continuing role and existence of that section, in the context of greater intensification and specialization of land uses in the area, parallel development of a network of green open spaces and links, and the need to improve the environment.

The ongoing importance of the expressway for moving persons and goods must be recognized before any decision can be made on whether the central section could be removed and, if so, under what circumstances. Even if discretionary use of autos in the area were to decline in line with the reduced road capacity, and if congestion levels remained stable, removing the central link in the limited-access highway system in and through the Central Area would further delay east-west vehicular trips — particularly by commercial truck, essential auto, and emergency vehicle — because speed limits would be reduced from 80 kilometres per hour to 50 or 60 kilometres per hour. In addition, the greater volume of east-west vehicular traffic on at-grade roads would create more conflict with north-south movements of pedestrians, cyclists, and vehicles.

THE TRANSPORTATION CHALLENGE

Given the *Toronto Central Waterfront Transportation Corridor Study*'s conclusion that the role of the Gardiner Expressway as a carrier of heavy trucks and as a commuter route is declining in both relative and absolute terms, the question — whether to relocate and redesign the Gardiner and Lake Shore Boulevard — is of much less consequence in transportation planning than was previously imagined. It is overshadowed by a much greater concern: if the Gardiner's role is diminishing, if the roadway obstructs opportunities, and if the road system cannot be expanded by very much, how will it be possible to sustain the movement and circulation necessary to maintain the quality of life and economic prosperity of the region?

To explore these questions, the team carried out two major planning exercises: first to explore, cost, and evaluate various concepts for modifying the Gardiner Expressway/Lake Shore Boulevard facility and, second, to explore various plans and proposals for expanding the transit system.

FINDING A SOLUTION FOR THE GARDINER EXPRESSWAY AND LAKE SHORE BOULEVARD

The team assembled, designed, and mapped a number of ideas for modifying the Gardiner Expressway and Lake Shore Boulevard. To do so, they compared each idea with the existing road structure and system, using the implications of four elements as basic criteria:

- the environment;
- land-use and urban design;
- transportation; and
- economy/finances.

Initially, there were nine different concepts, three each of three "families" (i.e., ways of retaining, removing or burying the Gardiner) were evaluated. Of the nine, two "best options" emerged: removing the central section of the elevated expressway and replacing it with surface roads, or retaining the expressway but relocating Lake Shore Boulevard and redesigning surface roads.

The team concluded that the waterfront would be most substantially improved as a place if the central section were removed and replaced by normal urban, grade-related streets. However, members were concerned that the reduced transportation service that would result might create too much stress on this important vehicular corridor, unless it were balanced by changes to land use and public transit.

The evaluation showed the strengths and weaknesses of each concept: for example, those that favoured land use had transportation drawbacks, while those that favoured road transportation would impede land-use and environmental objectives. It became clear that to maintain an appropriate balance between place and corridor, one that would meet place-making and environmental objectives while sustaining the diminished but still important role of the Gardiner/Lakeshore Corridor and a connected road system, a generic approach — retaining the entire Gardiner, removing it or burying it entirely — would not work.

The evaluation stimulated the team to find a solution that would maximize benefits for the environment, land use, and transportation in a balanced and economic way. This led it to consider a mixed concept in which the Gardiner is treated differently along its different sections, according to localized land uses and environment. For example: the Gardiner could remain elevated in some parts, be relocated in others, and be buried in still others.

This alternative would make it possible to relocate and redesign the Gardiner and Lakeshore appropriately, taking into account the various places through which they pass; it has another benefit: it would be possible to make changes in phases, as part of an integrated plan that would include more housing in the Central Waterfront and an expanded transit system.

TRANSIT AS THE WORKHORSE OF COMMUTER TRAVEL

The transportation carrying capacity of the Gardiner is a diminishing asset which must be balanced against the increasingly valuable asset of the waterfront as a a a more habitable and economically productive place.

Given that the Gardiner carries only about seven per cent of the Central Area's inbound morning peak-period trips, if it were removed the rest of the transportation system would be sufficiently flexible to absorb it — and does occasionally when maintenance closes the road system. It would have to absorb even fewer trips if additional surface roads and connections were created. Whether or not that happens, the most important point is that retaining the Gardiner at its current capacity will not begin to deal with the real transportation problem.

The fact is that travel to and through the Central Waterfront will grow and the number of residents there will double in the next two or three decades. These will have to be accommodated when governments do not have the resources to expand the road system very greatly. Therefore, the choice is not between one road system or another, but whether to take steps now to improve transit service so that people can continue to have convenient access to the city centre.

Table 10.1 shows why: choosing a single point on an expressway and in ideal conditions for each mode, one lane of automobiles on the expressway, with the current average occupancy of 1.2 people each, can carry only seven per cent of the passengers

Table 10.1 Capacity of various transportation modes

Transport mode	Persons carried past a point in one hour	Efficiency in relation to subway
Autos on one lane of the expressway		
1.2 occupants per auto	2,400	7%
4 occupants per auto	8,000	23%
Streetcar or bus on own right of way	15,000	43%
Commuter rail (GO Rail)	25,000	71%
Subway rail	35,000	100%

Source: IBI Group.

that can be accommodated on the Toronto subway. When the ratio of travellers to roads favoured travellers, at most this was a statistic of academic interest; in current circumstances, as more and more roads become chronically congested, it takes on greater and greater practical importance: a minor increase in transit capacity can numerically balance a major reduction in road capacity.

It is a matter of great good fortune that Toronto's rail corridors parallel the expressways for so much of their length, making it practical to convert commuters from road to rail. That has been evident over the years as GO Transit passenger volumes have continued to grow, and was most noticeable in September 1991, when GO Transit volumes increased during a TTC strike. Commuter travel is the most easily converted to transit; moreover, the majority of those using the Gardiner for peak-period travel are long-distance commuters, the market GO Transit is specifically designed to serve.

Of course, efficiency is not the only criterion for choosing a mode of access: people may choose on grounds of convenience, flexibility, privacy, and time, including waiting time. The ability to carry goods, and, more recently, the opportunity to conduct business by phone also make car travel attractive.

By contrast, a rail system is scheduled, and can neither pick up nor deliver from communities already designed to facilitate car travel; moreover, trains are often crowded. But a more extensive and better integrated transit system can minimize these disadvantages or at least offer as good or better convenience as congested highways. Flexibility can be improved if settlements are designed to encourage walking and transit — which can be done by placing sufficient quantities of housing and workplaces within walking distances of each other and of transit stops.

It is clear that our economic growth will depend substantially on our ability to develop a transportation system that takes into account the link between changes to the economic base of the waterfront/Central Area, and the constrictions imposed by the Gardiner's diminishing capability to serve those parts of the city. Projected travel demand needed to ensure an economically healthy region leaves no choice about drastically increasing the extent and amenity of the transit system: it must be done if the standard of liveability of the Central Waterfront, and of the city core and region as a whole, are to be maintained and improved. The choice is not whether to act, but whether to take steps now or simply react to problems that, inevitably, will have to be faced. Obviously the former is by far the better choice.

Because we will have to rely increasingly on transit in the future, we should plan now to provide sufficient capacity to absorb the traffic that results from stabilizing or reducing road capacity when redesigning the Central Waterfront road network.

A PLAN FOR TRANSIT

The last truly bold transportation initiatives in Toronto go back a generation or more, when the subways, commuter rail, and expressway systems were created. While the subway system and expanded commuter rail service have been fine-tuned in recent years, it is clear that the latter should continue to be expanded rapidly and that other bold initiatives are necessary to meet traffic needs in the core.

Therefore, the study team developed a conceptual plan for an expanded transit system to serve the Central Waterfront,

Map 10.7 Possible transit concepts

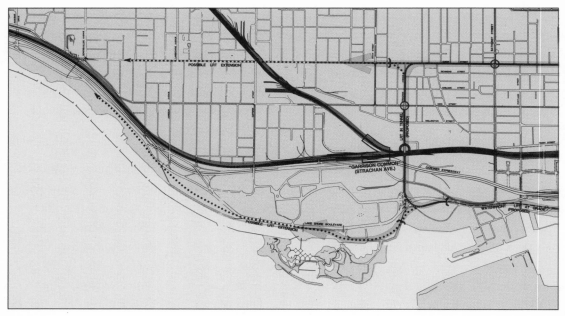

Legend:

GO Transit	Proposed LRT	Possible Subway
Existing Light Rail Transit (LRT)	Existing Subway	

Central Area, and greater region for generations to follow, just as the bold investments made by previous generations now serve us. The plan proposes the following major improvements:

- an expanded GO service centred on Union Station, with two new shoulder stations: one in Garrison Common (Strachan Avenue) and the other in the Lower Don Lands (Cherry Street);
- an expanded Waterfront LRT, extended to Park Lawn in the west and Greenwood in the east, combined with the GO service already suggested;
- introduction of a high-quality LRT Waterfront loop system along Queen Street, Cherry Street, Queen's Quay, and Strachan Avenue;

- extension of the Spadina subway to Union Station and the University Avenue subway to the waterfront; and
- other transit service improvements, such as high-occupancy vehicles (HOV)/express bus lanes, and more efficient, higher-capacity service on the King and Queen streetcar routes, etc.

The team concluded that:

Increasingly, transit is the key for economic development in large urban regions. It is, of course, essential that local and regional road access continue to be available for both automobile and truck traffic serving local land uses, but, increasingly, the key indication of accessibility is the availability of surface and

rapid transit services, particularly in Central Areas.

There are many examples of this reliance on transit: in New York City, the World Financial Center development at Battery Park in Lower West Side Manhattan was initiated a few years after the West Side Highway collapsed, despite the fact that the road was never replaced with a limited-access facility, because the developer knew that high-capacity rapid transit services were available. Similarly, the Canary Wharf development in the London Docklands is in an area not served by limited-access roads; the developer realized that high-quality rapid transit links are essential and, therefore, indicated a willingness to consider providing significant front-end funding for such facilities. Closer to home, rapid office/commercial development has occurred in the North York City Centre and more recently in the Scarborough City Centre following the extension of rapid transit lines to each of them, linking them to the downtown and the rest of the Greater Toronto region.

The Commission believes that the Central Waterfront must be recognized and treated as a valuable place, both for its own sake and for the benefit of the city and region. Already, more pedestrians and cyclists use the waterfront in the central core, because of the SkyDome and the residential community along Queen's Quay. East-west movement is also increasing, especially along the waterfront, as the result of recreational and cultural attractions that have been developed at Harbourfront. That trend will continue — pedestrian traffic, in particular, will keep increasing — and the need will grow for improved sidewalks, more streets that are pedestrian-friendly, and laneways transecting large blocks to facilitate pedestrian and cycle movement.

A PROGRAM TO INTEGRATE ENVIRONMENT, PLACE, AND CORRIDOR

The team of consultants concluded that the Central Waterfront would be improved as a place by a program including:

- a green infrastructure system of open spaces, parks, and links;
- improvements to the quality of the natural environment;
- a balanced and diverse mix of residential, employment, and recreational uses;
- pedestrian-friendly built form and streetscape designs that are more liveable, workable, and accessible, and that have legible public and private spaces;
- greatly improved public transit at both the regional and local scales;
- an interconnected and balanced road network;

- enhanced opportunities for economic competitiveness and renewal; and
- infrastructure capital and operating costs that are feasible because of the economic activity they create.

An important part of that vision is a redesigned and relocated Gardiner Expressway/Lake Shore Boulevard that strengthens links between the city and its renewed Central Waterfront and improves the area's quality as a place; at the same time, it will maintain and even improve its essential function as a corridor serving transit, rail and air passengers, auto travellers, truck, rail, and marine freight movements, pedestrians, and cyclists.

STAGE I

The team proposed Stage I of this program designed to achieve the improved links; in its words:

The study set out a range of transportation options, identified the environmental, land-use, urban design, and economic opportunities and concepts they help make possible, and assessed the required financial resources and related risks involved; it proposed a Stage I program aimed at achieving those opportunities in a cost-effective manner. The combined land-use transit system, road network, and environmental concept which could subsequently evolve would be compatible with various treatments of the Gardiner/Lakeshore facility, and the anticipated consequences of these were described. The Stage I program is designed to leave open the more promising options for the central section of the Gardiner/Lakeshore facility.

Map 10.8   Emerging green infrastructure in the Central Waterfront

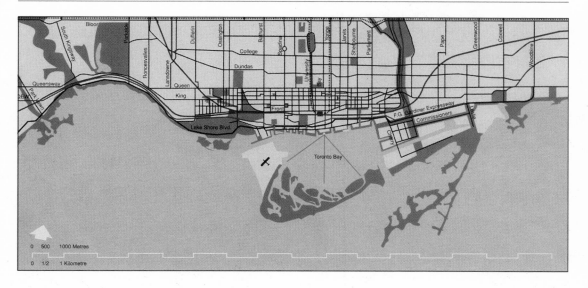

Implementation of the Stage I program will provide a considerably firmer basis than now exists for deciding on the most appropriate option, while moving purposefully to create a better place and corridor in the Central Waterfront.

Stage I programs and priorities are:

1. Green Infrastructure

The basic "green infrastructure" of parks, open spaces, and green links among them, plus steps to improve air, water, and soil quality and other environmental conditions, should be built as early as possible to begin the process of re-creating the Central Waterfront as a better place that, while part of the city, is connected to the water and to natural areas. These environmental programs should be implemented before or concurrently with the housing developments, in order to help attract residents to the area while ensuring that the open space system is completely achieved and protected.

2. Central Waterfront Housing and Economic Development

Another priority is a program for the delivery of as many as 3,000-4,000 housing units per year in the Central Area for the next 30 years, starting with appropriate designation of the lands.

Substantially increased Central Waterfront housing is essential to improve the quality of the Central Waterfront as a place, to moderate the growth of long commuter trips from suburban areas to the Central Area, and to help achieve an improved structure and quality of development throughout the region. At the same time, continuing development of employment and recreational uses is vitally important to maintain economic impetus. This includes developing the international trade centre and other economic development and tourism initiatives proposed in the Garrison Common study, establishing employment activities in the Railway Lands, and the mixed-use development

GO Transit plays an essential role in linking the centre and region

in other parts of the Central Waterfront described earlier.

3. GO Transit Expansion

Expansion of GO Transit service in the Lakeshore and Milton corridors and increases in Union Station's capacity, along with the Garrison Common shoulder station and related rail relocation, are essential to improve the relationship between the region and the centre and to serve the substantial increase in commuting and other trips to the centre that is anticipated, even if Central Area housing targets are met (and they will be much greater if the targets are not met).

4. Improved TTC Services

Significantly improved local transit is also essential to serve the residential and employment developments and circulation in the Central Waterfront; initially this can be bus services on the improved arterial road network with HOV lanes as appropriate. This would lead, over the medium term, to implementing other transit improvements such as a downtown LRT loop system linking to the Garrison Common (Strachan Avenue) GO Transit station and later to a Cherry Street GO Transit station.

5. Better Road Connections

The Front Street extension is required both for local land access and to allow direct regional access from the west to the Central Area north of the rail corridor without having to pass through the south/central section of the Central Waterfront, and should be in place to help carry traffic during the extensive construction work that will be required in the Central Waterfront.

Redesign and reconstruction of the Humber crossing bridges are required because of the deteriorating quality of the existing structures and related safety and operational imperatives.

The two continuous east-west arterial roads in the Central Waterfront, along with improved north-south streets and continuous, pedestrian-friendly sidewalks, walkways, cycle paths, and mid-block connectors, are essential to provide local access, create a legible framework, and re-establish visual and physical links between the city and its waterfront. This could include partial relocation of Lake Shore Boulevard from under the expressway, as well as related ramp changes to reduce further the barrier effects to the Gardiner/Lakeshore facility while leaving open the question of subsequently modifying the central section of that facility.

Timing and Funding

The goals of the Stage I implementation program would be to deliver the initial components of the green infrastructure and other program elements in five years. This includes: a continuous Greenway across the Central Waterfront, Roundhouse Park, etc.; 12,000-20,000 housing units in the Central Waterfront; a 50-per-cent expansion of GO Transit peak-period capacity on the key east-west lines, as well as augmented full-day service; the beginnings of improved feeder/distributor transit in the Central Waterfront, initially by means of buses using HOV

lanes as appropriate; and a more continuous arterial road network for land access by trucks, autos, surface transit, pedestrians, and cyclists.

This Stage I program would be the first giant leap in rejoining the Central Waterfront to both the city and the lake, making it a much better place to be rather than just to travel through, while still enabling it to fulfil its important function as a corridor. Additional facilities, such as the LRT loop system or its equivalent, would be in final design or possibly under construction.

It should be noted that the infrastructure elements listed above either have been included in municipal and/or provincial budgets, are currently being considered, or are part of the normal development process. The important point about this program is that it is based on an integrated concept of the Central Waterfront as a better place and corridor and moves purposefully to achieve that concept, building largely on projects and investments already proposed by individual governments and agencies, selected and modified in light of the overall concept.

Finding the key to sustainable, healthy urban places is essential; indeed it is probable that the ultimate success or failure of society as a whole to achieve sustainability will be determined by our cities.

Alberta. Urban Environment Subcommittee. 1988. *Environment by design: the urban place in Alberta.* N. p.: Environmental Council of Alberta.

STAGE II

While implementation of Stage I is under way, planners should prepare the second stage of the program. Elements of the second stage could include:

- continuing implementation of the green infrastructure system;
- further residential, mixed-use, commercial, industrial, and recreational development;
- further expansion of GO Transit services;
- construction of the LRT waterfront loop and the Cherry Street GO station; and
- redesign and relocation of the Gardiner Expressway and Lake Shore Boulevard consistent with plans integrating environment, land-use, and transportation on the waterfront.

Major public policy issues are at stake and decisions made (or not made) in the next few years will greatly affect the quality of Toronto's Central Waterfront and adjacent areas for two generations at least. It is clear that a new process is needed for planning and reaching necessary decisions and agreements, and for creating programs that will help achieve the bold plan within our grasp.

Within the context of integrating environmental, land-use, transportation, and economic issues across the Central Waterfront as a whole, it is useful to consider the various places that comprise the Central Waterfront, starting with its western gateway, Humber Bay. Projects, in addition to those already described in the Stage I program, are identified for each part of the water-front, to contribute to the critical mass of productive investment needed to help stimulate the region's economic recovery.

RECOMMENDATIONS

65. The Royal Commission recommends that the Province, Metropolitan Toronto, the City of Toronto, the City of Etobicoke, the Government of Canada, appropriate special purpose bodies, and the private sector negotiate a Waterfront Partnership Agreement or agreements to implement Stage I of the program to integrate environment, land use, and transportation in the Central Waterfront.

66. The Commission further recommends that, to expedite the implementation of Stage I, processes be designed to integrate approvals, consolidate capital budgets, and achieve concurrent decision-making by all levels and agencies of government.

67. Concurrent with implementation of Stage I, the parties should prepare a plan for Stage II of the program.

68. The City of Etobicoke, City of Toronto, Metropolitan Toronto, and the Metropolitan Toronto and Region Conservation Authority should participate in preparing the proposed shoreline regeneration plan, including the waterfront greenway and trail, and ensure that any other plans for waterfront areas are reviewed and/or developed in this context.

HUMBER BAY

The views across Humber Bay, particularly the vista of Toronto's skyline, are among the most striking in the region. The sense of place around the bay itself depends strongly on natural and visual attributes: the river and its banks, the curve and slope of the shoreline, the lake and distant perspectives. Collectively, these convey a sense of arrival and departure, an impression of natural beauty, and a vision of human settlement at the water's edge. Since the beginning, these three forces — nature, transportation, and settlement — have determined the use, development, and physical form of historic Humber Bay.

Its future will be determined, to a substantial degree, by these same forces, as they bear on the basic issues that currently characterize the area; these include the following:

- Humber Bay has a natural heritage in urgent need of remediation. (This issue is dealt with in more detail in the Environmental Conditions section of this chapter and in chapters 3 and 9 of this report.)
- Humber Bay's historic role as a place of human settlement for industry, recreation, and pleasure has been diminished and fragmented and must be revitalized.
- Humber Bay is a significant regional transportation corridor currently in need of change.
- Humber Bay has a trademark role as gateway to the central city, with a magnificent vista of the bay that must be appreciated and protected.

The mouth of the Humber had been a gateway at the beginning or end of ancient trails for aboriginal peoples long before the first European, Étienne Brûlé, arrived there in 1615. He had travelled south from Georgian Bay via the famous "passage de Toronto", along the banks of the Humber River. He and those who followed him saw the mouth of the Humber, and its access to Lake Ontario, as a crucial element in the European quest for riches from trade, saving souls, and strengthening (French and, later, English) notions of Empire.

More than 325 years after Brûlé — and after a mind-boggling sea-change in technology, culture, and settlement — that

> **T**he mouth of the Humber River and the shoreline to either side of it have long occupied a crucial position in the history of the development of Toronto. As a place in the wilderness, on the edge of the City or within the metropolis, the growth and physical form of the Humber Valley/High Park/Western Beaches Corridor has been predominantly influenced by the tension which has resulted from its concurrent perception as both a place to travel to — whether campground, trading station, pleasure ground or park — and a place to travel through — whether by canoe, foot, horseback, stagecoach, train, streetcar, automobile or bicycle.
>
> Garwood-Jones and Van Nostrand Architects Inc., Gerrard and Mackars Landscape Architects Inc., and B-A Consulting Group Ltd. 1991. *The Humber River/High Park/Western Beaches civic design study*. Toronto: Toronto (Ont.). Task Force on the Gardiner/Lake Shore Corridor.

Humber Bay, looking east from the Etobicoke waterfront to downtown Toronto

same sense of gateway and vista was captured by the remarkable planning and design of the Queen Elizabeth Highway.

The Queen Elizabeth Way was North America's first divided highway, begun in 1931 as a make-work project in a rapidly deepening Depression. In 1934, Tom McQuesten, the new provincial Minister of Public Works, his deputy, and the chief engineer, both named Smith, were joined in their determination to make the new road a thing of beauty, as well as an engineering masterpiece. A lawyer, McQuesten was known as the "artist-builder": he left his imprint on the Niagara Parks system, the Royal Botanical Gardens, the Peace and Rainbow bridges, and the Niagara Parkway. He and the Smiths conceived the QEW as a scenic parkway and public motorway with a wide planted median, limited access, cloverleaf interchanges, lighting, and landscaping. They hired sculptors and landscape

architects as well as engineers; bridges were embellished, views were preserved and enhanced. What it meant to the generations who used it has been eloquently recollected by Robert Stamp (1987), who was a boy at the time, in his book *The Queen Elizabeth Way: Canada's First Superhighway*:

We rolled over those magnificent bridges at Bronte Creek, Sixteen Mile Creek, and the Credit River. We passed straight through the Highway 10 intersection at Port Credit, thanks to that marvelous 1930s contribution to highway technology — the cloverleaf interchange.

Dusk might begin to fall as we neared the end of our journey. Car lights and roadside lights were turned on. The divided highway seemed every bit as safe in the dark as it did in broad daylight. Mom and Dad still referred to Highway 27 as Brown's Line. That intersection marked the beginning of

suburban Toronto with its small factories and industrial buildings hugging the sides of the road. Brightly-lit signs proclaimed Toronto's contribution to my childhood world: Lipton Tea, G. H. Wood: Sanitation for the Nation. All good things came from Toronto.

Then the Lion Monument loomed up in the median ahead of us. Hello Lucky Lion! Let the marble columns of Union Station welcome others; the QEW's stone lion was my favourite introduction to the city.

Finally, we swooped over the Humber Bridge, marked the Palace Pier on our right and caught a glimpse of our first red and yellow streetcar on the left. Ahead lay the bright lights of Sunnyside, the Exhibition, and downtown Toronto itself. It was all made possible by the Queen Elizabeth Way.

Vistas! Compared with other major city regions, Toronto has done very little to protect its vistas. Perhaps we've simply taken them for granted or, because of jurisdictional narrowness and fragmentation, perhaps their importance has not been articulated in a way that enables public discussion and opinion to inform public policy. Certainly,

as the Commission was reminded, time and time again, the importance of vistas has not been lost on people personally and emotionally as they go about their daily lives.

Humber Bay offers some of the most spectacular vistas on Toronto's waterfront — vistas that, in some cases, have been marred by thoughtless construction of infrastructure, buildings, and billboards. In other cases, as Robert Stamp says, some views have been made possible and even enhanced by road and rail travel.

Humber Bay has always been a transportation corridor. Eric Arthur (1986), in his landmark book, *Toronto, No Mean City* (as updated by Stephen Otto) reminds us that, "as we travel at speed over the Gardiner Expressway and the Don Valley, we are likely to forget that we are riding on the ancient "road system of the Indian, the coureur de bois and the traders."

In 1750, the first "Lakeshore Road" was cut out from the "beaten trails" to connect Fort Rouillé (near the present site of the CNE Bandshell) to Fort Toronto on the east bank at the mouth of the Humber; between 1798 and 1804, it was improved and became a public road with a ferry across the Humber in 1802 and a bridge in 1809. A stagecoach from York to Niagara was established in 1825.

In 1850, at the dawn of the great railway boom, Lakeshore Road, along with other regional roads in the Toronto district, was sold to private interests as a toll road. During the next 40 years, as the railroads transformed the new industrial city, roads fell into disrepair as the result of neglect, scandal, and recurring corruption. In 1890,

Vistas! Compared with other major city regions, Toronto has done very little to protect its vistas.

Lakeshore Road was turned over to the York County Council, but remained in relative disrepair until 1914-1916 when the new, provincially established Toronto-Hamilton Highway Commission virtually rebuilt the old road and paved it as Ontario's first motor traffic highway. It was 56 kilometres (35 miles) long and 5.5 metres (18 feet) wide. The road became the basis for a new industry and new development as motels and automobile-oriented restaurants sprung up along its route (particularly in the area close to the west bank of the Humber River), and the number of cars increased from 25 to 500 per day. In 1927, the road was widened to 26 metres (86 feet).

Meanwhile, the new magical world of electricity had spawned the electric street-car, which was previewed at the Toronto Exhibition in 1883. In November 1890, the Toronto and Mimico Electric Railway and Light Co. was formed to build and operate a street railway on Lakeshore Road and to sell electric power to people along its route. By July 1893, the Toronto Railway Company had taken over operations and extended the line from the Humber River to Mimico Creek and, the following year, as far as Long Branch and, later, Port Credit. The Long Branch service to Brown's Line continues to this day.

By 1894, the last horse-drawn streetcar had disappeared as new electric "radial" lines "radiated" out from the burgeoning City of Toronto. In 1891, the very ambitious Belt Line Railway Company line was estab-lished and opened to passenger traffic; it consisted of two loops, one for the Humber Valley and the other for the Don Valley, tied together by a line along the waterfront. In time, the company died, but parts of the Belt Line remained a part of the trans-portation system for more than 30 years.

In 1921, the public system was reorganized as the Toronto Transportation Commission; in 1953, with the appearance of the new Metropolitan Government, the TTC became the Toronto Transit Commission, with exclusive power to provide public passenger transportation in the metropolitan area, "other than steam railways and taxis".

Throughout the 19th century and the early part of the 20th, on both sides of the river, Humber Bay filled up with people in new settlements, villages, towns, and in special places for recreation: parks, pleasures, and public amenities.

Fort Toronto and Fort Rouillé had not survived the fall of New France in 1759. Fol-lowing the Toronto Purchase of aboriginal lands in 1787, Indian communities began to shrink and withdraw in the face of British expansion of the Town of York in 1793. By 1797, the new town had already expanded west along the waterfront to Bathurst Street.

In 1787, Jean Baptiste Rousseau had established a small farm and orchard on the east side of the Humber in present-day Swansea. Colonel Samuel Bois Smith came to Etobicoke in 1795 and led the way for new immigrants from the Napoleonic Wars and for Late Loyalists, who began to clear the land, construct the mills, and establish the farms of Etobicoke. In 1837, John Gardhome and his remarkable family came to homestead. They would be farmers, livestock breeders, politicians, teachers, and public servants for more than a century: in fact, in 1953 the first employee of the newly established Metropolitan Government was its Clerk, Wilbert Gardhome.

In 1847-1848, the "birth of municipal government in Etobicoke" took place at Montgomery's Tavern on Dundas Street West. John Howard built Colborne Lodge at High Park in 1837 and, almost 40 years later, gave his 66 hectares (165 acres) to the City as a public park. He persuaded his friend, John Ellis, to buy the adjoining land, including Grenadier Pond, and build his house overlooking both the pond and the lake. In 1858, with a population of about 3,000 people, the area was given a post office, called "Mimico", leaving the original "Mimico" settlement on Dundas to be renamed as "Islington".

By 1870, with the flow of the Etobicoke River diminishing so much that it could no longer power the mill wheels, steam had become the power source of choice. More-over, at a time when there were few indus-tries in Etobicoke, Humber Bay boasted three brickyards — Butwell, Price, and Maloney — which were located in a triangle south from Queen Street to Lakeshore, east of Salisbury Avenue (which later became Park Lawn).

In the 1870s, the little settlement at Humber Bay, just west of the Humber River near the lakeshore, became a "lovely resort for holiday-makers from Toronto" — and it remained that way until World War I. As Esther Hayes (1974) wrote in her book *Etobicoke from Furrow to Borough*:

> They came in crowds to dine and dance, to participate in games and sports, to picnic and to swim and fish or just paddle a canoe on the river. Starting from May 24, Queen Victoria's Birthday, an excursion steamer made scheduled trips daily from Toronto to the old wharf at the mouth of the Humber.

In winter, hockey, skating, and ice-boating became popular pastimes. Three hotels — the Royal Oak; the Nurse's Hotel, run by Charles Nurse; and Wimbleton House, run by John Duck — catered to the pleasures and needs of visitors. John Duck maintained a "menagerie", where he kept bears, deer, wildcats, mink, and other animals which, increasingly, were removed from human experience. The lower Humber River also became renowned for its market gardens; people crossed the river regularly to buy fresh produce.

In the latter part of the century, the City of Toronto expanded rapidly to the west; from about the 1850s, the area west of Dufferin and the Garrison Reserve to High Park and north of the lake, was a prestigious rural retreat. By the 1880s, Parkdale had become a "pre-eminent village of the Dominion". It became an independent municipality in 1879 and a decade-long debate began on whether it should remain separate or join the expanding City. The fight was between those who supported "home rule for Parkdale" and those who marched under the banner "Economy, Union, and Progress" and supported annex-ation. Major John Carlaw, a strong advocate of keeping Parkdale out of Toronto's grasp, warned that annexation would mean that "our waterfront, the glory of our town, would be polluted, the water supply made inferior, and the level of taxes would go up". He was not heeded and in 1889 the little Town of Parkdale, with its 225 hectares (557 acres) and 5,651 citizens, joined Toronto as the new St. Alban's Ward.

The Sunnyside strip was acquired in 1893 and by 1909 the City had moved its boundaries to the Humber Valley and the Village of Swansea. The Swansea Bolt Works, established in 1882 (which ultimately became the Steel Company of Canada), gave Swansea its start as a modern settle-ment. It built row housing for its workers, at the foot of Windermere Avenue, and donated the site for St. Olave's Church in 1886. The name of the "Windermere" Post Office was changed to "Swansea" in 1889.

William Rennie, who built his own house on John Ellis's land, founded the Presbyterian church on Morningside Avenue and built row housing for working people in different parts of the emerging village. After the severe recession at the beginning of the century, Swansea began to grow again and, by 1907, the old golf links that had marked several earlier landscapes began to sprout new houses. Swansea remained part of York Township until 1926, when it was established as a "self-governing" village. It would not be until many years later, in 1967, that Swansea, too, became part of the City of Toronto.

In the mid-1850s, the Toronto-Humber Railway Line had been established, causing a real estate "flutter" that led to plans by the Christian Socialist Movement to build a "Model Workingmen's Village" of solid, modest homes. Because of prevailing economic conditions, the project was not completed. However, the plans were dusted off again in 1906, when the Grand Trunk Railway built a major freight yard in East Etobicoke and, thereby, changed the area forever. Developers and builders were called in to create new homes and services; streets that had "gone to pasture" were re-established and new homes built on them. In less than a decade, Mimico and New Toronto emerged from being a rural to becoming an essentially urban community.

In all of the jostle and push of expansion, particularly in the early part of the new century, it became clear that competing demands of emerging transportation technologies and the need for new places to live, work, and play, in the face of jurisdictional confusion and inertia, made it imperative to reorder things along the waterfront.

In July 1912, the newly established Board of Toronto Harbour Commissioners was authorized to create plans for the waterfront and was given substantial powers to implement them. Much of the THC's work, of course, focused on rebuilding the central and eastern harbour area, which involved substantial land reclamation, construction of wharves, and deepening of the harbour to accommodate vessels that would use the proposed new Welland Canal.

Home Smith, a land developer and a member of the Commission from its inception (and its chair in the early 1920s) is generally credited with the 1912 waterfront plans. He certainly was no stranger to Humber Bay. In his time, he would develop some 1214 hectares (3,000 acres) of land along the banks of the Humber, including Riverside Drive, the Kingsway, Baby Point, and the Old Mill Tea Room. In 1928, to complement the CPR's new Royal York Hotel, he built St. George's Golf Course on the banks of the Humber. The THC began work in the Humber Bay area in 1917 and, within a decade, the whole area was transformed.

The plan was imaginative in scope, bold in design, and breathtaking in implementation. It gave coherence and balance to the claims of both corridor and place and understood the growing need for waterfront

> *The 1912 waterfront plan was imaginative in scope, bold in design, and breathtaking in implementation. It gave coherence and balance to the claims of both corridor and place and understood the growing need for waterfront recreation.*

recreation. It called for recreational facilities and parkland along the entire waterfront strip, from just west of Bathurst Street to the Humber River, with a six-kilometre (four-mile) long breakwall to control erosion and protect new uses.

As Mike Filey (1982) notes in his book, *I Remember Sunnyside*, by 1922 the Bathing Pavilion and Amusement Park had opened and almost 75 per cent of the Humber Bay section of the 1912 Waterfront Plan had been completed. Ultimately, the Harbour Commissioners developed 134 hectares (330 acres) — 46 hectares (113 acres) of protected waterways behind 5,482 metres (17,985 feet) of breakwall, 47 hectares (115 acres) of park, 35 hectares (86 acres) for sale or lease, and 6 hectares (16 acres) of dedicated streets. Two major thoroughfares,

Lake Shore Boulevard and Lakeshore Road, were laid out along the newly filled waterfront expanse that had been created by pumping 3,058,200 cubic metres (4,000,000 cubic yards) of sandy muck from the lake bottom and distributing it along a six-kilometre (four-mile) stretch of Humber Bay's waterfront shoreline. In time, the THC would build a new ballpark, Maple Leaf Stadium (1926) at the foot of Bathurst Street, and an airport on the Toronto Islands (1939).

Sailing, rowing, and canoeing facilities were developed as old clubs, displaced by the THC from Toronto Bay because of the harbour improvements, relocated west. The Argonaut Rowing Club, the longest continuously operating rowing club in Canada, established in 1872 at the foot of George Street, and later moved to the York

Sunnyside, Easter Sunday, 1949

SUNNYSIDE: A PLAYGROUND BY THE LAKE

A thundering and thrilling roller-coaster; a luxurious merry-go-round; tantalizing Honey Dew, hot dogs, and Downyflake doughnuts; bands, dances, and boat rentals at the Palais Royale — these were just some of the attractions at Toronto's Sunnyside Bathing Pavilion and Amusement Park, situated along Lake Ontario between the Humber River and Exhibition Place.

Not long after its inception in 1922, Sunnyside became known as a "playground by the lake". Children with bathing suits and towels in hand jumped on street cars and were transported, free of charge, to Sunnyside, where they enjoyed the 91-metre (300-foot) long swimming pool, the rides, and games of skill. Excited crowds flocked to the park grounds, participated in contests, entertained themselves and each other with concerts, strolled along the boardwalk or cheered entertainers and their outrageous acts, which included, for example, a female impersonators' competition and dancing bears.

Enjoying the lake and sandy beach, Sunnyside, 1926

Fond memories of the amusement park still linger in the minds of many Torontonians. Sam Sniderman (Sam the Record Man) recalls Sunnyside as "the focal point. . . for our courting and social activities . . . our only chance for a holiday resort". Radio and television personality Elwood Glover spoke of being taken to the amusement park ". . . where the lights and crowds and noise recreated . . . all the excitement of a county fair". He also recalled ". . . a bandshell with its back to the lake, where every Sunday night a People's Credit Jewellers broadcast would take place" (Filey 1982).

Seventy years later, it is still possible to walk through Sunnyside Park. The Palais Royale and the Bathing Pavilion are still intact and in operation. However, the glorious and exciting days that marked time spent at the park can no longer be captured. Most of historic Sunnyside was destroyed after World War II to make way for the Gardiner Expressway. A unique era, and a unique part of the City, are gone.

Source: Filey M. 1982. *I remember Sunnyside: the rise and fall of a magical era.* Toronto: McClelland and Stewart.

Street pier, was relocated to the foot of Jameson Avenue (which was then still connected to the waterfront). The Toronto Sail and Canoe Club, established in 1880, was relocated to the foot of Dowling Avenue, where it joined the Boulevard Club, which had been established in 1905 as the Parkdale Canoe Club. The Palais Royale was erected in 1920 and an entire generation "swung and swayed" and "jumped and jived" to Bert Niosi and Ellis McLintock and many other Big Bands. The Sunnyside Amusement Park, officially opened on 28 June 1922, was the "poor man's Riviera" and still exerts a powerful hold on the memories of the millions who went there. Mike Filey (1982) recalls the memories of a boy growing up in Swansea:

> Sunnyside was a world just outside our neighbourhood. From our house on Ellis Avenue, you walked to the bottom of the street, passing Catfish Pond and the Camels' Hump hills on the right and Grenadier Pond and High Park on the left. Just as you came out from under the railway bridge, by the old Lake Simcoe icehouse, you could feel the charge as the village met the lake.

> Across the short field and a narrow Lakeshore Road we would run to get to our first goal — the boardwalk! The boardwalk was the great pathway to imagined pleasures — a kind of yellow-brick road that stretched as far as the eye could see and where you could feel the excitement as the boards warmed your feet in the summer sun.

> And there it was! The water, the breakwall, the colours, the people, the smells, the happy noise — the sheer energy of it all. A world of rides, Honey Dew, music and chips with vinegar and salt.

By the late '40s, it had all begun to change. In 1948, a subcommittee of City Council tabled a report calling for a 19 kilometres (12-mile) long super highway from the Humber River to Woodbine Avenue. In 1953, the newly established Council of Metropolitan Toronto approved 13 kilometres (eight miles) of it; by 1955, the Frederick G. Gardiner Expressway, Canada's first full-scale urban freeway, was under construction and, by 1957, it was in operation.

The new expressway was a matter of great civic pride and understood to be the harbinger of economic and cultural progress. It was a part of the great program of growth of the 1950s, in which the new was clearly perceived to be of greater value than the old. Building the new transportation corridor sealed the fate of an already-deteriorating Sunnyside and began to significantly alter the vision of Humber Bay that had informed the 1912 Waterfront

---

The Gardiner Expressway was a part of the great program of growth of the 1950s, in which the new was clearly perceived to be of greater value than the old.

Plan. Coherence and balance began to slip away; the sense of the area as a place or series of places connected to the waterfront, to which neighbourhoods were attached and significant numbers of people would come for pleasure and recreation, gradually diminished as, more and more, Humber Bay become a corridor through which people passed on their way to somewhere else.

As a result of a central transportation corridor that comprises the Queensway, the railways, the Gardiner Expressway, and Lake

> **T**oday, from the regional perspective the western edge of the [Central waterfront] region is a sleeper — an area ripe for development, or possibly inappropriate development. There is an exciting opportunity and challenge for those concerned with the best use of this irreplaceable resource: the limited shoreline.
>
> Toronto Waterfront Charrette. [1989]. *Toronto Waterfront Charrette: blueprint for the future: a report to the agencies, property owners and residents of Metropolitan Toronto.* Toronto: Toronto Waterfront Charrette. Charrette Steering Committee.

Shore Boulevard, such historic public places as the Humber Valley and High Park, and such long-established urban Toronto neighbourhoods as Parkdale and Swansea, have been further isolated from each other and from the waterfront.

In the past few years — pushed as always by the forces of new land development, changes in transportation, and concern for environmental health — there has been considerable activity in the Humber Bay area and a number of studies that will profoundly affect its future.

In Etobicoke, the City Planning Staff's work on the official planning process has been supplemented by a *Lakeshore Overview Study* undertaken by the Butler Group (1991), and by two site-specific studies of the motel strip, one done by A. J. Diamond, Donald Schmitt and Company (1991) and the other by the Kirkland Partnership (1991). The Province of Ontario has declared the motel strip to be an area of Provincial Interest under the Planning Act.

The studies, and the negotiations and official processes involving them, were dealt with in the previous chapter; it is their effect on Humber Bay that concerns us here. The various proposals and studies include perspectives on priorities for environmental remediation, shoreline management plans, protecting vistas and regional view corridors, waterfront protection techniques, building heights, open space opportunities, transportation facilities, urban design, and detailed built form requirements. When placed in the context of the ecosystem approach accepted by the Province of Ontario, they should give considerable momentum to the efforts to rehabilitate and regenerate Humber Bay.

Recently, the City of Toronto (1991) established *The Humber River/High Park/ Western Beaches Civic Design Study* to:

> examine the means of improving the western end of the Gardiner-Lakeshore Corridor extending from Roncesvalles Avenue to the Humber River . . . to see how this section of the waterfront can be improved to once again serve as a meeting place of distinction along the Greater Toronto Waterfront.

Its objectives include:

- creating a major gateway to the City at the Humber River;
- improving the open space connections between the Humber River, the Western Beaches, and High Park;
- investigating the realignment of Lake Shore Boulevard between Roncesvalles Avenue and Ellis Avenue, and of the Queensway between the South Kingsway and Ellis Avenue; and
- proposing improvements to pedestrian environments, landscapes, and streetscapes in the transportation corridor.

It recommends the following civic design strategies, which are intended to improve vehicular, bicycle, and pedestrian access to, and movement through, the Gardiner/Lakeshore Corridor:

- two new waterfront trails along the waterfront: a new pedestrian board-walk and a new, separated bicycle path linking the City of Toronto with the City of Etobicoke;
- new pedestrian promenades along the north and/or south sides of both Lake Shore Boulevard and the Queensway;
- a direct new link between the Humber Valley trail and the new waterfront trails under the proposed new Humber bridges;
- the proposed extension of the Harbourfront LRT westwards to the Humber River along the Queensway;
- a new pedestrian and bicycle bridge from High Park, crossing the Queensway, the railway tracks, the Gardiner Expressway, and Lake Shore Boulevard, in order to provide direct access to the waterfront;
- improvements to the quality and amenity of at-grade vehicular, bicycle, and pedestrian access to the water-front at Windermere Avenue, Ellis Avenue, Colborne Lodge Drive, and Parkside Drive; and
- a new pedestrian deck and bridge at Roncesvalles Avenue that will link it directly to the waterfront.

Civic design strategies to improve the quality and amenity of public places within the corridor include:

Transportation corridor, 1990

- providing new urban parks in the Swansea, High Park, and Parkdale portions of the corridor;
- providing a new urban design structure for the potential redevelopment of the Stelco site;
- improving the civic and physical design of the proposed new Humber bridges and their environs, in order to establish a new gateway to Toronto and Etobicoke; and
- providing a series of new waterside plazas, piers, and monuments that will reinforce significant visual axes within the corridor.

Transportation strategies proposed in support of the civic design strategies include:

- realigning Lake Shore Boulevard north, in order to provide unimpeded pedestrian waterfront access on an additional 6.9 hectares (17 acres) of currently inaccessible parkland;

- providing improved at-grade parking facilities that will have direct access to and from Lake Shore Boulevard, for drivers visiting the Western Beaches in general, and Sunnyside Pavilion and the Palais Royale, in particular;
- providing improved pedestrian and vehicular access to the waterfront and/ or Lake Shore Boulevard at Roncesvalles Avenue, Parkside Drive, Colborne Lodge Drive, Ellis Avenue, Windermere Avenue, and the South Kingsway; and
- providing improved public transit access to the corridor, along both Lake Shore Boulevard and the Queensway.

The cities of Toronto and Etobicoke have joint stewardship with Metropolitan Toronto and the Province of Ontario in determining the future of Humber Bay. If we are to seize the opportunities that now present themselves on this historic part of Toronto's

waterfront, these authorities must begin to work with members of the public. Humber Bay is far too important to be severed and impaired by artificial planning jurisdictions.

RECOMMENDATION

69. The Royal Commission recommends that existing and future plans and studies for Humber Bay be integrated, within the context of the program for integrating environment, land use, and transportation in the Central Waterfront described in the previous section.

GARRISON COMMON

The portion of Toronto's waterfront we call Garrison Common is a loose cluster of places that evoke strong collective memories. It was here that the French built Fort

Aerial view of Garrison Common

Map 10.9 Historical elements

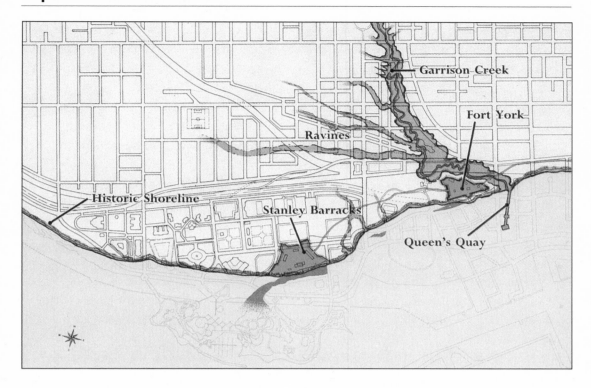

Garrison Creek

Fort York

Ravines

Historic Shoreline

Stanley Barracks

Queen's Quay

Rouillé in 1750 to support the fur trade. Forty-three years later, under the command of Governor John Graves Simcoe, the Queen's Rangers built Fort York to defend the new Town of York. At the time, the fort commanded the entrance to the harbour and was ideally situated to repel invaders. The name Garrison Common was used, at least until 1850, for the grassy area outside Fort York on which the soldiers grazed their cattle. It now refers to the area running north from the lake to Queen Street, west from Bathurst Street as far as Dufferin (and somewhat further west at its southerly end to take in all of Exhibition Place).

Other links to Canada's military history remain: the old Military Cemetery close to Fort York; the Fort York Armouries on Fleet Street, where soldiers trained in World War I, and which still houses several famous Toronto reserve regiments. There are the active facilities of HMCS York facing onto the lake and, just west of them, lovely Coronation Park, its majestic trees planted to honour the Canadian units that served in World War I.

In many ways, the area's industrial heritage is as rich as its military heritage. Canada's most successful clothing retailers had their workrooms in the area; nearby stood the warehouses of a large grocery chain. There was a brewery, and mills and factories, as well as the vast building in which Canada's first multinational company built farm equipment to be shipped worldwide.

The western end of the Garrison Common area is dominated by Exhibition Park, home to the Canadian National Exhibition, which has played a cherished role in Torontonians' memories since 1878. The remarkable Crystal Palace was built then as exhibition space to lure the annual Agricultural Association fair to the City. Although the building is long gone, its Victorian whimsy is echoed in the Music Building, the Bandshell, and the Horticultural Building.

The use of the area for exhibitions has continued for 113 years, luring generations of residents to its star attractions: two major annual exhibitions — one marking the end of summer, the other the beginning of winter.

South of the exhibition lands stands Ontario Place, the Province's answer to Expo '67. Built on stilts and strung out across three artificial islands, its architecture was described by William Dendy and William Kilbourn (1986), writing in *Toronto Observed*, as being "designed to amuse rather than impress". For 21 years, Ontario Place has attracted visitors to tour its exhibits, marvel at its large-screen cinema, and enjoy music, ballet, and pop concerts in a lakeside setting.

But the glories of yesterday's Garrison Common have faded: many industries have departed, and much of the land left behind lies empty. The most-used public venues — Exhibition Place and Ontario Place — are dominated for most of the year by hectares of empty parking lots. Major traffic corridors bisect the area and cut off links to the lake. Fort York is isolated, hidden behind the concrete span of the Gardiner, and the area's park system is not a system at all, just a disconnected series of green spaces.

Despite the shabbiness of some of its parts, the area's strategic location, rich history, and the extent of public ownership in it, provide enormous opportunities for regeneration. The Garrison Common area is 308 hectares (760 acres) in size, an area perched on the water's edge, clearly in transition, and in need of renewal.

All four levels of government are involved in the Garrison Common area, as is the private sector. When the Royal Commission first began to examine Garrison Common, it soon became apparent that there was no co-ordination of activities: each major player had plans and projects that, for the most part, were being pursued in isolation from each other. Nor was this a new problem: for decades, attempts at establishing a new plan for the area have failed, because of three factors: jurisdictional gridlock, lack of a clear economic development strategy, and lack of a co-ordinated physical plan — in short, lack of a shared vision.

The Commission reviewed problems and opportunities in the Garrison Common area and, in its *Watershed* (1990) report, called for development of an integrated master plan. In December 1991, Ruth Grier, minister responsible for the Greater Toronto Area, formally asked the Royal Commission to do just that.

A master plan would provide co-ordinated direction for all the political, investment, and design decisions needed to regenerate Garrison Common. In the Commission's view, a co-ordinated, ecosystem-based approach was needed in order to overcome

***D**espite the shabbiness of some of its parts, the area's strategic location, rich history, and the extent of public ownership in it, provide enormous opportunities for regeneration.*

Ontario Place

the fundamental challenges Garrison Common faces. There were six challenges:

1. To create a rich natural and human environment

Garrison Common occupies a major section of the Central Toronto Waterfront, but has a limited range of aquatic, terrestrial, and human environments. More than a third of the area's surface is covered by parking lots, roads or vacant industrial sites; 70 per cent of the land/water boundary is hard-edged. The Master Plan would ensure development and management of a complex and healthy ecosystem.

2. To make Garrison Common a vital part of the surrounding urban area

The publicly owned sections of the Garrison Common area — Exhibition Place, Ontario Place, and Fort York — are under-utilized and, in fact, the number of users has declined over the last ten years.

Much of the rest of the area — industrial and railway lands — is vacant. The Niagara and Parkdale neighbourhoods, which border the area, are cut off from Garrison Common and Lake Ontario by the transportation corridor. The Master Plan would facilitate connections between Garrison Common and the urban fabric around it, and would enhance its character as a unique place.

3. To guide major public infrastructure decisions and encourage investment in private development

Major public investments are being considered for Garrison Common, including: extending the Harbourfront LRT from Front Street; consolidating GO corridors; and making changes to the Gardiner/Lakeshore Corridor. A major new international Trade Centre is being planned for

Exhibition Place, substantial changes to the operation of Ontario Place are under way, and improvements are proposed for Fort York. The area would be dramatically transformed by collaborative planning among agencies, and by private-sector initiatives that would result from a strong vision for the area.

4. To promote the economic development of the region

Garrison Common has traditionally played a unique role in trade and tourism in the regional, provincial, and national economy. However, if Toronto and Ontario are to remain internationally competitive in these sectors, that role must be significantly reworked and expanded: trade and tourism draws are losing ground to comparable facilities in other jurisdictions. The Master Plan would focus on establishing a program of reindustrialization and strategic development of key sectors in the regional economy.

5. To enhance the attractiveness of Garrison Common

Garrison Common is unique: beautifully situated, with marvellous views of the lake, easy access to the water, and many magnificent buildings and landscaped areas; but much of its richness is neglected and undiscovered. The Master Plan would ensure that a consistently high standard of building design, composition, and landscaping is achieved, and that environmental quality becomes a goal in itself.

6. To co-ordinate long-term management of Garrison Common

The opportunity inherent in so much publicly owned land has not been realized because of the multiplicity of governments involved in the area. There is now a clear willingness to move towards a co-ordinated (and ultimately consolidated) management and development structure; the Master Plan would be the basis for doing so.

PROCESS

The *Garrison Common: Preliminary Master Plan* (Berridge Lewinberg Greenberg et al. 1991) was developed under the direction of a Steering Committee composed of representatives from all four levels of government and their respective boards and agencies. The work was carried out by a multidisciplinary group of consultants with expertise in urban planning, environmental design, transportation planning, and economic analysis. They met regularly with the Steering Committee, and held individual meetings with representatives of the area's landowners and residents.

An ecosystem approach was central to the development of the Garrison Common Master Plan. This meant that the consulting team had to look beyond immediate problems to broader issues affecting the area, and had to examine the interrelationship of the biophysical and human environments. Development of the Master Plan was based on the belief that incorporating natural systems into the planning process is essential to shaping a healthy human habitat.

In applying the ecosystem approach, a number of possible planning options were generated for Garrison Common. The net impact on and benefits for the whole system — natural, social, and economic — were evaluated for each one.

What the consultants have created is not "the final word" on Garrison Common, but a concept and a vision — a starting place from which to build for the area's future. Certainly, the preliminary response to the release of the report bodes well for a co-operative and constructive process involving the four levels of government and their agencies. There is considerable support, not only for the general thrust and vision of the Preliminary Master Plan, but for developing partnerships amongst the parties that will allow the plan to be finalized and action to begin.

DEFINING A NEW ROLE FOR GARRISON COMMON

One of the first tasks was to analyse the current role of Garrison Common and to develop an economic development strategy for the area. The resultant strategy is based on a recognition of the area's international, regional, and local potential; it has four major components:

1. Developing tourism for both domestic and international markets

Toronto's position as one of the top 10 tourist destinations in North America should be protected by a strong tourism strategy that would include development of new attractions for the enjoyment of visitors. Other than the SkyDome, there has been no significant new facility, event or amenity developed since the early '80s. The potential exists at Garrison Common to establish new cultural, sports, and entertainment facilities and new regional attractions (such as an aquarium), and to host festivals (such as Caribana, Mariposa, and a Winter Festival).

2. Expanding trade, particularly at the regional and international levels

The trade functions at Exhibition Place should be repositioned from the essentially local and regional, to become an internationally important venue. In part, this can be done by developing an internationally competitive trade and exhibition centre, which the city now lacks. The logical site is Exhibition Place.

A partnership of public- and private-sector interests are currently studying the issue intensely. The current proposal by Metropolitan Toronto involves renovating existing exhibition buildings and adding new, temporary exhibition halls for a total of approximately 139,350 square metres (1.5 million square feet) of space. Detailed planning will end in spring 1992 with the presentation of a business and design plan to Metro Toronto.

3. Reindustrializing old industrial areas, focusing on dynamic sectors of the new economy

Among the enterprises in Garrison Common that are now gone are Massey-Ferguson, Inglis, and Molson's. The loss, in just the last 10 years, of almost 2,000 jobs in the area — almost 15 per cent of total employment — leaves large and well-located tracts of land that provide a strong opportunity for Toronto's reindustrialization. They should be used as a resource on which new and leading-edge industry can be developed, encompassing the manufacturing, design, trading, and service sectors.

Toronto's position as one of the top 10 tourist destinations in North America should be protected by a strong tourism strategy that would include development of new attractions for the enjoyment of visitors.

Arts, Crafts and Hobbies Building, Exhibition Place

4. Developing communities by expanding existing, and creating new, residential neighbourhoods

There are significant opportunities in Garrison Common to create new residential communities, and to preserve and expand existing residential neighbourhoods. The Bathurst-Spadina neighbourhood section of the Railway Lands will reach as far west as Bathurst Street and offers the potential of expanding them westward into the Fleet Street lands. North of the track corridor, the basic street and open space pattern of the Niagara neighbourhood can also be extended west towards Strachan Avenue, using available public or vacant industrial land.

ENVIRONMENT

The condition of the aquatic environment along the waterfront is poor, and as indicated previously, a Remedial Action Plan is being developed in order to restore water quality. In Garrison Common, as elsewhere along the Central Waterfront, water quality and aquatic habitat are degraded: the lake water and bottom sediments are contaminated with nutrients, heavy metals, and organic chemicals. The area lacks fish habitat areas for spawning and feeding, although there is the potential for improving habitat within the breakwalls and in the Ontario Place lagoons. Poor connections between terrestrial habitats and the limited diversity of plant communities have resulted in sterile landscapes with limited ability to support wild-life and birds, and lacking in micro-climate protection and visual interest for people.

The transportation corridors, areas created by lakefill, and former industrial lands may have contaminated soils. Large areas of surface parking create problems with blowing dust, and traffic in the transportation corridor is a significant source of the area's air pollution.

Proposals for regenerating the natural environment in Garrison Common include strategies for improving water quality and open space. Reconfiguring the breakwaters and shoreline in and adjacent to the area would create a series of aquatic habitats, including wetlands and beaches. That would improve people's access and the quality of their experience along the Waterfront Trail. The wetlands would enhance fish habitat, and improve water quality by trapping sediments and excess nutrients. Building stormwater detention ponds would upgrade water quality in the nearshore areas of the lake.

There are many proposals to improve the quality and variety of open space, as well as the connections between open spaces — to create a "green network" that links the various open spaces in the area. The Waterfront Trail would provide east/west links and improve access to the shoreline of Lake Ontario. One possible route for the trail is along the perimeter of the islands at Ontario Place. A waterfront "canoe trail" would connect the Humber River to the Western Gap with potential links to the Toronto Islands and the Don River.

It is proposed that a Garrison Common trail be built, north from Coronation Park to Trinity Bellwoods Park, in order to establish a strong north-south connection with the lake. The trail would follow a series of existing and proposed parks and open spaces: a symbolic reference to Garrison Creek would be created, in the area where the creek and ravine once existed, through a series of stormwater management ponds, regrading, and revegetating with native woodland and meadow species.

The possible relocation of the Georgetown GO line further west would provide an opportunity to establish a green connection to Black Creek on the existing right-of-way.

Fort York would be better connected north to Trinity Bellwoods Park, east to the SkyDome and CN Tower, west to Exhibition Place, and south to the lake. Landscaping to recreate the original shoreline of Lake Ontario would be undertaken and could include symbolic shingle beach and water elements, a boardwalk link to Little Norway Park and the Western Gap, and relocation of the original Queen's Quay lighthouse to the site from its current home in Gore Park.

The existing sea of asphalt at Exhibition Place would be reduced and landscaped. At the west end of Exhibition Place, the integrity of the beaux-arts landscape would be maintained and enhanced by creating more pavilions-in-the-park and appropriate landscaping.

LAND USE

The plan proposes to continue and enhance the park and recreational character of Ontario Place, Exhibition Place, Coronation Park, and Fort York. The eastern end of Exhibition Place would be substantially redeveloped, with the creation of an upgraded Trade Centre, which would be designed to complement the surrounding

Figure 10.1 Preliminary Master Plan

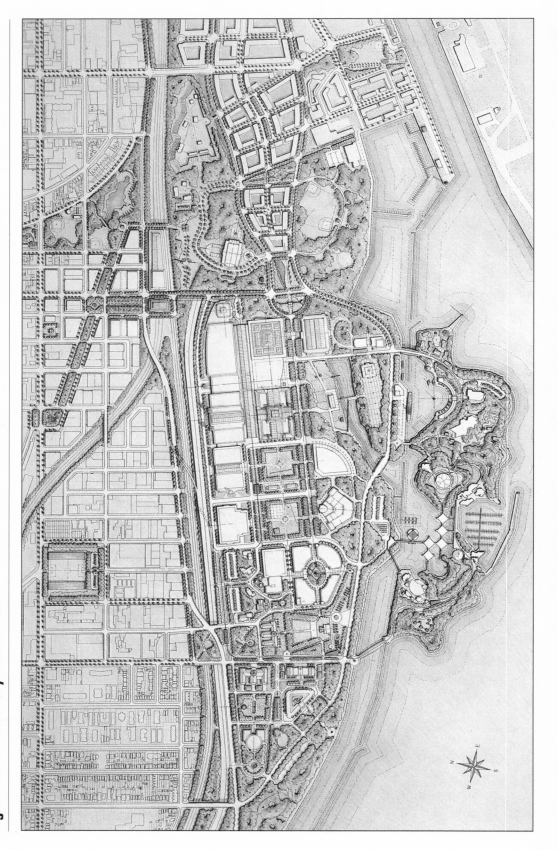

park. Infill buildings on the other major public lands would be developed on a scale and character consistent with those already established.

With an active Trade Centre to the north, there would be major opportunities to expand the scope of activities at Ontario Place. A year-round "Waterfront Village" with restaurants, shops, hotel, and a new Maritime Museum would diversify the facilities.

The Fleet Street lands would be the site of medium-scale mixed commercial and residential development as a transition between the higher-scale development proposed for the Railway Lands and the park-like environment of Fort York, Ontario Place, and Exhibition Place.

The Northern Reindustrialization Area would be revitalized west of Strachan Avenue, mainly with trade-mart related industries such as printing, graphics, film and communications. East of Strachan, a commercial/residential mix similar to that of Fleet Street is envisaged. Heights and densities would decline north and eastward to conform to the existing Niagara and Parkdale neighbourhoods.

TRANSPORTATION

One of the paradoxes of Garrison Common is that it has exceptional transportation facilities, but limited accessibility. Major road and rail corridors bisect the district, but it is hard to gain access on foot, by bicycle or even by car. The routes that pass through the area to serve downtown are serious barriers to movement in Garrison Common itself, and have a negative impact on its facilities.

One of the paradoxes of Garrison Common is that it has exceptional transportation facilities, but limited accessibility. Major road and rail corridors bisect the district, but it is hard to gain access on foot, by bicycle or even by car.

The preferred transportation solutions being offered for Garrison Common are based on the assumption that at least four major proposals now under active consideration would affect the area. These include: reconfiguring the Gardiner/Lakeshore; extending Front Street west; possibly realigning the two major GO lines and constructing a new combined station; and extending the Harbourfront LRT.

The preferred solution for the Gardiner is to keep it in its current alignment, but to relocate and redesign it, at least between Strachan Avenue and Bathurst. That is the area in which it constitutes a serious visual, physical, and experiential blight on Fort York. The Front Street extension should run west from Strachan Avenue to connect to Lake Shore Boulevard west of Exhibition Place. The Front Street extension would improve access to the northern reindustrialization area and would make it possible to downgrade Lake Shore Boulevard from six to four lanes, modified to create a scenic waterfront drive. Traffic speeds should be lowered and traffic lights should facilitate pedestrian crossings.

Proposed realignment of the Georgetown GO line to the west would greatly benefit Garrison Common. The *Garrison Common Preliminary Master Plan* proposes a single, integrated GO Transit station, servicing both the Lakeshore and Georgetown rail corridors, which would be built just north of the eastern end of the Exhibition grounds, and would allow passengers to connect directly with the Trade Centre. Connecting the Georgetown line to Lester B. Pearson International Airport would be a powerful component of transit infrastructure for Garrison Common and for Toronto.

Extending the Harbourfront LRT along the waterfront will mean better access to the recreational opportunities in Garrison Common. Because the revitalized exhibition and trade facilities will generate the presence of large numbers of people, a "people mover" system may ultimately be needed to link Ontario Place and Exhibition Place.

Connecting the Georgetown line to Lester B. Pearson International Airport would be a powerful component of transit infrastructure for Garrison Common and for Toronto.

To facilitate year-round use of Ontario Place, there will have to be improvements to the circulation system, to accommodate pedestrian, bicycle, and automobile traffic. The entry bridges, which are currently pedestrian bottlenecks, will have to be redesigned to make for easier traffic flows.

Most of the large surface parking lots that are so prevalent in Garrison Common would eventually be displaced. Instead transit would be enhanced and people would be encouraged to use it. Some surface parking lots — small, appropriately landscaped — would remain in Exhibition Place and Ontario Place and there might be opportunities to create a reservoir of off-peak parking north of the railway tracks.

Current land use, Garrison Common

Because Garrison Common now lacks a system of local streets, it has been proposed that the city grid pattern of streets from the north and east be extended into the area. Fleet Street itself would disappear, and The Esplanade would continue to the Princes' Gates. Lake Shore Boulevard would be slightly realigned to create a Princes' Gate Square in front of the eastern entrance to the Exhibition. Inside the gates, Princes' Boulevard would continue westward, providing a strong organizing element for the structures and activities to be established there.

HISTORICAL ELEMENTS

In addition to the already-described proposals for enhancing and recreating historical elements of Garrison Common, an open space connection with Trinity Bellwoods Park and northwest along the GO line would symbolically recreate Garrison Creek and link to Black Creek. The gesture of bringing water elements into Exhibition Place, Princes' Gate Square, and Fort York will recall historical connections to the original Lake Ontario shoreline.

Fort York could be given the prominence and setting it deserves by tying it into Garrison Common's green space network, relocating the Gardiner, improving access, providing symbolic links to the lake it once guarded, and creating better visual corridors. The Fort York Armoury could be used as the primary entrance to the Fort York park, and could become a more comprehensive military museum for Toronto.

There are many historical buildings in the area that should be preserved and reused. At Exhibition Place, the Horse Palace and the Coliseum could be successfully incorporated into the new Trade Centre. The fine buildings at the western end of Exhibition

Fort York

Place are sadly under-used and deserve permanent tenants. Potential uses include: a centre for the visual arts or educational, and environmental institutes; an aquarium; or permanent homes for major cultural institutions such as the Ontario College of Art.

The Maritime Museum needs a new location: it is too far from the waterfront and the current exhibition space is limited. This would free up Stanley Barracks for other functions, perhaps a unique meeting and reception centre, which would be enhanced by the re-creation of the original water's edge.

Other buildings that may have potential for new uses include HMCS York, as well as some of the area's remaining industrial buildings.

IMPLEMENTING THE PLAN

The Royal Commission's work, in collaboration with representatives of four levels

> **W**hile urban networks exist in space
> and time, urban partnerships contain
> the potential for relationships that
> can animate these networks. They
> include the governmental and the non-
> governmental; professional, technical,
> and voluntary associations; the busi-
> ness, corporate and informal sectors.
> Partnerships can exist on a permanent
> or temporary basis, they can be formed
> through statute or through an ad-hoc
> desire to achieve common goals.
> They can exist at a local level as well
> as internationally.
>
> Jacobs, P. 1991. *Sustainable urban development.* Montreal:
> Third Summit of the World's Major Cities.

of government and their respective boards and agencies, has generated a Preliminary Master Plan to guide decision-making and planning in Garrison Common. However, the greatest challenges still lie ahead. Implementing an integrated Master Plan for Garrison Common will require a process that resolves current jurisdictional fragmentation, and that avoids the uncertainties, slowness, and lack of co-ordination characteristic of conventional approval processes.

The first step is to subject the plan to full public and governmental review.

RECOMMENDATION

70. The Royal Commission recommends that integrated public hearings be held to review the *Garrison Common Preliminary Master Plan.* The hearings should be jointly sponsored by the participating governments and agencies.

During the course of the Garrison Common study, the Province and Metropolitan Toronto considered submitting a bid for Expo '98, a Class B World Fair. More recently, the possibility has arisen of hosting a 1996 exposition; the prospect of presenting Garrison Common to an international audience reinforces the need for the highest standard of environmental planning, building, and landscaping design. It also emphasizes the need to move beyond the complex approval processes under which the site is now regulated, to rethink the independent and often contradictory responsibilities of government agencies, and to move towards comprehensive planning and implementation.

RECOMMENDATION

71. The Royal Commission recommends that the results of the hearings be referred to the federal and provincial governments, Metropolitan Toronto, the City of Toronto, and interested private-sector parties, for their consideration with respect to the five-year capital construction program for regenerating Garrison Common. Such a program should include:

- projects designed to improve water quality and the diversity of open space in the area;
- improvements to the existing waterfront trail system, and connections north to Trinity Bellwoods Park (the Garrison Trail);
- a new GO station to service both the Lakeshore and new

Georgetown lines, link with
Lester B. Pearson International
Airport, and provide a connec-
tion to the Trade Centre at
Exhibition Place;

- a Trade Centre at the eastern
  end of Exhibition Place, and an
  emphasis on diverse, permanent
  uses for currently under-used
  buildings;
- improved connections at
  Ontario Place for pedestrians
  and bicyclists, development of a
  Waterfront Village and Maritime
  Museum, and a large-screen cinema complex; and
- programs designed to increase
  year-round accessibility and use of
  all amenities in Garrison Common.

TORONTO BAY

Toronto Bay has an extraordinary setting: its 400-hectare (1,000-acre) inner harbour is framed by a 250-hectare (625-acre)
island park, a picturesque regional airport,
a working port and the historic entrance to
the City's downtown, extending up to the
old shoreline at Front Street.

The Bay has been called Toronto's
"waterfront piazza". This appellation
reminds us again of the importance of
vistas in the art of place-making. Around
and across Toronto Bay are some of the
most magnificent vistas that this region
has to offer; looking outwards from the
City to the Lake, as well as looking at the

Toronto's "waterfront piazza"

City from the Islands, the Spit or the Lake itself.

Toronto Bay's individual places — diverse in character and function — have been changing fundamentally during the past 25 years and the area is being transformed. Their history, current forces of transition, and possible future roles are discussed in the following order:

- Railway Lands, which are now beginning to evolve into distinct neighbourhoods: City Place; Southtown; the Union Station/ Central Bayfront area; and emerging Central Park;
- Harbourfront lands, no longer an isolated enclave, but beginning to be integrated with surrounding areas;
- Toronto Island Airport; and
- Toronto Islands park and community.

RAILWAY LANDS

In its *Watershed* (1990) report, the Royal Commission examined the troubled 30-year history of the proposed Railway Lands redevelopment, discussed the basic features of the 1985 Part II Railway Lands Plan, adopted by City Council and the railways, and concluded that — in light of changes in the area, in the Financial District, and in surrounding areas — the plan should be reviewed.

In May 1990 Toronto City Council asked its Commissioner of Planning and Development to conduct such a review, in keeping with Planning Act requirements, and consistent with a provision in the Part II Plan itself.

A HISTORICAL OVERVIEW

Discussion on the future of the Railway Lands is hardly a recent phenomenon: the idea of removing 80 hectares (200 acres) of tracks separating City and lake has challenged planners, architects, developers, citizens, and politicians almost continuously for the past 30 years, and is hardly unique to Toronto. But a knowledge of the history of these lands is crucial to understanding the current situation and future opportunities.

The first major report on the lands in recent times was *The Core of the Central Waterfront*, prepared in 1962 for the City of Toronto Planning Board; it suggested decking the rail corridor and creating an expanded terminal. This idea was embodied in the 1963 Plan for Downtown Toronto, ultimately adopted by City Council in 1965. At the time, both CN and CP railways were building major new freight yards in the suburbs and, in 1968, they jointly produced a study, *Metro Centre*, for the redevelopment lands. It recommended relocating the rail corridor, demolishing Union Station, and building a new intermodal transportation terminal with considerable commercial and residential development. Thus began the three-decade debate that persists to this day.

Current arguments, however energetic, are only the most recent manifestations of a much older controversy: Toronto began on the lake and waterfront development has always been an important and controversial factor in the City's evolution.

> *T*he idea of removing 80 hectares (200 acres) of tracks separating City and lake has challenged planners, architects, developers, citizens, and politicians almost continuously for the past 30 years.

Virtually all the Central Waterfront, starting at Front Street, was created by extensive lakefilling that began in the City's early days; in the 1830s, public concern about the use of, and access to, the waterfront made the city council of the day apply for the patent of the waterlots, south of the former shoreline, to create a public, 30-metre (100-foot) wide, tree-lined promenade. Construction of this road, The Esplanade, did not begin for another 20 years, after wrangles between the municipality and various private interests. However, less than two years after The Esplanade opened in 1854, the City granted its southern 12 metres (40 feet) to the Grand Trunk Railway (now CN).

In 1855, a new railway station was built at Front and Bay streets. Lakefilling for the railways, shipping, and industry continued sporadically for the next half century. The many east-west railway tracks crossing the bottom of the busy city created dangerous and inconvenient level crossings at York,

Bay, and Yonge streets. In 1892, a bridge was built over the tracks at York Street, to permit pedestrian and vehicular access to the waterfront and minimize the effect of the rail barrier.

In 1904, the train station burned down in the Great Toronto Fire. Between 1905 and 1924, arguments continued among the CP and Grand Trunk railways, the City, the Toronto Harbour Commissioners, and the federal government on the design and location of a new station and whether there should be a raised or lowered rail corridor.

The Grand Trunk Railway supported the concept of raising the tracks on a viaduct allowing York, Bay, and Yonge streets to run under the tracks, a plan CP opposed. Its response was to build (and later vacate) its own station at Summerhill and Yonge.

In 1924, an independent commission recommended that the viaduct plan be implemented and the railway corridor was

Summer crowds crossing tracks at Bay Street, 1912

raised approximately six metres (20 feet). In 1927, Union Station as we know it today was opened, and more than 40 hectares (100 acres) of new land south of the station were created for rail yards. The freight line by-pass along the southern boundary, also on a raised viaduct, was constructed and then filled in to create a berm six metres (20 feet) high.

In the 1930s, and for the next 30 years, the THC continued its massive program of lakefilling south of the Railway Lands, for port and industrial uses. (It is ironic that, just as the railways were making plans to relocate their yards to the suburbs, Metropolitan Toronto, assuming the status quo, was building another waterfront barrier, the Gardiner Expressway.) Lake Shore Boulevard was constructed and, in 1963, the Gardiner Expressway opened. All the barriers to the waterfront we know so well today were firmly in place: the railway corridor and rail yards were functioning on lakefill six metres (20 feet) above the water, and the Gardiner/Lakeshore Corridor was operational.

THE 1970s

Beginning in the late sixties, CN and CP railways jointly created Metro Centre, a development company which presented a plan to the City for land owned by CN, CP, THC, the City, Metro, and the federal government. Not surprisingly, the issue of land ownership and control continually plagued plans.

The Metro Centre proposal was negotiated with the City, Metro, and the provincial government for four years and, by 1972, the Ontario Municipal Board had approved the plan for these lands. That year, construction started on the CN Tower.

In November 1974, CN shelved the development company's project, CP having left the partnership earlier.

In January 1976, the City adopted a new Central Area Plan, which called for special studies of the Railway Lands. At the Ontario Municipal Board, the railways argued that the City's plan was unacceptable and, by January 1978, Toronto City Council had proposed amendments to deal with the railways' objections. It submitted two new studies, *The Railway Lands: Basis for Planning* and *The Railway Lands: Proposed Goals and Objectives*, which were adopted by City Council after four months of public discussion.

THE 1980s AND 1990s

With the Central Area Plan approved by the OMB in June 1978, a Railway Lands Steering Group was created, chaired by the Honourable John Clement, then a member of the provincial Cabinet, and comprising representatives of all governments, as well as of the railways, to conduct detailed studies and co-ordinate the efforts of the many interested parties. By May 1982, the City's Department of Planning and Development had submitted a progress report, which effectively launched the formal preparation of the new Railway Lands Part II Plan.

The final report for the Railway Lands Official Plan and Zoning By-law was submitted to City Council in July 1985, followed in August by a report on the Memorandum of Conditions, which dealt with implementation aspects of the plan (land exchanges, infrastructure, cost-sharing, etc.).

The plan set out Council's policy for the Railway Lands:

They are to be developed as an integral part of the Central Area, in order to minimize the barrier effects of the road and rail corridor and the central city reunited with the waterfront.

They should satisfy a broad range of commercial, residential, institutional, cultural, recreational, and open space needs, while ensuring effective and efficient transportation services, including those by inter-city rail and commuter rail.

The plan divided up the 81 hectares (200 acres) of Railway Lands into 14 precincts, and allowed for high densities, particularly at the eastern end, where it envisaged the financial district would extend into the area, with buildings as high as those in the financial district.

One crucial aspect of the planning approval process was that Council created holding by-laws ("H" designations), under which environment and transportation issues would have to be studied before the subject lands were developed. Council viewed this as "fundamental to the proper planning and incremental development of the Railway Lands".

In January 1985, Premier Davis announced that a new covered baseball stadium would be located on the Railway Lands. Council had already adopted the Part II Plan, Zoning By-laws, and Memorandum of Conditions, and in March 1986, it approved the by-laws and agreements for the stadium. All these by-laws were debated at the Ontario Municipal Board in the summer of 1986 and were approved in December of that year.

In 1988, CN and Marathon Realty, the real estate subsidiary of CP, submitted separate applications to develop certain portions of the land and requested that the H designation be removed entirely from the Railway Lands. Early the next year, unable to get the City to respond, the applicants appealed to the OMB for a hearing, which the Board set for September 1990. But in April, City Council asked its Commissioner of Planning and Development for a report on processing applications for the Railway Lands. On 25 May 1990, he submitted a

Vacant lands offer new development possibilities

report recommending that the Official Plan Part II for the Railway Lands be reviewed, in order to consider the implications of many changes that had occurred since it was adopted.

The City's review did not intend to deal with the Railway Lands from scratch, but to assess the possibilities for improving the 1985 plan in the context of five major objectives:

- to improve the quality of the physical environment;
- to convert commercial uses to residential where appropriate;
- to identify locations for community services (schools and a community centre);
- to reflect advances made since 1985 in knowledge and understanding of environmental needs and processes; and
- to determine the development potential and feasible location for building over the rail corridor, as well as to take advantage of the opportunity of giving the south face of Union Station a civic portal, thereby making it a gateway to and from the Central Waterfront.

Modifications to the plan adopted by City Council include:

- measures to enhance the public domain, such as increased emphasis on north-south streets, greater setbacks, and more tree planting, to create pedestrian-friendly infrastructure and capture better sunlight conditions;
- reductions in the density and height of permitted development, as a consequence of the measures described above;

- conversion of commercial to residential use where appropriate, in order to support a better balance between place of residence and place of work in the City and the region;
- an enlarged Central Park adjacent to the SkyDome and including the Roundhouse;
- improved siting for the community park at the western end of the lands and designation of school sites alongside it;
- improved urban design around Union Station; and
- improved strategies for water conservation, energy efficiency, stormwater and groundwater management, waste management, and district heating and cooling.

Overall, the revisions have reduced the amount of development space by about 30 per cent, 371,600 square metres commercial and 278,700 square metres residential (four million square feet commercial and three million square feet residential). They also offer a better relationship between the Railway Lands and the waterfront, with improved pedestrian access, and better green and open space connections to and through the Harbourfront lands to the water's edge. As a statement of policy, the changes also accommodate the possible relocation and/or redesign of the elevated section of the Gardiner Expressway.

One of the owners, Marathon Realty, has also made provision for such a change, by proposing to begin development north of Bremner Boulevard. This phasing, together with setback provisions that Marathon is also willing to make, will allow both time and space to resolve the Gardiner issue in that area.

As the plans mature, it is evident that the Railway Lands can be subdivided almost naturally into three, possibly four, distinct neighbourhoods or areas. These are:

- **CityPlace**, CN Real Estate's lands west of John Street to Bathurst Street, an area that may become more residential and less commercial in character if the City's revisions are accepted by the Ontario Municipal Board;
- **Central Park**, an area of public amenities and attractions stretching from John to Simcoe streets, and including the CN Tower, SkyDome, the Metro Toronto Convention Centre (MTCC), the planned park, and Roundhouse Museum;
- **Southtown**, Marathon Realty's lands, running from Simcoe to Bay streets, which will function principally as a southerly extension of the Financial District; and
- **The Union Station Precinct**, the central intermodal terminus and interchange for the region, as well as a primary pedestrian and transit connection between the downtown and the waterfront.

The public interests and values inherent in two of these places, Central Park and the Union Station Precinct, are worth comment.

CENTRAL PARK

As a consequence of all the plans, modifications, and negotiations, the City of Toronto, as well as the other levels of government and the public agencies involved, now has a magnificent opportunity to create a Central Park worthy of the name, which could stretch from Front Street to the lake.

It would lie athwart the Railway Lands, as described earlier, and cross Bremner Boulevard, the Gardiner/Lakeshore Corridor, Queen's Quay West, and Harbourfront to the water's edge.

The northern 1.05 hectares (2.6 acres) of the park would consist of a landscaped deck over the rail corridor. The park would provide an attractive setting for the CN Tower, SkyDome, the renovated Roundhouse and the Convention Centre, an additional 7.3 hectares (18 acres); in the Harbourfront area, a further 2 hectares (5 acres) would be a green link to the water, either in the vicinity of York Quay Centre and Queen's Quay Terminal, or near Maple Leaf Quay.

An expansion of the Metro Toronto Convention Centre (MTCC), proposed by the provincial Crown corporation that runs the amenity, could be part of the park. Originally built with funds provided by the federal, provincial, and metropolitan governments during the 1980s, the convention centre has produced an operational profit every year since it was opened in 1985. The centre's board claims that the initial investment was recouped in two and-a-half years.

There is a wide array of conventions and meetings at the centre, which is an important source of business for Toronto's hospitality industry, attracting some two million visitors a year. But the MTCC has found that even with its 100,000 square metres (1.1 million square feet) of space, it cannot accommodate conventions, which keep growing in size, and loses business, including repeat business, that has outgrown MTCC's existing capacity.

The centre has therefore proposed to double in size by extending existing facilities southwards, under the Central Park. Planning feasibility studies have already shown

Proposed Convention Centre expansion

that this can be done attractively and both support and complement the City's objectives for the Central Park.

Furthermore, MTCC has indicated that, on the strength of its business record, it should be able to raise the bulk of the capital financing required for the project on its own account. It estimates that it would require less than one-third its construction costs in capital support from governments.

UNION STATION PRECINCT

In *Watershed*, the Commission expressed support for the Province's ongoing negotiations with Toronto Terminal Railways (TTR) to purchase Union Station and the adjacent rail corridor, and convert them for use as the central intermodal transportation facility for the Greater Toronto region, recognizing their strategic function and location. Although the negotiations have made progress, they were not complete as this was being written in December 1991. The Commission believes that it is critically important for the Province to own these assets.

HARBOURFRONT CORPORATION

The east-west railway tracks crossing the bottom of the busy City were only one of the barriers to public access and enjoyment of the waterfront. The realities of industrial, commercial, and port use of much of the land along the water's edge had brought gritty industries, wharves, and warehouses as well as the sprawling railway yards. More recently, the Gardiner Expressway and the imposing new structures of the Central Bayfront area threatened to form a concrete curtain along the waterfront, effectively blocking off the water even as they made access to the waterfront more difficult.

At a time when the federal government was concerned about the health of cities, and particularly about getting directly involved in maintaining and restoring their well-being, it decided during the election campaign of 1972 to acquire 40 hectares (100 acres) of land in the Toronto West Bayfront area as an urban park for the people of Toronto. The announcement drew comparisons between the potential of the site and the attractiveness of Vancouver's Stanley Park, Québec's Plains of Abraham, and London's Hyde Park — all parks in the traditional sense.

The lands acquired, subsequently known as the Harbourfront lands, were bounded by Lake Shore Boulevard to the north, York Street to the east, the harbour to the south, and Stadium Road to the west.

The federal action, taken without consultation, was adversely viewed by the Province and by local governments, thus setting the stage for conflict and requiring public consultations that delayed creation of a mutually agreed-on plan for several years. However, the importance of the site eventually brought the interested parties to the table and, in 1978, the federal government created Harbourfront Corporation to manage the task of developing the urban park.

It was clear that, if public access was to be restored, physical revitalization of the area would be necessary and that people would be drawn to the site only if activities attracted them. Harbourfront faced a twofold challenge: to redevelop the lands and to create programs and activities that would draw people to them. The dual mandates of real estate development and programming were initially viewed as complementary and even mutually dependent: development would pay for programming; programming would justify development.

In its early years, Harbourfront was a great success: increasing numbers of people were pulled to the site by imaginative and creative programs aimed at all age groups. Art shows, dance groups, craft demonstrations, poetry readings, and theatrical presentations vied for public attention. Costs were subsidized by the federal government, by real estate development, corporate sponsorships, and ticket sales. Harbourfront Corporation and its staff were justifiably proud of being able to offer quality programming at affordable prices.

Moreover, the early real estate developments were seen as being of high quality and very much in line with people's expectations. Renovations to the Queen's Quay Terminal and construction of the Admiral Hotel, Metro's marine police facility, and the King's Landing condominiums were perceived as good examples of urban design and renewal.

The need to satisfy increasing financial requirements for programming, as well as Harbourfront's wish to continue pursuing its goal of financial self-sufficiency, led it to a growing interest in the land development side of the business, ultimately manifested in high-rise buildings on the site.

But, as more buildings were developed, public concern grew, which, in 1987, led the City to impose a freeze on developments. Soon thereafter the federal government began a policy review of Harbourfront's role and mandate. Opposition to the high-rises at Harbourfront was exacerbated by high-rise developments on neighbouring waterfront sites between York and Yonge streets. Whether or not they were actually on Harbourfront lands, high-rises added to the growing sense that the public was being cut off from the lake and that the shoreline, rather than being used as a park for people, was becoming a housing tract.

A public review showed that people thought it was no longer appropriate for funding for Harbourfront's programming

Opposition to the high-rises at Harbourfront was exacerbated by high-rise developments on neighbouring waterfront sites. Whether or not on Harbourfront lands, high-rises added to the growing sense that the public was being cut off from the lake.

to come from the proceeds of real estate development. A number of deputants spoke to the issue at the public hearings in early 1989. In journalist June Callwood's words, making "programming. . .dependent upon putting up more ugly buildings seems to me to be a reprehensible way for it to have been planned".

With the Central Bayfront area east of Harbourfront becoming rapidly built up and major projects being planned for the Railway Lands, Harbourfront was no longer considered an isolated urban island. In its first interim report, the Commission concluded that the Government of Canada, having essentially accomplished what it set out to do in 1972, should implement the following three recommendations:

1. Harbourfront Corporation should be converted immediately to a new entity, Harbourfront Foundation, whose mandate will be to continue the provision of Harbourfront's wide variety of outstanding cultural, recreational, and educational programs, generally by:
    (a) programming its own activities;
    (b) providing facilities and support to other organizations who wish to use its amenities and expertise;
    (c) funding other organizations' programs which, in the opinion of the Board of Directors, are in the public interest and are compatible with a waterfront environment;
    (d) placing a stronger emphasis on marine and water-related programs and activities;
    (e) reflecting, maintaining, and preserving Toronto's waterfront and marine heritage; and

    (f) endowing the Foundation sufficiently to sustain the continuation of Harbourfront's programming activities.

2. The Harbourfront lands and properties should be planned with the City in accordance with the following principles:
    (a) A minimum of 16 hectares (40 acres) of land be made available immediately for parkland and be conveyed to the City, including a continuous waterfront promenade along the water's edge.
    (b) Provision of a community school site (acceptable to the appropriate school board) to serve the Harbourfront community and the surrounding area, for conveyance to the school board.
    (c) Provision of community facilities, including, but not necessarily limited to a community centre, medical clinic, library facilities, day-care and play space for children, and a place to worship.
    (d) The completion of Harbourfront Corporation's commitments with respect to assisted housing.
    (e) The allocation of sufficient lands and properties to support the Harbourfront Foundation's programming mandate, as defined in recommendation 1 above, and including additional program facilities, such as:
        (i) a nautical centre, with sufficient space to provide permanent accommodation for the sailing clubs and

Central Bayfront

schools currently operating out of makeshift facilities at Harbourfront; and

(ii) preservation of the Canada Malting silos, and consideration of their conversion to a civic museum.

(f) The further planning and development of the Harbourfront lands including links to adjacent areas such as Coronation Park, Molson's, Dylex, Loblaws, SkyDome, the Railway Lands, the financial district, and the Central and East Bayfront be included in the City's review of the Central Area Plan.

(g) No further building south of Queen's Quay West with the exception of low-rise buildings considered by the City to be in the public interest.

(h) An urban design plan be established as an integral part of Harbourfront's Official Plan amendments.

3. The federal government should work with the City, the Harbourfront Foundation, and other appropriate bodies to give effect to the changes arising from these recommendations. The lands, properties, and residual interests now managed by Harbourfront Corporation, and those still in the inventory of Public Works Canada should be held and administered by PWC on a temporary basis until appropriate agreements with the City are implemented.

The federal, provincial, and city governments moved quickly to respond to the recommendations. In November 1989 the Province declared a Provincial Interest

Learning to sail, Maple Leaf Quay

in the Toronto waterfront, citing excessive development and the need to preserve parkland for the public. In December 1989 the provincial Minister of Municipal Affairs advised Toronto's mayor not to implement an agreement the City and Harbourfront Corporation had made earlier that year to transfer parklands and buildings to the City. The minister then imposed a ministerial zoning order, prohibiting new construction on the Harbourfront site and asked the Premier's Special Advisor on the Waterfront, Duncan Allan, to review the agreement and bring forward a plan for Harbourfront that would serve the public interest, as recommended by the Royal Commission.

The report submitted by Mr. Allan in March 1990 to the Minister of Municipal Affairs recommended: creation of more parkland; unconditional funding of $28 million to the City for parkland improvements;

dissolution of Harbourfront Corporation, which would be replaced by the federal government with a new entity that had the sole task of providing public programs to be funded by an endowment; disposal of all federal assets in Harbourfront; and maintenance of the provincial zoning order until the public benefits were realized.

The City of Toronto signalled its broad support for the overall direction being taken and Harbourfront's board of directors voted unanimously to concentrate solely on programming. The federal government appointed Mr. W. Darcy McKeough to make recommendations on how the federal government should respond to the Province's views.

In November 1990 Mr. McKeough proposed a reorganization of Harbourfront that would split the Corporation's functions amongst three new entities: Harbourfront '90, a not-for-profit charitable company, which would carry on Harbourfront's cultural, recreational, and educational programs; a foundation that would manage the funds generated by disposing of Harbourfront Corporation or Crown non-program real estate assets still remaining and make annual payments of income to support the programming activities of Harbourfront '90; and the Harbourfront Disposition Company, which would dispose of Harbourfront Corporation or the Crown non-program real estate assets still remaining and turn the proceeds over to the foundation.

Mr. McKeough also recommended that parkland and funds for parkland improvements be given to the City of Toronto in the amounts and locations recommended by Mr. Allan's provincial review.

The McKeough recommendations were accepted by the federal government

School by the Water

Imagine yourself in grade four: you are on a boat, surrounded by your classmates, pulling up a vial of water from the bottom of Toronto Harbour so that you can assess the quality of its water. That type of learning experience is offered by School by the Water, a Harbourfront non-profit learning centre in York Quay Centre.

School by the Water has classes in urban studies and visual arts for students from kindergarten to college level. The urban studies program offers a hands-on opportunity to learn about the waterfront and the city's impact on it; through field trips and presentations, students are introduced to the history of the waterfront area and to its environmental, planning, and development issues. The material covered in a half- or full-day class at the school can form the basis for further regular classroom learning.

School by the Water has been active on the waterfront for 16 years and during that time, has offered many children a chance to explore Harbourfront, a vibrant part of Toronto where the city meets the lake. A small park area with trees and grass at the edge of York Quay has always been a favourite place to learn and play. Recently, however, the school was dismayed to discover that the trees were cut down for the expansion of the adjacent Molson stage. Fortunately, new trees will be planted and with time, will again provide a shady spot to relax and watch the lake.

In recent years, School by the Water has incorporated environmental issues into its curriculum. The visual arts program includes a sculpture-making workshop that utilizes "discarded" materials such as foam, plastics, and cardboard to help children in grades one to four absorb the value of recycling.

Lakewise, a program at School by the Water, was developed last year with the Harbourfront Marine Department; it focuses on Toronto's relationship with and dependence on Lake Ontario. Students visit the Toronto Islands and the Toronto Harbour, spending a day on the water where they can sample and observe the aquatic ecology of both. Aboard the passenger ship *Rosemary*, students investigate water quality, erosion, lakefilling, bird populations, and the effect of humans on them. The program was designed to foster appreciation of the natural environment and to help young people develop positive attitudes towards conserving natural resources.

School by the Water offers many city children a rare opportunity to experience the outdoors and learn about nature. By having contact with nature, and learning about the impact of the city on water quality, children learn about their role in maintaining a healthy environment. Moreover, children today may influence their parents, and later, when they are society's decision-makers, will perhaps bring with them a clearer understanding of how much is at stake.

and were being implemented by early 1991. Mr. McKeough agreed to manage disposition activities on behalf of the federal government, including negotiating with the City on lands that were no longer required by Harbourfront Corporation

Skating at Harbourfront

and were to be turned over to it; negotiating with developers on shifting proposed developments from the south side of Queen's Quay West to other locations; and disposing of remaining Harbourfront or Crown non-program real estate assets to raise funds for Harbourfront '90's endowment.

The Royal Commission's recommendation on planning and design issues was intended to reflect the fact that, no longer isolated, the Harbourfront lands should also be planned on an integrated basis with adjoining lands. Excellent design on the waterfront was also important. There was a need to deal with social issues in the area; and support for the City's parkland goals was worthwhile.

In 1991, having reached agreement with Mr. McKeough, the City of Toronto made formal application to the Ontario Municipal Board (OMB) for approval of a Zoning By-Law and Official Plan Amendment for the Harbourfront lands. Hearings began in November and were adjourned to February 1992.

Before the OMB can approve the application, Harbourfront Corporation and the developers must agree on relocating proposed developments from lands south of Queen's Quay West, and the City and Harbourfront Corporation must concur on the transfer of lands and money. If the OMB approves, and the Province lifts the zoning freeze, the Zoning By-Law and Official Plan Amendment will come into effect, facilitating full implementation of the Royal Commission's 1989 recommendations on the matter.

The second Royal Commission recommendation is also being addressed. The Official Plan and Zoning By-Law includes, for example: provision to designate more than 16 hectares (40 acres) of Harbourfront land as public park; permits a school on the east portion of Bathurst Quay, permanent community and day-care facilities on Bathurst Quay, the nautical centre to continue its activities on the Maple Leaf Quay and to relocate in part to John Street Quay; and replaces residential building site designations south of Queen's Quay West. In addition, the City has approved urban design criteria for building parcels in the Official Plan and Zoning By-Law and in specific Urban Design Guidelines.

The third and final Royal Commission recommendation on Harbourfront Corporation addressed implementation of the recommendations and transitional arrangements for management of the residual real estate interests. The approving of the Official Plan and Zoning By-Law Amendments and the lifting of the provincial zoning order on Harbourfront lands will allow disposition of the remaining Harbourfront and Crown non-program real property assets. As well as using proceeds from those sales to endow future programming, Harbourfront '90 will be free to seek out funding from such sources as the Canada Council or the private sector; pending establishment of Harbourfront '90's endowment, the federal government has agreed to make available to Harbourfront Corporation $8.8 million in each of three years, beginning in 1991.

Harbourfront '90 will be challenged to match future programming plans to available income; one way might be by seeking co-operation from other entities on the waterfront in joint endeavours that take advantage of Harbourfront '90's programming skills and experience.

Toronto Island Airport

The federal mandate given the Royal Commission specifically asked it to examine the future of the Toronto Island Airport (TIA) and related transportation services. Subsequent public hearings, held in early 1989, identified a number of issues including: access from the mainland, introduction of jet aircraft, noise, expansion of facilities and services, balancing general aviation and scheduled carrier use, as well

as management of the airport and subject lands. Ideas about the TIA's future ranged from phasing it out as quickly as possible to expanding it as much as possible. A detailed examination of these issues was needed before any recommendations could be made on the TIA's future.

In Publication No. 7, *The Future of the Toronto Island Airport: The Issues*, Royal Commission staff described the airport's origins and history, reviewed submissions to its January and February 1989 public hearings, and described some of the approaches it considered when reaching conclusions about the TIA. This was intended as the basis for further thought and discussion at the scheduled June 1989 public hearings; final recommendations were incorporated in the Commission's 1989 interim report.

A HISTORICAL OVERVIEW

The Toronto waterfront has been a factor in Canadian aviation since 1909, when the first amphibious aircraft landed at the Toronto harbour. By the 1920s, the Toronto waterfront was seriously being considered as a site for commercial aviation but it was 1937 before the City of Toronto approved construction of two municipal airports and, with the federal Department of Transport, agreed to locate a municipal airport on the Toronto Islands; the facility near the relatively distant village of Malton was merely a back-up in case of fog. (With its first terminal housed in a quonset hut, Malton expanded rapidly and, in 1983, was renamed Lester B. Pearson International Airport.) The City was responsible for half the construction costs of both projects and asked the Board of Toronto Harbour Commissioners (THC) to oversee construction and to operate the two airports.

In 1939, the City of Toronto leased its Malton operations to the federal Department of Transport but, at the Toronto Islands, the THC continued to act on its behalf as administrator and operator. During World War II, TIA became a Norwegian air base and, in the years following, as Malton grew, was used principally as a facility for training operators of light, private, and commercial aircraft.

In 1957, the City transferred ownership of Malton to the federal Department of Transport, in return for which the department promised to make major improvments to TIA's airport facilities; in 1961, the TIA site was extended east and west by lakefill and the promised facilities were built. The City agreed that the THC would act as principals in operating the Island Airport and, in July 1962, leased lands at TIA to the THC for 21 years.

TIA operations were generally unprofitable and, in 1974, the federal government agreed to the THC's request for a subsidy, subject to intergovernmental agreement on the airport's future. In March of that year the Joint Committee-TIA was convened, with representatives from the federal, provincial, Metro, and City governments, and from local community organizations.

The TIA Intergovernmental Staff Forum (ISF) was established in 1975 to provide technical assistance to the Joint Committee and to evaluate alternative uses for the airport; in turn, the ISF was directed by a Policy Steering Group, consisting of the federal and provincial ministers of transportation, the federal Minister of State for Urban Affairs, the Chairman of Metro Toronto, the Mayor of the City of Toronto, and the Chairman of the THC.

After examining a wide range of possible uses for the airport site, the ISF analysed three in detail: it could be used for general aviation only, general aviation and Dash 7 STOL service, or recreational use with or without housing.

In March 1977, when the ISF tabled its findings, the federal, provincial, and Metro governments favoured the general aviation/STOL option while the City wanted general aviation only. Further discussions did not resolve the disagreement.

Between February 1980 and March 1981, the Canadian Transport Commission (CTC), an independent body established to give the federal Minister of Transport advice on licensing commercial air services, held hearings on an application by Canavia Transit Inc., one of five carriers applying to operate STOL services between the Toronto Island, Montreal, and Ottawa. The City of Toronto intervened, on the grounds that changing Toronto Island Airport into the City's second commercial airport would run counter to municipal efforts to promote recreation and housing on the waterfront. Moreover, the City said, the costs of a STOL service would exceed any benefits it could provide.

The CTC concluded that the adequacy of air services in the Toronto/Montreal/Ottawa triangle should not prevent licenses for new carriers that would provide more convenient services to the travelling public and further justified the decision on the grounds of present and future public convenience and necessity.

Although the CTC was satisfied that a need existed for the service, it did not award a licence, both because of the City's opposition to the STOL and to construction of the necessary STOL infrastructure, and because

Transport Canada had not committed itself to upgrading the TIA or providing such infrastructure.

The airport's future remained uncertain until February 1981, when Toronto's City Council recommended that it accept advice given by the mayor: reach an agreement with the federal government and the THC to develop the airport for general aviation and limited commercial STOL service, provided the City's waterfront objectives can be protected.

In June 1981, a Memorandum of Understanding (MOU) was signed by the federal Department of Transport, the City of Toronto, and the THC, setting out conditions under which limited STOL passenger service could be established at the TIA. Two years later a 50-year Tripartite Agreement, which superseded the MOU, was signed by the City, the THC, and the Department of Transport, providing for continued use of City land at TIA for a public airport for general aviation and limited commercial STOL service. Under the agreement, jet-powered flights are permitted only for medical evacuations, emergencies, and during the Canadian National Exhibition Air Show. The agreement was amended in July 1985 to permit operation of the de Havilland Dash 8 aircraft at TIA.

The Toronto airport system comprises Pearson International, Toronto Island, Buttonville, and Downsview airports. (Existing airports in Hamilton, Oshawa, and Barrie were not included in the Royal Commission's analysis.) Of the two Toronto facilities serving a significant number of passengers — Pearson and Toronto Island — the latter represents about three per cent of total Toronto traffic and about five per cent of total domestic traffic. From 1977 to 1988, total movements at Pearson ranged from approximately 200,000 to 350,000, while they ranged from approximately 150,000 to 200,000 at TIA. More than half those at TIA were local, while the majority at Pearson were itinerant (i.e., travelling from one city to another).

The TIA is a regional facility: one, according to Transport Canada's definition, that supports a CTC class 1 single-plane service to a national or international airport, as well as direct non-stop scheduled or charter services to at least three other airports.

The majority of scheduled aircraft operating at TIA are turboprops. Because of closer proximity to downtown Toronto's business district, turboprops there can compete over longer distances with the generally faster turbojets operating from Pearson.

Because of the Western Channel, surface access to the airport has always been by passenger and vehicle ferries; improving surface access to Toronto Island Airport is a time-honoured subject of formal and informal studies. However, none of the many recommendations has ever actually been implemented, because the unanimity required by all parties is lacking.

The 1983 Tripartite Agreement forbids a fixed-link access in the form of a vehicular tunnel, bridge or causeway. It should also be noted that the Province, in keeping with its policy of providing surface access to airports, defrays the operating losses of the airport ferry. Commercial parking space for approximately 125 vehicles is provided on the mainland by the THC.

OWNERSHIP AND CONTROL

Ownership of the 87-hectare (215-acre) TIA site and its facilities is quite complex.

Toronto Island Airport

The jurisdiction in the original Crown grants and conditions changed over time, as the result of site expansion by lakefill in 1938 and 1962, changes that occurred when Metro came into existence, and the granting of leases.

The THC owns the largest portion of TIA lands: 65 hectares (162 acres) of land and 68 hectares (168 acres) of water. The City of Toronto owns a total of 19 hectares (48 acres) of land and 6.5 hectares (16 acres) of water. The federal government owns two small land parcels with a total area of two hectares (five acres). Parkland and waterlots south and east of the airport are owned by Metropolitan Toronto while unfilled lots west of the area are owned by the City and THC and are controlled by the Province.

In 1957, the City relinquished Malton Airport to the federal government in exchange for major improvements to TIA; it agreed that the THC would operate the TIA as principals and, in July 1962, leased all lands located at the airport to the THC for 21 years. On expiry of this lease, the Tripartite Agreement came into effect.

In 1974, the THC realized that airport revenues did not cover the combined operating costs of the airport and the airport ferry and asked the federal and provincial governments for subsidies as an alternative to closing the airport. Ottawa agreed to assume the TIA's operating losses until its future could be decided and the Province agreed to defray the operational costs of the ferry.

Under the 1983 Tripartite Agreement, the federal government is to consider requests to offset any deficits incurred by the THC in operating the airport during the term of the lease. If the City or the THC, because of a lack of funds, advises the minister it no longer wishes to be financially responsible for operating the airport, Ottawa has 90 days to indicate whether Transport Canada will take over operations. If the minister declines, the airport must be closed and lands currently owned by the federal government revert to the City; the City also retains the option to purchase the THC lands.

THE ISSUES

Since the 1970s, environmental issues have figured prominently in intergovernmental discussions on the airport, including many meetings about noise, urban design, and the City's concern that the airport might have an adverse effect on other waterfront uses, such as recreation and housing.

Noise is still the primary public concern, while there is little public comment about such consequences of the airport's presence as soil and water contamination from aircraft fuel, cars, and buses; lakefill; chemical pollutants; and run-off.

Several mathematical models have been developed to express, in a single index, the combined effect of the variables that influence human response to noise. One model, the Noise Exposure Forecast (NEF), has been adopted in Canada for controlling land use in the vicinity of airports. NEF values do not indicate actual noise levels but are a measure of the probable psychological response of an affected community to the actual noise generated by aircraft movements at a given location near an airport.

Official NEF contours are prepared by Transport Canada and published by the Canada Mortgage and Housing Corporation

as a guide for land-use planners. There is no statutory requirement for compliance with these standards, and no airport is legally required to operate in the manner assumed for purposes of preparing the noise forecasts. The significant NEF value for the TIA is 28, as stated in the Tripartite Agreement, which defines the maximum level of noise-related activity permitted as being tolerable to residents. According to the official 1990 NEF contour map, there are no residents living within the 28 NEF Contour. (See also the section on the Lower Don Lands.)

During its public hearings, the Royal Commission listened to different views on the TIA's dual role as the location for general aviation and limited STOL service: whether it should be maintained as is or give priority to one type of use over any other; whether the ferry is a bottleneck or a safety valve — which seems to depend on whether people think the airport should remain at its present size or be expanded — whether there should be a fixed link, for vehicles, pedestrians, or both; and whether TIA needs to be managed by a body other than the Toronto Harbour Commissioners.

The Royal Commission found no overwhelming public demand for any change in the airport's current role

The Royal Commission found no overwhelming public demand for any change in the airport's current role and made the following recommendations in its 1989 interim report:

- The Toronto Island Airport should continue its dual role serving general aviation and air commuter operations within the Tripartite Agreement.

- The City of Toronto, in consultation with Transport Canada, should consider whether to keep or replace the Toronto Harbour Commissioners as its agent in the management and operations of the Airport.
- Irrespective of the response to the previous recommendation, the City and Transport Canada should require improvements in the management of the Airport, including a new financial and accounting base and improved public and user consultation processes.
- A new plan should be prepared to reflect the role of the Airport as contemplated by the Royal Commission, ensuring that it remains at its existing scale within the waterfront environment, is cleaner and quieter, and is sensitive to the needs of its users.

In response to the recommendations, both the City of Toronto and a provincial-municipal committee commissioned studies to examine these and other related airport issues. Results are now being reviewed.

TORONTO ISLANDS

The Toronto Island Airport sits on the westernmost portion of Hanlan's Point, itself the westernmost of the Toronto Islands. Only two kilometres (1.2 miles) from the hustle and bustle of the city's financial core, the 14 islands, with their sheltered lagoons, ever-changing sand dunes, and stands of cottonwoods remain a unique sanctuary for city dwellers — in the words of M. J. Lennon (1980), author of *Memories of Toronto Island*: "10 minutes and 1,000 miles away".

When Governor Simcoe arrived in 1793 to carve the City of York out of the dense forest that lined Lake Ontario's shore,

The Toronto skyline still in sight, the islands offer a refreshing change of pace and scene

the islands were part of a 5.5-kilometre (3.5-mile) long peninsula that curved from the mouth of the Don River south and westward into the lake, where it formed a sheltered harbour. The peninsula was known to the natives as having curative powers; to Elizabeth Simcoe, these were her "favourite sands", to which she would retreat for healthy recreation — picnicking, painting or horseback riding.

Since the Simcoes' time the islands have continued to play a vital role in the recreational life of Torontonians. In the early 1800s, adventurous hunters and fishers used the peninsula to fish, trap muskrats, and shoot waterfowl. By 1833, Michael O'Connor had opened the first hotel — the Retreat; one of the hotel's selling points was its access by the first ferry — the horse-powered *Sir John of the Peninsula* — which eliminated the need for the arduous trek across the untamed mouth of the Don River. By the 1840s, fishermen's huts were scattered over the peninsula, and shortly thereafter, the first hardy homesteaders set up permanent camp.

Some ten years after the peninsula was severed from the mainland by a violent storm in 1858 to become "the Island", the City began to promote development there. The first summer house was built in 1872 by a prominent barrister, and thereafter many of Toronto's most distinguished citizens erected elaborate summer homes on Hanlan's Point and Centre Island.

Near the cottages at Hanlan's there was an amusement park; in the summer tens of thousands flocked daily to ride its roller-coaster, see the famous diving horse, watch baseball or lacrosse in the stadium or stroll along the boardwalk. The islands and the harbour provided endless opportunities for diversion — in the summer there was swimming, canoeing, rowing, fishing, and sailing, and in the winter, sledding, skating, and ice-boating.

The summer population of the islands expanded in the early 1890s when a tent community was erected at Ward's Island; by 1931, the City had allowed the tents to be supplanted by permanent dwellings. Thereafter, the number of year-round residents gradually grew, especially during the housing crisis following World War II, when additional dwellings were built on Algonquin Island.

In the 1950s, the islands had a "main street" on Centre Island, where there were hotels, a dairy, a barber shop, a hardware store, and a movie house. The three communities — Hanlan's, Centre, and Ward's — had community centres, sports teams, newspapers, and social functions. People lived on the islands year-round, sending their children to the Island School, commuting to the city by ferry in summer, tugboat in winter. There were people who lived on the islands, the man who delivered ice among them, who proudly claimed they hadn't been to the city more than a half-dozen times in their lives.

Just as the Toronto Islands have always been buffeted by the natural forces of wind and water that both shape and threaten them, they have been buffeted by human forces. For 150 years plans have been developed for the islands by successive city councils, harbour commissioners, and others. In the 20th century, most such plans envisaged dramatic changes in land use: apartment buildings linked to the city by tunnel and surrounded by parking lots, expressways running the length of the islands, or docks and warehouses for port activities.

In 1953, the newly created Metro Council developed the idea of turning the islands into a park and recreation area. Despite the vociferous arguments of island dwellers, by 1965 Metro had completed eviction procedures, compensated residents, and bulldozed 500 homes. The residents of the remaining 260 houses on Ward's and Algonquin islands decided to dig in and started a long and bitter fight to stay. Arguing that residential and recreational uses were not incompatible, the islanders fought eviction in the courts of law and public opinion.

In order to resolve the dispute, on 9 December 1981 the Province of Ontario introduced Bill 191, which was designed to allow the island community to remain until 2005. Ultimately, however, the Bill proved to be unworkable because it did not resolve such fundamental questions as ownership of the houses. In the fall of 1991, the Province gave notice that it would bring in new legislation for the islands, and that the legislation would create a Land Trust to act as landlord, and would permit as many as 110 new homes on the islands. Such legislation could help resolve the situation and provide much-needed security for the existing community.

Today's Toronto Islands are a rich, regional resource with lovely dunes and beaches, regionally rare plant forms, and varied fish communities.

Today's Toronto Islands are a rich, if somewhat under-used, regional resource. Their environmental resources include lovely dunes and beaches, regionally rare plant forms, and varied fish communities. The visitor can find clipped grass for picnicking and ball-playing, quiet lagoons in

Houses on Ward Island

which to watch turtles basking and night herons fishing, as well as opportunities for walking and bird-watching. There are active recreational facilities at Centreville, at the Long Pond rowing course on regatta days, and at the public marina and three yacht clubs.

Seven hundred people live in a vibrant, close-knit, car-free community on Ward's and Algonquin, and provide "eyes on the park". A water filtration plant services the city in the summer when water use is greatest. The live-in Island Natural Science School offers opportunities for Toronto students to spend an intensive week in natural science study. The Gibraltar Point lighthouse, built in 1808 on earlier orders from Governor Simcoe, stands as a historical link to the founding of the city, a reminder of the days when ship travel provided vital links between Toronto and the outside world. The lighthouse looks out over the island park to which Metro is trying to attract more visitors, a residential community poised for growth, and towards the evolving and changing waterfront of the City beyond.

LOWER DON LANDS

The Lower Don Lands are another sizeable part of Toronto's Central Waterfront that is clearly in transition. While usually thought of first in relation to shipping, heavy industry, bulk storage, and transportation, the Lower Don Lands have another side — a swath of green hugging the north shore of the Outer Harbour along Cherry Beach, to link up with the urban wilderness of the Leslie Street Spit.

Two hundred years ago, the Lower Don Lands could have been considered an

ecological unit: they comprised the lower reaches of the meandering Don River, the estuary at its mouth, and the peninsula to the south. The banks of the Lower Don were lined with water-loving trees and shrubs and surrounded by a forest of mixed deciduous and coniferous trees. The forest helped recharging of groundwater, controlled the rate of flow into the Don, prevented erosion of the banks, kept feeder streams cool, and helped to maintain a diverse fish community.

The river was the source of drinking water for mammals in the area, as well as providing spawning and feeding habitats for fish and other forms of aquatic life. The estuary at the mouth of the Don, known for many years as Ashbridge's Bay Marsh, was an ever-changing landscape of marshy vegetation, islands, and open water; it provided habitats for mammals, birds, fish, amphibians, and reptiles. The waters of the marsh were protected from those of the open lake by the peninsula, a natural sand bar that was breached during a fierce storm in 1858 to create today's Eastern Gap and the Toronto Islands. With the advent of European settlement, the organic unity of the Lower Don Lands was gradually eroded; today, having lost sight of the whole, we tend to think of the lands in terms of their separate pieces, as defined by roads, rail lines, and concrete dock walls.

There are six main components: the Lower Don, Ataratiri, the East Bayfront, the Port Industrial Area, the semi-natural areas of the Leslie Street Spit and the Outer Harbour's north shore, and the parklands of Ashbridge's Bay. While the future of the Lower Don Lands is unclear, there is no doubt that the area is on the verge of dramatic change. This section presents one vision of what that change could encompass.

Map 10.10 Lower Don Lands

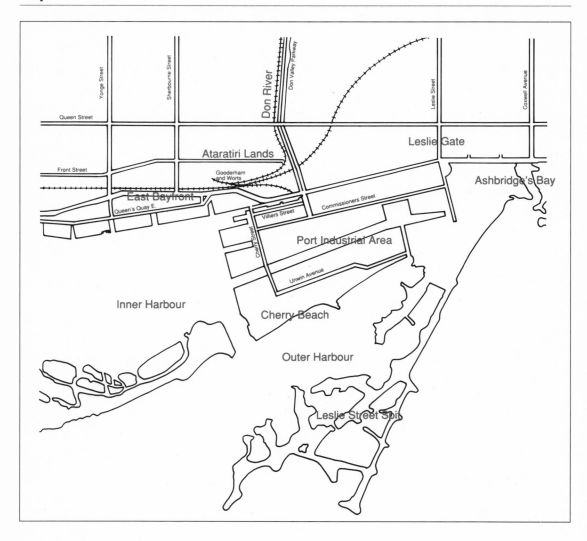

The boundary of the Lower Don River Valley is generally considered to be just north of the Bloor Viaduct. A great deal of the valley is used for utilitarian purposes — an expressway, two railways, an arterial road, utility right-of-ways, snow dumps, a few remaining heavy industries, transformer stations, and storage yards. Chain-link fences line the shores of the river, and log booms at its mouth contain the flotsam that surges down the river during rainstorms. Water and sediment quality in the river is poor,

as is wildlife habitat. Access to the shores is limited and uninviting, and only a few hardy souls walk or cycle along it.

Ataratiri is the name given to lands bounded, roughly, by Eastern Avenue on the north, the Don River on the east, the CN railway lines on the south, and Parliament Street on the west. At present, the area is occupied by a number of industrial users including railway yards, warehouses, factories, and scrap yards. In July 1988, the City of Toronto entered into an agreement with the Province of Ontario to develop 7,000 units of housing in the area, the City acting as planner and developer, and the Province as guarantor of funds necessary to acquire and develop the site.

The City now owns the entire 32.5-hectare (80-acre) site, having expropriated more than 40 private properties and having purchased the remaining third of the site from CP Rail and Canadian National Realty. Over the past three and-a-half years, the City has concentrated on the necessary planning needed to develop the land and design the future community. A great deal of time and money has been spent on assessing environmental conditions in the area and proposing solutions for the significant problems encountered there.

The East Bayfront is the area between the harbour and the Gardiner/Lakeshore Corridor between Yonge Street and Cherry Street. It is best characterized as a transportation corridor — a route to somewhere else, and currently not truly a "place". The East Bayfront is dominated by the Gardiner Expressway and Lake Shore Boulevard, which visually and practically cut off the areas to the north from the harbour.

Although the East Bayfront has been home to important port-related industry since it was created by lakefill in the 1950s, it has been declining for the last 30 years. Most marine terminals and wharfs are gone and the only remaining industrial uses are Redpath Sugar, and Lake Ontario Cement, together with the LCBO's storage and distribution facilities.

The Port Industrial Area lies south of the Gardiner/Lakeshore Corridor between Cherry and Leslie streets; it was built on lakefill placed in the former Ashbridge's Bay Marsh at the foot of the Don River, in accordance with the Toronto Harbour Commissioners' 1912 plan. The area was intended as Toronto's industrial heart — its link by ship, rail, and road to the outside world. That expectation was never fulfilled, however, when World War I and then the Depression intervened. Instead of being a manufacturing centre, the area came to be used mainly for bulk storage of coal, cement, and petroleum products. In recent years, many of the noisier, dirtier industries have left the area and it is ripe for change.

At the southern edge of the Port Industrial Area lies a thin strip of green, the semi-natural areas of the harbour's north shore; the western end is anchored by Cherry Beach, one of Toronto's cleanest beaches, which attracts bathers and boardsailers. Farther east, rowing and boating clubs hug the north shore and north of them is a vegetated strip of land through which the Martin Goodman Trail weaves. This area provides good-quality and varied habitat for wildlife, and attracts naturalists, cyclists, joggers, and walkers. Further east is the Leslie Spit, which was created by lakefilling. Left largely alone, the spit has evolved from a barren expanse of fill to become a rich and unique series of semi-natural habitats. A marina built by the THC to provide facilities for recreational boating protrudes into the Outer Harbour from the spit.

> *Left largely alone, the spit has evolved from a barren expanse of fill to become a rich and unique series of semi-natural habitats.*

VICTORY SOYA MILLS

In 1943, industrialist E. P. Taylor was looking for a site on which to build a new soybean processing plant to alleviate the wartime shortage of fats and oils caused by food and petroleum rationing. He had been named president of Victory Mills Ltd., a new company created from the Sunsoy Products branch of Canadian Breweries Ltd. Victory Mills soon leased a site at the southeast corner of Fleet and Parliament streets, ideally placed to receive and send shipments by rail, truck or boat. The plant built there was designed to extract and process soybean, linseed, and other vegetable oils to create products for human and animal consumption, as well as other products that would be processed further by other industries to make such goods as glue, paint, printing ink, and soap.

Despite wartime and post-war shortages of materials, construction of the new plant began almost immediately on the land, owned by the Board of Toronto Harbour Commissioners. Concrete silos were built first so that stockpiled soybeans could be available for processing as soon as the screw-press and solvent-extraction processes were ready to go into production. These silos have presided over the eastern edge of Toronto's harbour ever since.

The plant officially opened on 27 March 1946, and in 1947, Victory Mills purchased the site, as well as an adjoining parcel, from the THC. Over the years, the plant changed ownership twice: in 1954, Victory Mills was sold to Procter and Gamble Co. and renamed Victory Soya Mills, and in 1980 the company was resold to Central Soya Inc. of Fort Wayne, Indiana.

The importance of this processing plant should not be underestimated: the fact that it had been built, combined with a concerted campaign to encourage farmers to grow soybeans, precipitated immediate growth in the soybean market. In 1940, Canada produced 6,000 tonnes (220,000 bushels) of soybeans; by 1953, that figure had risen to 120,000 tonnes (4.4 million bushels). Demand for soy products changed little during the 1950s and '60s, then surged again during the 1970s, when people became aware that the consumption of vegetable fats was healthier than that of animal fats. In 1990, 25,000 soybean growers in Ontario produced 1.3 million tonnes (47 million bushels) of soybeans.

At the time it was closed in March 1991, Victory Soya Mills Ltd. was handling 400,000 to 540,000 tonnes (15 to 20 million bushels) of soybeans annually. The largest of three crushers in Canada, it processed soybeans into oil for margarine, cooking oil, and protein supplements for livestock feed.

Central Soya Inc. ceased plant operations, citing poor profits because of the Canada-United States free-trade agreement, government subsidies to a competing product (canola seed), and high municipal taxes.

Other conditions had also changed since E. P. Taylor carefully chose the plant's location: proximity to railroad and waterborne facilities is no longer advantageous in an era when road transportation dominates the movement of goods. Moreover, the Toronto waterfront was so developed that the plant was plagued with traffic problems.

To date, the site has not been sold. It is not hard to imagine what will happen when it is: now on the edge of the city core, the site will be redeveloped. The question is whether a way can be found to build for the future without razing our industrial past.

Sources: Stinson, J. and M. Moir. 1991. Built heritage of the East Bayfront. Environmental audit of the East Bayfront/ Port Industrial Area phase II, technical paper no. 7. Toronto: Royal Commission on the Future of the Toronto Waterfront. Draft.

Victory Soya Mills

East of Leslie Street is the Main Sewage Treatment Plant, a major employer in the area, and currently the subject of upgrading and expansion plans. The remainder of the Lower Don Lands — the lakefill parklands known as Woodbine Park and Ashbridge's Bay Park — are separated from the rest by Coatsworth Cut and the sewage treatment plant and are also disconnected from the residential neighbourhoods to the north. However, these parks, which include a marina as well as attractive landscaped areas in which to play, relax or picnic, are well linked to the Beach farther east by a boardwalk and greenspace.

Most of the Lower Don Lands are in limbo, with many former activities gone or in decline, and many recent studies and plans, in varying stages of completion, directed towards revitalizing this strategically placed area of the City.

In September 1991, in keeping with its plans to develop housing in Ataratiri, the City released its assessment of the environmental conditions in the area, along with a Part II Official Plan Proposal. The City has also addressed the Lower Don Lands in its

Cityplan '91 process and in the Gardiner Expressway East/Don Valley Sweep Civic Design Study (1990). The City of Toronto's Task Force to Bring Back the Don released its vision for the Lower Don Valley in August 1991.

Metro has made several studies of transportation in the Lower Don Lands (among them the Waterfront Transit Light Rail Extensions Feasibility Study (1990), and the Long Range Rapid Transit Network Study, which is a background study for Metro's new Official Plan); in addition, there is the *Revised Report on Metropolitan Interests in the Port Area*, development of a new Metropolitan Waterfront Plan, proposals to convert the Commissioners Street incinerator to an expanded recycling and transfer station, and Metro's environmental assessment for the Main Sewage Treatment Plant, in conjunction with a comprehensive report on the metropolitan sewage system.

The private sector is also active in planning for parts of the Lower Don Lands. For example, studies and proposals have been made for the Gooderham and Worts site, adjacent to Ataratiri; LeslieGate at the northeast corner of Lake Shore Boulevard and Leslie Street; expansion of the Lever Brothers property at the foot of the Don Valley Parkway; and several large sections of the Port Industrial Area, including St. Lawrence Park in its northwest corner, and Castlepoint at Polson Quay.

The THC prepared its Port Industrial Area Concept Plan in 1988 to foster economic development of this area, improve public access, and ensure the Port's future. A joint study of the economic impact of the Port of Toronto on the City of Toronto and surrounding jurisdictions was recently conducted by the Province, Metro, the City of Toronto, and the THC.

The roles of the THC and the Port of Toronto have also been studied extensively by the Royal Commission. Early in its mandate, the Commission realized it was time to formulate a new vision of the East Bayfront/Port Industrial Area. Because of concerns about pollution in the area, in its first interim report, the Commission recommended that an environmental audit be carried out on the lands. To protect the integrity of the Commission's study, on 17 October 1989 the Government of Ontario designated the area as one of Provincial Interest under the Planning Act. The process used to undertake the environmental audit was the Commission's first attempt to put the ecosystem approach into practice; the result was a persuasive example of how effectively this approach can be applied to research, analysis, and interpretation of information.

THE ENVIRONMENTAL AUDIT PROCESS

The environmental audit of the East Bayfront/Port Industrial Area was conducted from November 1989 to December 1991. Its purpose was to develop the best possible description and understanding of the environmental conditions in the East Bayfront/Port Industrial Area (within the inevitable limits of time and budget). It should be emphasized that this environmental audit was done before any decisions were made about future land uses — itself a radical departure from the norm.

Most land-use planning starts with a piece of land. In time, a developer comes along with an idea for a project — a condominium, an office tower, a mall — to put on that piece of land and if the environment is considered, it is through an environmental assessment of the project. The proponent considers what impact the project will have on the environment, and how that impact can be reduced or mitigated. One of the drawbacks of that way of planning is that it can lead to inappropriate uses of land.

By contrast, the environmental audit's first priority was to collect information on environmental conditions so that better decisions could be made later. In fact, the environmental audit team was not involved in decision-making about the future of the East Bayfront/Port Industrial Area: with the environmental information before them, however, others would be able to make fully informed decisions about land use.

A second fundamental difference in the Commission's environmental audit was its use of the "ecosystem approach" as a framework for research, analysis, and interpretation of information. As discussed earlier, the ecosystem approach focuses on relationships and examines how an area influences, and is influenced by, areas outside it. It also examines the effect of human actions on the ecosystem and, conversely, the possible effects of ecological conditions on human health. The ecosystem approach allowed the Commission to move beyond the compartmentalizing of traditional environmental management: instead of examining the state of the environment, the audit examined the state of the ecosystem.

In order to measure ecosystem health in the East Bayfront/Port Industrial Area,

The ecosystem approach allowed the Commission to move beyond the compartmentalizing of traditional environmental management: instead of examining the state of the environment, the audit examined the state of the ecosystem.

the team had to develop criteria, appropriate for the area, and for which information was available. Criteria and indicators used elsewhere were reviewed, including those in the Great Lakes Water Quality Agreement, the healthy cities concept, the Ecosystem Charter developed by the Rawson Academy, the Metro Toronto Remedial Action Plan goals, and the principles set out in *Watershed.*

Because humans are recognized as an integral part of the ecosystem, some criteria selected by the team were human-centred (anthropocentric) as well as biocentric. The criteria used included:

- habitat diversity, quantity, connectedness, and quality for wildlife;
- diversity and abundance of wildlife species;
- complexity of the food web;
- the presence of introduced species;
- adequate reserve of nutrients;
- levels of toxic chemicals in the ecosystem;
- effects of toxic chemicals on humans and wildlife;
- levels of dust, odours, and noise;
- variety, quality, and accessibility of opportunities for human activities;
- safety from environmental hazards;
- connectedness with the past; and
- aesthetics (urban form, perception of environment, natural features).

The way the audit was conducted was a third departure from the norm: in Phase I,

Figure 10.2   Ecosystem pathways

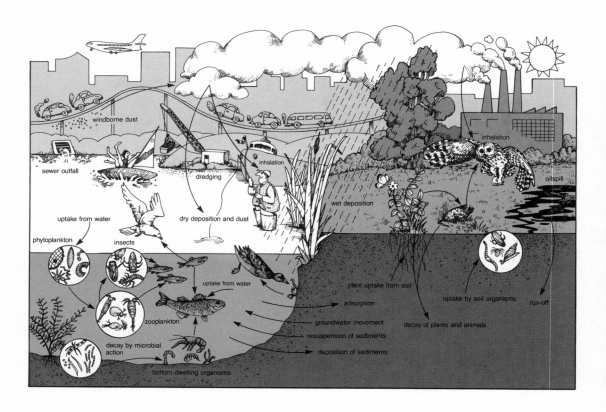

five work groups of experts collected existing information (and produced technical papers) on the atmospheric environment, water, soils and groundwater, natural heritage, and built heritage. During Phase II, working under the overall direction of a steering committee, seven work groups undertook further research to fill many previously identified gaps in data; they produced technical papers on the atmospheric environment, built heritage, hazardous materials, natural heritage, soils and groundwater, water and sediments, and ecosystem health.

In carrying out the audit, the Royal Commission was able to draw upon a wealth of talent and expertise. 93 people were involved in the steering committee and working groups: 53 public servants from four levels of government and agencies; 18 citizens from non-governmental organizations; seven from universities; three representing industry and labour; and 12 consultants from different fields. The work groups included staff from the federal and provincial governments, Metropolitan Toronto, and the City of Toronto. Also represented were the Toronto Harbour Commissioners, the Toronto Historical Board, the South East Toronto Industrial Awareness Organization (SETIAO), the Metropolitan Toronto and Region Conservation Authority, a number of community and environmental organizations, and ambulance, fire, and police services.

Significant effort went into attempts to integrate the results of the various working groups. Periodic meetings allowed members from different disciplines to interact and share information. Linking up these work groups were two "integrators", to ensure that work group members from each discipline recognized how its findings related to the concerns of others. For example, the integrators might ask members of the air group how air quality is affected by soil, industry, and transportation, or how it affects soil, water, wildlife or humans. The integrators later synthesized and interpreted all the information collected by the various disciplines, and the results were published in two reports, *Environment in Transition* (1990), which covered Phase I of the audit, and the audit's final report, *Pathways* (1991).

CHALLENGES AND OPPORTUNITIES IN THE LOWER DON LANDS

Many of the characteristics connecting different parts of the Lower Don Lands to each other can be considered both challenges and opportunities. The areas:

- share an interesting history;
- are generally underused;
- lie predominantly in the floodplain of the Don;
- have similar environmental problems;
- have poor links to the rest of the City; and
- for the most part, are owned publicly.

Over the last two centuries, human activities have dramatically shaped the physical environment of the Lower Don Lands. Where one now finds recycling plants or cranes, there was once a fertile marsh at the mouth of the Don River. Two hundred years ago natives fished with spears by lantern light in the Ashbridge's Marsh. European settlers caught fish, muskrats and turtles there, and market gunners shot fowl for the citizens of York. Simple frame cottages hugged the Lake Ontario shore.

The industrialization of the Lower Don Lands began in 1831, when James Worts came from England and established a grist mill at the eastern end of the harbour; the following year, Worts's brother-in-law William Gooderham arrived in York. The two went into business together and, in 1837, converted their flour mill to a distillery. As Gooderham and Worts, it operated until 1990, and left behind a cluster of industrial buildings of great historical and architectural value — one of the most important historic sites in Toronto.

By the 1880s, Ashbridge's Marsh was polluted from untreated human, animal, and industrial wastes, and its condition was becoming a civic concern. In response to the problems in the marsh and ongoing navigational problems in the harbour, the newly formed Toronto Harbour Commissioners (THC) drew up a plan to reclaim the northeast corner of the harbour and the marsh. The plan, unveiled in 1912, featured state-of-the-art docks, broad tree-lined avenues, and modern factories linked to the outside world by ship, rail, and road. The Port Industrial Area was to be Toronto's industrial centre, on land created from sand dredged from the bottom of the lake by the *Cyclone*, a massive dredge in what was considered one of the great engineering feats of its time.

The meandering Lower Don River was straightened and confined to a concrete channel, with a new mouth, an abrupt right-angle turn into the Keating Channel and

ASHBRIDGE'S BAY

Ashbridge's Bay, once one of North America's most important wetlands, was named after a family who came from Pennsylvania to the Town of York in 1793 and settled on the east bank of the Don River near the outflow into the bay. Today all that remains of the once-vibrant marshlands are the memories set down by hunters and naturalists who used the 520-hectare (1,285-acre) marsh.

When the Ashbridge family received its grant of land, the bay was a patchwork of large and small ponds with weedy lagoons, bogs and islands of bulrushes, water-lilies, arrowhead, marsh marigolds, cane grass, and duck weed. The Don River meandered through the delta marsh it had helped create. Shallow warm water, nutrients from the Don, and lush vegetation created ideal habitat for hundreds of species of wildlife. Early settlers "saw ducks so thick that when rising from the marsh they made a noise like thunder" (Barnett 1971).

The bounty of the marsh provided the small settlement of York with wild game. Less than a century later, with the invention of the breach-loading shotgun, hunters were able to slaughter wildfowl by the hundreds. Frank Smith, a member of the Toronto Ornithological Club from 1942 until his death in 1965, recalled how Bill Loam, a market shooter who made his living hunting and fishing in the marsh, would "come into his boathouse at night with the boat so full [of ducks] that there wasn't room for one more" (Fairfield 1991).

Frank Smith himself hunted in the marsh and said:

I have seen thousands of Muskrat houses built in it at one time and am safe to say that as many as ten to twelve thousand rats would be taken in one spring. . . . It was a problem catching Mud Turtles. The best way was undressing and taking a sack, walk in the water up to your armpits and when you stepped on a turtle you would duck under, get him and put him in the sack [sic]. I have taken as many as seventy-five to a hundred in one day in this way and sold them in the market for turtle soup (Fairfield 1991).

In the 1850s, storms broke through the sandy peninsula that separated the marsh from the lake, creating the Toronto Islands. Subsequent erosion problems induced the City in 1890 to build a breakwater on the western edge of the marsh, closing water circulation between marsh and harbour.

Sealed off from the lake, and the recipient of large quantities of industrial, human, and animal wastes, particularly from Gooderham and Worts's cattle byres, the bay became stagnant and polluted. Coatsworth Cut was opened at the east end of the marsh to improve circulation but a more permanent solution was proposed: fill the marsh to create lakefront industrial land.

In 1912, the City accepted plans by the Toronto Harbour Commissioners, and by 1930 garbage, building rubble, and sediment dredged from the harbour covered most of the marsh. The remainder was filled in the 1950s to make way for the Main Sewage Treatment Plant. Ashbridge's Bay, once home to a complex and rich wildlife community, has been replaced by salt and coal storage, oil tanks, industrial buildings, and vacant lots.

Inner Harbour. The river delta was replaced by new industrial lands, with docks, a ship channel, and a turning basin, as well as road and rail connections to the rest of the City.

Creation of the East Bayfront started much later, in the 1950s, after complicated negotiations among the Harbour Commissioners, the City, and the railways. The new land was used for docks, wharfs, and shipping-related industries, such as Redpath Sugar.

The physical restructuring of the Lower Don Lands continues today. Additions are still being made to the Leslie Street Spit, the four-kilometre (2.5-mile) long peninsula created from lakefill and begun in the early 1960s as a protective breakwater for an Outer Harbour. It soon became clear that Toronto had no need of a second harbour, and the spit has developed through natural succession into a rich wilderness area. The most recent land creation project in the Lower Don Lands is the Outer Harbour Marina, begun in 1986, to provide mooring slips for recreational boats, and a marina centre at the base of the breakwater.

Ashbridge's Bay with Toronto in the background

Though the splendour of the THC 1912 plan has faded, a rich industrial heritage remains: the plan's "armature" — the docks, bascule bridges, Ship Channel, bridges, railways, and roads — still forms a strong pattern on the land. Large structures such as silos, cranes, chimney stacks, and fuel storage tanks are dominant landmarks evoking past and some present industrial activities. The Gooderham and Worts buildings, the Palace Street School at the corner of Front and Cherry streets, and the former Bank of Montreal on Cherry Street are unique and worth preserving for their architectural merit. The industrial heritage manifested in the area's infrastructure and built form — in the grand scale of Commissioners Street, the pattern made by docks and seawalls, the cranes and tanks — should be treated with respect and, where possible, be used as the basis for future development.

The location of the Lower Don Lands is still strategic — minutes from downtown Toronto — but the area is underused, shabby, and neglected. Expropriations in Ataratiri have left blocks of empty buildings. Many industries, once long-term tenants in the East Bayfront/Port Industrial Area, have also departed, leaving behind empty structures or barren lots. On average, Toronto's industrially designated lands provide jobs for 79 people per hectare (32 people per acre); by contrast, density in the Port Industrial Area is only 11.6 employees per hectare (4.7 employees per acre).

The Lower Don Lands also provide a wide range of recreational activities: sailing, rowing, and boardsailing clubs cluster along the north shore of the Outer Harbour, larger boats are moored at the Outer Harbour Marina and Ashbridge's Bay Park, and Cherry Beach remains one of the Central Waterfront's cleanest for swimming. Naturalists haunt the area, while joggers, hikers, and cyclists use the Martin Goodman Trail, and some venture up the Lower Don Valley. Nonetheless, many of these recreational amenities are underused, in part because access is difficult and unattractive.

Virtually all the Lower Don Lands lie in the floodplain of the Don. If there were another regional storm of the magnitude of 1954's Hurricane Hazel, large parts of the area would be flooded to a depth of as much as one metre (three feet) of water, with some places being affected even more seriously. Modelling undertaken for the Ataratiri Environmental Evaluation Study showed that almost 3,800 dwelling units, and more than 900 businesses employing more than 23,000 people, are vulnerable to flooding in the Lower Don floodplain.

Under the Flood Plain Planning Policy Statement issued by the ministries of Natural Resources and Municipal Affairs, new development that is susceptible to flood damage is not normally permitted. However, municipalities may apply for special policy area status that allows controlled development in areas where new development cannot be restricted. The City of Toronto has applied for a special policy area in the Lower Don floodplain to permit development

> *The industrial heritage manifested in the area's infrastructure and built form — in the grand scale of Commissioners Street, the pattern made by docks and seawalls, the cranes and tanks — should be treated with respect, and used as the basis for future development.*

Map 10.11 Lower Don flood plain

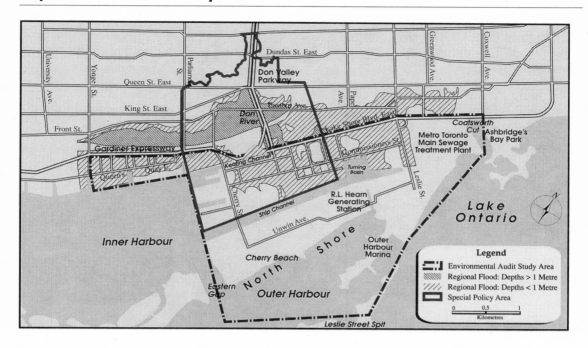

of Ataratiri, and a variety of measures are being considered to reduce the flood risk there.

The Lower Don Lands share other environmental problems: in many places, soils are contaminated with heavy metals and organic chemicals, in part because of the way lakefilling was done. For example, the Port Industrial Area was created from construction debris, sewage sludge, incinerator ash, and municipal garbage, as well as from sand. Construction of the Leslie Street Spit utilized earth fill from downtown Toronto (some of which was undoubtedly contaminated), and also rubble, incinerator and fly ash, and crushed battery casings. In the rail corridors, the Ataratiri lands, and the Port area, problems were compounded by spills, leaks, storage, and disposal of hazardous materials. When soil is contaminated, it is likely that the groundwater beneath it is contaminated as well.

The environmental audit of the East Bayfront/Port Industrial Area found some contamination of soils and/or groundwater at 27 of the 28 sites studied by the Royal Commission and by others (out of a total of 123 sites in the area). Although it is difficult to generalize — types and levels of contaminants vary greatly from site to site and across individual sites — these studies show that the soils and groundwater at some places are heavily contaminated. The MOE's cleanup guidelines are exceeded for a number of heavy metals: while there are no provincial guidelines for specific organic compounds, studies show that benzene, ethylbenzene, toluene, xylene, PAHs, and PCBs are present. At some sites, groundwater is contaminated with heavy metals and organic compounds as well as with free-phase floating petroleum products.

According to the *Ataratiri Draft Environmental Evaluation Study Report*

(Clarkin 1991), soil samples from more than 250 places in Ataratiri showed that about half the area does not currently meet guidelines for housing, commercial or industrial uses. Pollutants include metals, organic compounds such as polychlorinated biphenyls (PCBs), and coal tar. The highest levels of contamination occur in the western part of the area, where a coal gasification plant operated until the 1950s.

As in any industrial area, several thousand hazardous materials are used, stored or transported in the Lower Don Lands. Although there is insufficient information available to assess risks posed by these hazardous materials, the environmental audit showed that, in the past two years alone, 73 spills and fires involving hazardous materials were recorded in the East Bayfront/ Port Industrial Area.

Because the area is dominated by industry and transportation, air quality is poor in the Lower Don Lands. Odours from industry and the sewage treatment plant are a problem for nearby residents, and fugitive emissions of dust, volatile organic compounds, and metals from industry and traffic are a concern. Near the Gardiner/ Lakeshore Corridor and the Don Valley Parkway, preliminary modelling indicates that exceedances of provincial guidelines are likely for carbon monoxide, suspended particulates, and dustfall. Little is known about emissions or levels of trace organic compounds in the air.

Smog, including ground-level ozone, is a problem in the Lower Don Lands, as it is across southern Ontario, especially on sunny days in the late spring and summer.

In both Ataratiri and the Port Industrial area, noise is high enough to be a concern for residential use, but can be reduced to acceptable levels through building design and other measures. The major sources of noise are the traffic in the transportation corridors and, in the Port area, take-offs and landings from the Toronto Island Airport.

The levels of dust, odours, and noise along the north shore of the Outer Harbour are lower than in the industrial areas because so much of it is in recreational land uses.

In the Lower Don, Keating Channel, Inner Harbour, Ship Channel, and Turning Basin, water quality is poor and bottom sediments are contaminated with nutrients, heavy metals, and organic chemicals. Few fish can live in these waters, although over-wintering waterfowl congregate there because the water is warmer than elsewhere.

The water quality in the Outer Harbour is generally better than in the Inner Harbour, and sediments are cleaner. Unlike other Toronto beaches, Cherry Beach is rarely "posted", warning people not to swim.

Toxic chemicals are found in aquatic biota including benthic organisms, fish, and aquatic birds. There are restrictions on eating some sizes of eight species of fish found in the Lower Don Lands.

On land, the north shore of the Outer Harbour, the Leslie Street Spit, and several vacant lots in the industrial area have a variety of natural and semi-natural areas including beach and gravelly shorelines, wet meadows, open fields, willow thickets, stands of cottonwoods, and other habitats.

Thanks mostly to benign neglect, these areas have evolved to contain a mosaic of habitats in different stages of succession, providing excellent areas for breeding and migrating wildlife. Information collected for the environmental audit shows that they support a fairly complex food web: in the north shore area alone, there are some 330 species of plants, 260 of birds, 19 of fish, 12 of mammals, two of amphibians, one of snake, and 27 of butterflies. Similar numbers have been recorded for the Leslie Street Spit.

In contrast, the industrial areas of Ataratiri and the East Bayfront/Port Industrial Area are characterized by few kinds of habitats. Most are poor-quality — the occasional field between roads, parking lots, and industrial or commercial buildings. As a result, they support limited wildlife and a simple food web.

Moreover, although there is good-quality wildlife habitat, particularly in the southern parts of the Lower Don Lands, the spatial connections among habitats are poor. This is the case in east-west connections and, even more, in north-south connections with the important Don Valley corridor.

Links for human movement in the Lower Don Lands are just as poor as the wildlife habitat connections. The Gardiner/ Lakeshore Corridor effectively severs lands to the south from residential areas to the north. The Port Industrial Area is further cut off from the City by the Keating Channel. The Ataratiri area is effectively a cul-de-sac, constrained on three sides by the railway lines, the Don River, and the Adelaide Street ramps to the Don Valley Parkway.

Much of the land in the Lower Don Lands is publicly owned. The major land-owners in the Port Industrial Area are the THC, Metro Toronto, and Ontario Hydro. The Liquor Control Board of Ontario and the Ontario Provincial Police are landowners in the East Bayfront; CN and CP own the railway corridor and the yards south of Ataratiri. Ataratiri lands are now owned entirely by the City of Toronto.

In summing up the ecosystem health of the Lower Don Lands, it is fair to say that the area poses both significant challenges and opportunities for regeneration. The serious problems of contaminated soil and groundwater, air and water pollution, flood potential, dust, and noise must be addressed if the ecosystem is to be restored to health.

There are still significant gaps in our understanding of the environmental conditions in the area — gaps that must be filled. Moreover, jurisdictional, regulatory, and planning issues include a number of institutional obstacles that have contributed to environmental degradation and are road-blocks to remediation.

AN INTEGRATED PLAN FOR THE LOWER DON LANDS

In light of the challenges and opportunities in the Lower Don Lands, and the many studies and plans for individual parts of the area, it became obvious to the Royal Commission that an integrated plan is needed; piecemeal planning cannot deal effectively with issues such as flooding and soil contamination, rehabilitation of the Don River, access, and the need to stimulate economic recovery. An integrated plan would make it possible to:

- retain and enhance natural and built heritage;
- increase the diversity and intensity of uses;
- reduce the risk of flooding;
- share technologies for soil cleaning;
- share programs to monitor air pollution;
- improve links to the rest of the City;

Marsh and woodland habitat along the north shore of the Outer Harbour

- ensure that publicly owned lands are used for the maximum benefit of society;
- integrate the various planning exercises now under way; and
- assist economic recovery in the region.

Such an integrated approach would allow effective (and cost-effective) solutions that might not be appropriate or possible in planning for only one part of the Lower Don Lands. Integrated planning for the area allows consideration of the whole, rather than of a number of disjointed parts, by multiple agencies with different agendas and priorities.

The Ataratiri project is an illustration of the pitfalls of starting with a chunk of land and setting out to create a "project" on it — without integrated urban planning and in the absence of a sound initial understanding of environmental conditions. Ataratiri is economically handicapped,

encumbered by the costs of land purchased at the peak of the real estate boom; in addition, before it can proceed, millions of dollars will have to be spent for soil clean-up and flood-proofing. The greatest encumbrance, however, may well be the "megaproject" mentality: the inflexible, "all or nothing", predominantly single-use approach to development.

It may be tempting to view the Ataratiri site as if a single industry were simply being removed from an area that never had an urban pattern. But this land was once a piece of the city: it had streets, uses, activities, and history. Therefore, it makes little sense to treat it all at once and comprehensively. It would be better to develop housing in the area in a flexible, evolutionary way, as the "renovation" of an existing neighbourhood. Using this approach, changes would occur and improvements would be made, but the existing fabric would not be entirely eradicated. Life in the area would go on, while regeneration took place. Such gradualism may be frustrating to those who have a strong desire to see everything done "up front" but it does get the job done, in a more organic and economical way.

Such a flexible and incremental approach to development should be applied throughout the Lower Don Lands, within an overall framework that includes:

- improvements to environmental health, including a "green infrastructure" of civilized streets, parks, squares, recreational facilities, and green links; a flood management strategy; and remediation of air, water and soil;
- a transportation plan that provides for the needs of those outside the area while respecting the needs of those inside it (i.e., provides a balance between "corridor" and "place");
- a balance of land uses — residential, industrial, commercial, passive and active recreational — that integrates work and living places;
- a shared vision for economic development of the area, including clearly identified opportunities for private-sector participation and investment; and
- an integrated review and approval system.

ENVIRONMENTAL HEALTH

Given the environmental problems in the area, and current understanding of the need for a healthy environment, planning for the Lower Don Lands should begin with a strategy to restore environmental health. It would have four primary purposes: to lay out a "green infrastructure" of parks, open spaces, and green links; to address the

environmental problems facing the area; to minimize the impact of development on the environment; and to retain the area's natural and built heritage. A plan can be built on the knowledge accrued in the many studies and planning processes that have taken place in recent years.

A restored, cleaner Don River is central to this green framework; many of the water quality improvements will come from work to be carried out throughout the watershed under the Metro Toronto Remedial Action Plan; the Task Force to Bring Back the Don has laid the groundwork for physical changes that would improve access, aesthetics, and habitat, and contribute to improved water quality. (They are described in "Healing an Urban Watershed: The Story of the Don".)

In the Task Force's plan, the upper reaches of the Lower Don would become the Rosedale marshes; a small stone weir would create a marsh headpond; side ponds would be dredged to create marshlands for fish habitat. The floodplain would include a

The city contains in its form and functioning the traces of our history and of our collective memory; it holds the potential through which we can shape visions of our future. The strength of networks and partnerships lies in their potential to step outside the structures of conventional wisdom and the pattern of standard problem solving to formulate new problems and to articulate new opportunities.

Jacobs, P. 1991. *Sustainable urban development*. Montreal: Third Summit of the World's Major Cities.

The Lower Don

mixture of wetlands, meadows, and forested slopes. Revegetation of the side ravines would improve wildlife habitat, and trails would encourage passive recreational uses such as hiking and nature study. South of the new marshes would be the more formal, urban character of the channelized river: the water's edge would be richly landscaped with trees; stairs and ramps would provide access to widened pathways, separated from the railways by dense plantings.

The improved Lower Don would get a new mouth, in the Port lands south of the one that exists, with a gradual curve opening up to a re-created estuary. The delta and marsh would provide new habitat for aquatic life, passive recreational and educational attractions for people, and a wonderful setting for other uses. A wildlife corridor would continue south from the Don's new mouth to link with natural areas along the north shore of the Outer Harbour. Varied habitats there would

be protected and enhanced, and would be linked to the extensive natural areas on the Leslie Street Spit.

Green corridors would be wide enough to provide buffers between wildlife and human uses, and native plantings would be used to encourage ecological development of vegetation. Newly linked parks and green spaces in the East Bayfront would provide western connections between Harbourfront's public areas and the Don River green corridor. On the Lower Don Lands' eastern side, green links would improve what is now an unsatisfactory tie to the lovely recreational areas of Ashbridge's Bay Park and the Eastern Beaches beyond it.

One of the major environmental problems affecting almost the entire Lower Don Lands area is the potential for flooding. While it is hardly a new concern, attempts to deal with it over the years have been "band-aid" solutions: encasing the river in concrete (to reduce erosion and speed the flow of water), restricting new development in floodplains, and building berms do not address the root causes of high peak flows. Flooding has been exacerbated because the Don is used as a sewer to carry stormwater generated throughout the watershed.

An ecosystem approach to the flood problems on the Don would incorporate watershed-wide measures to reduce storm-water flow into the river. This fits with the goals and principles adopted under the Metro Toronto Remedial Action Plan, which includes measures such as use of stormwater detention ponds and redirection of residential downspouts from storm sewers to lawns. These may take longer to implement than other solutions, but they are probably cheaper, more equitable, and more beneficial in the long term.

Modelling shows that a severe storm would flood an area extending east from Yonge Street to a point past Greenwood Avenue, and would include most of the Port Industrial Area and the lands north to King Street. Obviously, there is a need to protect existing and proposed development in the Lower Don floodplain. The studies done for Ataratiri have identified a minimum flood protection package that would be needed before development could proceed; it includes placing fill on part of the Ataratiri site, widening the openings of four bridges over the Don, and constructing a floodway on the west bank of the Don River north of the Keating Channel. The costs of such measures should be borne by those who benefit from them.

Any plan to redevelop the Lower Don Lands must deal with the issue of contaminated soil and groundwater. A remediation strategy should be created for the entire area, building on the Royal Commission's environmental audit, and the City of Toronto's Ataratiri Environmental Evaluation Study.

An integrated soil and groundwater management strategy for the Lower Don Lands will allow clustering of sites for clean-up and an incremental approach, rather than one that insists on doing everything, everywhere at once. Clusters of sites should be identified on the basis of similar kinds and degrees of pollution, the potential for migration of contaminants from one site to adjacent ones or to nearby surface water, and expected future uses. Careful consideration should be given to the depth of soil to be remediated and appropriate standards of clean-up in relation to future built form, landscape types, range of activities, and likely health risks. The strategy should:

- be based on comprehensive, numerical clean-up guidelines that can be applied to the entire area, and that are appropriate for the intended end uses;
- be developed after a thorough review of information on the techniques available for clean-up of soils and groundwater, including work being undertaken by the Toronto Harbour Commissioners;
- ensure that detailed, site-specific investigations of soil and groundwater are undertaken prior to sale, lease or redevelopment of parcels of lands, and before decisions are made on the amount and type of remediation required;
- include the research needed to provide a better understanding of groundwater movement and contamination sources; and

- include an investigation of soil and groundwater quality in the natural areas along the north shore of the Outer Harbour and the development of an appropriate soil management strategy for these areas.

There are, as well, economies of scale that can be realized by considering the problem of soil and groundwater contamination on an area-wide basis. In addition, the potential exists to turn a challenge — the need to treat contaminated soil — into an opportunity. A soil treatment facility located in the area could decontaminate soils from across the Lower Don Lands and anchor development of soil cleaning expertise and technology that could be exported elsewhere.

The environmental audit raised many questions about air quality, questions that are applicable to the entire Lower Don Lands area. For example, it recommended that studies be conducted to assess noise levels, levels of toxic contaminants in air, and air quality in the vicinity of the traffic corridors. Such studies should be carried out for the area as a whole, and planning should include measures to reduce noise and improve air quality throughout the area.

Development of the Lower Don Lands should be designed to improve environmental conditions and minimize harmful effects. This would include such measures as:

- decommissioning and cleaning up plants, equipment, buildings, storage tanks, and underground pipelines;
- designing buildings and landscaping to improve microclimatic conditions and reduce energy use for heating and cooling;

- promoting access to public transit and providing liveable, pedestrian-oriented places;
- taking measures to reduce the quantity and improve the quality of urban stormwater run-off;
- encouraging natural landscaping that provides wildlife habitat and reduces the energy, chemicals, and water needed to maintain manicured landscaping; and
- requiring industries remaining in or coming into the area to use best possible management practices to control dust, noise, and odours, to deal with stormwater, as well as with hazardous materials, and to ensure workplace health and safety.

An environmental strategy for the Lower Don Lands area should build on the full potential of the natural and built heritage of the area. Existing wildlife habitats should be restored, protected, and enhanced, with connections improved between and among the Don Valley, Cherry Beach area, Leslie Street Spit, and Ashbridge's Bay.

Buildings of architectural or historical merit should be retained and reused whenever possible; and important aspects of the area's industrial heritage should be integrated into redevelopment. These measures will help the evolution of a distinctive place with memory, variety, and depth, where buildings, patterns, and structures of all ages co-exist, and natural habitats flourish.

TRANSPORTATION

As outlined in the section "Place and Corridor", the Royal Commission has recommended a program to integrate environment, land use and transportation in the Central Waterfront. Such a program would serve both regional and local needs, including the relocation and redesign of the Gardiner, improved public transit, and the establishment of city blocks and local streets in areas that are now just large chunks of land.

The transportation plan for the Lower Don Lands should mesh with the overall plan for the Central Waterfront, and strike a balance between the transportation needs of those outside the area and those within it. This would include, for example, maintaining the railway line that serves Redpath Sugar. It should address the need to improve north-south links from the Lower Don Lands to the residential areas to the north, improve access by local public transit, and improve routes for cyclists. With better connections and improved aesthetics, the Martin Goodman Trail will become part of the Waterfront Trail.

A redesigned Gardiner/Lakeshore Corridor will make possible a more interconnected and people-oriented urban street network with the necessary traffic capacity, create an appropriate framework for redevelopment, and improve the quality of streetscapes in the area. The Ataratiri Part II Official Plan Proposals recommend a pattern that incorporates existing streets and subdivides larger blocks to provide a finer-grained, more liveable framework for redevelopment.

It would be possible to build a Cherry Street GO station on a downtown LRT loop linked to a GO station at Garrison Common, to serve regional commuters. Improvements in local transit could include an eastern extension of the Harbourfront LRT, and improved bus service.

The other important transportation facility in the Lower Don Lands is the Port of Toronto. The Royal Commission has given a great deal of attention to this issue. (See *Persistence and Change: Waterfront Issues and the Board of the Toronto Harbour Commissioners* (1989) and the Commission's two interim reports.) In May and June 1989, it held hearings on the THC's role, mandate, and development plans, at which it received many submissions on such issues as accessibility, health and environment, the Port, ownership and land use, and the lack of accountability by the THC.

Once a major Great Lakes port, the Port of Toronto now ranks sixteenth nationally in terms of tonnage, and serves the local region, rather than having a national role. The long-term reduction in port traffic reflects changes to the commercial marine shipping industry: Toronto no longer makes economic sense as a principal destination for shippers. Nevertheless, a commercial port will always be essential to certain industries, on the waterfront and elsewhere, which receive raw materials and ship by water.

> The experiences that places make available to people, as we're learning, are an inheritance that has been entrusted to our care. Guarding these experiences and championing them, as we're also learning, are skills that are natural to people — because each one of us has direct access to the experiences that pour into us at any moment. So getting good at replenishing the places around us will just need a small stretch in our understanding.
>
> Hiss, T. 1990. *The experience of place*. New York: Alfred A. Knopf.

In its first interim report, the Royal Commission recommended that the THC's responsibility, jurisdiction, and mandate to operate the Port of Toronto be clearly separated from planning or developing lands that do not serve the port function on the waterfront. In its second interim report, *Watershed*, the Commission recommended that the THC continue to operate the Port, and that the port functions be consolidated on 40 hectares (100 acres) of land in the western part of the Port Industrial area, south of the Ship Channel. The remainder of the Port Industrial Area would be used for clean industry or mixed uses. The Commission also recommended that the mandate of the THC be clearly defined and supported by a strategically sound corporate plan, in order to rationalize use of public lands in the Port Industrial Area.

It has become apparent that there is a broad measure of support for strengthening the THC's accountability through amendments to the 1911 THC Act. The Royal Commission supports this approach. In late 1991, the THC entered into active negotiations to transfer lands surplus to its port operation requirements to the Toronto Economic Development Corporation (TEDCO).

In December 1991, the Honourable David Crombie, at the request of the federal Minister of Transport, agreed to bring together representatives of the THC, the City of Toronto, and the Department of Transport to produce a Memorandum of Understanding that will define the amount

Toronto Harbour Commissioners marine terminal

of land to be transferred from the Toronto Harbour Commissioners to TEDCO. It will also address the question of federal lands or jurisdiction, the possible future viability of the Port of Toronto, and any financial support that might be required.

LAND USE

A change in land use is occurring across the Central Waterfront: what were once single-purpose zones of industry and transportation are becoming a pattern of mixed uses embracing commercial, residential, recreational, industrial, and transportation elements.

Three of the nine *Watershed* ecosystem planning principles are particularly relevant to the Lower Don Lands: diverse, useable, and accessible. There should be diverse landscapes, places, wildlife habitats, and uses. Planning for the future should provide a local balance of employment and residential opportunities, thereby decreasing the need for commuting. This would suggest, for example, that commercial and compatible light industrial uses (such as graphics and printing) should be woven into the fabric of the Ataratiri site, just as they are now on King Street to the north. Finally, uses should permit public access and use of the water's edge.

Having mixed uses means there is a need to prevent conflicts in use: buffers have to be placed between sensitive uses and industry, especially sources of odours such as the Main Sewage Treatment Plant. They are also needed around sources of noise and air pollution such as the Gardiner/Lakeshore Corridor, the railway lines, and the Don Valley Parkway.

The City of Toronto's goal is to extend its physical centre to the waterfront.

Developing mixed residential lands at both ends of the Central Waterfront would be an appropriate bridge and/or extension of neighbourhoods in the Ataratiri, Bathurst/Spadina, and Harbourfront areas. Moreover, it might make for greater flexibility in the Ataratiri housing target, currently set at 7,000 units.

Given what we know about environmental conditions, not only in Ataratiri, but in the rest of the Lower Don Lands, there is a need to examine whether there are better, cheaper places to build some of the units. For example, could some of the housing be put in the East Bayfront, or St. Lawrence Park East, or the northwest corner of the Port Industrial Area, in association with other uses? (Redpath Sugar is an example of an important and clean industry that could be incorporated into a changed and intensified landscape, with appropriate separation from any residential uses.)

Preserving industrial land, and the jobs it can provide, is another goal of the City of Toronto. In *Watershed*, the Royal Commission recommended that a new industrial park be created in the Port Industrial Area, to exploit the area's potential for creating thousands of waterfront jobs. (This Lower Don Industrial Area is covered in greater detail later in the section on economic development.)

As well as dealing with housing and industry, a plan for the future of the Lower Don Lands must consider recreational needs and possibilities. A revitalized Don River Valley and a new Don delta have enormous potential as locations for hiking and biking trails, as well as for interpretive and educational centres and displays. In *Watershed*, the Commission recommended

Redpath Sugar in the East Bayfront

that 80 hectares (200 acres) of the Cherry Beach lands on the north shore of the Outer Harbour be transferred from the THC to the City of Toronto. There has been progress in this regard: the THC has transferred approximately half the land to the City of Toronto, which is developing a plan for managing it, intended to strike a balance between the needs of people and of wildlife.

Plans for the Outer Harbour area, including Cherry Beach, the north shore, and the Outer Harbour Marina, should also accommodate the requirements, including security of tenure, of the member clubs of the Outer Harbour Sailing Federation. As recommended in *Watershed*, the Royal Commission believes that, to avoid further adverse effects on users of the area — naturalists, windsurfers, and community club sailors — the Outer

Harbour Marina should not be expanded beyond its current capacity of 400 slips.

The Leslie Street Spit is the only accessible area on the Toronto waterfront large and wild enough to be described as an urban wilderness. It supports an astonishing variety of plants and animals, including a number of rarities: it has been colonized by nearly 300 species of vascular plants, and attracts 266 species of migrating, wintering, and breeding birds. In order to protect the integrity of the spit as a habitat for wildlife, it should be kept car-free and reserved only for uses such as passive recreation that are compatible with its urban wilderness character.

ECONOMIC DEVELOPMENT

An economic development strategy is crucial to revitalizing the Lower Don Lands and should include increased waterfront housing, increased employment opportunities in the area, and improved recreational facilities.

In the Ataratiri area, there should be greater emphasis on a wider variety of economic activities, including commercial, light industrial, recreational, and institutional uses, in addition to the current focus on housing. It may also be desireable to encourage temporary uses of some parts of the environmentally suitable land until the housing market improves. This would bring activity and some economic return, and help to demonstrate the desireability of the area.

If the market is allowed to respond to opportunities, synergies emerge. Once a sector is established in an area, it attracts spin-off uses; that will happen in Ataratiri, in the same way it has been occurring in the emerging design area at King/Parliament or the fashion district at King/Spadina. It is likely that entrepreneurs will see many interesting opportunities for a broad variety of uses in Ataratiri, as in other parts of the "shoulders" of downtown Toronto.

Another focus for increasing employment opportunities in the Lower Don Lands is the Lower Don Industrial Area, which can be created east of the new mouth of the Don River in the old Port Industrial Area on the land formerly owned or administered by the THC. With a consolidated Port, the surplus THC lands would offer new possibilities and opportunities for economic diversification in the City of Toronto. That is why, in its *Watershed* report, the Royal Commission recommended that these surplus lands be used to create a new waterfront industrial area, containing a Centre for Green Enterprise and Industry, to be both developed and managed by the Toronto Economic Development Corporation (TEDCO).

TEDCO, created by the City of Toronto, operates under a provincial charter with a mandate to create jobs, particularly on underutilized or surplus City property. Its board is made up of men and women from the business, labour,

Leslie Street Spit

environment, and public sectors. Management is able to fast-track the development process because of its intimate knowledge of the City's administrative workings.

While TEDCO's mandate is city-wide, it obviously is particularly important to the future of the new Lower Don Industrial Area. To be successful, industrial development agencies need to be at arm's length from the City and to have co-operation from municipal, business, and labour representatives. TEDCO is well placed in these respects: it is — and should continue to be — fully accountable to the City of Toronto, but it does enjoy an arm's-length relationship with the municipality. Its board should continue to include representatives from the City, Metro, business, environmentalist groups, and labour.

There are many waterfront opportunities for TEDCO: for example, it could collaborate with the World Trade Centre, which is part of a network of similar facilities in more than 50 countries. Importing and exporting "green technology" could be considerably enhanced by the World Trade Centre's expertise in promoting international trade and a new International Trade Centre in Exhibition Place would be a logical place for exhibitions and trade marts of green technology.

Given the need to remediate much of the soil in the Port Industrial Area, there is an opportunity to test available and new soil clean-up technologies in conjunction with the Centre for Green Enterprise and Industry. Such testing has the potential to provide Canadian companies with marketable experience in an area of growing concern in most economies.

The Lower Don Industrial Area could, in effect, become a showcase for future-oriented industries, operating on an environmentally sound basis, as Toronto heads into the 21st century. And given the public's concern about the quality of the environment, the former THC lands could be used to encourage industries that have operations or products geared to environmental protection and improvement.

The key to the burgeoning environmental industries sector lies in recognizing that current environmental problems represent an opportunity to profit — quite literally — from past mistakes. There is a need for new products and processes that will repair existing environmental damage and prevent it in the future — everything from industrial scrubbers to closed-loop systems for manufacturing. According to estimates, there are now more than 3,000 companies in Canada, generating more than $7 billion annually, that say they offer environmental products and services. In the United States, environmental industries do $100 billion of business annually and are said to constitute the country's third-largest industrial sector.

In Europe, an estimated two million jobs are associated with environmental industries and, given the horrendous environmental problems in eastern Europe, and rapid economic and political changes there, that number will probably rise rapidly. Furthermore, industrialization of the Third World will create an enormous demand for environment-related products and services.

If it is to play a major role in Canada's industrial future, Toronto must build and attract such industries — which is one of the tasks facing TEDCO. But merely competing for industry is not enough: Toronto has to be imaginative and daring enough to actually help create industries and products — and the jobs attached to them. To do this, it must provide a home for environment-related industrial research and development; a place where the growing number of people interested in the environment can get at least some of their training and education; where innovative techniques and products can be developed, tested, and manufactured; and where specialists in environmental marketing and distribution can be based.

Some of the industrial elements that might make up or contribute to a green industrial complex are already located in the Port Industrial Area: telecommunications, film, and television; electricity generation; and waste recycling, among others. In the winter and spring of 1989-90, the Commission sponsored two seminars on green enterprise and industry to explore development possibilities for these and other industries with government, business, labour, and academic experts.

As a result of these discussions, the Commission concluded that what is needed

is a catalyst to bring together the different sectors and interests and to convert potential into reality, to help make the Toronto of the 21st century what it has always been: a place of enterprise and industry, a liveable, workable city.

The catalyst could take the form of the proposed institute or a Centre for Green Enterprise and Industry, with its own building or buildings in TEDCO's Lower Don Industrial Area. Its mission would be to work with government, business, industry, labour, research scientists, environmentalists, and academic experts to promote green enterprise and industry in Toronto and in Canada. It would seek out firms interested in research and development related to environmentally sound or environment-specific enterprise and industry. Such a centre should be offered as a milieu for the world's leading scientists, from Canada and elsewhere, as well as for those involved in federal and provincial green industry development programs. On behalf of research and environmental agencies, they could develop projects appropriate to present and future needs and opportunities in the provincial and Canadian economies.

Among the federal agencies that should be encouraged to participate in and with the centre are: the Department of Industry, Science, and Technology; the Department of Energy, Mines, and Resources; the National Research Council; the Natural Sciences and Engineering Research Council; and Environment Canada. Provincial agencies should include the Ministry

> *The key to the burgeoning environmental industries sector lies in recognizing that current environmental problems represent an opportunity to profit — quite literally — from past mistakes.*

LESLIEGATE: RESPONSE TO THE ROYAL COMMISSION'S WORK

In 1990, IPCF Properties, a division of the Weston Group, proposed to intensify its use of a 2.4-hectare (six-acre) site at the corner of Leslie Street and Lake Shore Boulevard, currently occupied by a Loblaw's Superstore and an extensive parking lot.

However, it soon became apparent that the property, known as LeslieGate, has great local and subregional potential. Instead of pursuing traditional development options, IPCF decided to explore these possibilities within a development framework based on an ecosystem approach. Understanding that such an approach holds that "everything is connected to everything else", the framework seeks to link LeslieGate with the surrounding neighbourhood and, especially, with the waterfront.

A planning team began by examining the land use, built form, and physical environment of the surrounding neighbourhoods. The nearby area is predominantly mixed-use with residential — primarily low-rise, one-family houses mixed with the occasional apartment building to the north — and an industrial-commercial band along Eastern Avenue that extends south toward the lake in some parts.

The teams recommends integrating the LeslieGate site with surrounding communities through mixed-use development compatible with the existing scale: extending the urban grid south to the lakeshore, and providing at-grade pedestrian crossings. Offices, housing, and open space would be added to the Loblaw's store and parking lot to create a more diverse, economically and socially active centre for the area.

The team also suggests establishing a green corridor down Leslie Street to the Port Industrial Area. This "green, people-friendly" pedestrian spine, created by hard and soft landscaping, would ensure consistent treatment of the edge along Leslie, through the Port Industrial Area to the Leslie Street Spit.

Links to the waterfront would be enhanced by a "thoughtful, positive reinforcement of the pedestrian, cyclist, and vehicular connections across" and along Lake Shore Boulevard to Ashbridge's Bay. Connections between LeslieGate and the waterfront would be further improved if upper levels of future buildings on the site enabled people to see Ashbridge's Bay to the east and Lake Ontario to the south.

The kind of mixed-use development being proposed recognizes the growing importance of reducing distances between workplace, housing, and shopping. With the Loblaw's store remaining on-site, existing land uses would be maintained and a vital commercial enterprise would continue to contribute to the area's economic vitality.

IPCF Properties feels that LeslieGate can influence the future character of the area. Its location at the edge of the Port Industrial Area, near Cherry Beach and the Leslie Street Spit, gives LeslieGate potential as a gateway to the visual, recreational, and historical opportunities of the waterfront.

Source: Volgyesi + Propst Inc. 1991. *LeslieGate: a private sector response to ecosystem planning rational.* Toronto: Volgyesi + Propst Inc.

of Trade and Technology; ORTECH INTERNATIONAL (formerly the Ontario Research Foundation); and the Ministry of the Environment.

The centre would explore the possibility of attracting companies or organizations interested in gathering and disseminating information on environment-related statistics, experience, and trends. In helping to establish environmental information banks, TEDCO should work with the Greater Toronto Bioregion Research and Information Network (recommendation 24 in Chapter 3 of this report) and the United Nations Environment Program (UNEP), as well as with other international and national agencies responsible for gathering, reporting, and monitoring environmental information.

The centre would offer facilities for training and education, based on an ecosystem approach, to enterprise and industry, students at community colleges, and university undergraduate and graduate programs Canada-wide, for people planning careers in business or industry. In carrying out this part of its mandate, TEDCO should collaborate with community colleges in the Greater Toronto Area, including Ryerson, George Brown, and Humber, and with universities throughout southern Ontario, including Trent, Toronto, York, Windsor, Waterloo, and Guelph, all of which provide such education. In doing so, the centre would offer opportunities for direct contact among students, experts in research and development, managers, and workers in green enterprise and industry so essential to Toronto's future.

In addition to its negotiations with the THC, TEDCO has begun to define the role and mandate of the proposed Centre for Green Enterprise and Industry, including the development of a business plan. It is in this context that Commissioner Crombie has agreed to bring together representatives of the THC, the City of Toronto, and the Department of Transport to define the amount of land to be transferred from the THC to TEDCO, as well as related matters.

INTEGRATED REVIEW AND APPROVAL SYSTEM

As discussed in Part I of this report, regeneration of the Greater Toronto waterfront is hampered by the complexity of jurisdictions, planning, regulations, and approvals; this is certainly true of the Lower Don Lands. The environmental audit of the East Bayfront/Port Industrial Area included an analysis of the existing frameworks for stewardship and accountability, and found that regulatory and decision-making processes limit possibilities for adopting an ecosystem approach to planning and managing the area.

Similarly, planning for Ataratiri involves a lengthy and complex process. The City's Part II Official Plan Proposals (1991) describe a multi-year, four-stage approval process for development, to include:

- approval of the policy statements contained in the proposals document, together with a zoning by-law, development plan, and plan of subdivision for the entire Ataratiri site;
- approval of sub-areas consisting of several development blocks, provided that detailed environmental, flooding, and community service issues have been addressed;
- approval of each development block depending on completion of necessary pre-construction environmental clean-up;

- approval of individual development applications, provided that the building design satisfies concerns regarding noise, water conservation, energy conservation, waste reduction, reduction of automobile use, environmental remediation, and (where appropriate) floodproofing.

It is undoubtedly necessary to ensure that all public interests, including community services and environmental remediation, are thoroughly and carefully accommodated in redeveloping the Lower Don Lands. However it is also clear that ways must be found to structure the approvals process to provide the flexibility needed to respond to opportunities, integrate activities of different government agencies, and provide a greater degree of predictability and efficiency to encourage private-sector involvement. An integrated approach to the Lower Don Lands could help to free up some of the regulatory and jurisdictional problems currently hindering planning, approvals, and implementation.

RECOMMENDATIONS

72. The Royal Commission recommends that an integrated approach be taken to planning in the Lower Don Lands, based on the framework outlined above, and that it involve participation by all levels of government, as well as the private sector and the public.

73. The Royal Commission further recommends that the draft integrated plan provide a basis for public discussion involving federal, provincial, Metro, and City governments, the public,

private-sector landowners, neighbouring residents, and other interested parties.

74. An integrated process should be established to facilitate review and approval of remediation and development proposals by all levels and agencies of government.

CHAPTER 11:
SCARBOROUGH

In 1793 Elizabeth Simcoe, wife of the first lieutenant governor of Upper Canada, was impressed by the massive bluffs that lined the shoreline east of the colony's new capital: they reminded her of the scenic Yorkshire cliffs in Scarborough, England; the area was therefore given the name Scarborough. Designated a township in 1850, Scarborough became part of Metropolitan Toronto in 1953, and was officially declared a city in 1983.

The Scarborough waterfront comprises 20 kilometres (12 miles) or 40 per cent of Metro's shoreline. The area contains the highest proportion of single detached dwellings and owned housing along the Metropolitan Toronto waterfront.

The extent to which the Scarborough waterfront is already urbanized (primarily in single-family homes) and the presence of the bluffs makes it more difficult — although not impossible — to connect people to the water and to establish safe public access compatible with waterfront trail objectives. In fact, implementing a greenway system can take the established urban residential communities into account, respecting the limited opportunities available to protect

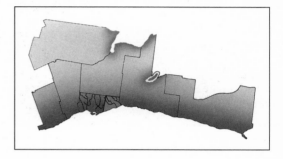

the cultural heritage of the people and the natural heritage of the bluffs. In this regard, a two-tiered waterfront trail linking to a regional greenway would be beneficial in the City of Scarborough.

A visit to Bluffer's Park, one of the most popular regional recreational parks, where one can fish, boat, sit on the rocks or simply stroll in the park admiring the striking views of the bluffs year-round; a fall walk in the Rouge Valley where one can encounter animals and view rare birds, or smell winter coming and see the wonders of nature at work as the leaves change colour; the serene feeling that comes from being surrounded by the history and artifacts at the Guild Inn with the peaceful view of the shimmering lake and the sun setting from atop the bluffs — these are only a few

At the foot of the bluffs, circa 1968

of the memorable experiences possible in Scarborough, a short distance east of the commercial and economic activity in downtown Toronto. In many instances, access to these places is limited and could be greatly enhanced if there were a regional greenways system across the waterfront and up the river valleys. (See Chapter 5 on Greenways.)

Natural topography has always contributed to defining urban form along this portion of the shoreline. The Scarborough Bluffs, which stretch as high as 100 metres (330 feet) in some places and account for 75 per cent of Scarborough's waterfront, are a unique heritage site the City and MTRCA strive to protect. An educational learning centre along the Scarborough waterfront, specifically focused on the various environmental processes operating there, would be

a marvellous opportunity to educate the public about the bluffs.

Only two major waterways in Scarborough flow into Lake Ontario: Highland Creek and the Rouge River. The Highland Creek — lying entirely within the City — drains an area of over 105 square kilometres (40 square miles). The Rouge River watershed, which covers more than 300 square kilometres (116 square miles), encompasses portions of six local municipalities. Its lower reaches are predominantly in northeastern Scarborough, and the river eventually forms the southeastern portion of Scarborough's political boundary.

The Rouge's spring-fed headwaters rise in the Oak Ridges Moraine, and flow rapidly down the moraine's shoulders. Many small streams come together on flat agricultural plains in Markham to form slower-moving major tributaries. Before the two main branches of the river, the Rouge and Little Rouge, reach Scarborough they form large, well-defined valleys, tumbling over boulders and rocks. Natural erosion processes have exposed geological features that are provincially significant, as well as distinctive bluffs that are as high as 40 metres (131 feet). In the last few kilometres before the Rouge River enters Lake Ontario, it broadens into the Rouge Marsh — the largest provincially significant area in Metropolitan Toronto — housing exceptional wildlife populations.

A 1991 draft MNR Ecological Survey of the Rouge Valley Park notes (Varga, Jalava, and Riley 1991):

Collectively, the lower Rouge valleys, lakeshore marshes and adjacent tablelands are the most significant system of linked natural areas along any of the lower river valleys draining into the [sic] northwestern Lake Ontario. The Rouge [in Scarborough] represents one of very few substantive corridors of natural space extending from the northwestern shores of Lake Ontario towards the interior of Halton, Peel, York, Durham or Metropolitan Toronto. The Rouge River and its valleys are exceptional among [other] watercourses from several points of view.

From one side of the valley to the other, the Rouge River corridor averages two kilometres (one mile) in width. The area contains a remarkable diversity of natural and rural heritage features and is especially important because of its proximity to Metropolitan Toronto — one of the last opportunities for ecological conservation on this scale in Metro.

The Rouge's spring-fed headwaters rise in the Oak Ridges Moraine, and flow rapidly down the moraine's shoulders. . . . The area contains a remarkable diversity of natural and rural heritage features . . . one of the last opportunities for ecological conservation on this scale in Metro.

Over the years, the Rouge River system in Scarborough has largely escaped urbanization and is a healthy and diverse ecosystem today. In the 1980s, proposals were presented to Scarborough Council to develop the Rouge tablelands in the city's northeast; after extensive study, Council decided to protect the area and designate it as Regional Natural Environment for rural uses. However, in adjacent and upstream areas, development has led to the destruction of woodlots and wetlands, has replaced tall grasses and other natural habitat with manicured lawns, and has introduced erosion and water quality problems due to inappropriate stormwater management.

In its first interim report (1989), the Royal Commission supported the views of many interest groups, recommending

Looking west from the Rouge Marsh

Map 11.1 Proposed Rouge Valley Park

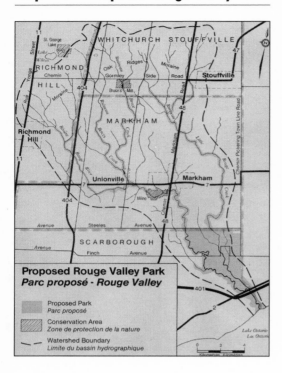

in the Rouge and Petticoat Creek watersheds (provincial land assembly), and tablelands along the top of the valleys.

Consultants have been commissioned to work with the appropriate agencies to examine the area's ecological and cultural inventory and assist in drafting management strategies. While the goal of creating a park has been declared and park planning has begun, it is possible that the land under study, especially in York Region, could be environmentally degraded by development of surrounding parcels of land.

The City of Scarborough is currently examining its secondary planning policies to ensure that areas adjacent to the park are adequately protected. The Advisory Committee has asked that these areas be protected in the interim, before degradation precludes future park options.

The health of the Rouge watershed and the long-term ecological integrity of the park depend on the extent and environmental sensitivity of development in the rest of the watershed. Proper controls such as stormwater management and protection of valley corridors, including adjacent tablelands, are essential. As part of its mandate, the Rouge Park Advisory Committee reviews development applications that will affect the park.

Obviously, development adjacent to the Rouge Valley should protect ecological processes and maintain the natural beauty of the valley. The natural profile of the skyline has been marred, in many urban valleys, by high-rises. Scarborough has begun to address this issue. Other municipalities with similar valley resources should ensure that appropriate height controls and development siting maintain and enhance views.

that the Rouge River Valley be protected as a natural heritage park. In March 1990, the provincial government announced its intention of creating a Rouge Valley Park and established an advisory committee on the subject. This professionally diverse group is responsible for drafting a park management plan for the portion of the park between Lake Ontario and Steeles Avenue (see Map 11.1.). The main goal is to ensure protection of the ecological integrity of the Rouge Valley Park and its natural, scenic, historic, and cultural values, through innovative planning, management, and use in the park and its environs (Rouge Valley Park Advisory Committee 1991).

By June 1992, the committee is to recommend a strategy and time-frame for protecting the park area and is likely to address extending its current northern boundaries to include publicly owned lands

The Guild Inn and the Scarborough Bluffs

The Commission supports the initial work undertaken on the Rouge Valley Park, and urges creation of a comprehensive strategy to ensure that, many years from now when the park is completed, it is ecologically healthy. Implementation of the strategy, which takes public input into account, should begin as soon as possible, even while planning proceeds for the northern half of the park.

As part of this process, thought should be given to a greenway protecting the

SCARBOROUGH'S GUILD OF ALL ARTS

The unpretentious gates on the Guildwood Parkway, along the waterfront in suburban Scarborough, are deceiving. The narrow driveway opens up and foliage gives way to reveal a picturesque inn surrounded by what seem to be Grecian artifacts and ruins.

The pieces of Grecian architecture, marble sculptures, and reliefs dispersed on the grounds of the Guild Inn look mysterious, arresting — and completely out of place. In fact, they are out of place: they were saved by Spencer Clark when the rest of the buildings of which they were a part were destroyed in the 1960s and '70s. They are all that remains of many of the finest examples of classical 19th-century architecture that were torn down to make way for designs from such contemporary architectural schools as Bauhaus.

One finds echoes of civilization's architectural past in four imposing columns on the north grounds of the Guild Inn. These Ionic columns and capitals, from a period prevalent in the fifth and fourth centuries B.C., once graced the Bankers Bond building, on a site now occupied by First Canadian Place, the tallest building in Canada, designed by Edward Durrell Stone.

Corinthian columns and capitals replaced Ionic in the fourth and third centuries B.C. Examples of the Corinthian style can be found in the salvaged marble columns at the Guild; they were once part of the Bank of Toronto, which stood on the site now occupied by Mies van der Rohe's Toronto-Dominion Centre and are among the 21 capitals and columns that form an amphitheatre, designed by the late Ron Thom, on the south grounds of the Guild Inn.

Although the practice of stone masonry has declined, the Guild — where many of the capitals, pediments, and bas-relief carvings are at ground level, albeit out of context — offers the opportunity to fully examine and appreciate the craftsmanship of the salvaged pieces.

There are more than 50 demolished buildings represented at the Guild, a monument to Spencer Clark and his vision of preserving at least some of Toronto's architectural past. The collection should be cherished and enhanced in every way possible.

Sources: Cowan, H. November 1984. "The ruins of winter." *City and Country*; The Spencer Clark Collection of Historic Architecture.

waterways and valleylands that feed into the Rouge River. This would help establish connections to significant natural areas such as the Oak Ridges Moraine and Duffin's Creek, conservation areas, and existing local and regional parks.

The Guild Inn, atop the bluffs on Scarborough's waterfront west of the Rouge River, houses a unique collection of architectural pieces. Established in 1932 by Rosa and Spencer Clark, the site was the original home for The Guild of All Arts, a thriving artists' colony. As Toronto's business buildings were being demolished over the years, Spencer Clark collected historic landmarks and kept them on the inn's grounds. He eventually sold the land and its buildings to the Province and Metro in 1978; Metro established the Board of Management of the Guild in 1983, to manage the property on its behalf. With the change in ownership came a change in direction in the vision of the site's future: recent proposals are that the inn be redeveloped as a substantially larger hotel/convention centre. However, formal plans have yet to be submitted to the City by Metro.

Scarborough's population has grown substantially — from 1,711 in 1900 to more than 267,000 in 1967 — and has risen by approximately 11 per cent since 1981; it is estimated to grow to more than 560,000 by 2001. The increase between 1990 and 2001 — more than 12 per cent — would be the greatest in any Metropolitan Toronto municipality, and greater than the increase in the region, estimated at eight per cent, for the same period.

In the early 1980s, population in the Scarborough waterfront grew moderately, at about one-third of that of the City; the number of children living in the area were evidence that it had the highest proportion of families in Scarborough.

Housing starts on the waterfront increased substantially in the late 1980s. In contrast to other municipalities in Metro, the Scarborough waterfront area has the lowest proportion of high-density residential housing. It is also the most exclusive waterfront in Metro, with the highest proportion of single detached dwellings — they comprise more than half the waterfront housing stock — and the highest proportion of ownership housing. Total employment in the Scarborough waterfront area rose by more than 50 per cent in the '80s.

WATERSHED UPDATE

In the past year, the City of Scarborough continued to address waterfront planning — and, indeed, city-wide planning issues — with an ecosystem approach, which has been well received at the political, bureaucratic, and community levels.

In October 1990, the Scarborough Waterfront Committee recommended adoption of the ecosystem approach, the nine waterfront principles, and other Commission recommendations as interim waterfront policies for Scarborough. Over the following nine months, public meetings were held and policies presented and discussed. In July 1991, City Council approved Official Plan Amendment 799, giving basic direction to activities along the city's 20 kilometres (12 miles) of waterfront and consistent with the Commission's views.

There is clearly no current agreement on the nature of regional co-ordination — a crucial step, in the Commission's view, in successful planning for the future. The City's view is that the leading role in local waterfront planning should remain in its hands, with regional co-ordination from Metro and continuing participation from MTRCA. It believes that Metro Toronto has not clearly defined its own role in waterfront planning, in the recently released *Planning Directions for the Metropolitan Waterfront: An Overview* (1991), which was intended to be the basis for discussion between Metro and other local municipalities on establishing a regional waterfront plan. Scarborough plans to continue to develop its waterfront on the basis of connectedness and safe public access, and is working with Metro, MTRCA, and others as necessary.

In its *Watershed* report, the Commission recommended that the environmental conditions of industrial areas such as the Johns-Manville site be investigated before being considered for redevelopment. The major issue currently facing the City is whether to retain industrial uses in the 60-hectare (150-acre) Centennial Industrial District adjacent to Lake Ontario. Lands north and east of the Centennial Industrial District are comprised of established residential communities, primarily of single-family homes.

As the Commission noted in *Watershed*, there is a potential "to establish a new residential area, the Port Union Community", on the Scarborough waterfront. Since then, the City has continued to deal with applications from developers and landowners seeking to redesignate and rezone industrial lands for alternate (primarily high-density residential) uses. In December 1990, Scarborough Council approved a Study of Options and Opportunities for the Development of the Centennial Industrial District.

PLANNING INITIATIVES

The purpose of the study, undertaken by City staff, is to assess the feasibility and desirability of retaining current industrial uses and to outline the next steps to be taken, based on desired land uses and capitalizing on waterfront opportunities. Terms of reference note that consideration should be given to appropriate land uses on the waterfront and that the Commission's nine principles should be implemented. The report is to be available early in 1992.

This is the City's most significant opportunity to enhance residential use and create a new waterfront community. The area, including the Rouge Hill GO station, has the most potential to bring people to the waterfront. Scarborough's decision about desired land uses should ensure that future development of the Centennial Industrial District is compatible with the waterfront. The historically significant old Port Union Village should also be restored and preserved in future plans for the area. The CNR line running along the shoreline now forms a barrier to Lake Ontario, and consideration should be given to ways of increasing public access.

Urban designers at a recent charette have suggested that the Centennial Industrial District also has potential as a gateway to the city for visitors arriving by water. A ceremonial entrance to the city would reflect the grandeur of the bluffs; it could connect to Scarborough City Hall via a tree-lined parade

Proposed ceremonial waterfront entrance at the foot of Port Union Road

route. Port Union Road could become the major organizing element of the community, anchored by nodes at both ends. A public facility at the water could include a gateway to the City and the beginning of a "ceremonial drive" from the waterfront to Scarborough City Hall; the north end could house a strong commercial node or other feature that delineated the entrance to a new Port Union community.

The Commission also made recommendations on redeveloping the publicly owned Guild Inn site. *Watershed* noted that local interests should be fully considered by the City of Scarborough in evaluating redevelopment proposals, and that such evaluations should be based on waterfront policies and should conform to the nine waterfront principles. An initial proposal by the lessee, including high-density development, met public resistance primarily from residents of the Guildwood community. Because Metro, the Guild Inn's owner, did not approve of the proposal, it was not submitted to the City. No revised proposal has yet been submitted.

Plans to redevelop the Guild Inn should not have an adverse impact on the surrounding community, which has existed since the 1950s. This is particularly true with respect to traffic and access to the waterfront, which should retain its existing natural, cultural, and small-scale characteristics.

If the Centennial Industrial District and the Guild Inn lands become engulfed by inappropriate, added elements of built form, chances for added public access and views to the water will disappear in key places along the shore. The City should ensure that approved built forms are sensitive to the water's edge, enhance views and vistas, and encourage people to visit the waterfront. Appropriate public amenities should also be provided and linear access connecting one part of the waterfront with the others should be a priority in preparing and reviewing all proposals.

The concerns that *Watershed* expressed about the focus of the Draft East Point Park Master Plan/Environmental Assessment and the environmental effects of lakefill, road access, traffic, and safety are being addressed. Following the release of *Watershed*, and while the Commission's review of shoreline regeneration was under way, MTRCA exercised more caution in proceeding with lakefill projects. In 1991, the Authority began to study the effects of proposed lakefill for East Point Park on water circulation, water quality, and adjacent intake/outfall pipes. This is scheduled to be completed by mid-1992.

As a potential major project requiring lakefill, East Point Park should be evaluated in the context of the Shoreline Regeneration Plan recommended in Chapter 4.

Added public concern has risen about including a Metropolitan Toronto sports

> **The danger, as we are now beginning to see, is that whenever we make changes in our surroundings, we can all too easily shortchange ourselves, by cutting ourselves off from some of the sights or sounds, the shapes or textures, or other information from a place that have helped mold our understanding and are now necessary for us to thrive.**
>
> Hiss, T. 1990. *The experience of place.* New York: Alfred A. Knopf.

facility complex in East Point Park. The proposed site would possibly destroy habitat for rare plants, such as the white bottle gentian, as well as for migrating birds, and other animals. Legally, the sports facility plan is an individual proposal, separate from the Conservation Authority's plan for the remainder of the park. In mid-1990, the provincial Ministry of the Environment granted Metro exemption of the sports facility from an individual environmental assessment, on the grounds that it met the criteria for municipal recreation projects with an estimated cost of less than $3.5 million. However, it should be noted that this decision did not include consideration of alternative locations or the likely effects of the facility.

The Ministry of the Environment has been asked to review the situation, and is currently considering whether the proposed sports facility should be subject to an individual environmental assessment, rolled into one that already exists for East Point Park, or if it should remain completely exempt. The Commission hopes the Ministry review will result in a process that recognizes existing studies and addresses the need for a comprehensive evaluation of the plans for the entire park, with a view to maintaining and enhancing the environmental integrity of the area.

For the past 32 years, planning in the City of Scarborough has been based on the 1959 Official Plan, which now has more than 800 amendments. The Commission believes that the plan should be revised, giving added emphasis to protecting and enhancing the natural environment, while addressing economic and community needs. Thought should also be given to protecting and enhancing Scarborough's waterfront and its

heritage; in this regard, a local waterfront plan is recommended for the City of Scarborough.

RECOMMENDATIONS

75. The Royal Commission recommends that the City of Scarborough, the Regional Municipality of Metropolitan Toronto and the Metropolitan Toronto and Region Conservation Authority review relevant documents including official plans and other waterfront-specific plans to ensure that they incorporate the ecosystem approach and nine waterfront principles described in Part I.

76. The Commission further recommends that the City of Scarborough, Metropolitan Toronto and MTRCA participate in preparing the proposed shoreline regeneration plan, including the waterfront greenway and trail and ensure that any other plans for waterfront areas are reviewed and/or developed in this context.

77. The Province of Ontario, the Regional Municipality of Metropolitan Toronto, and the City of Scarborough should negotiate a Waterfront Partnership Agreement in conjunction with appropriate authorities and agencies. It should:

   - clearly identify the roles and responsibilities of various agencies and authorities in developing and implementing plans for the Scarborough waterfront;
   - offer comprehensive waterfront and river valley policies, taking

into account the environmental vulnerability of the Scarborough Bluffs and the Rouge River Valley area. Such policies should outline ways to acquire, maintain, and provide access to land along the waterfront and up the river valleys. They could take the form of a waterfront plan and should be incorporated into the City's official and secondary plans;

- encourage continued development of a waterfront trail, including a two-tiered trail in Scarborough as part of the regional greenway and trail system, one route above the bluffs and one at their base. The system should also enhance access nodes to the waterfront, improve access to Bluffer's Park, and include facilities to educate the public on the geological processes that contributed to formation of the bluffs; and

- ensure that future land uses of the Centennial Industrial District are compatible with maintaining and enhancing the environmental integrity and public use of the waterfront. The opportunity to develop a new community that is integrated with the waterfront should be evaluated, and priority given to waterfront urban design guidelines. Consideration should also be given to ways in which the CNR line, which is a significant element in this area, can be better integrated to form a less obtrusive barrier to the waterfront.

78. The Province of Ontario, Metropolitan Toronto, and the City of Scarborough should ensure that any redevelopment of the Guild Inn respects and enhances its natural, historic, cultural and small-scale characteristics and maintains public acccess to the site.

CHAPTER 12: DURHAM

Durham Region lies east of York Region and Metro Toronto, partially surrounded by the shorelines of three lakes — Simcoe and Scugog, which are north of the Oak Ridges Moraine, and approximately 62 kilometres (39 miles) of Lake Ontario shoreline to the south.

The Regional Municipality of Durham came into being in 1974, a year after the Province of Ontario introduced the concept of regional government. Seven of the region's eight local municipalities are adjacent to water; of these, five — Pickering, Ajax, Whitby, Oshawa, and Newcastle — are adjacent to Lake Ontario. Durham encompasses about 40 per cent of the Greater Toronto bioregion's Lake Ontario shoreline, but is the most undeveloped region across the area, currently housing only about 20 per cent (about 70,000 people in 1986) of the total waterfront population.

The region is inside the boundaries of four conservation authorities: the Lake Simcoe Conservation Authority, the Metropolitan Toronto and Region Conservation Authority, the Central Lake Ontario Conservation Authority, and the Ganaraska Region Conservation Authority.

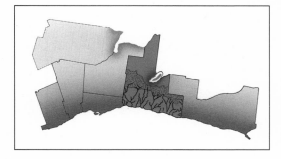

In this portion of the Greater Toronto bioregion, waters that flow into Lake Ontario include the Rouge River, Petticoat Creek, and Frenchman's Bay in Pickering; Duffin Creek and Carruther's Creek in Ajax; Lynde Creek in Whitby; Oshawa, Harmony/Farewell, and Black creeks in Oshawa; Bowmanville, Soper, Wilmot, and Graham creeks in Newcastle; and the Ganaraska River in Newcastle and Port Hope. There are Master Drainage Plans only for the Petticoat Creek and Carruther's Creek watersheds and a *Comprehensive Basin Management Strategy* (1990) for the Rouge River area.

The Durham shoreline comprises a variety of elements, including peaceful and relaxing natural areas, active urban parks and open spaces, new and old residential neighbourhoods and communities, marinas, large and small public utility buildings, and a significant industrial component.

The region's nature lovers and bird-watchers are among the many people who enjoy visiting such natural habitat areas as Frenchman's Bay and its surrounding marshes; the Petticoat Creek Conservation Area in Pickering; Carruther's Creek and its marshes in Ajax; and the Lynde Shores Conservation Area in Whitby. Lakeview Park in Oshawa, which has its recreational facilities and historical buildings, is well-used by families. In Newcastle, Darlington Provincial Park caters to passive and active park users with many natural open spaces. Wilmot Creek to the east is well-known for its superb salmon fishing.

The Town of Pickering offers examples of both old and new, ranging from modern residential subdivisions to country estates, and including hamlets andvillages with rural charm, rich farmland areas, and vast expanses of parkland and natural open space. Existing public facilities, such as the Pickering Nuclear Generating Station and the Duffin Creek Water Pollution Control Plant, are necessary structures on the waterfront and have become virtual built-form landmarks on Pickering's shoreline, visible from enormous distances along Lake Ontario.

Ajax has as much rural charm as Pickering, but is becoming increasingly urbanized. Future development should protect and enhance its natural and cultural heritage; current open spaces on the waterfront could be made more diverse, to provide a variety of experiences along the shore.

Approximately 70 per cent of Whitby's waterfront is publicly owned. Residents and nature lovers can enjoy watching wildlife in the rich vegetation and marshes of the Lynde Shores Conservation Area. To the east, the current Whitby Psychiatric Hospital lands are informally accessible to the public, and are currently being evaluated for institutional and residential redevelopment. The provincially owned site offers spectacular views of the Lake Ontario shoreline to the east and west; future changes to built form should maintain and enhance these views.

Plans call for future residential and recreational uses, including parkland and open space, on the dilapidated Whitby Harbour and surrounding lands east of the hospital site. The remainder of Whitby's waterfront is industrial, but the Town hopes that eventually it can ensure public access across the entire waterfront.

Almost 80 per cent of Oshawa's waterfront is owned by public agencies, about half of it — including the harbour area and the environmentally sensitive Second Marsh — by the Oshawa Harbour Commission; most of the remainder is public parkland or conservation authority land.

Lakefront Park West and Lakeview Park are the city's two major waterfront parks and future plans for the former include a water theme park and a marina. Natural amenities and the numerous children's recreational facilities are often used by nearby families.

The Town of Pickering offers examples of both old and new, ranging from modern residential subdivisions to country estates, and including hamlets and villages with rural charm, rich farmland areas, and vast expanses of parkland and natural open space.

Lakeview Park has a more natural environmental focus and historical background: the area is linked to extensive valleylands to the north and could be linked to the Oshawa Harbour area to the east. The property was formerly farmland, most of which was owned by the Henry family and by other early pioneers and their descendants; it was acquired and donated to the City by General Motors of Canada for use as a public park. The old buildings and their contents tell the story of Oshawa's history: the Henry House Museum, one of the oldest houses in Oshawa, was the home of Thomas Henry, a famous pioneering citizen, in the mid-1800s. Robinson House, built in the 1840s, is historic and has an unusual architectural design: originally a seaman's tavern that served sailors docking at the Port of Oshawa, in 1965 it was restored and established as an addition to the Henry House Museum. The Oshawa Historical Society plays a major role in ensuring that these buildings are preserved and restored.

The Newcastle shoreline is marked by Ontario Hydro's Darlington Generating Station and the St. Marys Cement facility. The vast remainder of the waterfront is currently given over to rural and natural areas, except at the Port Darlington Marina and the Wilmot Creek Retirement Community. In addition to fishing in Wilmot Creek, some residents use the vacant agricultural and waterfront lands for recreational purposes to discharge firearms. This is a concern for nearby residents.

Durham Region's population increased slightly in the early 1980s and is expected to grow by approximately 65 per cent from 1986 to 2001; it is currently estimated at 370,000. This forecast — based on factors including the growth rate of the regional economy and the distribution of regional population — is the highest predicted for any of the four Greater Toronto waterfront regions.

Urbanization in Durham is centred in three major nodes: Pickering/Ajax, Whitby/Oshawa/Courtice, and Bowmanville/Newcastle. The Bowmanville/Newcastle area will continue to grow the most. A large number of residents in Durham commute to Metropolitan Toronto by car or GO Transit. Any future eastward expansion of GO Transit would reduce the current proportion of automobile commuters.

Most of Pickering's waterfront area — extending south of Highway 401 to Lake Ontario from the Rouge River in the west to Duffin Creek in the east —is residential, mostly low-density, single-family homes. The town has the highest average household income on the Durham waterfront. Thirty-five per cent of Pickering's residents live on the waterfront and approximately two-thirds of them work in Metro. East of the Frenchman's Bay area, the waterfront is given over to industrial uses including the Pickering Nuclear Generating Station.

Almost all of the Ajax waterfront is also residential, with more than 60 per cent (more than 23,000 residents) of the town's total population living in the waterfront area — an increase of more than 20 per cent in five years, with the potential for more residential waterfront development. Much of the Ajax shoreline consists of waterfront open space, large areas that have accumulated over time.

Whitby has the lowest waterfront population in the Durham waterfront area, in proportion to total residents: less than five per cent of the town's residents live there. This is probably because so much

Duffin Creek at Lake Ontario

land in Whitby's waterfront area has been designated for industrial and institutional uses. Similarly, only about 15 per cent of Oshawa's 125,000 residents live in the waterfront area.

Because much of Newcastle's shoreline is undeveloped, only 29 per cent of Newcastle's 34,000 residents currently live in the waterfront area.

Major waterfront industry is located primarily in Whitby, Oshawa and Newcastle. East of Cranberry Marsh and the Lynde Shores area, most of Whitby's waterfront is given over to industrial uses including the Lake Ontario Steel Corporation (LASCO). In the late 1980s, 78 per cent of Oshawa's employment on the waterfront was in processing and machining occupations. The city continues to be a strong industrial base in the region, but will be greatly affected if and when downsizing occurs at General Motors of Canada, Oshawa's largest employer.

The Oshawa Harbour area also houses active port users including McAsphalt, Chieftain Cement, LASCO, and Courtice Steel; occasional users include General Motors of Canada, General Electric, Honda Canada, and Molson Breweries.

The two major employers in Newcastle are Ontario Hydro's Darlington Nuclear Generating Station and the St. Marys Cement operation.

THE REGION

The Region of Durham and its waterfront municipalities have a unique opportunity to preserve their natural shoreline, significant natural areas, and natural waterfront features, which are so abundant when compared to the remainder of the bioregion's waterfront. An ecosystem approach — considering the economy, the environment, and the community — and the Commission's principles have been endorsed by the Region and most of the area municipalities, providing a good basis for future growth and development.

WATERSHED UPDATE

In its *Watershed* (1990) report, the Commission urged the Province to negotiate one or more Waterfront Partnership Agreements with the Region of Durham, other levels of government, and other appropriate parties, in order to co-ordinate future activities along the waterfront. It also recommended that these agreements be closely linked to preparation of a Durham Waterfront Plan, which would include 17 environmental, economic, and community-oriented goals that should be reached as part of an ecosystem approach to planning. Since then, progress has been made in this regard.

Steps to establish strategies that will maintain and protect significant natural habitats have been taken in various parts of Durham Region:

- the Province of Ontario commissioned a study of the Frenchman's Bay area to evaluate the state of its environment; further study is proposed;
- Runnymede Corporation, landowners in the Carruther's Creek area, commissioned M. M. Dillon to prepare an Environmental Management Plan for the Carruther's Creek area;
- working on behalf of the surrounding landowners (including the Ontario Ministry of Government Services and the Region of Durham), Bird and

Hale environmental consultants (1991) completed an Environmental Management Plan for the Lynde Shores Major Open Space area in Whitby;

- a long-term management plan was completed for the Pumphouse Marsh in the City of Oshawa, with a view to preserving and protecting the existing ecosystem and enhancing the natural qualities of the marsh; and
- various studies have been undertaken on the Second Marsh; a steering committee is considering how to implement short- and long-term plans for rehabilitating, protecting, and preserving it.

Among the remaining natural areas along the waterfront that should be protected are McLaughlin Bay, the Wilmot Creek Mouth, and the Bond Head Bluffs in the Town of Newcastle.

The Region of Durham and its waterfront municipalities have a unique opportunity to preserve their natural shoreline, significant natural areas, and natural waterfront features, which are so abundant when compared to the remainder of the bioregion's waterfront.

REGIONAL PLANNING POLICIES

In 1991 the Region of Durham approved its revised Official Plan, which is being reviewed by the Province of Ontario. The revised Durham Official Plan generally endorses the nine waterfront principles and encourages a healthy working relationship with the local municipalities to implement environmentally, economically, and socially sound planning principles. The document includes general policies directed towards implementing an ecosystem approach, used to define some broad objectives. Emphasis is placed on the need to assess the cumulative impact of various types of development within the region.

Development on the Durham waterfront has often been done piecemeal, under general direction of the local waterfront municipality. It was the Commission's view, articulated in *Watershed*, (and with which Durham concurred) that the Region co-ordinate local waterfront plans in a regional context. Although discussions have been undertaken, no significant steps towards a regional waterfront plan have been achieved within the last year.

Action is needed soon on the Region's proposal to prepare a waterfront plan to encompass all or part of Durham's Lake Ontario waterfront, from Pickering to Newcastle, in an amendment to the Regional Official Plan. The Commission supports this initiative, which is to address earlier *Watershed* recommendations, recreational opportunities, public access, wetland conservation, and other issues.

Development proposals have been submitted for extensive tracts of waterfront land in such areas as Ajax, Whitby, and Newcastle, while smaller-scale projects have been proposed for Pickering. The Oshawa Harbour Area is also the subject of discussion on revitalizing the port area and increasing public waterfront use while maintaining the environmental integrity of the land.

Durham needs to assume a leadership role by offering planning that is environmentally sound, and takes into account the cumulative effects of economic activities and community development on the natural and built environments.

Local municipalities also need to have the tools to implement such an approach to planning at their level; furthermore, co-operative action is needed locally,

provincially, and federally, as well as amongst those levels, in concert with citizens and appropriate private-sector parties. This would ensure the necessary support and acceptance of environmental imperatives, the adoption of principles and the implementation of guidelines. For example, the region could work with local waterfront municipalities to implement a greenway strategy as a tool to protect ecological integrity and the natural areas which exist today. Inadequate alternatives include piecing together remaining parcels of land after each development has been approved or losing these areas to other uses such as golf courses.

Ontario Hydro has indicated its willingness to co-operate in ensuring safe access to the waterfront in areas near the Pickering and Darlington Nuclear Generating Stations in Durham and elsewhere on their waterfront lands.

As noted in Chapter 3, the Province has recognized the need to protect the moraine. An expression of Provincial Interest was made recently, interim guidelines for planning decisions were established, and a two-year study of long-term protective measures is scheduled to be completed in 1993.

The Durham Regional Plan recognizes the Oak Ridges Moraine as a major natural feature to be protected; a similar reference should be made to Durham's 62 kilometres (39 miles) of Lake Ontario shoreline, which is fairly developed in the west, but has expanses of relatively pristine waterfront land in the east, including bluffs that rise as high as 20 metres (66 feet).

In addition, significant natural areas, river valleys, and headwaters flowing south from the moraine should be protected as part of the Greater Toronto bioregion,

Newcastle shoreline

including the Altona Forest in Pickering and the Ganaraska River flowing through Newcastle and Port Hope into Lake Ontario.

TOWN OF PICKERING

Pickering was established in the early 1800s and the first town meeting was held there in 1811. Population had escalated to approximately 8,000 by the mid-1800s, and was double that a century later. As recently as the 1950s, farming was still the major source of wealth within the township. With the development of Highway 401, developers began scouting the area for land with residential promise and found it on the waterfront. The most westerly waterfront municipality in Durham, Pickering is home to more than 50,000 people today.

Pickering has traditionally relied on the MTRCA to take the lead role in planning and land acquisition for its eight kilometres (five miles) of shoreline. The conservation authority's ability to undertake these responsibilities successfully, as well as the historic debate over the ownership of Frenchman's Bay, has limited involvement in waterfront issues by the Town and its residents.

Debate about ownership of land under Frenchman's Bay and of part of the marshlands and the eastern shore, began in 1791 when the Township deeded parts of the bay to various people. By the mid-1800s, the deeds had been purchased by the Pickering Harbour and Road Joint Stock Company, which operated a busy commercial harbour in the bay until the 1920s.

The bay was purchased by the Pickering Harbour Company in 1965, but the argument has been made that, under the 1914 federal Beds of Navigable Waters Act, ownership of all such bodies of water reverted to the Crown in the absence of an express federal government grant or a legal determination; because neither of those was made when the Pickering Harbour and Road Joint Stock Company owned the bay in 1914, the argument goes, the property reverted to the Crown at that time.

The status of the ownership of the bay and municipal control over land-use proposals is currently being considered by the courts; therefore, plans related to these lands and water bodies are dependent on resolving legal issues.

WATERSHED UPDATE

In December 1990, Pickering Town Council responded positively to the Commission's report, and concurred with the ecosystem approach and the nine principles. It also agreed with other recommendations, such as the idea of a Waterfront Trail from Burlington to Newcastle, and an immediate review of the Ontario Trees Act.

The Province of Ontario, responding to an earlier *Watershed* recommendation for a study of Frenchman's Bay — and recognizing that there are concerns about balancing development and conservation in the area and that there is no integrated analysis of the problem — commissioned a report on the bay's capacity to support additional development.

The study, completed in June 1991 by the Heritage Resources Centre (Nelson et al.) at the University of Waterloo, concluded that many land-use and environmental changes have occurred in the bay area in the last 35 years, and that many more will occur in the future. It also noted that the land-use changes have had an adverse impact on the marshes and on other environmental qualities of the bay area.

It also concluded that added research, communication, and co-ordination among government agencies, citizen, and corporate groups were needed to discuss visions, goals, and objectives for the bay as a whole; this should be done before any decisions were made on which development proposals for the area should be allowed to proceed. In support of these conclusions, the report recommended that "a moratorium be declared on developments in the Bay and its borderlands until a co-ordinated conservation and development (sustainable development) strategy is prepared".

In the past few years, development in the Frenchman's Bay area has been challenged: residents have grouped together to speak against development, and the Town has begun to recognize that there is a lack of comprehensive policies and direction on the cumulative effect of development on the shoreline and the natural environment.

Response to the June 1991 *Frenchman's Bay, Ontario: Conservation and Sustainable Development* report includes general support from key provincial agencies, the Town of Pickering, and the MTRCA. They have agreed to put together terms of reference for the recommended sustainable development strategy.

In the meantime, the conservation authority and the Town are exploring the feasibility of acquiring land owned by Sandbury Building Corporation in the northeast end of Frenchman's Bay. Sandbury's current development plans include 39 townhomes on the tableland portion of the site, with public access on floodplain lands between the development and the bay. The site is currently designated for low-density residential use and would require rezoning if the project were to go ahead. The land at the north end of the bay, currently owned by the Pickering Harbour Company, is also subject to possible residential development

Frenchman's Bay

in the future on a site that includes environmentally significant marshes created by lake-filling many years ago.

Decisions regarding future land uses of the bay, including proposed development, should not be made until more is known about its environmental state.

LOCAL PLANNING INITIATIVES

In the near future, the Town of Pickering is likely to begin a comprehensive review of its 1981 District Plan; this is an important opportunity for the Town to revise its plan and to take the ecosystem approach it supported in its earlier response to *Watershed*.

The review should focus on establishing relationships among environmental, economic, and community features that would result in a healthier, more balanced ecosystem and improved quality of life.

Significant natural areas should be protected and enhanced, including the waterfront, major waterways, and Frenchman's Bay, while development proposals should be assessed to evaluate possible environmental effects.

TOWN OF AJAX

The present site of the Town of Ajax was once rolling farmland on the edge of Lake Ontario in Pickering Township. Used as an industrial site during the Second World War, the Town was later named after a British warship, HMS Ajax, symbol of courage and determination. Ajax became a post-war community; until 1950 it had no local government. It officially became a town in 1954, when the first Town Council and Public School Board were elected; in 1974, Ajax was amalgamated to include the former Town of Ajax, the Village of

Pickering, and portions of the Township of Pickering — which increased its size from less than 1214 hectares (3,000 acres) to more than 6475 hectares (16,000 acres). The combination of historic village homes, peaceful township farms, and a modern community make Ajax an interesting place in which to live, work, and play.

The town's population has grown from more than 23,000 residents in 1979 to more than 50,000 today, more than half of whom live in the waterfront area. Much of the six kilometres (four miles) of Ajax shoreline — from Duffin Creek east to Lakeridge Road — are given over to expanses of open space. This is the result of the Town's requirement of a 400-foot (122 metre) setback in numerous low-density residential neighbourhoods along the waterfront. MTRCA has also played a major role in managing these waterfront open spaces.

When Ajax residents look south from their waterfront neighbourhoods, they can see vast areas of manicured lawn between themselves and Lake Ontario. This view is disturbed in only one place along the residential waterfront, east of Harwood Avenue at the site of the Regional Water Treatment Plant. Proposed expansion of the plant would result in further encroachment of open-space lands. This use of waterfront lands is recognized as necessary, but is not acceptable to all nearby residents.

WATERSHED UPDATE

Last year, in addressing expansion of the Regional Water Treatment Plant, the Commission noted that "the proposed plant will mean a loss of existing green space and will create a visual barrier to the waterfront." It was recommended that "creative landscaping and building design should address these problems with a view to integrating the structure with the surrounding residential neighbourhood." The Commission continues to support this view, citing the Metropolitan Toronto's R. C. Harris Water Filtration Plant, the largest facility of its kind, as a good example of an exquisitely designed public building. Rather than being an eye-sore on the waterfront, the plant is considered by many people to be architecturally outstanding; its symmetry and terraced lawns are among its most engaging features. But it is only in the past decade that architects have recognized the success of this structure and begun to give it the accolades it deserves.

The Region recognizes the need to preserve and enhance access and views to the lake in designing its Water Treatment Plant and landscaping the site.

Durham Region is currently awaiting the outcome of the Ministry of the Environment's review of the environmental study report on expanding the regional water supply plant on the Ajax waterfront. The Ministry has received requests to "bump-up" the categorization of this project from a Class environmental assessment to an individual environmental assessment; and has extended the review period indefinitely. Recent concerns about high tritium levels have led the Region to plan a further study of water quality in the near future.

The combination of historic village homes, peaceful township farms, and a modern community make Ajax an interesting place in which to live, work, and play.

Elsewhere along the Ajax waterfront, residential development is likely to continue. Most notably, two parcels of waterfront land are available for development: a significant portion of lands owned by Runnymede Development Corporation Limited, located at the east end of Ajax including Carruther's Creek Marsh, a Class III wetland; and a block of land at the foot of Harwood Avenue, currently owned by Hi-Rise Structures Limited.

Initial development proposals released by Runnymede in June 1990 showed plans for a 95-hectare (234-acre) waterfront community, including a marina at the mouth of Carruther's Creek. Runnymede later voluntarily withdrew its development plans for the Carruther's Creek site, and are currently in the process of preparing new plans based on giving the environment priority. The Commission and the Town of Ajax agree that this is a commendable process, an example of how developers can adopt an ecosystem approach to the planning process, focusing on the existing natural environment and on ways to protect and enhance important areas; moreover, this can be done while still maintaining preferred densities and developing an economically feasible project that is sensitive to more appropriate built forms and provides public access to the water's edge.

In considering the Runnymede property along the Ajax waterfront, the Commission recommended a strategy that would maintain and protect Carruther's Creek; the transfer of the Class III wetland at the mouth of the creek to be managed by a public agency; creation of a suitable, publicly owned buffer to protect wetland; and acquisition of waterfront lands east of the creek by the Town of Ajax or MTRCA as a requirement of future development. The Commission continues to support these recommendations.

R.C. Harris Water Filtration Plant, Scarborough

Carruther's Creek, Ajax

East of Carruther's Creek and the Regional Water Treatment Plant, is the 3.7-hectare (nine-acre) parcel of land owned by Hi-Rise Structures, adjacent to open space areas on the waterfront.

Hi-Rise's development plans call for approximately 440 residential apartments in four 10-storey buildings stepped back from the shoreline and, in addition, other commercial and recreational buildings. The Official Plan and zoning designations for this site permit high-density residential and commercial uses, providing a marina is developed. Hi-Rise has submitted a proposal in keeping with the residential high density, but has asked that the marina obligation be dropped. Establishing a marina in this location would require comprehensive environmental studies and a significant volume of either lakefilling or dredging.

The Commission is of the opinion that the current development plan is not designed in an environmentally sensitive manner, and would like to see the proposal modified to incorporate an ecosystem approach similar to that of Runnymede Development Corporation. Plans should be consistent with the existing open and accessible character and scale of the Ajax waterfront.

The Town of Ajax should reconsider the appropriateness of designating the Hi-Rise lands as high-density residential and of the marina requirement, taking into account the issues discussed in this report, which would have to be addressed before the Province would approve a marina and other development on this site.

LOCAL PLANNING INITIATIVES

Planning in the Town of Ajax is currently guided by the 1978 District Plan. The plan, while requiring a 400-foot (122-metre) setback in developments along the shoreline, is not based on an environmental framework. Instead, general environmental policies are contained in the Durham Regional Official Plan and the policies of local conservation authorities.

Ajax has relied heavily on MTRCA for waterfront land acquisition and maintenance; as a result of the setback provision for development along the shoreline, vast expanses of open space are maintained by the conservation authority, primarily for passive recreational uses such as walking, jogging or bicycling along the shoreline. There is an opportunity to use these spaces to provide green connectors between natural environmental areas such as Duffin Creek and Carruther's Creek. However, such corridors would have to be heavily vegetated, preferably with native plant associations to create diverse wildlife habitat.

Ajax Council is still considering the *Watershed* report, but Town staff generally endorse the ecosystem approach and the nine principles. Because the Town would benefit from implementing such an approach, they should review the District Plan to incorporate the appropriate principles; the review should include a waterfront plan that is appropriate to the Town's needs, incorporating: environmental protection of the shoreline, natural areas, and rivers flowing into the lake; appropriate land uses on the waterfront; and greenway connectors within the Town and linking it to surrounding municipalities.

TOWN OF WHITBY

In 1852 Whitby, which is adjacent to and east of Ajax, took its name from the seaside town in Yorkshire, England. Officially incorporated in 1855, it had a population of almost 3,000 people shortly thereafter; by the 1950s, Whitby was home to more than 15,000 people and now has quadruple that number. By 2001, population is expected to approach 100,000.

Today, the town's eight kilometres (five miles) of Lake Ontario shoreline stretch roughly from Cranberry Marsh east to Corbett Creek; watercourses entering the lake at Whitby include Lynde Creek, Pringle Creek, and Corbett Creek. Among the most important natural areas along the waterfront are Cranberry Marsh and the Lynde Shores Conservation Area.

WATERSHED UPDATE

Over the past year, Coscan's Harbour Isle residential development in the Town of Whitby has been hotly debated because of issues including access, massing, height, and density. In *Watershed*, the Commission recommended that continuous public access to the Whitby Harbour waterfront be incorporated into the project's plans. The following December 1990, the Province of Ontario endorsed the waterfront trail and the Commission's nine principles.

The Town of Whitby later approved plans for the Coscan project. which did not conform to the recently endorsed policy. The provincial Ministry of Municipal Affairs indicated its intention of filing a zoning appeal with the Ontario Municipal Board, using the non-compliance as grounds.

The disagreements between the Town of Whitby and the Province of Ontario were eventually resolved to everyone's satisfaction. The then Mayor Bob Attersley noted that, "through a tremendous effort of all parties concerned, we met a mutual agreement. . . . I am proud that the municipality, the [Province] and the Developer were able to mutually agree on this project."

The revised Harbour Isle development proposal has been amended to include a public walkway around the entire site, a public parkette, an at-grade public walkway from Brock Street to the water's edge allowing public access through the project, and an overall reduction in the number of residential units from 791 to 734.

The Lynde Shores Secondary Plan area, located just west of Whitby Harbour, has also been under much study in the past year. In 1990, consultants were commissioned by landowners including the Region of Durham, the Province of Ontario (Ministry of Government Services) and the private sector to undertake an environmental management plan (EMP) for the area.

This comprehensive study identifies and documents environmentally sensitive and culturally significant areas, and assesses the potential impacts of development on the biophysical and cultural resources of within the Lynde Shores Secondary Plan area. It also makes recommendations for establishing and managing these areas as major open space lands. These lands are to be maintained or enhanced as development proceeds.

This Environmental Management Plan was prepared to fulfil Ministry of the Environment requirements to grant an environment assessment exemption to the Ministry of Government Services which, as a Crown ministry involved in planning and developing provincial lands, would normally undertake a full environmental assessment. The EMP is also a policy requirement of the draft secondary plan.

PLANNING INITIATIVES

The Town of Whitby has undertaken a review of its 1974 Official Plan and recently completed the third phase of a five-phase study, *Development of Strategies and Options* (M. M. Dillon et al. 1991). In the first and second phases background information was compiled and a policy review and assessment were begun; the last two phases will propose and finalize a Draft Official Plan and accompanying policies.

The Town's development strategy endorses the ecosystem approach, and will focus on a number of elements including, but not limited to:

- moving towards achieving sustainable development through the adoption of appropriate goals and policies;
- adopting the principle of land stewardship to protect land and water resources from the negative impact of inappropriate use or premature development;
- adopting "best management" practices to manage, enhance, and conserve Whitby's natural resources;
- establishing linked parks and open-space systems, primarily through the Oak Ridges Moraine, the Lake Iroquois shoreline, the Lake Ontario waterfront, and Heber Down Conservation Area, and a system of greenways comprising valleylands, parks, utility corridors, and open-space systems; and
- encouraging conservation and protection of water bodies, fisheries, wetlands, forest, and woodlots.

The Commission believes that the steps taken by the Town of Whitby in revising their Official Plan mark substantial progress and trusts that these will lead to comprehensive policies that strengthen continued economic growth and ensure maintenance of healthy urban and rural areas in the town.

CITY OF OSHAWA

The City of Oshawa began as a clearing in the forest wilderness on the north shore of Lake Ontario, known from the early until the mid-19th century as Skae's Corners. In 1849, when it became a separate municipality known as Oshawa, the population was about 2,000.

Industrial progress began in 1876 when Robert McLaughlin, a carriage builder, moved to Oshawa to begin the McLaughlin Carriage Company; beginning with this small factory, business progressed and in 1918 the McLaughlin Carriage Company was sold and merged with the Chevrolet Motor Car Company of Canada, to form General Motors of Canada Limited. Today, the company has Canada's largest automobile plant, located on the Oshawa waterfront.

General Motors of Canada today is a waterfront-friendly industry, helping to protect the Oshawa Second Marsh located adjacent to its corporate headquarters and establishing the McLaughlin Bay Wildlife Reserve. Native vegetation is being planted and trails are being created; the area will soon be open to the public. The active protection of the marsh evolved over the past few decades, gaining support from governments and the private sector. In June 1991, General Motors received the Pickering Naturalists' Conservation Award for continued efforts to design headquarters that would be compatible with protecting the marsh — building height, glazing, and lighting were designed keeping in mind migrating birds; moreover, the headquarters development protects the Second Marsh with a berm/swale complex and silt ponds to control run-off.

The Oshawa waterfront area comprises almost eight kilometres (five miles) of Lake Ontario shoreline, stretching from Corbett Creek to McLaughlin Bay. Major local areas of environmental importance and waterways flowing into Lake Ontario include the Oshawa Second Marsh, Pumphouse Marsh, and Oshawa Creek. The Oshawa Harbour Area is also a major component of the city's waterfront.

Oshawa Harbour Commission lands currently include the Oshawa Harbour area and the Second Marsh; many people feel that the harbour area includes industrial uses that are unwanted next to a recreational area, Lakeview Park, that is likely to be used increasingly in the future. Most cargo traffic is located on the east side of the harbour, next to the environmentally sensitive Second Marsh. The future role of the harbour area is currently being studied by the City.

Over the past decade, the port has undergone major changes in cargo mix and users: in the early 1980s, St. Marys Cement relocated its high-volume coal shipments from the Oshawa port to its own private facility in Newcastle. Since that time, its salt storage, regional distribution, and other uses have also moved to the St. Marys Cement dock.

WATERSHED UPDATE

The Commission recommended a review of the 1984 Oshawa Harbour Development Plan to better define the role of the port in light of potential alternate land uses. The Commission further recommended that, if it were decided that the industrial/commercial port function was no longer warranted, the Oshawa Harbour Commission should be disbanded and its lands transferred to the City of Oshawa for development based on an approved plan that conforms to the nine principles.

General Motors headquarters building near the Oshawa Second Marsh

Since those recommendations were made, the City of Oshawa has begun a comprehensive planning study of the Southeast Oshawa area, including the Oshawa Harbour, the Second Marsh, and surrounding lands. The review is geographically divided into two areas: the Oshawa Harbour area lands and the balance of the land north and east of the harbour, including the Second Marsh.

The harbour study for the port area, undertaken by Malone Given Parsons for the City of Oshawa, examined the role and economic viability of the existing port, to determine preferred future land uses for the southeast Oshawa Harbour area. They applied the ecosystem approach outlined in Watershed, and considered port issues in the context of the environmental condition of the lands, the port's economic future, its local and regional roles, and issues that would affect the community, including public access and use of the waterfront. The study's key conclusions are that:

- a mix of cultural and recreational uses would be the most appropriate long-range plan for the port;

- a mix of industrial and non-industrial uses is a viable shorter-term strategy for servicing port industrial functions in the near future, recognizing that sustainable development requires a balance of economic and environmental changes;

- implementing the broader objectives for long-term use of the port lands (which is still anticipated) would mean moving current Oshawa port functions to an alternative harbour;

- the Port of Oshawa can continue to operate in an economically viable and self-sustaining way until a clear alternative exists;

- a Waterfront Partnership Agreement, consistent with the Commission's *Watershed* recommendations, would be the most appropriate way to ensure that the government and private landowners co-operate in implementing this (or an alternative) plan; and

- the 1984 Oshawa Harbour Development Plan and related studies were over-ambitious and cannot be supported by current or projected market demand.

The balance of the Southeast Oshawa lands were examined in a study by City of Oshawa staff. Existing land uses are primarily open space and industrial; the area includes the environmentally sensitive Second Marsh and other significant natural open-space areas. The main issues for the Southeast Oshawa study area are the need for long-term planning, soil contamination and other environmental constraints, and preservation and enhancement of natural areas, particularly the Second Marsh.

The Southeast Oshawa studies are currently undergoing departmental, agency, and public review. Following this part of the process, the City of Oshawa will make recommendations on the future role and function of the Oshawa Harbour and appropriate land-use concepts. The region's economic objectives include maintaining Oshawa Harbour as a commercial port facility until studies have been completed. If these studies support transferring port activity from Oshawa to the St. Marys Cement dock facility in Newcastle, the region may reconsider the role of Oshawa Harbour.

An additional phase of the harbour study will entail land-use and design options and implementation guidelines. It is the Commission's view that the future role of the harbour area should be decided on in an appropriate environmental context; in turn, successfully implementing the City's emerging plans will depend on its ability to bring all parties together at the earliest possible stage. Certainly, it is advantageous for the City to do so from the outset: discussing appropriate recommendations and agreeing on ways to implement a preferred option

by establishing consultations among various provincial ministries, the Oshawa Harbour Commission, the Town of Newcastle, and the Region of Durham.

The City of Oshawa's 1987 Waterfront Development Plan has been particularly successful in providing guidance for establishing and implementing a local trail system that will eventually link the city's downtown to its waterfront.

Planning for the entire city is governed by its 1987 Official Plan. This plan should be revised with a view to incorporating the ecosystem approach, and protecting and enhancing the natural environment, while promoting economic growth and community development.

TOWN OF NEWCASTLE

The Town of Newcastle was established when regional government was introduced in 1974; today, it encompasses three major urban areas: the villages of Newcastle, Bowmanville, and Courtice. Of these, Newcastle and Bowmanville are located near Lake Ontario.

In 1794 the first settlers to the Town of Newcastle arrived in Bowmanville (known as Darlington Mills until the 1830s). The area was named after Charles Bowman, a Scots merchant from Montreal who bought the local store and considerable amounts of land in the town. Bowmanville was incorporated in 1853, and became a town in 1858. By 1878, it had a population of approximately 3,500; today, with more than 14,000 residents, it is the largest urban area in Newcastle.

The Village of Newcastle, incorporated in 1856, was founded in the mid-1800s by people who wished to capitalize on its location close to the Grand Trunk Railway, which had been constructed from Toronto to Montreal between 1853 and 1856. The railway brought business to the village: brickyards, builders, and cabinetmakers, among them. Major fires in 1877, 1891, and 1896 destroyed several buildings and many local businesses, not all of which were rebuilt as the village struggled to revive itself. In the 1960s it had a population of more than 1,500, and it is estimated to have 2,500 people today.

The total population of the Town of Newcastle exceeds 45,000 and is expected to be more than 65,000 by 2001. With much of its waterfront undeveloped and its hinterland a mix of urban and agricultural areas (and some industrial uses), the Town has a great opportunity to maintain much of its current natural state.

The Town of Newcastle encompasses most of the Durham Shoreline, with more than 30 kilometres (19 miles) of waterfront, most of it undeveloped, from McLaughlin Bay east to Port Granby. Other substantial portions of Newcastle's waterfront lands are taken up by Darlington Provincial Park, the Darlington Nuclear Generating Station, St. Marys Cement, and the Wilmot Creek Retirement Community.

WATERSHED UPDATE

Local Council first approved the Official Plan for the Township of Darlington in 1960 (renamed, in 1985, the Town of Newcastle Official Plan). This plan, approved in part by the Province of Ontario in 1986 and 1987, currently includes policies for the three major urban areas: environmental and commercial, industrial, and institutional. It does not include policies or land-use designations for the waterfront or rural areas within Newcastle, portions of which are to be developed in the short and long term, as noted in the revised regional Official Plan.

In recommendations related to the Town of Newcastle, *Watershed* urged that approvals for proposed residential, commercial, industrial, tourism or recreational projects on the Newcastle shoreline be suspended until a local waterfront plan is prepared for the entire waterfront, unless such development proposals conform to the goals and objectives of such a plan and to the Commission's nine principles. Since the recommendations were made, the Town has not approved any waterfront projects.

A review of the Newcastle Official Plan was begun by staff and the first public meeting on it was held in September 1991. The Commission supports the initiative to update the Town's planning policies and reshape them to conform with the regional plan, focusing on managing growth and maintaining and improving the quality of life. A comprehensive study of the town's waterfront area is also under way and a study of the Bowmanville waterfront area is being completed.

The Commission supports this approach which will help the Town guide development of Newcastle and its waterfront area in a way that is most beneficial to those places and to the people in them. It believes that, in future, the Newcastle waterfront could offer an exciting mix of natural and built environments, and a diversity of land uses that are sensitive to their natural surroundings and that range from industrial to residential, mixed-use, and recreational, as well as natural and urban open spaces.

St. Marys Cement: Industry on the Waterfront

In 1912, a construction materials company, St. Marys Corporation, was founded in St. Marys, Ontario. Today, it is an important Canadian corporation, operating in Canada and the United States.

Since the late 1960s, St. Marys has run a quarry and cement plant on the Bowmanville waterfront in Newcastle. In 1973, the company was permitted to extract materials on the site under the Pits and Quarries Control Act. The following year, St. Marys acquired a provincial waterlot to create docking and storage facilities. In 1988, the plant produced approximately 500,000 tonnes (492,000 tons) of cement, about 8.5 per cent of the provincial total.

To remain internationally competitive, St. Marys plans to expand the capacity of the Bowmanville plant, at a cost of $160 million, so that it can produce from 2,000 to 5,000 tonnes (1,968 to 4,920 tons) of cement per day; the company has asked the Province to sell it a 32-hectare (80-acre) waterlot immediately west of the existing dock, so that it can enlarge its port facilities to accommodate two maximum-sized bulk carriers. Such facilities are important to enable the company to continue exporting to U.S. markets and they would also meet the bulk cargo needs of other Canadian companies. Furthermore, there is long-term potential for St. Marys to provide a deep-water port at the dock.

However, expanding St. Marys dock and quarry operations would affect wildlife habitat and the adjacent residential community. The company is aware of the value of the natural environment and intends to consider the site's natural attributes in planning future operations. For example, it proposes to compensate for the loss of relatively poor fish habitat, which would result from enlarging the dock, by creating an experimental lake trout spawning shoal in consultation with government and non-government wildlife experts. Similarly, consideration will be given to ways of maintaining wetland values if future quarry expansion affects Westside Beach Marsh, a Class II wetland on the St. Marys site.

By carefully designing the proposed dock, the company hopes to minimize environmental effects; it will monitor the fish shoal and potential effects of the new dock, including erosion and sediment movement.

The concerns of nearby residents include impaired vistas, dust, storm drainage, noise, and vibration from industrial operations, as well as shoreline erosion. St. Marys Cement is attempting to meet these by building landscaped berms, and by good housekeeping practices that will reduce dust and noise. It has expressed its willingness to work with various government agencies and the community at large to protect the environment while successfully operating an industry on the waterfront.

The *Watershed* report also noted that, before any recommendation could be made on future expansion of the St. Marys Cement dock facilities on the Bowmanville waterfront in Newcastle, further detailed analysis was needed. In 1989, St. Marys applied to the Ministry of Natural Resources to acquire an additional (32-hectare)

80-acre Lake Ontario waterlot that would give it the space needed to expand existing dock facilities through lakefilling. At the present time, the Province is considering whether the proposed fill should be subject to an environmental assessment.

The recommended Greater Toronto bioregion shoreline regeneration plan (Chapter 4) will also help prepare a framework within which to guide the future of the Newcastle waterfront area.

GREENWAYS

The Oak Ridges Moraine, as it reaches southeast towards the Trent River, has been used as a northern boundary in describing the Greater Toronto bioregion. However, in Durham Region it becomes obvious that there is at least one additional bioregion which should also be considered: the one encompassing the watersheds north and east of the moraine (including the green links between the three regional urban areas in Durham south of the Moraine), up to Lake Simcoe and Lake Scugog (see Map 12.1).

There is an opportunity for Durham's regional urban areas to be separated by natural areas of vegetation, and providing wildlife habitat as well as connectors to a regional greenway system, linking the major natural elements of the bioregion.

To date, the Region of Durham has not been very involved in developing the Waterfront Trail endorsed by the Province, but it supports creation of a greenway system linking public access on the waterfront to the river valleys and enhancing natural features in the major open-space system, working with local municipalities and other appropriate agencies to reach these goals.

Map 12.1 Regional greenway concept, Durham

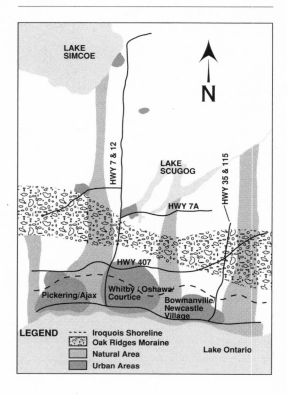

Among the key areas in which there are opportunities to develop portions of a Durham greenway system in the near future are:

- publicly owned lands in the Lynde Shores area, stretching into Cranberry Marsh and the Whitby Psychiatric Hospital lands on the Whitby waterfront
- Oshawa waterfront lands surrounding the Second Marsh, which could include public access for educational purposes; and
- those waterfront lands for which there are development proposals, because they offer opportunities for acquiring public rights of way. The Town of Newcastle has the most potential in this respect.

79. The Royal Commission recommends that Durham Region, its local municipalities, MTRCA, CLOCA and GRCA continue to review relevant documents including official plans, secondary plans and other waterfront-specific plans to ensure that they incorporate the ecosystem approach and the nine principles described in Part I.

  The review should include, but not be limited to:

  - a regional waterfront plan encompassing all of Durham's Lake Ontario shoreline;
  - a review of the Pickering District Plan; and
  - a review of the Ajax District Plan and preparation of an Ajax waterfront plan.

  Prior to establishing a comprehensive Durham waterfront plan, waterfront projects should be approved only if proponents show that the development is consistent with the ecosystem approach, the nine principles in Part I and recommendations in Part II.

80. The Commission further recommends that Durham Region, the towns of Pickering, Ajax, Whitby, and Newcastle, the City of Oshawa, MTRCA, CLOCA and GRCA participate in preparing the proposed shoreline regeneration plan, including a waterfront greenway and trail, and ensure that any other plans for waterfront areas are reviewed and/or developed in this context.

81. The Province of Ontario should negotiate one or more Waterfront Partnership Agreements with the Regional Municipality of Durham, local municipalities, other levels of government and their agencies, and appropriate private-sector bodies, to manage future waterfront activity. While different municipalities are at different stages of waterfront planning, the Waterfront Partnership Agreements should be closely linked to preparation and implementation of the regional waterfront plan, and should include:

  - clear identification of the roles and responsibilities of various agencies in implementing waterfront plans in Durham, with the Region taking the co-ordinating role;
  - a review of the design of proposed regional water supply and sewage facility plans along the waterfront, to ensure that they do not detract from other waterfront objectives;
  - strategies to protect and maintain significant natural habitats including:
    - Frenchman's Bay marshes;
    - Carruther's Creek mouth;
    - Lynde Creek mouth;
    - Pumphouse Marsh;
    - Oshawa Second Marsh;
    - McLaughlin Bay;
    - Wilmot Creek mouth; and
    - Bond Head Bluffs;
  - endorsement and implementation of the recommendations made for Frenchman's Bay, in

its *Conservation and Sustainable Development* report, after consultation with the public and with such appropriate agencies as the Town of Pickering, the Region of Durham, MTRCA and the Province of Ontario;

- a regional greenway and trail strategy consistent with recommendations in Chapter 5. This regional greenway and trail system should extend from the Oak Ridges Moraine south to Lake Ontario and north to Lake Simcoe and Lake Scugog.

The natural areas between the three regional urban nodes — Pickering/Ajax, Whitby/Oshawa/Courtice, and Bowmanville/Newcastle — should be re-established and kept in a natural state (see Map 12.1);

- transfer of the Class III wetland at the mouth of Carruther's Creek and a suitable buffer, to a public agency to be managed as a protected wetland; and acquisition of waterfront lands east of the creek by the Town of Ajax or MTRCA, prior to future development; and

- options and implementation strategies for the future of the Oshawa Harbour area; this process should include informtion on soil and groundwater contamination, appropriate clean-up standards for proposed future land uses, alternative remediation techniques, and cost/benefit analyses of the options.

EAST OF DURHAM

As noted in chapter 1, the *Watershed* report focussed on the waterfront of the Greater Toronto Area. However, with a broader understanding of the ecological features of the bioregion we now venture east of Durham to the Trent River. The Towns of Port Hope, Cobourg, Colborne, Brighton and Trenton are located along Lake Ontario in the County of Northumberland. To date, the Commission has been in contact with the towns of Cobourg and Port Hope, and includes comments specific to these areas here.

TOWN OF PORT HOPE

Port Hope is located at the point where the Ganaraska River meets Lake Ontario. In 1793, the first 27 settlers arrived in what was originally named Smith's Creek, and was later renamed Port Hope, in honour of Colonel Henry Hope, a lieutenant governor of the colony. By 1834, the town's population had grown to 1,517 and, by the mid-1900s, it had reached 6,327. Currently, Port Hope has a population of about 11,830 people, which is expected to increase by about 36 per cent over the next decade.

The Ganaraska River contributed significantly to the economic development of Port Hope: historically, it provided the power for saw and grist mills and clean water used by distilleries, making Port Hope a thriving centre of industry and trading until the beginning of the 20th century, when competition from larger centres became increasingly fierce.

Today, the Ganaraska River, which flows to Port Hope southeast from the

EARLY ECOSYSTEM PLANNING: THE GANARASKA WATERSHED

Although concepts like the ecosystem approach, watershed planning, and quality of life may seem to be new additions to our mental maps, they have existed and been applied for many decades. The 1944 Ganaraska Watershed report is an early and exciting example of their use; while terminology has changed in the years since then, many ideas and goals remain unchanged.

In 1941, citizens concerned about the environmental health of Canada, and of Ontario in particular, met at what later became known as the Guelph Conference to formulate a conservation program and lobby government. The Dominion and Ontario governments responded by agreeing to collaborate in a survey of the Ganaraska watershed and to publish a follow-up report. But another 48 years passed before the two governments actually established a joint inquiry including land-use matters: this Royal Commission on the Future of the Toronto Waterfront. One of the most significant innovations of the original Ganaraska study – the use of natural boundaries, rather than political boundaries, to determine land-use planning borders – has been used by the Royal Commission.

The Ganaraska was chosen as an example of conservation study for all of Canada. Among the most significant environmental matters of the time were related issues of erosion and flooding; toxic pollution, urban sprawl, and atmospheric change still lay in the future. Instead, terrible years of drought had alerted people to the vulnerability of Canada's soils. Photographs show the desert-like northern reaches of the Ganaraska watershed, with its sand dunes and washed-out gullies.

While those who carried out the Ganaraska study in the 1940s did not use the term "ecosystem approach" (it had yet to be coined), that they understood its value is evident in even a single paragraph of their report:

> Natural resources form a delicately balanced system in which all the parts are inter-dependent, and they cannot be handled piece-meal. The present situation requires the co-ordination of existing relevant knowledge and its amplification where necessary, and then the development of a comprehensive plan for treating the natural resources on a wide public basis.

The study's first step was to connect existing environmental problems with historical land-use patterns in order to gain a better understanding of the nature and extent of problems. In the early 19th century, lumber was Ganaraska's main industry: between 1793 and 1861, 38 saw mills operated in the region. Agriculture spread in the wake of the felling of forests. Together, these two land uses helped create erosion and flooding problems in the Ganaraska watershed. Without tree roots to bind the soil, and trees to soften the impact of falling rain, soils were easily washed away. And without tree roots to trap moisture, rain or sudden snow melts led to torrential floods, resulting in heavy property damage and occasional loss of life.

Following a survey of the climate, soils, farms, natural areas, vegetation, wildlife, areas suffering from erosion, and land uses (similar to today's "state of the environment" reports), recommendations were made to rehabilitate the watershed. They included reforestation of approximately 8,100 hectares (20,000 acres) — particularly of the delicate soils of the Oak Ridges Moraine — water retention ponds, improved agricultural practices (which included a recommendation that fragile soils be taken out of production), and the creation of several recreational centres. With the end of World War II in sight, the report's authors saw these remedial measures as providing important job creation opportunities for returning soldiers.

The report also called for provincial legislation that would combine the best features of two existing conservation programs "so that conservation projects on needy areas may be initiated immediately after the necessary local requirements of the Act are compiled with the municipalities concerned." Two years later, in 1946, the Ontario government responded and passed the Conservation Authorities Act.

Source: Richardson, A. H. 1944. *A report on the Ganaraska watershed: a study in land use with plans for the rehabilitation of the area in the post-war period.* Toronto: Ontario. Dept. of Planning and Development.

The desert-like northern reaches of the Ganaraska Watershed, circa 1940s

Oak Ridges Moraine in Newcastle, is an important recreational resource, home to thousands of rainbow trout and other species. Fishers come to the Ganaraska to participate in an annual salmon hunt or other fishing events.

Portions of the lower Ganaraska River are subject to erosion and severe annual flooding. Therefore, Port Hope has constructed concrete and stone channels to hold flood waters and has recently completed the Caven Street Erosion Control Project. This involved lining the river banks with armourstone to prevent erosion.

The waterfront area west of the Ganaraska is occupied by a beach parkette and by the Eldorado/Cameco uranium refinery. The latter industrial site is characterized by noise, odours, and contaminated soils, discouraging public use of the lakefront and commercial, residential, and other land uses in the vicinity.

East of the Ganaraska River are a sewage treatment plant and the Esco industrial area, which includes an abandoned paint factory. Most of the remaining land along the eastern shoreline is publicly owned, providing recreational opportunities for fishing, hiking, boating, and swimming. Clear access routes leading to and connecting waterfront areas are limited and are currently being considered by the Town.

The Port Hope Harbour at the mouth of the Ganaraska River is a spawning ground in spring and fall for a number of fish species, including brown trout, rainbow trout, lake trout, and Pacific salmon. Unfortunately, harbour waters and sediments are contaminated by radionuclides from former radium and uranium refining operations, as well as by high levels of phosphorus, nitrates, and metals. The levels of many of the contaminants exceed the Guidelines for Open Disposal of Dredged Materials set by the Canada-U.S. Great Lakes Water Quality Agreement. At present, the harbour is the focus of a Remedial Action Plan (RAP).

East of Port Hope Harbour is Gage Creek, which also flows from the Oak Ridges Moraine. There is a wetland area at its mouth that contains marsh vegetation including wetland tree species. Tests of the creek and nearby areas indicate poor water quality with high levels of nutrients and bacteria, as well as maximum summer temperatures that are too high for rainbow trout.

Conceptual plans have been prepared for remediating Gage Creek and other contaminated sites in the Port Hope area. The federal government will select and prepare a storage site for contaminated materials, a process that could be completed within five years, and clean-up will begin after this time.

In February 1991, the Town of Port Hope released *Town of Port Hope: Waterfront Master Planning Study*, which emphasizes the need to enhance tourism and recreation, and recommends that planning policies be altered to ensure that the Town's waterfront areas become a focus for public use. According to the master plan, policies of the Port Hope Official Plan should ensure that environmentally sensitive areas are protected, diverse land uses co-exist along the river and lakefronts, and that public access and recreational opportunities on the waterfront are improved. These goals are supported by the Commission as they are in accordance with the nine principles for waterfront regeneration.

In response to the waterfront study, the Town of Port Hope council approved formation of the Port Hope Waterfront Implementation Committee which is now involved in its first project, construction of a new harbour on the east side of the mouth of the Ganaraska. The purpose is to improve the Town's economy and enable Port Hope's citizens to reclaim the waterfront as a people place; the new facilities might also attract more tourists to Port Hope, increasing the Town's revenue and generating new jobs.

A lakefront park and a public marina with facilities that include a restaurant are planned for the new harbour. The town proposes to use lakefill in some places to provide areas for onshore marina facilities; planning for the Port Hope waterfront should be guided by the shoreline regeneration plan described earlier in this report.

A Greenways Subcommittee was formed by the Town to co-ordinate the planning and development of walkways and paths along the lakefront, Gage Creek, and the Ganaraska River. It has fully endorsed the waterfront trail concept described in *Watershed* and in the provincial report, *The Waterfront Trail: First Steps from Concept to Reality* (Reid et al. 1991). Members of the subcommittee are currently engaged in rehabilitating the Gage Creek Wetland area in order to restore its natural elements (marsh, waterfowl nesting areas) and to develop trails linked to the proposed waterfront network.

TOWN OF COBOURG

Originally named Amherst, the Town of Cobourg was founded in 1798 and renamed to honour the marriage of Princess Charlotte to Prince Leopold of Saxe-Cobourg. By the 1830s, the community had established itself as a regional centre with a population of about 1,000; by the middle of this century, population had increased to 7,818. Today it is home to more than 15,000 people, which is expected to increase by about 20 per cent in the next decade.

Cobourg has a number of public buildings of architectural and/or historical significance: Victoria Hall, also known as the Town Hall, was completed in 1860 and remains an impressive example of mid-Victorian architecture, embellished with detailed carvings. The Hall is the home of the Northumberland Art Gallery and the Victoria Hall Concert Hall. Cobourg's Old Victoria College, established in 1836,also has historical resonance: its first president was Reverend Egerton Ryerson, an educator who attracted many visitors, including actors and musicians, to the college, and who went on to establish Ontario's school system.

Construction of a harbour in the 1840s on Cobourg's beach stimulated the town's growth and the harbour soon became a busy port from which iron ore and other products were exported. A century later, after World War II, industry expanded and Cobourg became the home of several leading international companies in Canada, including General Foods and Curtis Products. However, commerce in the harbour had declined by the 1950s and development plans for alternative uses of the land have since been proposed.

Among concerns about the present condition of the Cobourg Harbour area is the presence of contaminated soil on industrial sites in the harbour lands, most of which is attributed to oil and gas spillage from storage tanks. The Town of Cobourg recognizes the need to develop and enhance the harbour area so that it becomes more accessible, usable, and attractive for residents and tourists.

In late 1990, the mayor of Cobourg asked Town staff to review *Watershed* with a view to adapting and applying its recommendations to the Cobourg waterfront area. The staff report, which endorsed the relevant *Watershed* recommendations, found that some recommendations could have implications for the town's future, while others could be adopted by policy documents or implemented through departmental programs. For example, an ecosystem-based policy to deal with waterfront issues could be included in the Official Plan, as could a policy for a waterfront trail. The staff report has been approved by council and steps are being taken to incorporate specific *Watershed* recommendations into the Town's planning.

A Harbour Area Secondary Plan (1989) has been approved by the Town of Cobourg and by the Province of Ontario. It will guide development of the harbour area, based on principles of accessibility and attractiveness to residents and tourists. The plan also notes that development should support the downtown, physically and commercially, and should maintain the town's existing scale and character. Proposed improvements include creation of parkland, promenades, pathways, and a plaza; expansion of marina facilities; and development of mixed land uses.

The Town of Cobourg will have opportunities to improve its harbour area and waterfront in the short and long term. The Commission believes that future development should be guided by comprehensive policies that deal with issues including, but not limited to, environmental protection, shoreline regeneration, appropriate land-use designations, and incorporation of public access.

There is an opportunity for Northumberland County and its member municipalities, especially the towns along Lake Ontario, to participate in future studies on the Greater Toronto bioregion.

Colborne, Brighton and Trenton, the County of Northumberland, the Ganaraska Region Conservation Authority and the Lower Trent Region Conservation Authority participate in preparing the proposed shoreline regeneration plan (Chapter 4), including a waterfront greenway and trail, and ensure that any other plans for waterfront areas are reviewed and/or developed in this context.

RECOMMENDATIONS

82. The Royal Commission recommends that the towns of Port Hope and Cobourg, the County of Northumberland and the Ganaraska Region Conservation Authority continue to review relevant documents including official plans, secondary plans, and other waterfront-specific plans to ensure that they incorporate the ecosystem approach and the nine waterfront principles described in Part I.

83. The Commission further recommends that the towns of Port Hope, Cobourg,

REGENERATION AND RECOVERY

THE INTRODUCTION OF SUSTAINABLE DEVELOPMENT WILL HAVE A REVOLUTION-
ARY EFFECT AS FAR REACHING AS THE INTRODUCTION OF STEAM, ELECTRICITY AND
ELECTRONICS IN THEIR TIME. IT IS ABOVE ALL AN INTELLECTUAL REVOLUTION. (A
REPORT FROM 45 LEADING INDUSTRIALISTS TITLED *RESHAPING EUROPE*.)

This assessment of the impact of sustainable development on the future of their continent by leading European industrialists squares exactly with the conclusions of the Royal Commission's 1990 interim report, *Watershed*: the environment and the economy are mutually dependent. Economic development and good quality of life cannot be sustained in an ecologically deteriorating environment.

The way we choose to treat the Greater Toronto waterfront is critical: if governments, the private sector, and individuals recognize — and act on — the need to resolve past environmental problems and forge strategies to protect the waterfront now and in the future, we will indeed have crossed a watershed.

In the 18 months since the Commission published its *Watershed* report, the Greater Toronto regional community, and Canada itself, have been passing through a difficult phase of self-doubt and uncertainty —

prompted, in part, by the constitutional discussions and, as well, by the downturn in the economy and the sluggish recovery.

In his introductory essay to *The Fourth Morningside Papers*, author-broadcaster Peter Gzowski (1991), speaking about Canada's current problems, says:

I don't know the answers. I'm not even sure — yet that I know all the questions, which as a radio guy, I'm better at than I am at answers anyway. I think they're there, though. I think there is a way out of the mess we've got ourselves into. I don't imagine Canadians will ever be quite the same as we were before, but when I think about that I think of a golf story I know, in which a man is coming in from the 18th hole and someone asks him if he's played his usual game, and he answers, "I never do".

"The way we were before", in other words, is really a whole lot of ways, and which ones you think — or thought — were important always depended on where you were and what was weighing on your mind at the time.

For what it's worth, I think we need a victory now. Desperately. By "victory" I mean only something that goes right, something we can agree on, even if it's only the process by which we try to mend things and not — yet — the contents of a new deal. To use a sports term, we have to turn the momentum around. We have to get some people together to say, "Look, we agree on these things, now maybe we can get down to what Lester Pearson used to call 'expanding the common ground.'"

What is true on a national level is also applicable to Toronto and the experience of the Royal Commission. As its work developed and expanded over three years, the Commission became more and more impressed with the hopes, dreams, talents, needs, and frustrations of

the people and organizations we worked with: municipal and regional governments, federal and provincial ministries, business and labour leaders, environmentalists, community activists, and citizens from all walks of life. All are interested in working towards Peter Gzowski's "victory". All want to get on with the job of developing the waterfront; planning and building for sustainability; implementing the environmental imperatives; and regenerating historic and special places.

This fourth section of the final report brings together all these perspectives and proposed solutions in a strategy for implementing this report.

The strategy involves six basic steps:

1. Adopt the ecosystem approach, and the nine waterfront principles (clean, green, useable, diverse, open, accessible, connected, affordable, attractive).
2. Establish or adjust waterfront plans to ensure they reflect the ecosystem

Mouth of Duffin Creek, Ajax

approach and the principles —
i.e., plan for sustainability.

3. Secure intergovernmental co-operation,
   agreements, and commitments on
   what needs to be
   done, the priori-
   ties, who does
   what, and the
   time-frames for
   design, con-
   struction, and
   delivery.

4. Consolidate capi-
   tal budgets and
   pool resources
   as necessary to move projects forward.

5. Create the framework and conditions
   for private-sector involvement; capitalize on its enterprise, initiative,
   creativity, and capability for investment.

6. Establish partnerships: among governments, and between the public and
   private sector, in accordance with
   planning and project requirements.

As far as the first two steps are concerned, the ecosystem approach is a way
of doing things as well as a way of thinking;
adopting its values and philosophy leads to
different ways of doing things. Increasingly,
these values are being accepted by governments, by many companies in the private
sector, and by the community at large. The
ecosystem approach is the cornerstone
of *Our Common Future*, the report of the
World Commission on Environment and
Development (1987), and is reflected in the
mandate of the many round tables that were
created in response to it.

In 1978, the International Joint
Commission included a commitment to
restore and maintain the integrity of the

*As its work developed and expanded
over three years, the Commission became
more and more impressed with the
hopes, dreams, talents, needs, and
frustrations of the people and
organizations we worked with.*

Great Lakes Basin ecosystem as part of
the renewed Great Lakes Water Quality
Agreement. The goal of the federal
government's Green Plan for a Healthy
Environment (1990)
is to balance
economic growth
with an environment
that sustains life
today and for
future generations.
In responding to
Watershed, the
Government of
Ontario adopted, as provincial policy, the
ecosystem approach to planning.

This final report contains many examples of government agencies, businesses,
landowners, and developers modifying plans
and activities to accommodate this approach.
The result is a smoother, faster system of
project approvals and decisions, which
means easier, more efficient investment
and job creation that offers better results
for the environment and for the economy.

Step three in the strategy calls for
intergovernmental co-operation, agreements,
and commitments. The sheer number of
public agencies involved on the waterfront
(more than 75 by the Royal Commission's
count) has led to fragmentation, gridlock,
and a lack of public accountability. The idea
that there must be sweeping reform of
public jurisdiction and administration to
reduce the number of agencies and the
levels involved as a necessary precondi-
tion of regenerating the waterfront, is
hardly new:

The eyes of the administration are
focused on the waterfront.

In the formative years of Metro
politicians and planners looked north,

457

Runnymede Development Corporation Limited and the 'Environment-First Approach' to Planning

Runnymede Development Corporation Limited owns 95 hectares (234 acres) of land bordering Lake Ontario in Ajax. In the summer of 1990, it proposed a residential subdivision for the site, comprising approximately 600 single-family dwellings, 130 town-houses, 1,300 condominiums, and other uses including a hotel, marina, office and retail space, and recreational areas.

At that time, however, the developers were not fully aware of the impact the project would have on the environment, particularly on the existing ecosystems of the Carruther's Creek Marsh and the Ajax Warbler Swamps, both of which lie within the boundaries of the property. These natural areas, designated as regionally and provincially significant, would have been damaged and a planned 250-berth marina would have been especially harmful to the marsh.

After discussions with government agencies and local interest groups, Runnymede voluntarily withdrew its proposal and re-evaluated the project; it decided to implement a new strategy, stressing an "environment-first approach" and developing a new and innovative plan for the property.

This process began with an assessment of the property's physical and biological features. Based on that information, a document outlining the environmental guidelines for planning was prepared; it established the net acreage that can be developed by preserving the Ajax Warbler Swamps and creating two buffer zones around the marsh. The 60- to 90-metre (197- to 295-foot) wide buffer will preserve existing grassland areas that are important for nesting migratory birds, and establish an outer reforestation zone that will restrict pedestrian access and shelter the marsh from adjacent development lands.

The results of the study were reviewed with local authorities, agencies, and interest groups before the company began work on an Environmental Management Plan (EMP). The purpose of the EMP is to find ways to mitigate potential harm to the marsh and woodlot as a result of developing the future residential community.

Concurrent with preparing the EMP, Runnymede is developing subdivision concepts. At this writing, it is refining a final concept that will include a variety of low-, medium-, and high-density residential units with a small neighbourhood commercial facility. A 122-metre (400-foot) wide park is proposed along the shoreline to include pedestrian links to the west and, ultimately, to the east.

Runnymede's "environment-first approach" embraces the principles for a healthy waterfront as outlined in *Watershed*, which will be reflected in the proposed community in a number of ways: maintaining the wetlands and constructing stormwater ponds to filter water from urban run-off will assure that it is clean and green. Bikeways and path-ways connecting to the marsh, and a lake driveway permitting transit, will enable the area to be more accessible, useable, and open. To the north, a proposed wildlife corridor would link habitats of the Ajax Warbler Swamps to another complex to the east.

The project will also be diverse and affordable, accommodating a range of activities and housing types. Finally, by maintaining and enhancing existing natural features, Runnymede will create an attractive community that offers a high quality of life for future residents.

Carruther's Creek Marsh

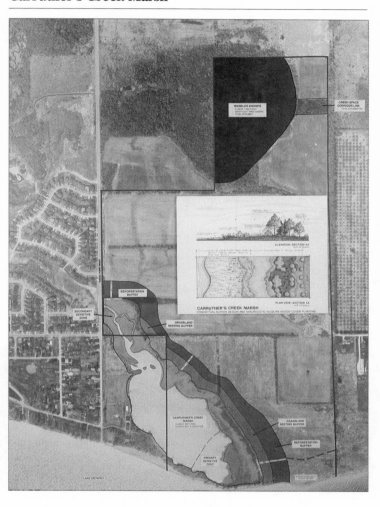

east and west in an attempt to keep pace with the exploding residential and commercial development. And while they did this, the waterfront — about 20 miles of shoreline — was chopped up and jurisdiction was split among several bodies. . . .

It resulted in piecemeal development. Toronto City Council became aware of the problem and recognized the hodge-podge of development on its doorstep. . . . It directed its Planning Board to prepare a report.

Out of this concern, the Greater Toronto Branch of the Community Planning Association of Canada stepped into the breach. . . . As food for thought the association proposed a master plan for harbour development. It recommended the creation of an authority to supervise development of the whole waterfront from end to end.

In the meantime a metropolis of 1.5 million persons is sweltering in the midsummer heat, and swimming along the 20 mile stretch of waterfront has been banned because of pollution.

This is a comparatively small problem but it is evidence that there is a problem.

This call for an authority "to supervise development of the whole waterfront from end to end", taken from an article by Raymond Hill in the *Telegram* of 24 July 1959, was never heeded. And there is little reason to believe that, if it had been, the result would have been workable — for many reasons.

After close and careful consideration of public administration of the waterfront, the Royal Commission has concluded that no single level of government can or should be in control of it. The issues are too complex, cut across too many boundaries, involve too many scales and levels: local, provincial, national, and international; they cannot be left in one pair or even in several sets of hands. Even if it were theoretically desirable to do so, the question of whose hands would control the waterfront would be a matter as delicate and as fraught with difficulty as finding the answer to our constitutional predicament — and take just as long!

Public administration of the waterfront is a shared responsibility and should remain so, each government — federal, provincial, and local — performing its role within its jurisdiction in partnership with others. That is not to say that there should

Darlington Provincial Park, Newcastle

not be and cannot be changes and adjustments to public institutions. The Commission's recommendations to modify the roles and mandates of Harbourfront Corporation and the Toronto Harbour Commissioners, which were accepted by the Government of Canada and are now in the process of being implemented, are just two examples of such essential changes.

In the overall scheme of things these are relatively minor adjustments, of course, and others may be necessary in future. The real key to the public administration of the waterfront is the round-table process — one that brings together all the parties at the appropriate time, publicly and openly, so that public values can be debated and determined, and various agencies made accountable. Indeed, the ecosystem approach demands this.

In its *Watershed* report, the Royal Commission proposed that:

> This process of bringing governments and people together should begin with the Government of Ontario. The Province should recognize the Toronto Regional Waterfront as a Provincial Resource and commit itself to a policy and program of waterfront regeneration. The representatives of government and government agencies, and the scores of interest groups and individuals who came before the Commission — and who consistently called for strong provincial leadership, collaboration, and resources on which new provincial-municipal partnerships

could be constructed — would applaud and support such a declaration.

The agreements would be created across the waterfront, where appropriate, and up the river valleys, as necessary. While there would obviously be common elements among them, the exact form, nature, composition, and time-frame of the agreements would, of course, depend on the issues being addressed and the regeneration opportunities being pursued in each municipality.

The federal government should also consider participating in these agreements, where appropriate. It now has an outstanding opportunity to apply its commendable commitment to the environment in practical ways. Under the Great Lakes Water Quality Agreement, Canada and the United States have specific responsibilities for water quality in the Great Lakes, including, of course, Lake Ontario. Canada also has other responsibilities according to federal-provincial agreements, such as the RAPs.

Both before and after the release of Watershed, the Province showed leadership; it responded quickly and strongly in a variety of ways to the ideas in both interim reports, including:

- adopting the ecosystem approach and the nine principles as waterfront policy;
- approving and acting on the Waterfront Greenway/Trail;

The real key to the public administration of the waterfront is the round-table process — one that brings together all the parties at the appropriate time, publicly and openly, so that public values can be debated and determined, and various agencies made accountable.

- agreeing to set up the Waterfront Regeneration Trust and to enter into such Waterfront Partnership Agreements with municipalities, the federal government, and other parties as are necessary to achieve waterfront goals.

The Government of Canada also indicated a willingness to act within its jurisdiction in partnership with others, and continued to move on the Commission's recommendations. It, too, adopted the ecosystem approach (in the Green Plan, for example, which the Government is currently considering as it applies to the Greater Toronto region). It made organizational changes to Harbourfront Corporation and began making alterations to the Toronto Harbour Commissioners, as recommended by the Royal Commission.

Canada Post, which is a federal Crown corporation, negotiated a strategic land transaction in Mississauga that will help advance that City's waterfront plan. Other federal departments have been receptive to consideration of, and possible support for, various waterfront initiatives such as an international exhibition and the International Trade Centre. In December 1991, the federal government asked the Commissioner to bring parties together to prepare a Memorandum of Understanding on the future of the Port lands and the Toronto Harbour Commissioners.

Municipalities and conservation authorities also reacted positively, generally accepting the principal recommendations of *Watershed*, developing their own ideas for their waterfronts within a broad regional framework, and signalling their willingness to enter into partnerships. For example:

- Halton Region, the City of Burlington, the Town of Oakville, and the Halton Region Conservation Authority have an effective partnership on the waterfront, and are working to implement such waterfront projects as "Windows-on-the-Lake" and securing strategic properties.
- The City of Mississauga assembled an intergovernmental consortium to negotiate a major waterfront land transaction with Canada Post Corporation.
- The City of Etobicoke and several developers and landowners in the area have made enormous efforts to complete the plans and secure approvals for redevelopment of the motel strip.
- Metropolitan Toronto is developing a waterfront plan. It is placing priority on developing its interests in the Garrison Common, and is helping to co-ordinate the Waterfront Trail across the Metropolitan waterfront.
- The City of Toronto, having negotiated with Harbourfront Corporation, the Toronto Harbour Commissioners, and the owners of the Railway Lands, has obtained 61 hectares (150 acres) of land for parks and the financial resources to develop them. Added to Metro's waterfront parks and those of MTRCA, these comprise a base for developing the green infrastructure on the Central Waterfront, as recommended in Chapter 10.
- Scarborough actively participated in the action to save the Rouge Valley and is co-operating with MTRCA and others in developing the plan for Rouge Park.
- Municipalities in Durham Region — Pickering, Ajax, Oshawa, Whitby, and Newcastle — have taken steps, in

co-operation with others, to balance protection and development of their respective waterfronts in ways suitable to their particular circumstances:

– Pickering is working with the Province to help sort out the administrative and legal framework of Frenchman's Bay.

– Ajax is co-operating with Durham Region to find the best design solution for the regional water treatment plant and its surrounding area.

– Oshawa, in concert with the federally appointed Harbour Commission, is examining the

Toronto Islands Park

options for the future of its harbour.

- Whitby has asked the Province to approve a major redevelopment project for the eastern edge of its harbour and, with the Province and other landholders, is completing plans for Lynde Shore.
- In co-operation with its regional counterpart, Newcastle is completing its first plan for the as-yet largely undeveloped shoreline in a way that supports industry and protects environmental values.
- Durham Region is establishing a new plan that includes the waterfront as a regional focus for the constituent municipalities.

• East of Durham, Port Hope is starting to implement its waterfront master planning study, emphasising economic renewal, tourism, recreation, and the protection of environmentally sensitive areas. Cobourg has a secondary plan for its harbour area including mixed uses, marina expansion, parks, and tourism opportunities.

Clearly, the possibilities of extended intergovernmental co-operation look good; there are signals that all governments in the region are searching for the pathway to economic and environmental regeneration. This is not from some shallow desire to climb on the environmental bandwagon, but because they recognize that new ways of thinking and of doing things, as proposed in the six basic steps of the regeneration strategy, offer the only path forward.

It is also important to consider the economic implications of an ecosystem approach. The Commission held discussions on the regional economy in 1991; these indicated that:

• Toronto's recovery is important, not only for the metropolis itself, but because of its significance to the provincial and national economy.

• It is evident that the continuing weakness of Toronto's largest traditional trading partners (Québec and the United States) may inhibit or delay an export-led recovery.

• Manufacturing's share in the region's employment is still shrinking; many experts believe some fundamental structural change is under way and that many of the manufacturing jobs that have disappeared since the last economic downturn will never return, which means that we must develop a new manufacturing base, after identifying the new industries that can replace lost jobs.

• To the extent that the service sector is dependent on general economic conditions, including strong interprovincial and international trading conditions that remain weak, this sector is unlikely to lead the region's recovery.

• Tourism, the region's second largest industry, is also depressed and will remain so as long as Toronto's prices are high in comparison to those of its competitors, and as long as Toronto lacks new tourist "products" to attract domestic and international customers.

• The construction industry has probably been hardest hit of all sectors: since the real estate boom came to its abrupt end, it has suffered an unemployment rate as high as 40 per cent.

The economic downturn has been difficult, and in some cases devastating, for the individuals, families, and corporations directly affected; nonetheless, Torontonians, like other Canadians, are still optimistic about themselves and their communities. For example, in his weekly column in the *Globe and Mail*, on 9 November 1991, David Olive wrote:

> Incredible. In the midst of widespread lay-offs and plant closures, unprecedented cynicism directed at governments and signs that their country is on the verge of cracking up, Canadians appear to be pronouncing themselves mightily pleased with the way their lives are going.

> Certainly there are worse ways of starting a week than to read, as we did on Monday, the upbeat findings of a *Globe and Mail*–CBC News poll of 2,631 Canadians conducted between Oct. 21 and 28. If we are to believe this survey, an astonishing 91 per cent of us feel we have a good or very good quality of life. Two-thirds of Canadians are confident we'll have enough money to cover future expenses. Nine of 10 people polled say they're satisfied with their communities as good places to live. And 51 per cent say their jobs give them a great deal of satisfaction, with an additional 38 per cent saying they get at least some satisfaction from their work. The poll results cut across both genders, and all ages, regions and income levels.

The Commission believes that, if this is an accurate reflection of the state of the regional economy and of the way people in

Constructing Queen's Quay station for Harbourfront LRT, Toronto

Greater Toronto view themselves and their community, there is a basis for action. A program for regenerating the waterfront — utilizing our human and financial resources, built on what we have learned about the ecosystem approach and dealing with environmental issues — will help stimulate the regional economy. The three elements of this proposed program are to:

- build new infrastructure compatible with the environment;
- deliver a long-range housing program on the Central Waterfront and around GO stations elsewhere along the waterfront; and
- develop green enterprise and industry.

The first element of the program is the recognition, common among the different levels of government as well as the private sector, that the region has been living for more than 15 years without maintaining appropriate levels of investment in its basic infrastructure. For example, the Board of Trade of Metropolitan Toronto, in its 1991 annual report, has been among those who argue that inadequate investment in infrastructure is one of the threats to the economic status of our community. The resulting backlog is potentially very damaging unless there is prompt action to restore a better balance in investment priorities. If a program could be agreed on and put in place now, it would have a useful counter-cyclical impact and stimulate the economy.

The idea of using an appropriate infrastructure to help the Greater Toronto region recover its economic health is hardly new: reconstruction of the Sunnyside boardwalk and the early work on the Queen Elizabeth Way were used to combat the Depression of the '30s; reforestation of the Ganaraska helped the region weather post-war difficulties; and the Government of Canada's $2.4 billion Special Capital Recovery Program helped pave the way for the economic prosperity of the mid- and late 1980s.

A broad range of infrastructure is needed, and much of it should be in water-front areas, including "green infrastructure" (the greenway and trail, parks, and other open spaces); environmental management and control (water and sewage treatment plants and systems); transportation (expansion of commuter rail services and urban transit); and new and expanded facilities for tourism, trade, and convention business.

Many of these elements of infrastructure have been clearly identified by various governments; some projects now in various stages of the design and approvals process could be accelerated.

The second element of the strategy involves housing, in the Central Waterfront area as well as in other parts of the water-front — for example, clustered round GO stations. The Commission's Publication No. 15, the *Toronto Central Waterfront Transportation Corridor Study*, (discussed in Chapter 10 of this report), as well as other studies and planning reports carried out for the Commission and for the City of Toronto, Metropolitan Toronto, and the Province came to the conclusion that a substantial housing program is needed in the Central Waterfront area.

The consulting team that prepared Publication No. 15 calculated that construction of 3,500 units of housing a year on or close to the Central Waterfront (in line with the volumes proposed in Cityplan '91) would stimulate an annual construction investment of $400 million and produce 7,000 person years of direct and indirect employment annually. The team proposed that this level of effort be maintained over the next 20 to 30 years, and said there is sufficient land — some 304 hectares (750 acres) — in the Central Waterfront area to accommodate this additional population.

Such a program would also be more benign environmentally than allowing sprawl to continue unchecked. It would help reduce growth pressures for long commuting trips to the Central Area via the Central Waterfront, would encourage greater use of transit, help to create a richer urban experience, and greatly reduce land consumption in the suburbs.

The third element in the proposed program is to create green industry and enterprise in the region. This is already happening to some extent, but its full potential is only beginning to dawn on people. In

Little Sugar Creek Greenway, downtown Charlotte, North Carolina

order to explore and carry out productive investment in industry, services, and jobs, a Centre for Green Enterprise and Industry in the Lower Don Lands was proposed by the Commission in the *Watershed* report.

Chapter 10 of this final report discusses additional studies and activities related to the concept that have appeared since the publication of Watershed. It also identifies some green industry possibilities: telecommunications, film and television, design and graphic arts, waste recycling, among them. New products and processes are suggested that will repair existing environmental damage and prevent it in the future — everything from industrial scrubbers to closed-loop manufacturing systems.

Green industry can be considered in a broader context as well: cleaning up a Great Lake or a regional watershed; decontaminating polluted soils; expanding a GO system instead of an urban expressway; redeveloping obsolete industrial and transportation lands in the inner city for housing and mixed use rather than taking over agricultural land on the periphery — all are green enterprises.

If governments can agree on a proposed program for recovery and are prepared to enter partnerships, there are numerous opportunities along the waterfront for projects large and small, public and private. Private-sector projects that are based on the principles and practices of the ecosystem approach and that conform to municipal waterfront plans should be approved expeditiously. Small-scale public projects that are within the scope and the budgets of individual public agencies should also be identified for early implementation.

A substantial number of major strategic projects are beyond the financial capabilities of single agencies or levels of government, particularly given the very tight fiscal constraints that all governments face. These would require intergovernmental — and, in some instances, public/private-sector partnerships — to become reality.

While these projects are proposed for various places along the waterfront, and appropriate partnerships should be maintained or formed to carry them out, the majority are slated for the Metropolitan Toronto waterfront. That is where the most extensive land transitions are occurring, where the environmental strains are the heaviest, and where economic opportunities are greatest.

Stage I of the Central Waterfront program, integrating environment, land use, and transportation, would provide the core for a recovery program here.

The Central Waterfront offers four major redevelopment opportunities: at Humber Bay, Garrison Common, the Central Transportation Corridor, and the Lower Don Lands. Within each of these areas, major multi-million-dollar projects are being proposed or planned by various public- and private-sector proponents. They include:

- major parks and open-space expansion, including a greenway and trail connections;
- expansion and upgrading of environmental management and control systems (water and sewage works);
- flood control measures;
- expansion of commuter rail and local transit systems, as well as new stations for GO Transit and additional subway lines;
- improvements to arterial roads, expressways, and bridges;
- railway relocation;
- housing and mixed-use developments, such as Etobicoke's Harbour Village, Garrison Creek, CityPlace, Southtown, St. Lawrence Park, and Castlepoint at Polson's Quay;
- additional commercial cultural, recreational, and entertainment facilities in Exhibition Place and Ontario Place;
- upgrading and expansion of convention, tourism, trade, and business facilities; and
- possibly, an international exhibition (Expo '96, '97 or '98).

The costs of the public elements are substantial: for example, as of December 1991, Metropolitan Toronto's waterfront capital budget alone includes $1.2 billion of works in progress, $1.1 billion of works to which some commitment has been made, and a further $700 million of works that could be done in the next five years, but for which there is no current commitment.

The City of Toronto and the Province also have multi-million-dollar projects on

Windward Co-op and Little Norway Park, Bathurst Quay, Harbourfront, Toronto

their books. The Province has given high priority to the new GO Stations, for instance, while the City of Toronto has its own high-priority, multi-year capital project in the $350-to-$400-million Sewer System Master Plan, which will virtually eliminate combined sewer overflows and will control and treat stormwater run-off.

Which brings us to the fourth step in the strategy: given the range, size, and complexity of these capital projects, the tight budgetary restraints facing all governments, and the urgent need for both economic recovery and environmental regeneration, there is only one way to proceed.

Governments must get together promptly, agree on plans, projects, and priorities, consolidate their capital budgets, and pool resources. They must then create conditions under which the private sector will willingly bring its resources to bear, in order to create investment and jobs.

Fortunately, this has already begun. The round-table process initiated by the Royal Commission for the environmental audit, the Garrison Common Preliminary Master Plan, and the Toronto Central Waterfront Transportation Corridor Study brought together governments and private-sector interests. The process is now at the point where the four governments on the Central Waterfront — the Province, Metropolitan Toronto, the City of Toronto, and the City of Etobicoke — are beginning to exchange information on capital plans and to look at the use of their extensive public lands along the waterfront as equity they could put into public-private partnerships. The Government of Canada has committed to do its share in its own jurisdiction.

If governments agree quickly, the fifth of the six steps that comprise the strategy will have been reached and this will create the conditions for step six: establishing partnerships among governments, and between the public and private sectors, in accordance with planning and project requirements.

The Commission believes that the conditions are present for creating a critical mass of public and private sector activity, once governments agree on plans and projects to be implemented so that the private sector can design, finance, and construct them. This will "jump-start" environmental regeneration and contribute to economic recovery, providing both short- and long-term jobs along the waterfront and in the region.

To obtain the maximum benefits from the proposed strategy, an agreed intergovernmental process for co-ordination, including the establishment of appropriate Waterfront Partnership Agreements, and possibly one or more development "vehicles" to support public and private initiatives, will be needed.

Co-ordinating efforts and establishing partnerships should include, local, regional, provincial, and federal governments, as appropriate; special authority agencies; private-sector interests; and community groups. Any development instruments should operate at arm's length from governments and should adopt a business approach to their mandates.

> *Governments must get together promptly, agree on plans, projects, and priorities, consolidate their capital budgets, and pool resources. They must then create conditions under which the private sector will willingly bring its resources to bear, in order to create investment and jobs.*

EPILOGUE

It is difficult to think of another period in our history when the incidence of change has been so great and the opportunity to do it right has been so exceptional.

In offering its perspective on places along the waterfront of the Greater Toronto bioregion, and in recommending specific courses of action to regenerate them, the Commission is guided, of course, by the principles and values of the ecosystem approach.

They are based on certain fundamentals that we need to keep reminding ourselves are there: that hydrology, topography, and climate set the fundamental conditions for human habitation and that, if respected, these conditions give our places unique shape and character. We also need to remind ourselves that nature exists in cities, that there are still the wild places and natural systems — rivers, creeks, valleys, hills, shorelines, and vacant lots — in which, healed and cared for, life-giving regeneration can occur.

We need to take advantage of the new thinking already being practised in our suburban places: beginning as essentially residential enclaves, dependent in the main on the core city for jobs, they made commuting a way of life. But over time, many suburbs have begun to emerge as important places of employment, social diversity, and cultural energy. Now, the new approach calls for greater integration and intensity of land use and built form, energy conservation, and public transportation. This regeneration of the suburbs, which is occurring around the world, may propel our suburban places into the role they always promised they would play: offering the best of both worlds, city and country!

We need to remember the value of maintaining our landscapes: natural landscapes born of ecological processes and meeting our need for environmental balance; working rural landscapes in which goods are produced to feed us and future generations; and city landscapes that remind us of our cultural heritage and a way of life that enriches us all.

We are responsible for the consequences of our own actions — to ourselves and to other people, to other generations, and to other species. The ethic that justifies moving in, using up, throwing away, and moving on is no longer acceptable.

> *We are responsible for the consequences of our own actions — to ourselves and to other people, to other generations, and to other species.*

We believe, with Toronto architect Jeffery Stinson that, "our history is imbedded in everything we build"; that valuing what has been will make us more careful as we plan what is to be.

When we assume that "progress" means degrading our natural and built heritage, that it's better to "start all over again", we are always in danger of wiping out collective memories. In consequence, we often reduce our history to personal genealogy and visit European, Asian, and African places to link ourselves with the past — of which so little remains in our local experience. Moreover, when the winds of change blow, we are not rooted enough to know what is important to us or our sense of ourselves and how to defend it. As a result, our places become indistinguishable from other modern places in the western world and people — even those who have lived in one place all their lives — find themselves increasingly disconnected from it.

We need to understand the evolutionary way: there is no ultimate perfect city and, inevitably, our changes will be changed by those who come after us. We need to understand that change comes as a better friend when it is done within an overall context of continuity.

We need to understand and appreciate our natural and human heritage — making a careful inventory of what we have, reusing and recycling what we can, developing what we require, and weaving the new into the old.

Our current path is unsustainable. Both our economy and our environment are under stress; we are sacrificing the future to mask the reality of the present. It is the Commission's view that, done effectively and imaginatively, the process of regeneration will not only contribute to the husbanding of our resources for economic recovery, but will also give us places where unique features are enhanced rather than homogenized and where "development" and "conservation" become kindred ideas that bring us together.

Finally, in this report, we have tried to keep in mind the Olympian insight of Lewis Mumford (1938) in his great work, *The Culture of Cities.*

Cities are the product of time. They are the molds in which men's lifetimes have cooled and congealed, giving lasting shape, by way of art, to moments that would otherwise vanish with the living and leave no means of renewal or wider participation behind them. In the city, time becomes visible: buildings and monuments and public ways, more open than the written record, more subject to the gaze of many men than the scattered artifacts of the countryside, leave an imprint upon the minds even of the ignorant or the indifferent. Through the material fact of preservation, time challenges time, time clashes with time: habits and values carry over beyond the living group, streaking with different strata of time the character of any single generation.

The city is a fact of nature. But [it] is also a conscious work of art, and it holds within its communal framework many simpler and more personal forms of art. Mind takes form in the city; and in turn, urban forms condition mind. For space, no less than time, is artfully reorganized in cities: in boundary lines and silhouettes, in the fixing of horizontal planes and vertical peaks, in utilizing or denying the natural site, the city records the attitude of a culture and an epoch to the fundamental facts of its existence. The dome and the spire, the open avenue and the closed court, tell the story, not merely of different physical accommodations, but of essentially different conceptions of man's destiny. The city is both a physical utility or collective living and a symbol of those collective purposes and unanimities that arise under such favoring circumstance. With language itself, it remains man's greatest work of art.

Appendix 1:
Orders in Council

CANADA

PRIVY COUNCIL

P.C. 1988-589

Certified to be a true copy of a Minute of a Meeting of the Committee of the

Privy Council, approved by Her Excellency the Governor General

on the 30th day of March, 1988.

WHEREAS there exists a historic opportunity to create a unique, world class waterfront in Toronto;

AND WHEREAS there is a clear, public understanding that the challenge can only be achieved with more cooperation among the various levels of government, boards, commissions and special purpose bodies and the private sector;

AND WHEREAS the Intergovernmental Waterfront Committee has identified a number of urgent matters that must be studied and dealt with;

AND WHEREAS the Government of Canada has certain jurisdictional and property responsibilities in the area:

Now therefore, the Committee of the Privy Council, on the recommendation of the Prime Minister, advise that the Honourable David Crombie be authorized to act as a Commissioner effective from June 1, 1988, and that a Commission, to be effective from that date, do issue under Part I of the Inquiries Act and under the Great Seal of Canada, appointing the Honourable David Crombie to be a Commissioner to inquire into and to make recommendations regarding the future of the Toronto Waterfront and to seek the concurrence of affected authorities in such recommendations, in order to ensure that, in the public interest, Federal lands and jurisdiction serve to enhance the physical, environmental, legislative and administrative context governing the use, enjoyment and development of the Toronto Waterfront and related lands, and more particularly to examine

(a)   the role and mandate of the Toronto Harbour Commission;

(b)   the future of the Toronto Island Airport and related transportation services;

(c)   the issues affecting the protection and renewal of the natural environment insofar as they relate to federal responsibilities and jurisdiction;

.../2

474

(d)   the issues regarding the effective management
        of federal lands within the Toronto Waterfront
        area; and

(e)   the possible use of federal lands, facilities,
        and jurisdiction to support emerging issues,
        such as the proposed Olympic Games and World's
        Fair; and,

The Committee do further advise that the
Commissioner

(a)   be directed to seek full consultation with all
        interested parties and especially the Province
        of Ontario and the City and Metropolitan
        Governments;

(b)   be authorized to adopt such procedures and
        methods as he may from time to time deem
        expedient for the proper conduct of the
        inquiry;

(c)   be assisted in the conduct of the inquiry,
        where appropriate, by the officers and
        employees of the various departments or
        agencies of the Government of Canada;

(d)   be authorized to sit at such times and in such
        places as may be required and to rent such
        space and facilities as may be required for
        his staff, in accordance with Treasury Board
        policies, in both Ottawa and Toronto;

(e)   be authorized to engage the services of such
        staff and technical advisors, including
        counsel, as he may consider necessary or
        advisable, at such rates of remuneration and
        reimbursement as may be approved by Treasury
        Board;

(f)   be authorized to engage the services of such
        experts and other persons as are referred to
        in section 11 of the Inquiries Act who shall
        receive such remuneration and reimbursement as
        may be approved by Treasury Board;

(g)   be authorized to publish special studies as
        may be appropriate from time to time and to
        submit interim reports to the Governor in
        Council as may be required;

                                        ...3

P.C. 1988-589

- 3 -

(h)   be directed to submit his report in both
        official languages to the Governor in Council
        with all reasonable dispatch, but not later
        than June 1, 1991; and

(i)   be directed to file the records and papers of
        the inquiry as soon as reasonably may be after
        the conclusion of the inquiry, with the Clerk
        of the Privy Council.

CERTIFIED TO BE A TRUE COPY - COPIE CERTIFIÉE CONFORME

CLERK OF THE PRIVY COUNCIL - LE GREFFIER DU CONSEIL PRIVÉ

Ontario
Executive Council

Order in Council

On the recommendation of the undersigned, the Lieutenant Governor, by and with the advice and concurrence of the Executive Council, orders that

WHEREAS the Province of Ontario recognizes the importance of the Interim Report and recommendations of the federal Royal Commission on the Future of the Toronto Waterfront, of which the Honourable David Crombie is Commissioner;

AND WHEREAS, in the spirit of returning the waterfront to the people, the Commissioner has recommended that there be intergovernmental management and co-operation, that the mandate of the Toronto Harbour Commission be refocussed and that the Toronto Harbour Commission lands and Provincial lands in the central waterfront be "pooled" for the purpose of carrying out a comprehensive environmental evaluation to assist in determining the most appropriate future uses of these lands;

AND WHEREAS the Commission's Interim Report acknowledges the environmental significance of the waterfront and the ecological dependence of the waterfront on the headwaters, source areas and river valleys which drain into Lake Ontario;

AND WHEREAS the Commission's Interim Report also recognizes the extensive socio-economic pressures which characterize waterfront development and the importance of rational planning and development of the waterfront on the future quality of life and well being of hinterland areas;

AND WHEREAS the Province of Ontario recognizes the Provincial interest in a number of key aspects of the Commission's next phase (Phase 2), including ensuring that the natural environment is fully considered and given due weight in any deliberations regarding future development options for the waterfront, that open space and continuous public access are fundamental components of future waterfront development and that transportation and broader quality of life issues associated with the sustainable socio-economic development of the fastest growing economic area of the country are effectively managed;

O.C. 2465/89

- 2 -

AND WHEREAS there are significant provincial land holdings which are integral to future waterfront development;

AND WHEREAS the Province of Ontario wishes to collaborate with the Federal Government in Phase 2 of the Royal Commission's work in order to achieve the objectives set out in the Royal Commission's Interim Report and to avoid any confusion regarding the position of the Province of Ontario on the need for coordinated and sensitive development of the waterfront and to avoid duplication in public hearings processes;

AND WHEREAS it is considered expedient to cause inquiry to be made under the Public Inquiries Act, R.S.Q. 1980, c. 411 concerning the following matters associated with the Toronto Waterfront, which matters are hereby declared to be of public concern;

AND WHEREAS such inquiry is not regulated by any special law;

NOW THEREFORE pursuant to the provisions of the said Public Inquiries Act a commission be issued to appoint the Honourable David Crombie a Commissioner:

1. to inquire into and recommend initiatives to preserve and create continuous public access to the water's edge extending from the eastern boundary of the Region of Durham to the western boundary of the Region of Halton;

2. to inquire into and make an environmental evaluation of those Toronto Harbour Commission lands and adjacent Provincial lands recommended to be pooled in the aforesaid Interim Report;

3. to inquire into and make recommendations on issues associated with management and development of the pooled and other appropriate waterfront lands, including:

    (a) appropriate allocation of waterfront lands to various uses, i.e. housing, open space, industrial and commercial uses;

478

(b) waterfront transportation in the context of the regional transportation system;

(c) housing and community development on the waterfront; and

(d) employment and job opportunities relating to the waterfront;

4. to inquire into and recommend waterfront related initiatives to preserve and enhance the quality of the environment and the quality of life for people residing in the greater metropolitan area extending from the eastern boundary of the Region of Durham to the western boundary of the Region of Halton;

5. to inquire into and recommend financing proposals and other mechanisms to link and integrate the waterfront to the upstream watersheds in the aforementioned locations.

AND THAT the Commissioner shall complete his inquiry and assessment and make recommendations and deliver his report by June 1, 1991;

AND THAT all Government Ministries, Boards, Agencies and Commissions shall assist the Commissioner to the fullest extent in order that he may carry out his duties and functions, and that he shall have authority to engage such counsel, experts, technical advisors, investigators and other staff as he deems proper, at rates of remuneration and reimbursement to be approved by the Management Board of Cabinet;

Recommended _____ Concurred _____
Minister of Municipal   Chairman
Affairs

Approved and
Ordered _____October 12, 1989_____   _____
          Date   Lieutenant Governor

P.C. 1991-479

CANADA

PRIVY COUNCIL

Certified to be a true copy of a Minute of a Meeting of the Committee of the Privy Council, approved by His Excellence the Governor General on the 14 March, 1991

WHEREAS the Royal Commission on the Future of the Toronto Waterfront was directed to submit a report to the Governor in Council embodying its findings, recommendations and advice on or prior to June 1, 1991;

AND WHEREAS the Commission will not be in a position to submit its report on or prior to June 1, 1991.

THEREFORE, the Committee of the Privy Council, on the recommendation of the Prime Minister, pursuant to Part I of the Inquiries Act, advise that a commission do issue amending the commission issued pursuant to Order in Council P.C. 1988-589 of March 30, 1988 by deleting therefrom the following paragraph:

"AND WE DO HEREBY direct our said Commissioner to submit his report in both official languages to the Governor in Council with all reasonable dispatch, but not later than June 1, 1991;"

and by substituting therefor the following paragraph:

"AND WE DO HEREBY direct our said Commissioner to submit his report in both official languages to the Governor in Council with all reasonable dispatch, but not later than December 30, 1991;"

CERTIFIED TO BE A TRUE COPY - COPIE CERTIFIÉE CONFORME

CLERK OF THE PRIVY COUNCIL - LE GREFFIER DU CONSEIL PRIVÉ

Ontario
Executive Council

Order in Council
Décret

On the recommendation of the undersigned, the Lieutenant Governor, by and with the advice and concurrence of the Executive Council, orders that:

Sur la recommandation du soussigné, le lieutenant-gouverneur, sur l'avis et avec le consentement du Conseil des ministres, décrète ce qui suit :

WHEREAS the Honourable David Crombie was appointed a Commissioner under the *Public Inquiries Act* by Order in Council 2465/89;

AND WHEREAS that Order in Council states that the Commissioner is required to complete his inquiry and assessment and make recommendations and deliver his report by June 1, 1991;

AND WHEREAS it is deemed necessary and in the public interest to extend the period of appointment of the Commissioner;

NOW THEREFORE the Commissioner, the Honourable David Crombie, shall complete his inquiry and assessment and make recommendations and deliver his report by December 31, 1991. The directions contained in the Order in Council 2465/89 continue to apply in all other respects.

Recommended _____
Minister of
the Environment

Concurred _____
Chair

Approved and Ordered ___March 20, 1991___
Date

_____
Lieutenant Governor

O.C./Décret   536/91

APPENDIX 2:
ANNOTATED BIBLIOGRAPHY

ROYAL COMMISSION PUBLICATIONS

In addition to this final report, the Commission has published 15 major discussion papers, two interim reports, 11 working papers, and 12 technical papers. In general, each one summarized plans and initiatives in a subject area; highlighted issues that require the attention of all levels of government if the waterfront is to achieve its highest potential; and identified new opportunities that could be pursued if there were greater co-ordination in the work of all governments and public authorities.

The Royal Commission also published 13 issues of the *Newsletter* of the Canadian Waterfront Resource Centre (ISSN 0840-9846), in order to increase public awareness of issues and policy directions.

DISCUSSION PAPERS

1. *Environment and Health: Issues on the Toronto Waterfront.* 1989. Royal Commission on the Future of the Toronto Waterfront. Environment and Health Work Group. ISBN 0-662-16539-2. DSS cat. no. Z1-1988/1-41-1E.

    Examines the existing policy framework as it affects environment and health in relation to Metropolitan Toronto's waterfront and suggests improvements. Focuses on six topics that illustrate many of the environmental and

health issues of the waterfront ecosystem: water quality, lakefilling, heritage preservation, natural areas and wildlife, public involvement, and jurisdictions. Recurrent themes include the principle of sustainability, the goal of virtually eliminating toxic substances, and the ecosystem approach. Bibliography.

2. *Housing and Neighbourhoods: The Liveable Waterfront.* 1989. Royal Commission on the Future of the Toronto Waterfront. Housing and Neighbourhoods Work Group. ISBN 0-662-16936-0. DSS cat. no. Z1-1988/1-41-2E.

    Discusses housing and neighbourhoods on or close to the Metro lakeshore: opportunities exist for protecting the environment and enhancing existing neighbourhoods while, at the same time, doubling the waterfront population through sensitive intensification of present communities and careful development of new neighbourhoods. Identifies key policy goals, and makes recommendations on how these can be achieved in terms of affordability, planning and design controls, government co-ordination and accountability. (Includes statistics which are updated in the Royal Commission working paper, *Greater Toronto Region and Waterfront: Community Overview.*)

3. *Access and Movement.* 1989. Royal Commission on the Future of the Toronto Waterfront. Access and Movement Work Group. ISBN 0-662-16937-9. DSS cat. no. Z1-1988/1-41-3E.

    Proposes a network of transportation types to and along the waterfront, with particular attention to the way modes interact and support one another. Included in this transportation framework are waterfront transportation centres, where different forms of transport come together, and where there are possibilities for development and access to the water. Discusses many kinds of networks: trails and walkways, bicycles, parking lots, streetcars and buses, GO Transit — as well as waterfront scenic drives, extensions of north-south roads, visual access, recreational boating, and cruises. Maps include: existing transportation infrastructure; the proposed transportation framework; local issues on the Metro Toronto waterfront; and local issues on the central area waterfront. Bibliography.

4. *Parks, Pleasures, and Public Amenities.* 1989. Royal Commission on the Future of the Toronto Waterfront. Parks, Pleasures, and Public Amenities Work Group. ISBN 0-662-16936-0. DSS cat. no. Z1-1988/1-41-4E.

    Looks at open space and recreational issues along the Metropolitan Toronto waterfront. There is an inventory of existing recreational facilities along the waterfront, followed by an examination of policies, plans, and projects currently in effect or under active consideration by various public agencies, private developers, and other waterfront interests. Identifies new opportunities to improve public enjoyment of the waterfront, emphasizing general policy goals and implementation strategies. Useful appendices include "Institutional Framework" information on mandates, powers, and approaches of the major waterfront agents on the waterfront, at all levels of government. Reading list.

5. *Jobs, Opportunities, and Economic Growth.* 1989. Royal Commission on the Future of the Toronto Waterfront. Jobs, Opportunities, and Economic Growth Work Group. ISBN 0-662-16939-5. DSS cat. no. Z1-1988/1-41-5E.

    Recommends a working waterfront for Metropolitan Toronto, examines plans for the 12 geographical areas on the waterfront, and identifies the major issues and redevelopment opportunities related to those plans. Proposes policy initiatives that might be used to encourage industries to remain or relocate on the waterfront. Bibliography.

6. *Persistence and Change: Waterfront Issues and the Board of Toronto Harbour Commissioners.* 1989. Royal Commission on the Future of the Toronto Waterfront. Steering Committee on Matters Relating to the Board of Toronto Harbour Commissioners. ISBN 0-662-16966-2. DSS cat. no. Z1-1988/1-41-6E.

    Focuses on issues associated with Toronto's port and waterfront, examining issues in terms of their history and the future, with a view to developing a broad perspective on the port and, more generally, the Toronto waterfront. Not all waterfront issues considered in this report are exclusively within the mandate of the Toronto Harbour Commissioners (THC), but because they are important to the community as a whole, they may shape expectations of the THC. Covers such issues as access, environment and health, the port, ownership, land use, and accountability.

7. *The Future of the Toronto Island Airport: The Issues.* 1989. Royal Commission on the Future of the Toronto Waterfront. ISBN 0-662-17067-9. DSS cat. no. Z1-1988/1-41-7E.

    Evaluates issues involving the Toronto Island Airport, related transportation services, the need to develop strategic options that will meet the needs of the aviation companies, the travelling public, and the overall interests of all users of Toronto's waterfront. Describes the airport's origins and history, reviews submissions of more than 50 deputants at

Commission hearings on the airport, and proposes a number of approaches to making decisions about the airport's future. Bibliography.

8. *A Green Strategy for the Greater Toronto Waterfront: Background and Issues: A Discussion Paper.* 1990. Royal Commission on the Future of the Toronto Waterfront. ISBN 0-662-17671-5. DSS cat. no. Z1-1988/1-41-8E.

    Complements Royal Commission Publication no. 4, *Parks, Pleasures, and Public Amenities*; summarizes information on current ecological, recreational, and public uses and values along the Greater Toronto waterfront and associated river valleys, as well as the progress of public agencies in maintaining or creating waterfront open space and recreational facilities. Identifies gaps in and barriers to a linked system of waterfront and valley-land green spaces, and discusses issues and opportunities that should be addressed by a Green Strategy, as well as actions necessary to implement such a strategy. Three appendices: summary of regional and local municipality waterfront policies; regional and municipal planning documents and related studies; and specific issues and opportunities in waterfront municipalities. Bibliography.

9. *Waterfront Transportation in the Context of Regional Transportation: Background and Issues.* 1990. Royal Commission on the Future of the Toronto Waterfront. ISBN 0-662-17730-4. DSS cat. no. Z1-1988/1-52-2E.

    Discussion paper describes existing and potential future transportation demand, facilities, and services, for the Greater Toronto Area and for the GTA waterfront in particular. Presents examples of interactions between provision of transportation infrastructure and land use. The final chapter poses questions which can serve as criteria in developing and evaluating alternative transportation concepts for the waterfront. Maps include existing transportation infrastructure, and Lake Shore Corridor transportation concept.

10. *Environment in Transition: A Report on Phase I of an Environmental Audit of Toronto's East Bayfront and Port Industrial Area.* 1990. Royal Commission on the Future of the Toronto Waterfront. ISBN 0-662-17847-5. DSS cat. no. Z1-1988/1-52-3E.

    Using the ecosystem approach, Phase I of the environmental audit seeks to understand connections and interactions among terrestrial, aquatic, and atmospheric components of the environment and human activities in the East Bayfront/Port Industrial Area. Existing information on environmental conditions in the study area is reviewed, information gaps are identified, and a number of options for research in Phase II are proposed. Publication accompanied by Phase I technical papers: *Atmospheric Environment, Built Heritage, Natural Heritage, Soils and Groundwater, Aquatic Environment.*

11. *Pathways: Towards an Ecosystem Approach: A Report on Phases I and II of an Environmental Audit of Toronto's East Bayfront and Port Industrial Area.* 1991. Royal Commission on the Future of the Toronto Waterfront. ISBN 0-662-18577-3. DSS cat. no. Z1-1988/1-41-11E.

    Phase II of the audit provides a better understanding of the environmental conditions of the East Bayfront/Port Industrial Area. Describes the physical structures of the study area ecosystem, including their historical development. Examines how the ecosystem functions, and makes a preliminary assessment of ecosystem health. Discusses the ecosystem approach, the notion of ecosystem integrity, and the ways in which decisions are made about ecosystems, including issues of stewardship and accountability. Proposes 29 recommendations toward improving ecosystem integrity in the East Bayfront/Port Industrial Area. Includes maps and bibliography. Publication accompanied by Phase II technical papers: *Atmospheric Environment, Built Heritage of the East Bayfront, Ecosystem Health: A Biophysical Perspective, Hazardous Materials, Natural Heritage, Soils and Groundwater, Water and Sediments.*

12. *Planning for Sustainability: Towards Integrating Environmental Protection into Land-Use Planning.* 1991. Royal Commission on the Future of the Toronto Waterfront. ISBN 0-662-18929-9. DSS cat. no. Z1-1988/1-41-12E.

Discusses better ways to integrate environmental and land-use planning in order to promote environmentally sustainable economic development adequate to the needs of the region during the next decade. Examines various problems in Ontario's existing land-use planning and environmental assessment process, and the need for reform. Suggests reforms that could immediately improve the system, and calls for a public inquiry to study and consult on the issues before any recommendations can be made to government on whether and how to develop a fully integrated system. Appendices, including one, 'Towards an Ecosystem Approach to Land-Use Planning', that proposes a way in which growth and development could be planned.

13. *Shoreline Regeneration for the Greater Toronto Bioregion.* 1991. Royal Commission on the Future of the Toronto Waterfront. ISBN 0-662-18981-7. DSS cat. no. Z1-1988/1-41-13E.

Examines policies, practices, technology, and methods available to regenerate shoreline areas. Addresses the public's desire for the benefits of shoreline modification and its desire to avoid the negative consequences of previous projects. Suggests that correction can come only from a co-ordinated, planned approach based on the conviction that the benefits of regeneration will far exceed the effort expended. Recommends leadership by the two senior levels of government in development and implementation, and public input to achieve understanding, acceptance, and support for the goals, objectives, and constraints of the plan. Bibliography.

14. *Garrison Common: Preliminary Master Plan.* 1991. Royal Commission on the Future of the Toronto Waterfront. ISBN 0-662-19121-8. DSS cat. no. Z1-1988/1-41-14E.

Offers innovative recommendations for regenerating the environment and economy of Garrison Common and enhancing surrounding neighbourhoods. Covers such sites as Fort York, Exhibition Place, Ontario Place, Coronation Park, HMCS York, the Tip Top Tailor building, the old Loblaw's warehouse, the Massey-Ferguson works, and the Molson holdings. Seeks to establish year-round use of the area, high-activity, public, urban waterfront parks, making the Common a permanent home for a wider range of regional outdoor/indoor events. Appendix and bibliography published separately.

15. *Toronto Central Waterfront Transportation Corridor Study.* 1991. Royal Commission on the Future of the Toronto Waterfront. ISBN 0-662-19248-6. DSS cat. no. Z1-1988/1-41-15E

Sets out transportation options for the Toronto Central Waterfront; identifies the environmental, land-use, urban design, and economic opportunities and concepts they help make possible; the required financial resources and related risks; proposes a program aimed at achieving these cost effectively. Envisions a redesigned and relocated Gardiner Expressway/Lake Shore Boulevard facility to help strengthen the links between the city and its renewed Central Waterfront and to improve the area's quality as a place, while maintaining and enhancing its essential function as a transportation corridor. Maps.

Interim Report, August 1989. 1989. Royal Commission on the Future of the Toronto Waterfront. ISBN 0-662-17215-9. DSS cat. no. Z1-1988/1E.

The Royal Commission's first interim report discusses the future of the Toronto Island Airport; the role, mandate, and development plans of the Harbourfront Corporation; the role and mandate of the Toronto Harbour Commissioners, as well as various environment and health issues. Findings are based on research studies and public hearings, at which more than 300 groups and individuals made submissions. Interjurisdictional recommendations ensure that public benefits are among the considerations shaping future development of the waterfront. Bibliography. A working paper, published separately, is *An Index to the First Interim Report of the Royal Commission on the Future of the Toronto Waterfront, August 1989.*

Watershed: Interim Report, August 1990. 1990. Royal Commission on the Future of the Toronto Waterfront. ISBN 0-662-18012-7. DSS cat. no. Z1-1988/1-62-1990E.

    Watershed, the Royal Commission's second interim report, calls for an ecosystem approach to planning the waterfront and the Greater Toronto bioregion; provides nine guiding principles; and directs 80 recommendations to various levels of government. Written in three main sections: explaining the ecosystem approach and analysing the state of the health of the Greater Toronto bioregion; proposing principles that should guide policy and planning; addressing area-wide and area-specific issues. Submits that the Greater Toronto waterfront from Burlington to Newcastle should be clean, green, useable, diverse, open, accessible, connected, affordable, and attractive. Index and references.

WORKING PAPERS

    Working papers provide a public forum for addressing various waterfront issues that warrant research and discussion.

1.   Merrens, H. R. 1989. *A Selected Bibliography on Toronto's Port and Waterfront.* Royal Commission on the Future of the Toronto Waterfront. ISBN 0-662-17596-4. DSS cat. no. Z1-1988/1-42-1E.

    Intended as a guide to the diversity of material pertaining to Toronto's port and waterfront produced in recent years by a variety of people, including scholars, journalists, architects, planners, engineers, and others. Bibliographical entries.

2.   Clark, N. J. 1990. *An Index to the First Interim Report of the Royal Commission on the Future of the Toronto Waterfront, August 1989.* Royal Commission on the Future of the Toronto

Waterfront. ISBN 0-662-17597-2. DSS cat. no. Z1-1988/1-42-2E.

    The 600 headings include personal names, government bodies, corporations, geographical locations, and subject terms.

3.   Munson, W. 1990. *Soil Contamination and Port Redevelopment in Toronto.* Royal Commission on the Future of the Toronto Waterfront. ISBN 0-662-17729-0. DSS cat. no. Z1-1988/1-42-3E.

    Draws attention to the legacy of soil contamination left by Toronto's industrial past. Planning decisions for redeveloping the Port Industrial District will need to consider the relative clean-up costs for different uses. Topics include soil contamination, quality of fill material, clean-up costs, port redevelopment schemes, the planning debate, and environmental audits.

4.   Lemon, J. 1990. *The Toronto Harbour Plan of 1912: Manufacturing Goals and Economic Realities.* Royal Commission on the Future of the Toronto Waterfront. ISBN 0-662-18005-4. DSS cat. no. Z1-1988/1-42-4E.

    Considers why the Toronto Harbour Commissioners (THC) chose manufacturing as the centrepiece of its 1912 plan for the Port Industrial Area and, specifically, what kinds of high value-added industry they hoped to attract. Explains why bulk storage and processing predominated instead.

5.   Greenberg, K. and G. Sicheri. 1990. *Toronto's Moveable Shoreline.* Royal Commission on the Future of the Toronto Waterfront. ISBN 0-662-18160-3. DSS cat. no. Z1-1988/1-42-5E.

    Examines settlement along the shores of Lake Ontario during the first half of the 19th century, in order to define the nature of early relationships between the City of Toronto and its waterfront. These are compared to conditions that evolved along the central waterfront, as lakefilling continued into the 20th century, in an effort to understand how this has altered the relationship between the metropolitan area and its waterfront. Identifies

challenges to establishing necessary city/
waterfront links.

6. Gertler, M. S. 1991. *Toronto: The State of
   the Regional Economy*. Royal Commission
   on the Future of the Toronto Waterfront.
   ISBN 0-662-18888-8. DSS cat. no. Z1-1988/
   1-42-6E.

   Analyses the state of Toronto's economy
   from a regional perspective, describing recent
   structural changes to employment, investment,
   output, and income throughout the region in
   the past 20 years. Identifies current and future
   challenges to the region's economic health
   and underlines the need to realign our way
   of thinking about economic growth and
   government's role in fostering it.

7. Munson, W. 1991. *The Disposal of Coal Ash at
   Toronto's Outer Harbour*. Royal Commission
   on the Future of the Toronto Waterfront.
   ISBN 0-662-18902-7. DSS cat. no. Z1-1988/
   1-42-7E.

   Examines land creation at Toronto's
   Outer Harbour, specifically through the use
   of coal ash from the R. L. Hearn thermal generating station. Places the Toronto experience in
   the broader context of world-wide use of waste
   materials in creating urban land, and comments
   on the potential environmental implications
   of this practice. Maps and bibliography.

8. Davies, K. 1991. *Towards Ecosystem-based Planning:
   A Perspective on Cumulative Environmental Effects*.
   Royal Commission on the Future of the
   Toronto Waterfront. ISBN 0-662-19085-8.
   DSS cat. no. Z1-1988/1-42-8E.

   Explores how cumulative environmental
   effects can be addressed in environmental
   planning and management in the Greater
   Toronto bioregion. These are defined as
   including social, economic, and biophysical
   considerations, as well as the interactions
   among them. Lists individuals and organizations familiar with cumulative environmental
   effects, and initiatives related to those effects.
   Bibliography.

9. Klinger, X. 1991. *Metropolitan Toronto
   Winter Waterfront Study*. Royal Commission
   on the Future of the Toronto Waterfront.
   ISBN 0-662-19138-2. DSS cat. no. Z1-1988/
   1-42-9E.

   Presents a strategy for enhancing
   and increasing year-round public use and
   enjoyment of the Metropolitan Toronto waterfront. Discusses policies, guidelines, and low-
   cost initiatives that could be implemented by
   local and regional municipalities, and by conservation authorities in order to enhance waterfront accessibility, diversity, connectedness, and
   usability during the colder months. Bibliography.

10. Garland, G. 1991. *Greater Toronto Region
    and Waterfront: Community Overview*. Royal
    Commission on the Future of the Toronto
    Waterfront. ISBN 0-662-19148-X. DSS cat.
    no. Z1-1988/1-42-10E.

    Analyses key social and economic issues
    on the greater Toronto waterfront, and makes
    policy proposals. Focuses on population
    growth, household incomes, housing trends,
    employment and journeying-to-work according
    to mode of transportation. Includes statistical
    municipal and waterfront area community
    profiles. Bibliography.

Desfor, G. 1990. *Urban Waterfront Industry, Planning
and Developing Green Enterprise for the 21st Century:
A Report of the Symposium Held on November 16, 1989*.
Royal Commission on the Future of the Toronto
Waterfront. ISBN 0-662-17640-5. DSS cat.
no. Z1-1988/1-52-1E.

Summarizes discussions at a symposium
convened to consider new ideas for developing environmentally sound industry on Toronto's port lands.
Examines past and current issues, problems, and
trends related to industry in the port area. Details
potential obstacles to environmentally sound
industrial development, and proposes policies likely
to overcome them and to encourage appropriate
industry in the port lands. Bibliography.

APPENDIX 3:
WATERSHEDS

Appendix III summarizes existing information about the watersheds draining into Lake Ontario in the Greater Toronto bioregion. Six conservation authorities are responsible for them; from west to east, they are: Halton Region Conservation Authority; Credit Valley Conservation Authority; Metropolitan Toronto and Region Conservation Authority; Central Lake Ontario Conservation Authority; Ganaraska Region Conservation Authority; and Lower Trent Region Conservation Authority. Except for the area covered by Lower Trent Region Conservation Authority, which was mapped by the Ministry of the Environment, maps were provided by the conservation authorities involved.

Population figures for each watershed were calculated using 1986 census tracts and watershed boundaries: watershed boundaries were outlined on the census tract maps; census tracts inside a particular watershed were identified; and population numbers recorded. In areas where census tracks straddled watershed boundaries or extended beyond the GTA borders, estimates were made of the percentage of the census tract lying within the watershed boundary and, on that basis, the population was calculated for that portion: if only 20 per cent of the census tract fell within a watershed boundary, only 20 per cent of that census tract's population were counted as part of the watershed's population.

In order to provide a brief overview of the range of existing watershed studies and plans, the Commission asked the conservation authorities to indicate whether they have undertaken studies or plans regarding erosion/flooding, water quality, habitat, and individual watersheds. In addition, in the 1980s, most conservation authorities had prepared overall plans for their areas of jurisdiction.

The last column, labelled "jurisdictions", shows that most watersheds include several municipalities and that — when undertaking planning and management on a watershed scale — there is a need for intermunicipal co-operation.

Existing Watershed Information[1]

Watershed	Area (km²)	Population[2] (1986)	Erosion/ Flooding	Water Quality	Habitat[3]	Watershed Studies[4]	Jurisdictions[11]
Halton Region Conservation Authority							
Grindstone Creek	86	8,220	—	x	x	—	H(Burl); H-W(Flam)
Falcon Creek	4	6,570	—	x	x	—	H(Burl)
Indian Creek	22	23,550	—	—	x	—	H(Burl)
Hager Creek	8	3,500	x	—	x	—	H(Burl)
Rambo Creek	21	9,230	x	—	x	—	H(Burl)
Roseland Creek	9	12,730	x	—	x	—	H(Burl)
Tuck Creek	12	15,000	x	—	x	—	H(Burl)
Shoreacres/ Appleby Creeks	25	13,240	x	—	x	—	H(Burl)
Sheldon Creek	18	14,940	x	—	x	—	H(Burl,Oak)
Bronte McCraney / Fourteen Mile / Taplow Creeks	352	40,800	x	x	x	Fourteen Mile Creek and McCraney Creek Watershed Planning Study (Draft)	H(Burl, Milt, Oak); Well (Pusl)
Sixteen Mile Creek	350	65,460	—	x	x	Just beginning	H(Milt, Oak)
Morrison/ Wedgewood Creeks	24	9,060	x	—	x	—	H(Oak)
Joshua Creek	22	5,210	—	—	x	Process underway	H(Oak)
Credit Valley Conservation Authority							
Credit River	850	355,220	x	x	x	Credit Valley Water Management Strategy	H(Milt, HH, Oak); P(Miss, Bramp, Cal); Duff (Mono); Well(Erin)
Metropolitan Toronto and Region Conservation Authority							
Etobicoke Creek	212	210,200	x	x	x	—	P(Miss, Bramp); MT(Etob)
Mimico Creek	92	167,010	x	x	x	TAWMS[5]	P(Miss); MT(Etob)
New Toronto Creek[6]	14	30,030	—	—	—	x	MT(Etob)

Watershed	Area (km²)	Population[2] (1986)	Erosion/ Flooding	Water Quality	Habitat[3]	Watershed Studies[4]	Jurisdictions[11]
Metropolitan Toronto and Region Conservation Authority *(continued)*							
Humber River	910	520,040	x	x	x	TAWMS; ARCH[7] initiatives underway	P(Miss, Bramp, Cal), MT(Etob, York, Tor, NY); Y(Vau, King, Aur)
Don River	363	929,400	x	x	x	TAWMS; studies underway	MT(York, Tor, EY, NY, Scar); Y(Vau, RH, Mark)
Lake Ontario[8]	—	400,200	—	—	—	—	MT(Tor, Y, Scar); D(Ajax, Whit, Osh, New)
Highland Creek	109	332,120	x	x	x	—	MT(Scar); Y(Mark)
Rouge River	333	99,400	x	x	x	Rouge Strategy	MT(Scar); Y(RH,Aur, Mark,W-S); D(Pick)
Petticoat Creek	29	7,240	x	—	x	Master Drainage Plan	MT(Scar); Y(Mark); D(Pick)
Frenchman's Bay	22	27,950	x	x	x	Proposal for funding	D(Pick)
Duffin Creek	293	28,800	x	x	x	—	D(Pick, Ajax, Ux)
Carruther's Creek	38	13,490	x	—	x	Master Drainage Plan	D(Pick, Ajax)
Central Lake Ontario Conservation Authority							
Lynde Creek	135	20,080	x	x	x	—	D(Whit)
Pringle Creek	29	7,600	x	x	x	—	D(Whit)
Corbett Creek	15	12,050	x	—	x	—	D(Whit, Osh)
Oshawa Creek	120	51,090	x	—	x	—	D(Osh)
Harmony/ Farewell/ Black Creeks	105	62,140	x	x	x	—	D(Osh, (New)
Robinson Creek	6	390	x	—	x	—	D(Osh, New)
Tooley Creek	11	780	x	—	x	—	D(New)

Watershed	Area (km²)	Population[2] (1986)	Erosion/ Flooding	Water Quality	Habitat[3]	Watershed Studies[4]	Jurisdictions[11]
Central Lake Ontario Conservation Authority *(continued)*							
Darlington Creek	17	1,170	x	—	x	—	D(New)
Westside Creek	6	3,050	x	—	x	—	D(New)
Bowmanville Creek[9]	169	6,990	x	—	x	—	D(New)
Soper Creek[9]	169	8,450	x	—	x	—	D(New)
Ganaraska Region Conservation Authority							
Wilmot/Orono/ Hunter/Stalker Creeks	98	3,220	x	x	x	—	D(New)
Graham/ Mullingan/ Crooked Creeks	78	3,280	x	x	x	—	D(New); N(Hope)
name unknown	9	—	x	—	x	—	D(New)
Bouchette Point Creek	17	—	x	x	x	—	D(New)
Port Granby Creek	19	—	x	x	x	—	D(New)
Crysler Creek	4	—	x	—	x	—	N(Hope)
Wesleyville Creek	10	—	x	—	x	—	N(Hope)
Morish Creek	34	—	x	x	x	—	N(Hope)
name unknown	9	—	x	—	x	—	N(Hope)
Ganaraska River	259	3,190	x	x	x	—	D(New); N(Hope)
Gage Creek	46	—	x	x	x	—	N(Ham)
name unknown	3	—	x	—	x	—	N(Ham)
name unknown	5	—	x	—	x	—	N(Ham)
name unknown	—	—	—	—	x	—	N(Ham)
Cobourg Brook/ Baltimore Creek	119	—	x	x	x	—	N(Ham, Hald)
Midtown Creek	6	—	x	—	x	—	N(Ham)
Brook Creek	15	—	x	—	x	—	N(Ham)
name unknown	6	—	x	—	x	—	N(Ham)
name unknown	12	—	x	—	x	—	N(Ham, Hald)
Lower Trent Region Conservation Authority[10]							
Barnum House Creek	—	—	x	—	—	—	N(Hald)
Shelter Valley Creek	—	—	x	—	—	—	N(Hald)
Colborne/Salem/ Butler/Proctor/ Smithfield Creeks	—	—	x	—	—	—	N(Hald, Cram, Bright)
Trent River	—	—	—	—	—	—	Hast; N; Pete
name unknown	—	—	—	—	—	—	N(Mur)
name unknown	—	—	—	—	—	—	N(Mur, Bright)

NOTES

x : Information exists in reports and in some instances in data files. Information varies in age, quality, and quantity.

— : No information exists.

1. Existing watershed information as of November 1991. Watershed information and boundaries provided by Conservation Authorities.

2. Population data restricted to population in watershed within GTA boundaries.

3. Habitat includes information on Environmentally Significant Areas (ESAs), fisheries and other wildlife.

4. Studies noted are only for individual watersheds, not the watershed plans undertaken during the 1980's for the entire area of the conservation authority's jurisdiction.

5. TAWMS: Toronto Area Water Management Strategy.

6. New Toronto Creek runs through an underground pipe: no watershed information available.

7. ARCH = Action to Restore a Clean Humber.

8. Lake Ontario Watershed drains land between the Humber River and Don River Watersheds, and between Don River and Highland Creek Watersheds. No creeks currently drain this area.

9. Together Bowmanville and Soper Creeks have a watershed area of 169 km^2.

10. In the Lower Trent Region Conservation Authority only major watersheds are included. The LTRCA has not mapped watershed boundaries.

11. Jurisdictions

H-W=Regional Municipality of Hamilton-Wentworth
Flam=Town of Flamborough

W=County of Wellington
Pusl=Township of Puslinch
Erin=Township of Erin

Duff= County of Dufferin
Mono=Township of Mono

H=Regional Municipality of Halton
Burl=City of Burlington
Milt=Town of Milton
HH=Town of Halton Hills
Oak=Townof Oakville

P=Regional Municipality of Peel
Miss=City of Mississauga
Bramp=City of Brampton
Cal=Town of Caledon

MT=Municipality of Metropolitan Toronto
Etob=City of Etobicoke
Tor=City of Toronto
York=City of York
EY=Borough of East York
NY=City of North York
Scar=City of Scarborough

Y=Regional Municipality of York
Vau=City of Vaughan
King=Township of King
RH=Town of Richmond Hill
Aur=Town of Aurora
Mark=Town of Markham
W-S=Town of Whitchurch-Stouffville

D=Regional Municipality of Durham
Pick=Town of Pickering
Ajax=Town of Ajax
Ux=Township of Uxbridge
Whit=Town of Whitby
Osh=City of Oshawa
New=Town of Newcastle

N=County of Northumberland
Hope=Township of Hope
Ham=Township of Hamilton
Cram=Township of Cramahe
Hald=Township of Haldimand
Bright=Township of Brighton
Mur=Township of Murray

Pete=County of Peterborough
Hast=County of Hastings

APPENDIX 4:
ILLUSTRATION CREDITS

INTRODUCTION

p. 3
Toronto Skyline, view from the Toronto Islands
Metropolitan Toronto and Region Conservation
Authority

p. 8
Bluffer's Park Marina, Scarborough
Dr. J. D. Murray

p. 15
Watersedge Park, Mississauga
Debbie Williams, Royal Commission on the Future of
the Toronto Waterfront

CHAPTER 1

p. 20
no caption
Lisa Ohata, Royal Commission on the Future of the
Toronto Waterfront

p. 22
Greater Toronto bioregion
Acart Graphic Services Ltd.; Royal Commission on the
Future of the Toronto Waterfront

p. 24
Muskrat
Gerald King

p. 27
Pickering Nuclear Power Station
Ontario Hydro

p. 41
Ecosystems
Keir Consultants Inc.; Barrett and Kidd, *Pathways:
Towards an Ecosystem Approach: A Report of Phases I and
II of an Environmental Audit of Toronto's East Bayfront
and Port Industrial Area*

p. 43
This community could be anywhere in North America
Suzanne Barrett, Royal Commission on the Future of
the Toronto Waterfront

p. 44
A distinct and memorable place, Kensington Market
City of Toronto Archives

p. 55
*Pond in the Black Creek Valley provides stormwater
management and wildlife habitat*
Sarah Kalff, Royal Commission on the Future of the
Toronto Waterfront

p. 56
Niagara Escarpment, near Milton
C. Boucher

CHAPTER 2

CHAPTER 3

Filling in Ashbridge's Marsh
City of Toronto Archives

An early flood on the Don
City of Toronto Archives

Forks of the Don today
Peter Gill

p. 236
History of Development in the Don Watershed
Hough Stansbury Woodland Ltd.

Development continues in the headwaters
Hough Stansbury Woodland Ltd.

p. 237
Golf course under construction
Hough Stansbury Woodland Ltd.

Keele Valley Landfill
Hough Stansbury Woodland Ltd.

The Ross Lord Dam and reservoir
Hough Stansbury Woodland Ltd.

Restricted access — lower Don
Hough Stansbury Woodland Ltd.

Expressways at the river's mouth
Hough Stansbury Woodland Ltd.

p. 238
Allowing nature to regenerate
Hough Stansbury Woodland Ltd.

p. 239
Preserving historical links
Hough Stansbury Woodland Ltd.

Preserving natural remnants
Hough Stansbury Woodland Ltd.

pp. 239–242
Figures 10–17
Hough Stansbury Woodland Ltd.

p. 243
Farmland in the headwaters
Hough Stansbury Woodland Ltd.

pp. 244–249
Figures 18–28
Hough Stansbury Woodland Ltd.

p. 250
A typical storm sewer outfall
Hough Stansbury Woodland Ltd.

pp. 251–253
Figures 29–31
Hough Stansbury Woodland Ltd.

p. 254
Top
Rollo Myers

Lower Rosedale flats
Hough Stansbury Woodland Ltd.

p. 255
Top
Rollo Myers

Lower Don channel
Hough Stansbury Woodland Ltd.

p. 256
Connecting the watershed
Hough Stansbury Woodland Ltd.

p.257
no caption
City of Toronto Archives

p. 258
Top
Hough Stansbury Woodland Ltd.

Bottom
Hough Stansbury Woodland Ltd.

PART III: PLACES

SELECTED BIBLIOGRAPHY

A. J. Diamond Donald Schmitt and Company. 1991. *Etobicoke motel strip study.* Toronto: Ontario. Ministry of Municipal Affairs.

Acres Consulting Services Limited and Project Planning Associates Limited. 1974. *The Halton-Wentworth waterfront study: concepts for waterfront development.* N.p.: Waterfront Co-ordinating and Technical Committees.

Ajax (Ont. : Municipality). 1989. *Office consolidation copy of the district plan of the Town of Ajax planning area.* Ajax: Ajax (Ont. : Municipality).

Alberta. Urban Environment Subcommittee. 1988. *Environment by design: the urban place in Alberta.* N.p.: Alberta. Environment Council of Alberta.

Arthur, E. 1986. *Toronto, no mean city.* Revised by S. A. Otto. Toronto: University of Toronto Press.

Association of Conservation Authorities of Ontario. [1991]. *A conservation strategy for the conservation authorities of Ontario.* N.p.: Association of Conservation Authorities of Ontario.

BA Consultants Ltd., Hough Stansbury Woodland, and The Kirkland Partnership Inc. 1990. *Gardiner Expressway East/Don Valley sweep civic design study.* Toronto: Toronto (Ont.). Task Force on the Gardiner/Lake Shore Corridor.

Barrett, S., and J. Kidd. 1991. *Pathways: towards an ecosystem approach: a report of phases I and II of an environmental audit of Toronto's East Bayfront and Port Industrial Area.* Publication no. 11. Toronto: Royal Commission on the Future of the Toronto Waterfront.

Berridge Lewinberg Greenberg et al. 1991. *Garrison Common: preliminary master plan.* Publication no. 14. Toronto: Royal Commission on the Future of the Toronto Waterfront.

Bird and Hale Ltd. 1991. *Environmental management plan: Lynde Shores Secondary Plan area: final report.* Toronto: Bird and Hale Ltd.

Board of Trade of Metropolitan Toronto. 1991. *Annual report 1991.* Toronto: Board of Trade of Metropolitan Toronto.

Bonis, R. R. (ed.). 1968. *A history of Scarborough.* Scarborough: Scarborough Public Library.

Bosselmann, P., et al. 1990. *Sun, wind, and pedestrian comfort: a study of Toronto's central area.* Cityplan '91 report no. 25. Toronto: Toronto (Ont.). Planning and Development Dept.

Buchanan, I. D. 1991. *Presentation for Royal Commission on the Future of the Toronto Waterfront.* Maple: Ontario. Ministry of Natural Resources.

Butler Group (Consultants) Inc. 1991. *Lakeshore overview study South Etobicoke: draft report.* Etobicoke: Etobicoke (Ont. : Municipality).

Byer, P. H., R. Gibson, and C. Lucyk. 1989. *The adequacy of the existing environmental planning and approval process for the Ganaraska watershed.* Toronto: Ontario. Environmental Assessment Advisory Committee.

Canada. 1990. *Canada's green plan for a healthy environment.* Ottawa: Government of Canada.

Canada. Environment Canada, Canada. Dept. of Fisheries and Oceans, and Canada. Health and Welfare Canada. 1991. *Toxic chemicals in the Great Lakes and associated effects.* Toronto: Canada. Environment Canada, Canada. Dept. of Fisheries and Oceans, Canada. Health and Welfare Canada.

Canada. Office of the Auditor General. 1990. *Report of the Auditor General of Canada to the House of Commons.* Ottawa: Canada. Office of the Auditor General.

Canada. Parliament. *Cultural property export and import act.* 1974-75-76, c. 50, s.1. Ottawa: Government of Canada.

———. 1911. *The Toronto Harbour Commissioners act, 1911, 1-2 George V, assented to 19th May 1911.* Ottawa: Government of Canada.

———. 1988. *Canadian environmental protection act.* Ottawa: Government of Canada.

———. 1989. *Fisheries act.* R. S., c. F-14, s. 1. Ottawa: Canada. Dept. of Fisheries and Oceans.

Canada/Ontario Agreement respecting Great Lakes Water Quality Board of Review. 1985. *Canada/ Ontario Agreement respecting Great Lakes water quality.* N.p.: Canada/Ontario Agreement respecting Great Lakes Water Quality Board of Review.

Canadian Medical Association. 1991. *Health, the environment, and sustainable development: the role of the medical profession.* Ottawa: Canadian Medical Association.

Carson, P., and J. Moulden. 1991. *Green is gold: business talking to business about the environmental revolution.* Toronto: HarperCollins.

Clarkin, W. 1991. *Ataratiri draft environmental evaluation study report.* Toronto: Toronto (Ont.). Housing Dept.

Cobb, J. B., and H. E. Daly. 1989. *For the common good: redirecting the economy toward community, the environment, and a sustainable future.* Boston: Beacon Press.

Cobourg (Ont.: Municipality). 1989. *Amendment no. 24 to the Official Plan of the Town of Cobourg: Harbour Area Secondary Plan.* Cobourg: Cobourg (Ont. : Municipality).

Davies, K. 1991. *Towards ecosystem-based planning: a perspective on cumulative environmental effects.* Working papers of the Canadian Waterfront Resource Centre, no. 8. Toronto: Royal Commission on the Future of the Toronto Waterfront.

Dendy, W., and W. Kilbourn. 1986. *Toronto observed: its architecture, patrons, and history.* Toronto: Oxford University Press.

Doering, R. L., et al. 1991. *Planning for sustainability: towards integrating environmental protection into land-use planning.* Publication no. 12. Toronto: Royal Commission on the Future of the Toronto Waterfront.

Durham (Ont. : Regional municipality). *Review of the Durham Regional Official Plan.* Whitby: Durham (Ont. : Regional municipality).

Environics Research Group and Synergistics. 1991. *Top-line summary of research conducted on behalf of the Royal Commission on the Future of the Toronto Waterfront.* Toronto: Synergistics.

Etobicoke (Ont.). Council. 1990. *Official Plan of the Etobicoke planning area: the motel strip: amendment no. C-65-86: secondary plan revised May 1990*. Etobicoke: Etobicoke (Ont.). Council.

Etobicoke (Ont.). Planning Dept. 1983. *The Mimico study*. Etobicoke: Etobicoke (Ont.). Planning Dept.

_____. 1988. *The motel strip: Official Plan of the Etobicoke planning area*. Etobicoke: Etobicoke (Ont. : Municipality).

Eyles, N., and B. Clark. 1988. "Last interglacial sediments of the Don Valley brickyard, Toronto, Canada, and their paleoenvironmental significance." *Canadian journal of earth science*.

Eyles, N., and N. Williams. 1989. *The sedimentary and biological record of the last interglacial/glacial transition at Toronto, Canada*. N.p.: Geological Society of America Special Publication.

Filey, M. 1982. *I remember Sunnyside: the rise and fall of a magical era*. Toronto: McClelland and Stewart.

Fleisher Ridout Partnership Inc., Arcop Architects Inc., and Hemson Consulting Limited. 1988. "Port Industrial Area concept plan." *Port of Toronto news* 35 (3).

Fryer, M. B. 1989. *Elizabeth Postuma Simcoe, 1762-1850, a biography*. Toronto: Dundurn Press.

Garwood-Jones and Van Nostrand Architects Inc., Gerrard and Mackars Landscape Architects Inc., and B-A Consulting Group Ltd. 1991. *The Humber River/High Park/Western Beaches civic design study*. Toronto: Toronto (Ont.). Task Force on the Gardiner/Lake Shore Corridor.

Gertler, M. S. 1990. *Toronto: the state of the regional economy*. Working papers of the Canadian Waterfront Resource Centre, no. 6. Toronto: Royal Commission on the Future of the Toronto Waterfront.

Goad, C. E. 1984. *Mapping of Victorian Toronto*. Sutton West, Ont.: Paget Press.

Gzowski, P. 1991. *The fourth Morningside papers*. Toronto: McClelland and Stewart.

Halton (Ont. : Regional municipality). 1990. *A greenlands strategy for Halton*. Oakville: Halton (Ont. : Regional municipality).

_____. Planning and Development Dept. 1982. *The Halton waterfront plan*. Oakville: Halton (Ont. : Regional municipality). Planning and Development Dept.

_____. 1991. Land stewardship and healthy communities: a vision for the 90's and beyond. Halton Region Official Plan review report B4. Oakville: Halton (Ont. : Regional municipality). Planning and Development Dept. Draft.

Hamilton-Wentworth (Ont. : Regional municipality). Hamilton Beach Advisory Committee. 1991. Hamilton Beach neighbourhood plan. Hamilton: Hamilton-Wentworth (Ont. : Regional municipality). Planning and Development Dept. Draft.

Hancock, T. 1990. *Towards healthy and sustainable communities: health, environment and economy at the local level*. Toronto: York University. Faculty of Environmental Studies.

Hayes, E. 1974. *Etobicoke from furrow to borough*. Etobicoke: Etobicoke (Ont. : Municipality).

Hill, R. 1959. "A master plan for the shoreline." *The Telegram*. 24 July.

Hiss, T. 1990. *The experience of place*. New York: Alfred A. Knopf.

Hough, M. 1989. *City form and natural process: towards a new urban vernacular*. London: Routledge.

_____. 1990. *Out of place: restoring identity to the regional landscape*. New Haven: Yale University Press.

Hough Stansbury and Woodland Limited. 1987. *Port Credit harbour and waterfront study.* Mississauga: Mississauga (Ont.). Planning and Building Dept.

IBI Group et al. 1990. *Greater Toronto Area urban structure concepts study.* Toronto: Greater Toronto Coordinating Committee.

_____. 1991. *Toronto Central Waterfront transportation corridor study.* Publication no. 15. Toronto: Royal Commission on the Future of the Toronto Waterfront.

International Joint Commission. 1978. *Great Lakes water quality agreement of 1978.* Ottawa and Washington: International Joint Commission.

_____. 1982. *Biennial report under the Great Lakes water quality agreement of 1978.* Ottawa and Washington: International Joint Commission.

_____. 1986. *Third biennial report under the Great Lakes water quality agreement of 1978 to the Governments of the United States and Canada and the States and Provinces of the Great Lakes Basin.* Ottawa and Washington: International Joint Commission.

_____. 1988. *Revised Great Lakes water quality agreement of 1978 as amended by protocol signed November 18, 1987.* Windsor: International Joint Commission.

_____. 1990. *Fifth biennial report under the Great Lakes water quality agreement of 1978 to the Governments of the United States and Canada and the State and Provincial Governments of the Great Lakes Basin.* Ottawa and Washington: International Joint Commission.

International Joint Commission. Great Lakes Science Advisory Board. 1991. *1991 report to the International Joint Commission.* Windsor: International Joint Commission.

International Joint Commission. Great Lakes Water Quality Board. 1991. *Cleaning up our Great Lakes: a report from the Water Quality Board to the International Joint Commission on toxic substances in the Great Lakes Basin ecosystem.* Windsor: International Joint Commission.

_____. 1991. *Review and evaluation of Great Lakes RAP: remedial action plan program 1991.* Windsor: International Joint Commission.

International Joint Commission. Virtual Elimination Task Force. 1991. *Persistent toxic substances: virtually eliminating inputs to the Great Lakes.* Windsor: International Joint Commission.

Jackson, C. I., and D. Runnalls. 1991. *The Great Lakes in the 1990s: an environmental scan for a renewed Canada-Ontario agreement.* Ottawa: Ontario. Ministry of the Environment, Canada. Environment Canada.

Jacobs, P. 1991. *Sustainable urban development.* Montreal: Third Summit of the World's Major Cities.

Kanter, R. 1990. *Space for all: options for a Greater Toronto Area greenlands strategy.* Toronto: Ontario. Ministry of Natural Resources.

Kirkland Partnership. 1991. *Etobicoke motel strip secondary plan: urban design supplement.* Etobicoke: Etobicoke (Ont. : Municipality).

Klinger, X. 1991. *Winter waterfront: year-round use in Metropolitan Toronto.* Working papers of the Canadian Waterfront Resource Centre, no. 9. Toronto: Royal Commission on the Future of the Toronto Waterfront.

Lennon, M. J. 1980. *Memories of Toronto Island: 10 minutes and 1,000 miles away.* Cheltanham: Boston Mills Press.

Little, C. E. 1990. *Greenways for America.* Baltimore: Johns Hopkins University Press.

Lynch, K. 1981. *A theory of good city form.* Cambridge: MIT Press.

M. M. Dillon Limited, and Ecologistics Limited. 1991. *Town of Whitby Official Plan review and update study: phase 2: policy review and assessment report.* Whitby: Whitby (Ont.). Planning Dept.

M. M. Dillon Limited et al. 1990. *Town of Whitby Official Plan review and update study: phase 1: background information.* Whitby: Whitby (Ont.). Planning Dept.

_____. 1991. *Town of Whitby Official Plan review and update study: phase 3: development strategies and options report.* Whitby: Whitby (Ont.). Planning Dept.

M. M. Dillon Limited, Natale Scott Browne Architects, and MIE Marine Engineers. 1991. *Town of Port Hope: waterfront master planning study.* Port Hope: Port Hope (Ont. : Municipality).

Malone Given Parsons Ltd. et al. 1991. *Oshawa harbour study: area no. 1 component of the southeast Oshawa planning study.* Oshawa: Oshawa (Ont. : Municipality).

Martin, L. 1991. *Presentation by ARCH to the Metropolitan Toronto Works Committee about coordinated action on water quality.* Etobicoke: Action to Restore a Clean Humber.

Maryland Greenways Commission. 1990. *Maryland greenways — a naturally better idea.* Annapolis: Maryland Greenways Commission.

McCormick Rankin et al. 1991. *Burloak secondary plan.* Oakville: Halton (Ont. : Regional municipality).

McHarg, I. L. 1969. *Design with nature.* Garden City: Natural History Press.

McKeough, W. D. 1990. *Harbourfront: report to the Honourable Elmer MacKay.* Toronto: Canada. Public Works Canada.

Metro Toronto Remedial Action Plan. 1988. *Environmental conditions and problem definition.* Toronto: Metro Toronto Remedial Action Plan.

_____. 1990. *Draft discussion paper on remedial options.* Toronto: Metro Toronto Remedial Action Plan.

_____. 1991. *Strategies for restoring our waters.* Toronto: Metro Toronto Remedial Action Plan.

Metropolitan Toronto and Region Conservation Authority. 1978. *Colonel Samuel Smith Waterfront Area master plan.* Downsview: Metropolitan Toronto and Region Conservation Authority.

_____. 1989. *The greenspace strategy for the Greater Toronto region: a conservation vision for the 21st century.* Downsview: Metropolitan Toronto and Region Conservation Authority.

_____. 1990. *A comprehensive basin management strategy for the Rouge River watershed.* Downsview: Metropolitan Toronto and Region Conservation Authority.

Metropolitan Toronto (Ont.). Planning Dept. 1991. *Planning directions for the Metropolitan waterfront: an overview.* Toronto: Metropolitan Toronto (Ont.). Planning Dept.

_____. 1991. *Towards a liveable metropolis: a discussion paper in the metropolitan plan review series.* Toronto: Metropolitan Toronto (Ont.). Planning Dept.

Metropolitan Toronto (Ont.). Waterfront Technical Committee. 1967. *The waterfront plan for the Metropolitan Toronto planning area.* Toronto: Metropolitan Toronto (Ont.). Planning Board.

Millward, R. E. 1990. *Report to Toronto City Council about the desirability of conducting a review of the official plan part II for the railway lands.* Toronto: Toronto (Ont.). Planning and Development Dept.

Mississauga (Ont.). Planning and Building Dept. 1989. *The office plan of the City of Mississauga planning area: office consolidation.* Mississauga: Mississauga (Ont.). Planning and Building Dept.

Mississauga (Ont.). Waterfront Planning Team. 1990. *Fundamentals: the basis for the Mississauga waterfront plan.* Mississauga: Mississauga (Ont.). Planning and Building Dept.

_____. 1990. Implementation: strategies to realize the Mississauga waterfront plan. Mississauga: Mississauga (Ont.). Planning and Building Dept. Draft.

_____. 1990. Vision 2020: a plan for the Mississauga waterfront. Mississauga: Mississauga (Ont.). Planning and Building Dept. Draft.

_____. 1991. *Draft Mississauga waterfront plan: results of agency review and public consultation.* Mississauga: Mississauga (Ont.). Planning and Building Dept.

Moffat Moffat and Kinoshita et al. 1978. *Colonel Samuel Bois Smith waterfront area master plan.* Downsview: Metropolitan Toronto and Region Conservation Authority.

Moore/George Associates Inc. 1987. *Hamilton Beach concept plan.* Hamilton: Hamilton (Ont.). Hamilton Beach Steering Committee.

_____. 1987. *Oshawa waterfront development plan.* Oshawa: Oshawa (Ont.). Planning Branch.

Mumford, L. 1938. *The culture of cities.* New York: Harcourt, Brace and Company.

Municipal/Industrial Strategy for Abatement. MISA Advisory Committee. 1991. *Water conservation in Ontario: implementing the user pay system to finance a cleaner environment.* Toronto: Ontario. Ministry of the Environment.

Nelson, G., et al. 1991. *Frenchman's Bay, Ontario: conservation and sustainable development.* Waterloo: University of Waterloo. Heritage Resources Centre.

Newcastle (Ont.). Dept. of Planning and Development. 1989. *The Official Plan of the Town of Newcastle: consolidated office copy.* Newcastle:

Newcastle (Ont.). Dept. of Planning and Development.

Nuala Beck and Associates Inc. 1991. *The new "big picture".* Toronto: Nuala Beck and Associates Inc.

Olive, D. 1991. "A discourse on events: even in these gloomy times, Canadians still prepared to count their blessings." *The Globe and Mail.* 9 November.

Ontario. 1980. *Niagara Escarpment planning and development act. Revised Statutes of Ontario, 1980.* Toronto: Government of Ontario.

_____. 1980. *Topsoil preservation act. Revised statutes of Ontario, 1980.* Toronto: Government of Ontario.

_____. 1987. *Conservation authorities act. Revised statutes of Ontario, 1980. Chapter 85 as amended by 1983, chapter 8, s. 20.* Toronto: Government of Ontario.

_____. 1989. *Environmental assessment act. Revised statutes of Ontario, 1980. Chapter 140 as amended by 1988, chapter 71, s. 18.* Toronto: Ontario. Ministry of the Attorney General.

_____. 1989. *Planning act, 1983. Statutes of Ontario, 1983. chapter 1 as amended by 1983, chapter 82; 1984, chapter 32, s. 21; 1985, chapter 16 and 1989, chapter 5 and certain regulations thereunder.* Toronto: Ontario. Ministry of the Attorney General.

_____. 1990. *Trees act. Revised statutes of Ontario, 1980. Chapter 510.* Toronto: Ontario. Ministry of the Attorney General.

Ontario. Environmental Assessment Board. 1980. *Environmental assessment act hearing: Colonel Samuel Bois Smith Waterfront Area master plan.* Toronto: Ontario. Environmental Assessment Board.

Ontario. Ministry of Municipal Affairs. 1985. *Niagara Escarpment plan.* Toronto: Ontario. Ministry of Municipal Affairs.

Ontario. Ministry of Natural Resources. 1991.
*Implementation guidelines for Oak Ridges Moraine
within the Greater Toronto Area.* Toronto:
Ontario. Ministry of Natural Resources.

Ontario. Tree Bylaws Advisory Committee. 1991. *Final
report of the Tree Bylaws Advisory Committee.*
Toronto: Ontario. Ministry of Natural
Resources.

Ontario Wild Life Working Group. 1991. *Wild life strategy for Ontario.* Toronto: Ontario. Ministry of
Natural Resources.

Oshawa Harbour Task Force. 1984. *Oshawa Harbour
development plan: a report to the Oshawa Harbour
Commission.* Oshawa: Oshawa Harbour
Commission.

Oshawa (Ont.). Dept. of Planning and Development.
1987. *Office consolidation copy of the City of
Oshawa Official Plan.* Oshawa: Oshawa (Ont.).
City Clerk's Dept.

_____. 1991. *Southeast Oshawa planning study area
no. 2 component: final report.* Oshawa: Oshawa
(Ont.). Dept. of Planning and Development.

Pickering (Ont. : Municipality). 1989. *Office
consolidated copy of the district plan for the district
planning area of the Town of Pickering.* Pickering:
Pickering (Ont. : Municipality).

Porter, M. E. 1990. *Competitive advantage of nations.*
New York: Free Press.

Proctor Redfern Bousfield and Bacon Consultants.
1967. *The waterfront plan for the Metropolitan
Toronto planning area.* Toronto: Metropolitan
Toronto (Ont.). Planning Board.

Reid, R., et al. 1991. *The waterfront trail: first steps from
concept to reality.* Toronto: Ontario. Office of the
Premier.

Reid, R., R. Lockhart, and B. Woodburn. 1990.
A green strategy for the Greater Toronto waterfront.
Publication no. 8. Toronto: Royal Commission
on the Future of the Toronto Waterfront.

Richardson, A. H. 1944. *A report on the Ganaraska
watershed: a study in land use with plans for the
rehabilitation of the area in the post-war period.*
Toronto: Ontario. Dept. of Planning and
Development.

_____. 1974. *Conservation by the people: the history of
the conservation movement in Ontario to 1970.*
Toronto: University of Toronto Press.

Rouge Valley Park Advisory Committee. 1991. *Park
options: Rouge Valley park project.* Scarborough:
Rouge Valley Park Advisory Committee.

Royal Commission on the Future of the Toronto
Waterfront. 1989. *The future of the Toronto Island
Airport: the issues.* Publication no. 7. Toronto:
Royal Commission on the Future of the
Toronto Waterfront.

_____. 1989. *Interim report.* Ottawa: Royal
Commission on the Future of the Toronto
Waterfront.

_____. 1990. *Environment in transition: a report on
phase I of an environmental audit of Toronto's East
Bayfront and Port Industrial Area.* Publication
no. 10. Toronto: Royal Commission on the
Future of the Toronto Waterfront.

_____. 1990. *Watershed: interim report.* Ottawa: Royal
Commission on the Future of the Toronto
Waterfront.

Royal Commission on the Future of the Toronto
Waterfront. Shoreline Regeneration Work
Group. 1991. *Shoreline regeneration for the Greater
Toronto bioregion.* Publication no. 13. Toronto:
Royal Commission on the Future of the
Toronto Waterfront.

Royal Commission on the Future of the Toronto
Waterfront. Steering Committee on Matters
Related to the Board of Toronto Harbour
Commissioners. 1989. *Persistence and change:
waterfront issues and the Board of Toronto Harbour
Commissioners.* Publication no. 6. Toronto:
Royal Commission on the Future of the
Toronto Waterfront.

Sale, K. 1985. *Dwellers in the land: the bioregional vision.* San Francisco: Sierra Club.

Sandwell Swan Wooster Inc., Beak Consultants Limited, and EDA Collaborative. 1990. *Lake Ontario shoreline management plan.* Toronto: Central Lake Ontario Conservation Authority, Ganaraska Region Conservation Authority, and Lower Trent Region Conservation Authority.

Scarborough (Ont.). Planning Dept. 1988. *Official plan: office consolidation.* Scarborough: Scarborough (Ont.). Planning Dept.

Stamp, R. M. 1987. *The Queen Elizabeth Way: Canada's first superhighway.* Erin: Boston Mills Press.

Stinson, J., and M. Moir. 1991. Built heritage of the East Bayfront. Environmental audit of the East Bayfront/Port Industrial Area phase II, technical paper no. 7. Toronto: Royal Commission on the Future of the Toronto Waterfront. Draft.

Suzuki, D. 1991. "We need to make life in the big city liveable." *The Toronto Star.* 21 September.

Toronto Area Watershed Management Strategy (TAWMS). Steering Committee. 1986. *Humber River water quality management plan, 1986.* Toronto: Ontario. Ministry of the Environment.

Toronto Harbour Commissioners. [1913]. *Toronto waterfront development, 1912 to 1920.* Toronto: Toronto Harbour Commissioners.

Toronto (Ont.). Council. 1990. *By-law respecting the prohibition and regulation of the use, recovery and disposal of certain products, material, and equipment containing or manufactured with chlorofluorocarbons, halons, or other ozone depleting substances: office consolidation.* Toronto: Toronto (Ont.). City Clerk.

Toronto (Ont.). Healthy City Office. 1991. *Evaluating the role of the automobile: a municipal strategy.* Toronto: Toronto (Ont.). Healthy City Office.

Toronto (Ont.). Healthy Toronto 2000 Subcommittee. 1988. *Healthy Toronto 2000: a strategy for a healthy city.* Toronto: Toronto (Ont.). Dept. of Public Health.

Toronto (Ont.). Planning and Development Dept. 1985. *Railway lands part II: final report — official plan statements and zoning by-law.* Toronto: Toronto (Ont.). Planning and Development Dept.

_____. 1991. *Ataratiri part II official plan proposals.* Toronto: Toronto (Ont.). Planning and Development Dept.

_____. 1991. *Cityplan '91 proposals report.* Toronto: Toronto (Ont.). Planning and Development Dept.

Toronto (Ont.). Planning Board. 1962. *The plan for downtown Toronto.* Toronto: Toronto (Ont.). Planning Board.

_____. 1963. *The core of the Central Waterfront: a proposal by the City of Toronto Planning Board.* Toronto: Toronto (Ont.). Planning Board.

_____. 1970. *Metro Centre.* Toronto: Toronto (Ont.). Planning Board.

_____. 1978. *The railway lands: basis for planning Toronto.* Toronto: Toronto (Ont.). Planning Board.

_____. 1978. *The railway lands: proposed goals and objectives.* Toronto: Toronto (Ont.). Planning Board.

Toronto (Ont.). Task Force to Bring Back the Don. 1991. *Bringing back the Don.* Toronto: Toronto (Ont.). Task Force to Bring Back the Don.

Toronto (Ont. : Municipality), Toronto Harbour Commissioners, and Canada. Transport Canada. 1983. *Tripartite agreement: to provide for the continued use of certain parcels of land at Toronto Island for the purpose of a permanent public airport for general aviation and limited commercial*

STOL (short take-off and landing) service operations.
Toronto: Toronto (Ont. : Municipality),
Toronto Harbour Commissioners, and Canada.
Transport Canada.

United States. Council on Environmental Quality.
1990. *Twentieth annual report.* Washington, D.C.:
United States. Council on Environmental
Quality.

United States. National Park Service. 1990. *Economic
impacts of protecting rivers, trails, and greenway corridors: a resource book.* San Francisco: United
States. National Park Service.

United States. President's Commission on Americans
Outdoors. 1987. *Americans outdoors: the legacy,
the challenge.* Washington, D.C.: Island Press.

Varga, S., J. Jalava, and J. L. Riley. 1991. *Ecological survey of the Rouge Valley Park.* Aurora: Ontario.
Ministry of Natural Resources. Draft.

Weller, P. 1990. *Fresh water seas: saving the Great Lakes.*
Toronto: Between The Lines.

Whyte, W. H. 1968. *The last landscape.* New York:
Doubleday and Company.

World Commission on Environment and Development.
1987. G. H. Brundtland, chairman. *Our
common future.* Oxford and New York: Oxford
University Press.

INDEX

Local Architectural Conservation Advisory Committee, 198

Long Branch Village (Etobicoke, Ont.), 296

Lower Don Lands (Toronto, Ont.), 252, 305, 385-386, 389, 393, 395-402, 404-405, 407-409, 411, 413-414, 467-468

Lower Trent Region Conservation Authority, 168, 453

Lynde Creek (Whitby, Ont.), 195, 202, 427, 447

Lynde Creek Shores marsh (Whitby, Ont.), 222

Lynde Shores (Whitby, Ont.), 446, 464

Lynde Shores Conservation Area, 195, 222, 428

Lynde Shores Secondary Plan, 440

M. M. Dillon Ltd., 431

Main Sewage Treatment Plant (Toronto, Ont.), 145, 318, 389-390, 407

Malone Givens Parsons Ltd., 442

Malton Airport (Toronto, Ont.). *See* Lester B. Pearson International Airport

Maple Leaf stadium (Toronto, Ont.), 345

Marathon Realty Company Limited, 367-368

Marie Curtis Park (Etobicoke, Ont.), 281, 286, 291

Marina del Rey development project (Etobicoke, Ont.), 294

marinas, 155, 279, 395, 438, 451

marshes, 24, 152, 158, 251, 253, 278, 314, 393, 401-402, 431, 433, 435, 441. *See also* wetlands

Martin Goodman Trail, 257, 387, 396, 405

Maryland, 180, 193

McGuinness site (Etobicoke, Ont.), 296-297

McHarg, Ian L., 66

McKeough, W. Darcy, 374, 376

McLaughlin Bay (Ont.), 155, 431, 447

McLaughlin Bay Wildlife Reserve, 441

McNichol estate (Burlington, Ont.), 266

McQuesten, Thomas Baker, 340

Metro Centre, 364

Metro Centre (Toronto, Ont.), 366

Metro Toronto Convention Centre, 369-370

Metro Toronto Remedial Action Plan, 25, 64, 94, 130-134, 136, 143-147, 157, 391, 401, 403

Metro Toronto Remedial Action Plan. Public Advisory Committee, 131, 134

The Metropolitan Museum of Art (New York, N. Y.), 214

Metropolitan Toronto and Region Conservation Authority, 51, 80, 94, 131, 154, 158, 160, 174, 184, 190, 197, 199, 281, 287, 294, 301-302, 338, 416, 421, 423-424, 427, 433-434, 436-437, 439, 447-448, 462

Metropolitan Toronto (Ont.), 52-53, 80, 131, 313, 424-425, 462, 469

Metropolitan Toronto (Ont.). City Council, 15, 64, 131, 137, 293, 296, 301, 307-308, 328, 338, 350, 362, 366, 384, 399

Metropolitan Toronto (Ont.). Dept. of Public Works, 300

Metropoll Report, 16, 128-129, 185, 194, 208, 213, 263, 284

MGS. *See* Ontario. Ministry of Government Services

Microclimate, 95, 209, 211, 223, 404

Miller, Sarah, 129

Mimico (Etobicoke, Ont.), 289, 293-294, 343

Mimico Creek (Etobicoke, Ont.), 131, 292

The Mimico Study, 294

mink, 108

mirex, 104

MISA. *See* Municipal/Industrial Strategy for Abatement

Mississauga (Ont.), 218, 279, 462

Mississauga (Ont.). City Council, 13, 277, 281, 285-287

Mississauga (Ont.). Mayor, 281

Mississauga Waterfront Plan: Results of Agency Review and Public Consultation — Draft, 279, 282-283, 285

mixed uses, 218, 267, 319-320, 334-335, 338, 401, 406-407, 442, 444, 453, 467-468

MMA. *See* Ontario. Ministry of Municipal Affairs

MNR. *See* Ontario. Ministry of Natural Resources

MOE. *See* Ontario. Ministry of the Environment

Moir, Michael, 79

Mono (Ont.). Town Council, 50-51

moratoria, 7, 13, 149, 173, 293, 434

Morris, David, 173

Morrison Creek (Oakville, Ont.), 266

MOT. *See* Ontario. Ministry of Transportation

Motel Strip (Etobicoke, Ont.), 218, 291, 296-299, 304, 348, 462

Motel Strip Secondary Plan, 295, 298-299

Moulden, Julia, 36-37, 326

MTCC. *See* Metro Toronto Convention Centre

St. Lawrence Park (Toronto, Ont.), 390, 407, 468

St. Mary's Cement Corporation, 429-430, 441, 443-445

stakeholders, 10, 13, 46-48, 51, 81, 134, 146, 171

Stamp, Robert M., 340

Steel Company of Canada, 343

Stinson, Jeffery, 79, 470

STOL. *See* Short Take-off and Landing

stonehooking, 151

stormwater, 132, 135, 240, 243, 250, 285, 314, 403, 418

stormwater run-off, 132, 236, 237, 250-251, 314, 404, 469

Strachan Avenue (Toronto, Ont.), 332, 336, 359

Strategies to Realize the Mississauga Waterfront Plan: Implementation, 282-283

streets, 309, 319, 321-322, 361

Sunnyside Amusement Park (Ont.), 346

Superior Park (Etobicoke, Ont.), 294

sustainable development, 38-40, 45, 52-53, 60-61, 76, 81-82, 440, 455, 457

Sustainable Urban Development, 76, 174, 274, 362, 401

Suzuki, David, 157

Swansea (Toronto, Ont.), 305, 343-344

Task Force on the Gardiner/Lakeshore Corridor, 307, 339

Task Force to Bring Back the Don, 80, 136, 193, 238, 252-255, 390, 401

TEDCO. *See* Toronto Economic Development Corporation

THC. *See* Toronto Harbour Commissioners

Third Biennial Report under the Great Lakes Water Quality Agreement of 1978 to the Government of the United States and Canada and the States and Provinces of the Great Lakes Basin, 129

Three-Rod Law, 151

Tommy Thompson Park (Toronto, Ont.),. 7, 155, 305. *See also* Leslie Street Spit

Topsoil Preservation Act, 89

Toronto (Ont.), 4-5, 462

Toronto (Ont.). City Council, 7-9, 13-14, 52, 131, 145, 308, 316, 327-328, 338, 343, 350, 362, 364-368, 371-375, 377-382, 386-387, 389-390, 395-396, 399, 406-408, 410, 413, 459, 462, 468-469

Toronto (Ont.). Healthy City Office, 35, 49

Toronto (Ont.). Commissioner of Planning, 367

The Toronto and Mimico Electric Railway and Light Company, 342

Toronto Area Watershed Management Strategy, 1986, 132, 135-136

Toronto Belt Line Railway Company, 342

Toronto-Buttonville International Airport (Toronto, Ont.), 379

Toronto Central Waterfront Transportation Corridor Study, 16, 304-305, 308, 310, 316-319, 322, 329, 466, 469

Toronto Economic Development Corporation, 13, 406-407, 409-410

Toronto Hamilton Highway Commission, 342

Toronto Harbour Commissioners 2, 7-9, 13-14, 152-153, 165, 253, 344-345, 365-366, 377-382, 387, 390, 393, 395, 399, 403, 405-410, 413, 461-462

Toronto Harbour Commissioners Act, 406

Toronto Historical Board, 392

Toronto Inner Harbour (Toronto, Ont.), 132, 153, 363, 395

Toronto Island Airport, 7-9, 305, 364, 377-379, 381-382, 398

Toronto Island Airport. Intergovernmental Staff Forum, 378

Toronto Islands, 150, 153, 168, 221, 301, 305, 314, 316, 364, 377-378, 382-385

Toronto, No Mean City, 341

Toronto Observed, 352

Toronto Outer Harbour (Toronto, Ont.), 396, 398, 402, 404, 408

Toronto Purchase, 342

Toronto Terminal Railways Corridor, 370

Toronto, The State of the Regional Economy, 30, 45

Toronto Transit Commission, 324, 334, 342

Toronto Transportation Commission, 328, 331, 336, 341

Toronto Waterfront Regeneration Land Trust, 13, 15, 170, 462

Towards a Liveable Metropolis, 50

Towards Ecosystem-Based Planning: A Perspective on Cumulative Environmental Effects, 76

Town of Port Hope Waterfront Master Plan Study, 451